Garrie L. Tufford

Search for the PAST

Search

for

the

AN INTRODUCTION TO PALEONTOLOGY

Prentice-Hall, Inc. 1960

James R. Beerbower

Department of Geology
Lafayette College
Illustrated by the author

PAST

Englewood Cliffs, N.J.

Search for the Past,
An Introduction to Paleontology
by James R. Beerbower
© 1960
PRENTICE-HALL, INC.
ENGLEWOOD CLIFFS, N.J.

LIBRARY OF CONGRESS

CATALOG CARD NO.: 60–5040

PRINTED IN THE UNITED STATES OF AMERICA

79728

PREFACE

𝒯his book is an attempt to answer some general questions about paleontology: What is it? What do paleontologists do? What are the conclusions of paleontology? The first two of these are essentially personal questions, for no two paleontologists have the same view of their field or the same methods. To an extent, then, this book is an argument for certain ways of looking at fossils, of interpreting their significance, and of utilizing those interpretations. As an argument it requires participation, resistance, and criticism by the reader. To encourage these attitudes, I have tried to present each argument with its antithesis. "But," "however," "although," and "on the other hand" are sprinkled liberally through the text.

I hope this approach will result in intelligent skepticism toward not only the special viewpoints advanced here but toward paleontologic principles, methods, and conclusions in general. Since this is a book about what paleontology is—not what it might be—I have presented what I believe to be the most widely accepted of these generalities. I have emphasized, however, statistical analysis and certain "model" approaches that have not as yet been used in many studies. Although this emphasis may mislead, it at least gives a picture of paleontology as a developing science, not as a static set of rules and classifications. (I beat some dead horses—I hope the more sophisticated will forgive me.)

This is a book about paleontology, that is, the study of ancient life, not just about fossils. Even with many illustrations and examples, it can be only a weak substitute for studying fossils, observing their structure, classifying them, and interpreting their environment and evolution. In an attempt to give a more vivid picture of these activities, I have included a "stream of consciousness" description of some of them. In other cases, I used tape recordings of classroom discussion as a basis for the textual discussion. But these expository techniques are still only substitutes for field trips, museum work, and original papers, and they may mislead as well as guide.

The imperfections of this book will, I hope, stimulate the reader to correction by reference to other sources or by independent thought. Again I hope the reader can remedy the defects—certainly such difficulties are part of the nature of modern paleontology.

ACKNOWLEDGMENTS

The author of a textbook must ultimately be more editor than original writer. His creative function is in the selection and organization of material rather than in the development of novelties. The editor of a scientific journal is "backstopped" by his panel of experts; the author of a textbook must receive an equivalent service from his critics. If the selection and organization of this book has value and validity, a large measure of credit goes to Ralph G. Johnson and J. Marvin Weller, both of the Geology Department, the University of Chicago, who detected my errors, suffered my eccentricities of style, restrained my enthusiasms, and contributed their own ideas. I should like further to acknowledge the assistance of Maurine Lewis and Michael Sundermeier of Prentice-Hall; their cooperation, patience, and enthusiasm were invaluable.

JAMES R. BEERBOWER

CONTENTS

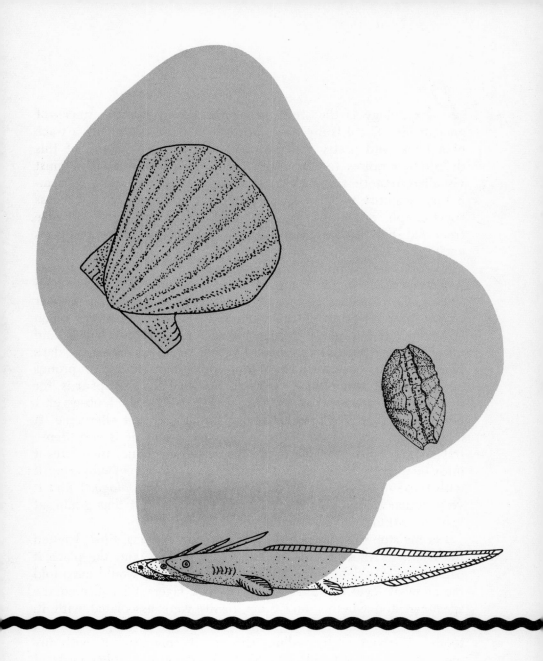

1. FOSSILS *and* SCIENCE

*P*aleontology is the study of fossils. Fossils are the traces of ancient life. There is my book, in thirteen words—but only a trace of a book, and pretty well petrified at that. Explanation of this definition requires ten thousand times thirteen words. You must visualize Aristotle turning a fossil shell in his hands, and a contemporary scientist with calipers, calculating machine, and a mass spectograph, examining the same shell. And you must visualize from that shell the living beast on the sea floor, five million centuries ancient.

Paleontology comprises fossils and men and ideas about fossils. As I write this, I juggle in my left hand a paperweight, a three-inch square of rock, collected last summer in West Virginia (a number on the rock refers to my field notes, including where and when collected). It is a piece of coarse sandstone, with much clay and mica between the quartz grains. On one surface I can see a dark blue structure consisting of a button-like base and two prongs perhaps a half an inch long. Is this a fossil? Well, perhaps it is, for it resembles some part of an animal. What else can I observe? I test it with dilute hydrochloric acid, but it does not effervesce. It is, therefore, not calcite. Seen under a hand lens, it is very dense but not too hard. It is too dense for vertebrate bone; therefore, it must be a tooth. What kind? Perhaps a shark's tooth? Comparing it with those illustrated in Romer's *Vertebrate Paleontology,* I find it very similar to one type named *Xenacanthus*—if not that group, at least something very close to it.

Let me stop this reverie now and retrace the steps. First, I noted the characteristics of the fossil, the rock it is in, and the place it came from. My field notes, if I had dug them out, would have told me at what level in the sequence of rock layers I'd collected the specimen and whether any other fossils were associated with it. Then I made an intuitive jump to "It's a fossil—maybe a shark tooth." Without really willing the act, I compared it with my memories of other fossils and of the hard (preservable) parts of recent animals. Finally, I checked my hunch by comparison of this fossil with others illustrated in a reference book.

If it had been a shell or a leaf impression, the process would have been the same: to observe and compare. This is the basic method, the skeleton, of paleontology.

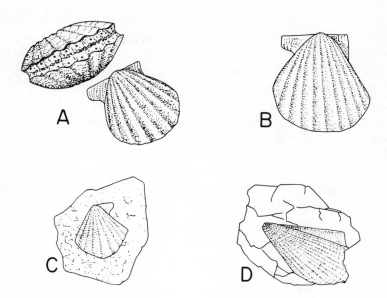

Fig. 1–1. *SIMILARITY OF RECENT ANIMALS AND FOSSILS. A)* Two recent clams, lower one lying on one side with one valve of shell visible; the other, edge-on, with both valves and some of the viscera shown. *B)* Shell of a similar clam collected from ocean bottom sediments. *C)* Somewhat similar shell from late Mesozoic rocks. *D)* Shell from middle Paleozoic rocks. Note that the shell has "ribs" and an "ear" like A, B, and C, although its shape is considerably different.

But the skeleton without the flesh of life is dead—and deadly to our interest. Ink scribbled in a notebook, measurement, chemical analyses, all the paraphernalia of precise observation and hours devoted to comparison with pictures and descriptions in reference books or with identified specimens won't recreate the living shark. The paleontologist must apply his imagination and reason to reconstruct the living past from the traces of the once-living. From observations, imagination suggests certain hypotheses to account for their nature, and reason judges, from a set of given rules, which hypothesis is most probable.

THE CHARACTERISTICS OF FOSSILS

Fossils resemble, to a greater or lesser degree, modern organisms, or rather parts of those organisms. Fossils are found only in sedimentary rocks (some of the rare exceptions are discussed below), and these rocks are derived from sediments like modern ones in which similar organisms are sometimes buried after death. Finally, different kinds of fossils are associated in the rocks in the same way in which different organisms are now associated in life or in burial.

Many fossils resemble modern organisms in composition and form, some even in microscopic detail. The shell of a clam living in a tidal channel is very like the shells cast up by waves along the beach and like the shells buried by sand high on the beach. In turn, similar shells occur in the partly consolidated rocks from a hill beyond the shore, and still others—though perhaps less similar —in a dense sandstone on a distant mountain (Fig. 1-1). Or a section of a fossil beneath a microscope may show the fine details of cellular structure (Fig. 1-2).

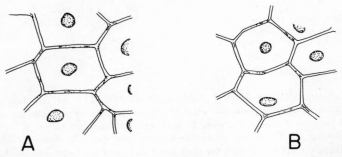

Fig. 1–2. *PRESERVATION OF CELLULAR STRUCTURE.* A) Section of skin of a fossil frog from the Eocene of Geiseltales. B) Section of skin of recent frog showing polygonal cells with bounding membrane and central nucleus. Magnification of both about 600 times. (A. after Schindewolf.)

Other structures found in rocks, however, are less obviously fossils (Fig. 1-3C), and some that originated by inorganic processes (crystallization, compaction, etc.) resemble animal or plant structures (Fig. 1-3A, 1-3B). There is no very sure way of identifying these anomalous objects; but, as a rule of the thumb, fossils have a more complex organization of parts, resemble other objects from the same rocks in general form and detailed structure, and show evidence of burial by the surrounding sediments. In contrast, inorganic structures are no more complicated than crystal growths, vary greatly in form or detail (or both), and may cut across the sedimentary beds or show other evidence of later formation.

If similarity of form extends to microscopic features, you might expect equal similarity in chemical composition. Decay, oxidation, reduction, solution, and the activities of other organisms, however, destroy or alter the normal composition before, during, or after burial. The organic compounds are least stable and are preserved only in special circumstances (the frozen mammoths of Siberia) or as traces in shell or bone. The inorganic compounds (calcium carbonate, silica, etc.) from which some animals construct their skeletons resist destruction or alteration but yield to prolonged exposure to air, water, and organic activity on the surface or to chemical activity after burial. Because of this attrition, observed in action now, only a small proportion of the animals living at any time were preserved as fossils, and most of these in fragmental and altered form.

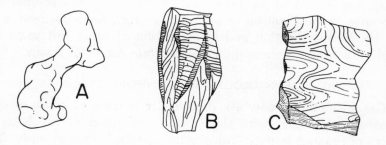

Fig. 1–3. *CONCRETIONS AND FOSSILS.* A) Chert concretion. B) Cone-in-cone concretion. C) Fossil calcareous algae. Both concretions cut across the beds in which they were found. The fossil lay in the plane of the bedding.

The fossil shark's tooth mentioned on the first page illustrates these characteristics, for it resembles the teeth of modern sharks in form and in composition (the stable inorganic compound), but it also illustrates something else: the association with rock type and other fossils. One would expect to find fossils in sedimentary rocks, since these are formed by deposition on the earth's surface, but the association goes further than that. For just as sharks' teeth of this kind are found only in certain sandstones, shales, and limestones, so any one kind of fossil is limited to certain rocks. Rock characteristics reflect the environment at the place of deposition and the life environment of the fossil—or at least the environment into which it was washed for burial. The structure of the fossil also tells something of the place in which the animal lived, so that interpretation of environment based on rock association becomes a check against interpretation based on fossil characteristics. The two usually come out quite close, and those that fail to jibe—like the armored, terrestrial dinosaur in marine limestones—can be explained by transportation after death.

The association of different kinds of fossils in the same rocks is also similar to that anticipated from a knowledge of modern animal and plant associations. Again anomalies exist, but these usually have a logical explanation. Coral reef associations, fresh water lake associations, shallow marine associations—all persist in the fossil record.

But granite gneiss associations? Absurd, of course, but some igneous and metamorphic rocks do contain fossils. Lava flows cover trees and animals, and, even if the flesh and skeleton are burnt away, the form may be preserved as a mold in the cooling lava. Likewise, metamorphism of sedimentary rock tends to destroy fossils by recrystallization and by distortion of form, but some relatively low-grade metamorphic rocks retain traces of fossils.

THE PALEONTOLOGIST AND UNIFORMITARIANISM

The question I'd now ask rhetorically is whether these observations are consistent with the original definition of fossils as the traces of organic activity. You should answer, "Yes, obviously. They resemble modern organisms in form, composition, and occurrence." Particularly, certain forms, structures, and chemical compounds exist at present only as parts of organisms or as results of organic activity. Therefore their occurrence in rocks demonstrates the existence of organisms in the past. If this interpretation is correct—and it could be disproved only by finding all of these features developing in association without organic intervention—a further set of principles must be sought. These principles should extend the hypothesis and permit its application to detailed problems of paleontology. If someone decided that fossils were formed under the influences of the stars (as suggested by some late medieval philosophers), he, as a "paleoastrologer," would seek rules to relate the character of fossils to the movement of the planets. He might assume that certain fossil shapes were the results of specific conjunctions: that the heart urchin was associated with Venus, perhaps, and that fossils were formed first near the mountain tops, nearer the heavenly spheres. Reason would then have rules by which it might constrain imagination.

Just so, paleontologists need a set of rules. If fossils derive from living things, it seems logical to assume that life processes were the same in the past as they are at present. The observations summarized above imply this concept although a different set of processes might conceivably give rise to these same structures and associations. The test then is to see whether this first principle of "biological uniformitarianism" serves to predict in a simple manner the results of further observations. Many of the following chapters will be concerned directly or indirectly with the testing of biological uniformitarianism as a working principle.

But biological uniformitarianism forms only a part of a broader concept of uniformitarianism. Presumably rivers flowed to the sea in the Cambrian as they do now—flowed, cutting valleys and building deltas. Rain fell, rocks weathered, and waves broke along the shore. In general, geologists assume that the same physical and biological processes occurred in the past as at present, and they arrive thus at the familiar dictum: the present is the key to the past. Although an assumption, certainly, it agrees with observation and serves usefully in the interpretation of earth history.

Rivers, however, flow at different rates and carry different amounts and kinds of sediment. Rocks weather rapidly or slowly and in different ways as proportions of moisture and temperature vary. The biological processes vary in their rates and in their interactions. Probably the rates and combinations were about the same, but "about" covers a wide range of variation. Further, man's knowledge of earth (and biological) processes is limited by his short period of observation. If you lived so rapidly that a minute spanned your life, could you say that the hour hand of the clock moved? Or that the alarm mechanism had significance if you did not hear it ring? In the same way, an event that occurred but once in a billion years might be inexplicable, or a process that acted slowly over that same period might be unrecognized. Uniformitarianism, therefore, is a working principle essential to paleontologists but not an invariable rule or a scientific law.

FOSSILS AND ANIMALS

These "normal" processes acting through billions of years have shaped the earth and its life to the present form. The paleontologist concerns himself with the history of that shaping. Yet as the chisel of a sculptor obliterates in succeeding blows its earlier marks, so these processes obliterate the traces of their own action, leaving for the paleontologist only the smallest sample of the past on which to base his reconstruction. Properly, he desires a complete recon-struction, a jungle from which one may hear the roar of lions and a coral reef through which undulate varicolored fish. Further, as a biologist, he wishes to know the details of the living system in some exact, quantitative fashion. How then does one bridge the gap between a few fossils broken from a rock and the living world which they represent?

If there were a time machine, he might move back through successive moments in time to take measurements, stop along some Cambrian shore to count the trilobites, note what they eat, observe their growth, and measure the chemistry and physics of the water in which they live. These measurements, although only a few of the very many possible, would serve to describe a living system. If he can make some of the same measurements on the fossils that remain as traces of that system, they will serve in the same fashion to describe, to characterize. Then, if the relation between measures and the dynamics of the living system are understood, he has a reconstruction.

Obviously, most of the desirable measures cannot be made on fossils. Of these trilobites, perhaps one in a hundred thousand is fossilized, and when fossilized, only the skeleton of a complex ani-mal is left. Likewise lost are the soft-bodied creatures that lived beside the trilobite, on some of which it fed. Little evidence is left in the rocks of currents, or temperature, or salinity of the water; but some things may be undisturbed, like the proportion of one kind of trilobite to another and the type of bottom sediment over which they lived. The paleontologist searches, therefore, for such meaningful measurements.

Moreover, some measures or characteristics are closely related to others in modern biological systems. If one of these can be determined from the fossils, then others may be estimated. For ex-ample, a complex molar pattern exists characteristically only in mammals that eat grass. A fossil tooth with such a pattern suggests grassland although no fossil seed or stem is found. If the limbs of the fossil mammals from the same rocks are fitted for rapid running, this would also indicate an open plain, a grasslands environment. In this fashion a meaningful description of the biological system is built up, using one or more measures to estimate others.

I should note though, that these measures are made on small samples of the living system. The shark's tooth in my paperweight

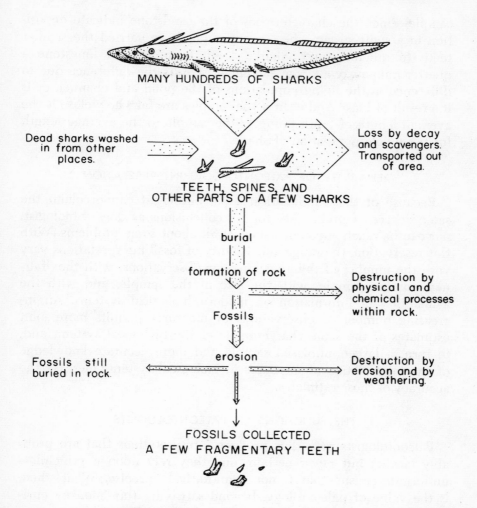

MANY HUNDREDS OF SHARKS

Dead sharks washed in from other places.

Loss by decay and scavengers. Transported out of area.

TEETH, SPINES, AND OTHER PARTS OF A FEW SHARKS

burial

formation of rock

Destruction by physical and chemical processes within rock.

Fossils

erosion

Fossils still buried in rock.

Destruction by erosion and by weathering.

FOSSILS COLLECTED A FEW FRAGMENTARY TEETH

Fig. 1–4. *FOSSILIZATION.* Only a very small percentage of the biological world is preserved in the fossil record. Most of the animals and plants that lived alongside these sharks were not fossilized.

(Fig. 1-4) was only one of several in the sandstone outcrop. Others must be present, buried in the hill; and still others must have been in the rock trucked from the road cut and covered now in the fill across the valley. I have only a sample of the fossils actually in the rock layer. Is it a fair sample, or is it in some way biased? I picked up this specimen because the tooth was unusually large and well preserved, a method of collection hardly insuring an unbiased sample. Since the characteristics of the sandstone indicate deposition in a swift stream, the current might have carried the smaller teeth to quieter water. Sharks' teeth from a pond limestone a quarter-mile away average smaller in size. Is the difference due to difference in the living populations of the pond and channel, or is it a result of bias? And even if the samples are fair, how close is the average length of tooth prong in the sample to the average length for the whole population of sharks?

RELIABILITY OF PALEONTOLOGIC INTERPRETATION

Because of these difficulties, a paleontologist cannot claim the same degree of probability for his conclusions as does a biologist, nor can he reach any conclusions at all about some problems. With this reservation, the range and validity of fossil interpretations vary with the number of different kinds of observations, with the "fairness" of the sample, with the size of the sample, and with the availability of information on modern biological systems. An increasing number of observations or measures permits more joint estimates of the same characteristic of the biological system; and, in turn, a larger, unbiased sample and more accurate knowledge of the interrelation of measures in biological systems increase the accuracy of those estimates.

THE FUNCTIONS OF PALEONTOLOGISTS

Paleontologists may thus produce interpretations that are probably correct but never certain, and they rely upon a principle—uniformitarianism—that is not quantitatively precise. What, then, is the value of paleontology, beyond satisfying the "monkey curiosity" of the paleontologists?

Certainly paleontology has an importance, justified in practice, to geology as a whole. William Smith discovered, more than 150 years ago, that certain types of fossils were associated with definite units of a sedimentary rock sequence, a sequence determined by superposition of bed on bed, and therefore could be used to determine the relative age of rocks.* Subsequently, fossils were found to characterize certain ancient environments and could be used

---

* Füchsel partly anticipated Smith's work; Cuvier and Brongniart developed a similar technique at about the same time as Smith.

to determine past geographic relationships and the physical evolution of the earth's surface and climate.

The value of paleontology to its other related discipline, biology, is less fundamental but exists none the less. Since life has a historical context represented by paleontology, no understanding of a modern biological system is complete until its historical development is known. Further, paleontologists can discern certain general patterns of evolution from this historical record. Finally, the relation of evolutionary changes to changes within the biological system and its environment suggest problems in evolutionary dynamics and solutions to these problems.

Beyond this, however, paleontology is an adventure, an exploration into the jungles of the past. Because it is our own past and our own history, it forms for each one of us an immediate, personal mystery. In solving that mystery we see ourselves in the perspective of time.

REFERENCES

Adams, F. D. 1954. *The Birth and Development of the Geologic Sciences.* New York: Dover.

Bucher, W. H. 1953. "Fossils in Metamorphic Rocks," *Geol Soc. of America, Bulletin,* Vol. 64, pp. 275-300; 997-999.

Camp, C. L. and G. D. Hanna. 1937. *Methods in Paleontology.* Berkeley: University of California Press. "Methods," as used here, implies techniques of collection and preparation.

Elias, M. K. 1950. "The State of Paleontology," *Jour. of Paleontology,* Vol. 24, pp. 140-153.

Krumbein, W. C. 1955. "Experimental Design in the Earth Sciences," *Trans. American Geophysical Union,* Vol. 36, pp. 1-11. A very technical but very important paper on the sampling problem in geology.

Schindewolf, O. H. 1950. *Grundfragen der Paleontologie.* Stuttgart: Schweizerbart. A stimulating, difficult book on some of the major problems of paleontology.

Simpson, G. G. 1953. *Life of the Past.* New Haven: Yale University Press. A simple but sophisticated treatment of the material covered in the first eight chapters of this book.

Swinnerton, H. H. 1947. *Outlines of Palaeontology,* 3rd ed. London: Arnold.

Williams, H. S. 1895. *Geological Biology.* A neglected but very important introduction to modern ideas in paleontology.

Woodford, A. O. 1956. "What Is Geological Truth?" *Jour. of Geological Education*, Vol. 4, pp. 5-8.

Zittel, K. A. 1901. *History of Geology and Paleontology to the End of the Nineteenth Century*, trans. M. M. Ogilvie-Gordon. New York: Scribner. Important but ponderous.

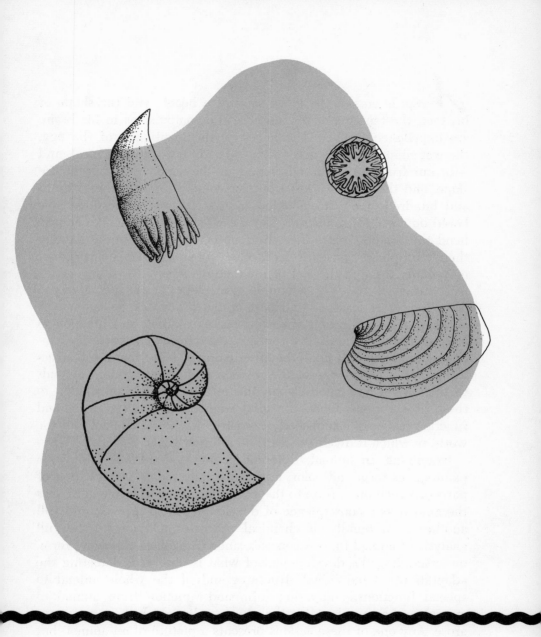

2. The SHAPES of ANIMALS

$\mathcal{A}$ reptile crosses the moist sand of a beach, and the shape of his foot, the tensions of his muscles, the compulsions in his brain, are imprisoned forever. The ancestry, the incubation of the egg, the wet summer of the first year of life, the just finished meal, and —for our frustration—the coarseness of the sand, the angle of the slope, and the moisture left from an evening rain—all these things and hundreds more are molded in the shallow impressions now bared on a slab of sandstone. But we who study the track comprehend the smallest part since the factors, in their subtlety and by their multiplicity, obscure each other. We recognize our prisoner only dimly through this net of interacting causes.

The track is, however, a sample of a living animal and relates to the observer at least a small part of the history of the animal. A skeleton or a shell are, in the same sense, samples, and function in interpretation of the lives of which they formed a part. This interpretation depends upon the observation of fossil shape and structure, upon a knowledge of the relation of form of modern animals to their lives, and finally upon the relation of this knowledge to these observations. Once the vital connection between form and function has been established, reconstruction of the animal and the world in which it dwelt proceeds on a firmer basis.

Examining an animal, different people see different things; a painter sees form and color; a biologist may see an organization of parts or a relation of form to the environment; another biologist sees the animal as a consequence of development and growth, and still another as a bundle of chemical processes. Obviously, the full analysis of animal form is complex since it involves observing form, understanding the development of what is observed, detecting the adaptations of individual structures and of the whole animal to special functions, comparing form and function from animal to animal, and comprehending the processes by which the adaptations arose. Any one of these actions presents a picture of an animal, but each by itself is an incomplete picture, like a single photograph taken to represent a whole continent.

ANIMAL ORGANIZATION

Any one of these particular ways of looking at an animal has its own rules and methods which yield comparable results applied to any animal. A student of form (a morphologist) observes a single individual, a solitary coral from a reef in Bahamas perhaps, in the same way as he would a Kodiak bear from Alaska. I can use a description of the coral to illustrate this viewpoint and method.

The coral is first of all a blob of color and an aggregate of matter distinct in character from the matter about it (the water) and from the matter beneath it (the sea floor). A closer look distinguishes a skeletal cup which supports the remainder of the animal (Fig. 2-1).

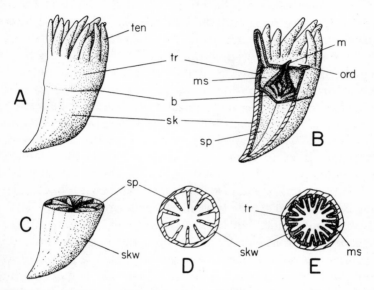

Fig. 2–1. *STRUCTURE OF A SOLITARY CORAL. A)* External form. *B)* Section cut down through body and skeleton. *C)* Skeleton. *D)* View of skeleton from above. *E)* Section cut across skeleton and body just above base. Skeleton widely crosshatched; body wall and mesentaries closely crosshatched. Note that septa and mesentaries alternate and septa are covered by folds of body wall. Abbreviations: *b,* base; *m,* mouth; *ms,* mesentary; *ord,* oral disk; *sk,* skeleton; *skw,* skeletal wall; *sp,* septum; *ten,* tentacle; *tr,* trunk.

The skeleton consists of a *wall* (a cone, really) and of *septa* which are vertical plates extending inward from the wall toward a central axis. Both wall and septa consist of the mineral aragonite and are hard and rigid. Resting on and partly within the cup, the *trunk* of soft, living, tissue rises as a hollow cylinder from the *base*. The skeleton is outside the living tissue, i.e., an external skeleton, and the base and lower part of the trunk accommodate the septa by folding over each plate. The upper end of the cylinder is closed over by the *oral disk* which has a single central opening, the elongate *mouth,* and a circle of *tentacles* along the juncture of trunk and oral disk. The cylinder is partitioned within, albeit incompletely, by *mesentaries* which alternate with the infolds over the septa and which, like them, are vertical sheets that extend inward toward the axis of the cylinder.

The ordering of the septa, mesentaries, and tentacles about a central axis establishes a basic *radial symmetry* for the coral (Fig. 2-2). If the symmetry were perfect, any mesentary or septa should have an identical mate on the other side of the body in the plane defined by the structure and the central axis. Most of the mesentaries and septa are repeated in this fashion, but certain irregularities exist—some are mirrored through a plane that divides the body into equal halves, and these irregularities of radial symmetry define a plane of *biradial symmetry,* a "right" and a "left." This plane is shown by certain of the mesentaries and septa and by the elongation of the mouth. The axis of radial symmetry lies by necessity in the plane of biradial symmetry. The septa and mesenteries at one end of this plane differ in detail from those at the other end so the biradial symmetry itself is imperfect. In addition to having a right and a left the coral, then, also has a "front" and a "back." To the original axis of radial symmetry, one adds an axis of "right—left" and an axis of "front—back," all three perpendicular to each other. The addition of the "front—back" axis establishes a third kind of symmetry, *bilateral,* with a plane of symmetry, the same plane as the biradial. Men, grasshoppers, and clams are all organized in this fashion with a plane of bilateral symmetry dividing their bodies into equal halves. The axes and planes of symmetry furnish a basic organization for the coral. The morphologist describes the animal then by reference of various structures to the axis of symmetry, the base at one end, the oral disk at the other, and to the plane of symmetry. Further, the individual structures are ordered with respect to one another—the mesentaries to the septa, the tentacles to the mesentaries, the mouth to the tentacles. He depicts the general form of the coral or any other organism as a number of parts, each of distinctive shape with a definite spatial arrangement (and with a definite number), and analyzes the adaptations of the animal with reference to the form and arrangement of the parts.

The division of part and function extends to finer details of these units. For example, the body wall of the coral consists of two layers of microscopic units (Fig. 2-3), the cells, each with a bounding

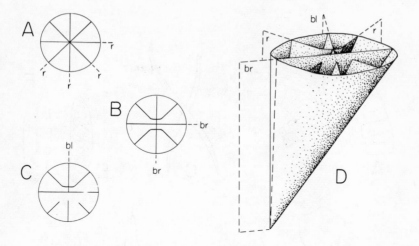

Fig. 2–2. *SYMMETRY IN A CORAL SKELETON.* Various types of symmetry shown by arrangement of septa. A) Radial *(r)*; each septal pair represents a plane of symmetry. B) Biradial *(br)*; two planes of symmetry at right angles. C) Bilateral *(bl)*; a single plane of symmetry with "right-left" and "front-back" directions. D) Lateral view of coral. Bilateral symmetry perfect, biradial and radial imperfect.

membrane, a fluid interior (the *cytoplasm*) in which granules of different types float, and a central dense *nucleus*. The outer layer of cells (the *epidermis*) is bound to the inner (*gastrodermis*) by the jelly-like *mesoglea* which includes scattered cells. The epidermis covers the entire outer surface of the coral, including the base, tentacles, and oral disk; the gastrodermis lines the internal cavity, the *coelenteron*, and also forms the mesenteries. Most of the coral's tissue consists of simple brick-like *epithelial* cells, but some, more fiber-like, muscular cells lie in bands or layers among the epithelial cells; other, delicate, thread-like units serve for perception and communication; still others are modified for the production of glandular secretions. Also scattered among the cells of the epidermis are cells bearing hair-like *cilia* that maintain a constant though weak current by their movement. Finally, abundant on the tentacles and scattered over the remainder of the body are the *nematocysts*. These remarkable structures consist of a capsule enclosing a coiled slender tube armed with barbs. The tube may be discharged from the capsule against prey or an enemy, and, at the same time, a toxic fluid is ejected from the tube. All these various cells and some other types not described are organized to form the living tissue of the coral.

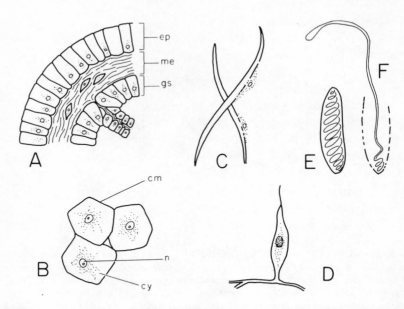

Fig. 2–3. *CORAL TISSUES AND CELLS.* A) Section of body wall. B) Epidermal cells, section parallel to body surface. C) Muscular cells. D) Nerve cell. E) Nematocyst, unexploded. F) Nematocyst, exploded. Abbreviations: *cm,* cell membrane; *cy,* cytoplasm; *ep,* epidermis; *gs,* gastrodermis; *me,* mesoglea; *n,* nucleus.

Other kinds of animals lack radial symmetry and nematocysts but possess other types of symmetry and cells in their places. These differences however do not obscure basic similarities, for although a man lacks nematocysts (unfortunately perhaps for comfort in a crowded bus), he still consists of cells with nuclei (and a few without), specialized for certain functions and arranged in layers and organs. Some of the smallest animals are not divided into cells (or are unicellular) and though composed of distinctive parts lack symmetry or even constant order in their arrangement. Even for these the method of description remains the same.

To summarize: The morphologist describes animal form in terms of arrangement, shape, size, and number of distinct parts and clarifies his description with illustrations.

THE PRESERVATION OF FORM

I should now ask the question, "what happens to form after the coral's death?" The variables are the stability of the molecules in various parts of the animal, the activity of scavengers such as bacteria, the chemistry of environment, the rate of burial, the physical and chemical characteristics of the entombing sediments, the changes in physics and chemistry during rock formation, and the varied geologic agencies acting up to the time that the fossil is collected. Not a very simple problem.

The living tissue, with its framework of unstable organic molecules, decays readily and attracts scavengers. Parts composed of these tissues are seldom found as fossils and then only under very special conditions. In a very few fossils, the tissues are found intact (frozen mammoths in Siberia) or partly intact (mummified animals in late Pleistocene desert caves), but, more often, they are seen as impressions or carbonized films in fine grained sediments. Although the form has been considerably distorted by crushing in these fossils, a fairly reliable restoration "in the round"—which yields a great deal of information about animals and animal parts otherwise unknown as fossils—is possible.

Skeletal parts are much more common as fossils, and, consequently, groups with skeletons form a disproportionate part of the fossil record. Insects, some other arthropods, sharks, some other vertebrates, and a number of other animal groups possess skeletons of organic material. The same limits apply to fossilization of these as to fossilization of living tissue generally, but these skeletal materials, because of their greater hardness and resistance, are more commonly fossilized as impressions or films than are soft tissues.

Skeletons of inorganic compounds such as calcite, opaline silica, and tricalcium phosphate constitute the most common type of fossil. These may also be distorted by crushing and very frequently are altered in composition and/or microstructure. Breakage of the skeletal parts or departures from expected proportions or symmetry compose the usual measures of crushing. Examination of modern animals gives some idea of the proportions and symmetry to be expected in their fossil relatives, and close examination, in some cases of thin sections under a microscope, may disclose actual bending or slippage along microfaults. Again, variation in proportions and symmetry in fossils otherwise similar provides a measure of distortion, but some variation occurs even without distortion. Finally, the character and structure of the sedimentary rock may indicate the amount and direction of distortion. For example, fine grained shales undergo a good deal of compaction, and most of the fossils in them are quite flat, whereas sandstones are little compacted and contain fossils "in the round."

The process of petrifaction (Table 2–1)—indeed the whole problem of fossilization and nonfossilization—is rather a mystery. Some skeletons are preserved unaltered even with some proportion of organic compounds remaining (Abelson, 1957), but others either are impregnated with additional minerals, recrystallize altering microstructure, are replaced altogether by mineral infiltration, or occur simply as casts in cavities left by solution. Most recrystallizations, replacements, and casts have lost some of the details of skeletal structure and so limit studies of form in such fossils. On the other hand, unaltered or impregnated fossils preserve skeletal details and give more information, but even for these knowledge of the over-all form of the living animal is restricted.

TABLE 2–1

The Nature of Fossilization

Preservation without alteration	
Organic compounds	
Soft parts	Frozen; mummified. Such finds are rare and limited largely to Pleistocene deposits.
Skeletal parts	Organic constituents of bone or shell. Chitin in arthropods, graptolites, and some other invertebrates. Cartilage in some vertebrates.
Inorganic compounds	
Calcium carbonate:	
Calcite	Fairly stable, found in many invertebrate phyla.
Aragonite	Moderately stable, rare in rocks older than Mesozoic. Corals and molluscs.
Tricalcium phosphate	Brachiopods, arthropods, vertebrates. Quite stable.
Silica (opaline)	Moderately stable. Rare in rocks older than Cenozoic. Sponges and some protozoans.
Altered in fossilization	
Organic compounds	
Soft parts	Films of carbon. Rare. Found in fine shales deposited in anerobic environments.
Skeletal parts	Carbonized. Particularly the chitinous skeletons of arthropods and graptolites.
Inorganic compounds	
Permineralized	Deposition of minerals in interstices of skeleton. Commonly $CaCO_3$. Less frequently SiO_2, glauconite, iron compounds, etc.

| Recrystallized | Less stable inorganic compounds alter in physical form to more stable state without change in chemical composition, e.g. aragonite to calcite. May be very common mode of preservation, but difficult to distinguish from replacement. |
| Replacement | Removal of original skeleton material by solution and deposition of new compounds, carbonates, silica, iron compounds, etc., in its place. Very common—intergrades with permineralization and recrystallzation. |

Preservation as molds or casts
Organic compounds

| Soft parts | Imprints in fine-grained laminated shales and lithographic limestones. |
| Skeletal parts | Imprints or casts. |

Inorganic compounds

| Molds | External and internal molds formed by sediment around or within skeletal parts (Figure 2-4). |
| Casts | Filling of mold after skeletal parts are dissolved (Fig. 2-4). Intergrades with replacement. |

Evidences of animal activities

Tracks	Mode of locomotion. Preserved as molds and casts.
Burrows	Animal habitat and behavior. Mode of burrowing. Preserved as molds and casts.
Coprolites	Fossilized excrement. Diet. Structure of gut. May be preserved in any of ways in Table 2–1.
Borings and tooth marks	Evidence of predation.

Unfortunately, interpretation of the mode of preservation depends upon apparent preservation of structure, or on similarity in structural detail and composition to living relatives of the fossil group. If fine details are preserved and the composition is the same as in modern forms, presumably the skeletal material is unaltered. Since the skeleton is unaltered chemically and the composition is the same as living relatives, the composition of the skeleton has remained the same throughout the history of the group. And around and around the reasoning goes.

Two avenues would appear to lead out of this intellectual traffic circle. Among many recent animals, the microstructure of the skeleton is correlated with organic construction—that is to say, the crystals in the skeleton are arranged in a definite order different from that in inorganic crystal growths. A thin section of the fossil under a petrographic microscope may show this distinctive ordering of crystal axes, but some individual ions can probably move in and out of these crystal lattices without disturbing the arrangement as a whole. In consequence, some changes in composition might occur without any indication in microstructure—experimental data on the extent of such changes is badly needed.

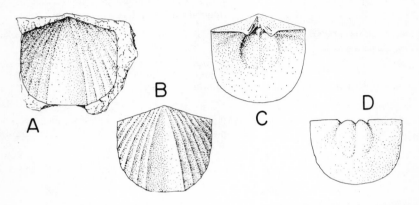

Fig. 2–4. *FOSSIL MOLDS AND CASTS.* Types of fossil preservation shown by a brachiopod shell. *A)* External mold—the impression of the shell in the rock. *B)* Cast—external surface—formed by replacement of original shell material. *C)* Cast—internal surface. *D)* Internal mold—impression formed by the inner surface of the shell on the mud or sand that filled the interior of the shell.

The occurrence of organic compounds within inorganic shell or bone likewise provides a measure of alteration. Most, if not all, of these are more sensitive to physio-chemical changes than the inorganic constituents. If a scale of sensitivity for such compounds under geologic conditions were available (a start on such a scale has been made—see Abelson, 1957), a parallel scale of degrees of alteration could be constructed.

Because distortion of form and alteration of composition modifies the characteristics of the "sample" of the living animal, the paleontologist attempts to evaluate these modifications by some of the criteria given in the preceding paragraphs. Sometimes the interpretation of these modifications is useful in itself. The distortion of a mammalian skull tells something of the forces imposed upon it; the replacement of a shell is related to the geochemistry of the sediment and the subsequent rock formation. But more often the interpretation separates these modifications as "accidents" of fossilization from the more important features produced by organic growth and related to organic function.

DEVELOPMENT OF FORM

Since a coral consists of units with a definite spatial arrangement, the topography of the animal may be mapped—the axes and planes of symmetry as the grid; the major units as the dominating hills and valleys; and the different cells as contours of the living landscape. This topography is obviously more strictly organized than any real land surface—the very word *organism* implies this—and it must develop as does a landscape in some orderly fashion but with more efficient control.

How does this development concern a student of fossils? I would answer, in a general way, that he cannot grasp the significance of form (and its variation and transformation in time) without understanding its development. More immediately, many fossils are of immature animals. The method of study depends on the manner of growth of these animals.

The development of all organisms is similar and consists of cell proliferation, growth, and differentiation. These activities generate the major units of the body. In the coral, this is most simply seen in the colonial types. In these a layer of tissue connects the individual animals that compose the colony. Acceleration of cell proliferation and of cell growth forms new individuals as buds from this layer. The cells divide, grow, and redivide. Shortly, these processes become localized within certain portions of the bud so that the major structures of the mature coral appear; for example, there is a localization with the body wall of the bud at the positions adjacent to the mesenteries of the nearby adults. Here the cells divide more rapidly; produce, as a consequence, a ridge projecting into the body cavity, and ultimately grow to form mesenteries. At the same time, the simple cells of the bud change and differentiate into the types characteristic of the adult.

In budding, the new cells formed by division possess the same kind of hereditary material as the parent cells. Obviously each one of the new cells has identical heredity. If they grow and divide at different rates or if they develop into different kinds of cells, they do so in spite of their heredity. The control of mesentary position by the location of adjacent mesenteries suggests that the external environment of the cell triggers a particular growth rate or a particular kind of differentiation.

Analysis of sexual reproduction and consequent development suggests other factors and controls. The sex cells, formed in the gastrodermis (the inner cell layer) of the adult coral, have only half of the hereditary material of the parent cell. After maturation, these cells are released into the water where fertilization occurs. Since each cell, both egg and sperm, bears only half the normal complement of hereditary material, the fusion of the two brings the amount of hereditary material up to the original level.

This initial cell of the new individual now divides in the same manner as the cells in asexual reproduction. The replication continues until a hollow ball of cells is formed (Fig. 2-5). The ball then folds into itself so that an elongate, cup-shaped individual is developed with a body wall of two layers of cells. The mesentaries develop in pairs in the central cavity; the animal settles to the bottom; a basal plate of aragonite forms, and the initial septa appears beneath the intermesenteric spaces. Then the development of tentacles and additional mesentaries and septa elaborate the structure.

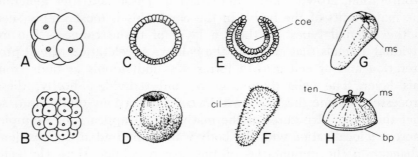

Fig. 2–5. *DEVELOPMENT OF CORAL. A)* Early, eight cells. *B)* Many celled. *C)* Many celled, hollow ball stage. Section cut across embryo. *D)* After infolding of one side of ball to form embryonic coelenteron. *E)* Cross section showing embryonic coelenteron. *F)* Slightly later stage somewhat elongated and ciliated (*cil*). *G)* Formation of initial mesentaries (*ms*). *H)* Embryo after formation of flat basal plate (*bp*). First tentacles (*ten*) present.

Here again the development is orderly, though more complicated than asexual budding. But this order, characteristic of both asexual and sexual reproduction and development, is mutable. If several buds produced by a single individual are separated, but are allowed to develop in the same environment, the process of development and the form of adult will be similar in each bud. On the other hand, if a series of fertilized eggs are placed in the same environment for development, the process and the adults will differ in details. Since the asexual buds have identical heredity and fertilized eggs differ in heredity, biologists conclude that the hereditary material controls, in some fashion, the pattern of development.

But not completely, for asexually produced buds placed in different environments will develop in different ways. This is most obvious when the gross size is modified by modifying the amount of food available, but other factors such as temperature or chemistry of the water are also effective. Apparently, heredity determines the potentialities of growth and development, but environment regulates the specific manner in which an individual develops. Further, each cell has, as a part of its environment, the other cells of the organism, and its position in the developing organism conditions its physiology and structure. In this fashion, the activity of the cells in the mesentaries of the colonial corals induces the formation of mesentaries in the developing bud. Studies of other animal groups and of plants show the same results and demonstrate that the generalization is valid throughout the organic world.

STUDIES OF GROWTH AND DEVELOPMENT IN FOSSILS

Paleontologists rarely have evidence of the early stages of development in fossil animals, but are able to observe the later stages in many groups (Fig. 2-6). The preservation of growth stages depends upon the appearance of hard parts, the skeleton, in the immature individual. In animals that reproduce by budding, such as the colonial corals, the skeleton developes soon after the bud forms. For example, the four septa of the coral, *Tetradium*, close across the center of the skeleton in the upper, mature part of an individual and divide the tube-like skeleton into four parts. Each of the parts continues above this level as an independent unit, and four new septa appear in each of the new tubes. This division must reflect the division (fission, really) of a mature individual by inward growth of the septa and of the body wall folds over the septa.

In nearly all sexually produced individuals, the development of the skeleton is relatively late—after the basic structure has been formed—so that the paleontologist has a record of the growth of the skeleton and related organs but not of their initial development.

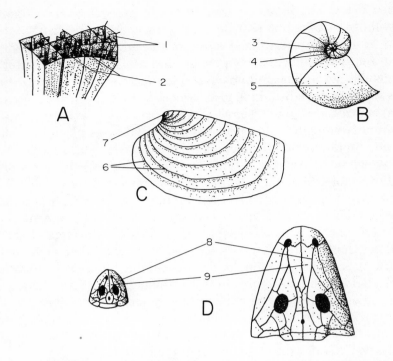

Fig. 2–6. *GROWTH STAGES IN FOSSILS.* A) A colonial coral, *Tetradium*. The vertical plates (1) grew inward and divided the original skeletal tube into four new tubes (2) each of which contained a separate individual. As the individual grew in size, the tube was built upward. B) Cephalopod shell. Initial chamber of shell (3) in center of spire. As animal grew, it built a partition (4) across the back end of the chamber and added new material at its open end. The animal always lived in the last built chamber (5). C) A clam shell. The valves of the shell increase in size by growth at margins. Successive stages in growth are recorded by concentric growth lines (6). Initial shell indicated by number 7. D) Young and mature amphibian skulls. Growth by addition along juncture (8) of separate bony plates (9). Growth pattern can be determined only if skull of young individual of same kind is found. Note changes in proportions of skull.

A single fossil may preserve this record if the animal increased skeleton size by abandoning the old skeleton and building a new one on to it (corals, bryozoa, cephalopods, and so on), or if the animal remodeled without completely destroying the old structure (pelecypods).

The trilobites (and other arthropods) increase skeleton size by shedding the old structure and building a new one. In studying these groups the paleontologist collects a series of these moults—from one individual or more likely from a number of related individuals—illustrating the transformation from the larva to the adult (Fig. 2-7). Similarly, a series of fossils is necessary to determine growth in vertebrates and echinoderms (Fig. 2-6). In these groups the animal remodels its skeleton without shedding, and does it in such a way that it destroys nearly all traces of the antecedent form. The fossil series, therefore, represents a number of individuals which died at different stages in their development. For this reason, differences between animals in the sequence may be either differences in stage of development or in individual pattern of development. Studies of growth in recent animals help to distinguish the two kinds of difference, but such series are always difficult to analyze.

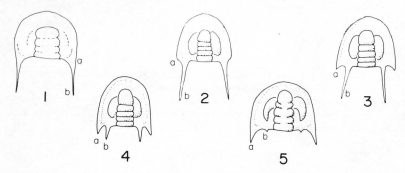

Fig. 2–7. *GROWTH AND DEVELOPMENT IN FOSSILS.* The external skeleton of the trilobite head. Each specimen is a moult shed by the animal as it outgrew the external skeleton. In theory these could all be from the growth of a single animal. Note change in proportions and in spines (*a* and *b*). *1)* Very early, one millimeter in length without the spines. *2)* Two millimeters length. *3)* Three millimeters length. *4)* Five millimeters length. *5)* Thirteen millimeters length.

The method of analysis used depends primarily on the mode of growth. For structures that originate, disappear, or are extensively remodeled during development, a simple description of the structure, its position, and its time of appearance relative to other structures suffices. A trilobite growth series considered in this way consists of a description of the number and position of the paired spines on the head shield, relative to size, number of body segments, development of the eyelobe, and so on (Fig. 2-7). However, much of the modification in form during development results from changes in proportions of structures already present. The oversized feet of adolescent boys and dogs illustrate this sort of development, ordinarily called *relative growth*. Relative growth may be measured by modification of a coordinate system where the positions of certain points are plotted on a grid and the change in relative position distorts the shape of the grid (Fig. 2-8). More simply, two dimensions can be measured on individuals in the growth series. In this

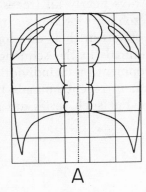
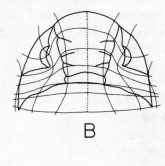

A

B

Fig. 2–8. *RELATIVE GROWTH.* Deformation of grid shows modification of form in development of adult trilobite *(B)* from larval *(A).* Close spacing of lines in B indicates relatively slow growth in that region and direction; wide spacing indicates relatively rapid growth. (After Piveteau, ed. *Traité de Paléontologie,* Copyright, Masson et Cie, Paris. Used with permission.)

TABLE 2–2

RELATIVE GROWTH IN BRACHIOPODS

Measurements of shell length and width on a series of 22 specimens

Specimen	Length (mm.)	Width (mm.)
1	7.8	6.3
2	3.7	3.8
3	7.0	6.8
4	2.8	3.1
5	7.0	6.5
6	7.7	7.3
7	8.6	8.8
8	9.9	9.3
9	11.3	10.0
10	14.4	13.9
11	16.7	14.9
12	16.5	15.5
13	14.7	13.0
14	9.4	8.3
15	16.9	15.0
16	15.3	14.2
17	7.2	6.9
18	6.5	7.0
19	7.0	7.0
20	5.2	6.0
21	4.4	4.6
22	2.7	3.2

fashion, length and width were measured on a series of 22 brachiopods (Table 2–2). Each pair of measurements from an individual
was then plotted on a graph (Fig. 2-9). The points form a cloud
elongated in one direction. A line drawn through the trend of the
cloud expresses the relative growth of width with respect to length.
The line can be expressed mathematically in the form:

$$y = a + bx^a$$

This line does not express the change in a single brachiopod but is a
sort of a summation of growth in several individuals of the same
kind.

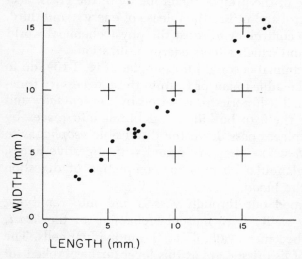

Fig. 2–9. *RELATIVE GROWTH.* Plot of length and width measurements on a series of fossil brachiopods. Each circle represents a pair of measures made on one specimen.

So far I have described growth and development in terms of the
resulting adult morphology. The distinction is useful for literary
purposes, but becomes misleading if applied too literally; the organism at any given stage in its life history is a functioning system
wth form adapted to function. It happens that, in the early stages, a
primary function is growth, but this depends on the other functions
—a dead larva is rarely capable of growing into a live adult. An animal, consequently, is to be considered a four dimensional system—
the immediate three dimensioned form and the time dimension of
development.

FORM AND FUNCTION

The ultimate function of any organism is survival, if not as an
individual at least in survival of its kind. All the others, including

growth and development, are implied in survival. And the converse of survival implies limits of tolerance beyond which lies death for the individual or race. Knowledge of animal functions, of the relation of form to function, and of these limits of tolerance, contribute most of the information necessary to interpret ancient environments and geography.

What do animals need? Food, first, or, more formally, a source of energy. This involves search, and, by implication, the means of search, the moving tentacles of the coral, and the hunting spiral of the hawk, or the movement of the elk to mountain pastures; it involves also the seizure of the prey or the cropping of the grass. Second, an ability to control and utilize the release of energy; and third, ability to adjust to, to control, or to resist the physiochemical world of which it is a part and which affects energy utilization.

But what does one animal, a squid for example, (Fig. 2-10), do to survive and what is the adjustment of form to these necessary functions? The prey, a small fish perhaps, is seized by the *tentacles* and drawn to the mouth, there to be killed and bitten into pieces by the horny *beak*. The pieces pass down the distensible *esophagus* to the muscular *stomach* where they are mixed with digestive juices, and, thence, to the glandular *coecum* for completion of digestion and absorption into the blood.

The blood is pumped out through vessels and into ramifying passages of the body cavity by a muscular chamber of the *heart*, and finally the food becomes available to the individual cells. The shattered molecules of fish tissue are at this level further broken for the energy that lies in the breaking, and some of the molecules or parts of them are recombined to build the tissues of the squid. These transformations, however, require free oxygen that can only be acquired outside the animal, so the blood, in its path through the body, passes through the delicate filaments of the *gills*. Oxygen in solution in the water diffuses through the thin gill walls into the blood and is carried with the food molecules to the cells.

The energy yielding reactions and the molecular syntheses, which require these reactions, are controlled within the cell by enzymes. The production of enzymes in turn is controlled by the hereditary materials acting within the cellular system. And so the tissues are built or repaired.

Each cell, however, poisons itself with the by-products of these reactions. The wastes of cellular activity, of course, diffuse back

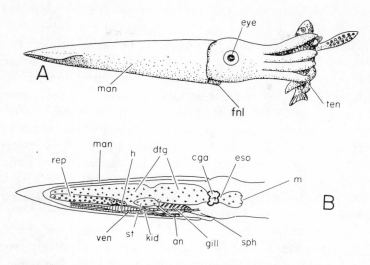

Fig. 2–10. *ANATOMY OF THE SQUID.* A) Squid capturing fish. B) Internal anatomy, one side of mantle and one gill removed. Different functional systems shown by different patterns on drawing. Nerves extend from cerebral nerve centers (heavy outline) to all parts of the body. Arterial (vertical lines) and venous (stippled) blood vessels likewise branch to different organs. Abbreviations: *an*, anus; *cga*, cerebral nerve centers; *dtg*, glandular part of digestive tract; *eso*, esophagus; *eye*, eye; *fnl*, funnel; *gill*, gill; *h*, heart; *kid*, kidney; *m*, mouth; *man*, mantle; *rep*, reproductive system; *st*, stomach; *ten*, tentacle.

into the bathing blood, but the concentration there must be reduced by the filtering action of the *kidneys* and by diffusion of the gaseous wastes back into the surrounding water.

And so you have energy, its controlled release and utilization, and maintenance of a stable environment for each cell. But what of the fish? How did it come to the reach of the tentacles? Or how came the squid to be in oxygenated waters? The prey must, therefore, have been perceived, a retinal image in the complex eye of the squid, an image coordinated to the need for food in the central nervous system and then related to pursuit. The muscular cone, the *mantle,* that surrounds the viscera of the squid relaxes; water flows into the cavity between mantle and viscera; and, on the command of impulses from the cerebral and the visceral nerve centers, the mantle contracts. The water is forced out through the narrow opening of the funnel in a jet, and the squid darts after its prey with rapid pulsations of the jet system. In the same manner the squid will seek to escape a larger fish or toothed whale, aided by a screen of "ink" expelled into the water to distract or blind the pursuer.

In general then, the squid through its behavior adjusts to, controls, or resists the modification of its environment beyond its limits of tolerance. Ultimately however, the environment will exceed these limits; the water becomes too warm or cold, prey too scarce, or an enemy too swift. Then survival becomes that of race rather than individual, and reproduction the ultimate means of survival. In the squid, the sexes are separate and the eggs and sperm are produced by specialized tissues. The sperm after maturation are introduced into the mantle cavity of the female by a specially modified tentacle of the male. The fertilized eggs are released into water and development initiated.

One can construct a general list of life functions from this analysis of the activities in and of a squid. First, food getting; second, the digestion of the food in preparation for use by the cell; third, acquisition of oxygen, that is, broadly, respiration; fourth, circulation of nutrients and oxygen to the cellular level; fifth, utilization of the nutrients; and sixth, excretion of wastes from cellular activities. These are the necessary functions of any life, but all organisms known at present also perceive features of the external world, relate these features, however, crudely to the requirements of survival, and behave on the basis of these relations. Further, all organisms have some protective mechanisms, and finally contribute (usually directly) to reproduction, and, thus, to maintainance of the race.

ADAPTATION AND ITS INTERPRETATION

Adaptation occurs in all organisms, but is expressed in different fashion in each. The squid as a vigorous predator has highly developed eyes; the clam as a sluggish bottom dweller needs only the slightest ability to perceive "light or not light." The tiger needs claws; the antelope hoofs. Each animal has an adjustment of form (and also of physiology and behavior) to its mode of life. It is, in biological terms, *adapted* to a particular set of these general functions, and therefore has narrower limits of tolerance than life taken as a whole.

If the relation between form and function is recognized, if the limits of tolerance implied in a specific body structure are recognized, the form of fossils assumes more than abstract significance.

In this framework, bilateral symmetry is not only a definition of repetition of parts; it is an index to the general mode of life of the fossil. The reconstruction of function in fossil animals depends ultimately on observation of the function-form relationship among modern animals, but the reasoning in a specific reconstruction is more complex than this simple statement indicates. An interpretation of the functional relationships of the "sabre-tooth tiger" demonstrates this complexity.

The "sabres" which were enlarged canines (Fig. 2-11) probably served to kill animals for food as do the smaller canines of modern cats and dogs. They are similar in form and thus probably similar in function; i.e., one reasons by analogy between canine of the lion and canine of the "sabre-tooth." The analogy is strengthened if an enlarged canine is associated with a carnivorous diet in other groups of animals, but some animals with such canines are not carnivores (baboons, for example) so only a probability can be established, not a certainty. Thus additional study is necessary.

The lower jaw is so articulated to the skull that it can be dropped through more than 90° and free the full length of the "sabre" for a stabbing motion. No modern forms have a similar articulation, but analysis from a strictly mechanical viewpoint demonstrates the possibility of this type of action. As a consequence, the reconstruction is based on mechanical analysis of structure as well as on analogy of form.

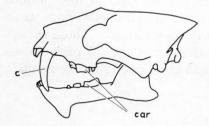

Fig. 2–11. *SKULL OF A SABRE-TOOTHED CAT.* Note enlarged canine teeth (c) and shearing teeth (car) for cutting flesh. (After Matthew.)

The structure of the "sabre tooth cat" in other portions of the skeleton resembles that of modern cats. We can say, then, that the two are "related," without attempting at this point to define "related." Observation of modern animals demonstrates that closely related animals are likely to be similar in behavior and in details of the soft anatomy. The "sabre-tooth" is more likely than not a carnivore because of this close relationship to living carnivores.

Further comparison with modern organisms and analysis of

mechanical details of skull and limbs establishes rather conclusively that this peculiar fossil cat was a carnivore. But wait! Another paleontologist suggests that the "sabre-tooth" ate carrion, not living prey, and argues that the structure of the jaw shows the muscles used in biting (analogy and mechanical analysis) were relatively weak and that the elongated canines functioned in tearing partly decayed flesh. Further, the "sabre-tooth" cats known from the LaBrea tar pits in California were probably attracted to the tar seeps by the large animals caught there who were dying or dead. Here you can note the introduction of an additional mode of reasoning, a consideration of the association of the fossil with other animals and with the environment of deposition.

The first interpretation seems most probable, but the second is certainly not impossible. The conflict is unlikely to lead to duels, nor is the existence of alternate interpretations an uncommon situation in paleontology. The point is that one can only give a probable answer, or choose the least improbable.

Because the fossil yields a very partial kind of information about the living animal, interpretations of function are likely to be equally partial. Complex skeletons closely related to a variety of functions provide much grist for the mill of interpretation. Thus the habits, habitats, and environments of most fossil vertebrates are known in detail; they are far less well known in corals or clams.

Another difficulty arises from lack of information on habits of living animals. Zoologists have described the form of most animal groups in at least moderate detail, but the function of various structures is less often inferred, much less demonstrated. Those groups of fossils that lack close living relatives pose special problems as do those with structures without analogues among living animals, related or not.

REFERENCES

Abelson, P. H. 1957. "Organic Constituents of Fossils," *Geol. Soc. of America, Memoir 67*, Vol. 2, pp. 87-92.

Carter, G. S. 1951. *A General Zoology of the Invertebrates*. London: Sidgwick and Jackson. Deals principally with invertebrate physiology, development, and function.

Clark, W. E. LeGros, and P. B. Medawar. 1945. *Essays on Growth and Form Presented to D'Arcy Wentworth Thompson*. Oxford: Clarendon Press. A series of papers illustrating morphologic techniques and philosophy.

Dacqué, E. 1921. *Vergleichende biologische Formenkunde der Fossilen niederen Tiere.* Berlin: Borntraeger. Function, form, and environment in fossil invertebrates.

Deecke, W. 1923. *Die Fossilisation.* Berlin: Borntraeger. Processes and results of fossilization.

Eager, R. M. C., and D. H. Rayner. 1953. "Relative Growth in Shells of the Fossil Family Anthracosiidae in Upper Carboniferous Times," *Linnean Soc. London, Proc.,* Vol. 164, pp. 148-173. One example of many studies made of relative growth.

Foldyna, J. 1957. "Use of a Stereoplotter STD-2 in Paleontology for the Morphological Evaluation of Fossil Shells," *Photogrammetric Engineering,* Vol. 23, no. 5.

Palmer, A. R. 1957. "Ontogenetic Development of Two Olenellid Trilobites," *Jour. of Paleontology,* Vol. 31, pp. 105-127. A recent study of growth patterns in a group of fossil arthropods.

Olson, E. C. and R. L. Miller. 1958. *Morphological Integration.* Chicago: University of Chicago Press. A technical treatment covering statistical methods of study.

Sawin, P. B. 1946. "Morphogenetic Studies of the Rabbit. III. Skeletal Variations Resulting from the Interaction of Gene Determined Growth Forces," *Anat. Record,* Vol. 69, pp. 183-200.

Switzer, C. and A. J. Boucot. 1955. "The Mineral Composition of Some Microfossils," *Jour. of Paleontology,* vol. 29, pp. 525-533.

Thompson, D. W. 1942. *Growth and Form.* Cambridge: Cambridge University Press. A classical work on the form of animals.

Vinogradov, A. P. 1953. (Translation) "The Elementary Chemical Composition of Marine Organisms," *Sears Foundation Marine Research Memoir,* No. 2.

Also see book by Buchsbaum cited at the end of Chapter 3.

3. FORM and CLASSIFICATION

J have used the phrases "similarity to modern forms," "comparison of form," "relationship to modern animals," and with intent, have avoided definition of "similarity," and neglected to explain how one "compares." I've also written about corals, squids, and sabre-tooth tigers. But how does one distinguish between them, and, perhaps, why?

The "why" is easier; I needed nouns for verbs; I wanted to say "the squid swims"; not the — swims; but paleontologists need to do more. If someone says, "bring me that whatchimacallit in the corner," he is obviously referring to an object and one he can point out if necessary. If, however, he says, "bring me a whatchimacallit," the matter becomes more difficult since you don't know whether a "whatchimacallit" talks, has four legs and a top, or rolls over and plays dead. He's still talking about an object, but since there are several dozen objects in the room, he must describe the desired object. Therefore, he says, "Bring me the brown object with four legs and a top," (presuming you and he have already agreed what those nouns and their modifiers mean) and you drag a table across the room. He may then say, "Bring me the object like that whatchimacallit from the next room," and you understand that there exists a class of objects anyone of which is called a "whatchimacallit" and with a definable set of characteristics.

The process of comparison and classification is thus a constant part of mental activity and is unusual in paleontology and biology only in the conscious attention paid to it. Paleontologists compare organisms and the things they do, and as a consequence of the comparison say that animal *B* is more like animal *A* (called a squid) than it is like *C* (called a clam). Therefore, everyone calls *B* a squid also. If the natural world were completely continuous, the boundaries between groups in such a classification would be arbitrary, and you might find, with good luck, one organism that shared equally the features of *A* and *C*. Most people feel, however, that the world is not completely continuous (which doesn't prove that it isn't) and so attempt to classify along what appears to be natural divisions between groups of objects.

Since the process of classification is first of all an intuitive grouping and only later a conscious analysis of similarity and difference, any discussion is difficult. Probably each person develops, through examination of a series of organisms, an idea of a common *structural plan* which lies beneath the multiple variance of detail; that is, he deals with a population of objects each differing from the other but with limits on those differences. Zoologists recognize that land vertebrates have four limbs as part of their structural plan, but some land vertebrates may have only two limbs (dogs, for example, are occasionally born without forelimbs). One could properly consider such individuals to be freaks, but since they possess the other features of the structural plan of "dogness," one classifies them with four-legged dogs. On the other hand, if a large number of two-legged dogs were known, the structural plan implied by the word "dog" would no longer include "four legs." Once the idea of "dogness" is developed, one names the class which is characterized by this idea. Consequently, the student of "dogness" attempts to rationalize his intuitive grouping (as I just did in talking about the number of legs) by making a list of characters that a "dog" has and no "non-dog" has; it is a list that defines through inclusion and exclusion.

The basis for this intuition varies, moreover, with the purpose of the classification. A painter, in the color composition of a picture, is not interested in "dogness" as such, but rather in color; so he derives a classification of "brownness" that includes some dogs, cats, and cows as well as innumerable other objects but excludes yellow dogs, green cats, and purple cows. What is the difference? Both the painter and the dog fancier certainly are classifying the same objects (though probably not the same "impressions of objects"). It lies in the purpose of the classification and the particular relationship between the classifier and the object classified. Therefore, the painter weighs the similarities and differences on the basis of color relationships; the dog fancier, possibly, on the probable results of breeding animals.

THE CLASSIFICATION OF ANIMALS

Enough for the theory of classification! The paleontologist bases his classification on the form of fossils and weighs similarities and differences on a scale of relationship he calls an evolutionary transformation. In comparing the form of fossils, he establishes a correspondence of parts by similar orientation of axes, planes of symmetry, and poles, by arrangements that appear to attain maximum correspondence, and by the function of parts. Or, simply, he matches head with head, eye with eye, lens with lens. Further, he recognizes a subdivision of parts that contributes to subdivision of the structural plan; the head, therefore, is a more "basic" part of the structural plan than the eye, the eye more basic than the lens. In addition, animals, enduring and changing in time, must be compared in development so that similar stages in development are matched and the patterns of development themselves compared. As the comparison goes on, the weighing of the results in terms of the evolutionary postulate begins. Since the evolution of organisms is a complex process, discussion of this weighing is postponed to a further section of the book. It suffices here to recognize that evolutionary relationships of descent and of common ancestry are bases of any modern classification.

Finally, a formal classification is derived, its precise form determined by the psychology of the classifier but following some generally accepted rules. The paleontological classification, or, perhaps better, the biological classification of organisms, follows a hierarchial system, i.e., the smallest subdivisions are organized into larger groups and these into still larger ones. Since the classification depends on recognition of a structural plan, each category in the classification has a distinctive structural plan; the subdivisions of a large unit share the common plan of the larger unit and are distinquished from one another by differences imposed as details of the over-all plan, and the larger unit derives its structural plan from the elements common to its subdivisions (Fig. 3-1).

Because the classification depends upon evolutionary relationships it also expresses these relationships. The smallest subdivisions have undergone only slight evolutionary transformation from the other subdivisions in the same group; the larger groups have evolved far from their common source. Unfortunately, the formal method of classification now used was developed before the theory of evolution, and so the taxonomist (the classifier, one who deals in classifications, taxonomies) is tormented by some incompatibilities of method and theory.

The various categories are named in this fashion with the most inclusive at the top:

Kingdom
   Phylum
      Class
         Order
            Family
               Genus
                  Species

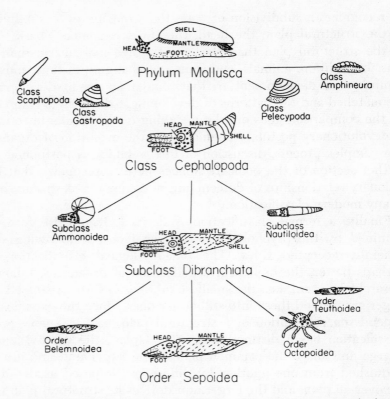

Fig. 3–1. *THE CLASSIFICATION OF ANIMALS.* The molluscan structural plan includes a *shell* lined by a *mantle,* a *head,* and a muscular *foot.* The cephalopod plan includes a tubular shell divided into chambers and tentacles derived from the foot, as well as a head and the mantle. The dibranchiate plan includes a small, chambered *shell* enclosed within the large, thick, and muscular *mantle,* as well as tentacles and a head. The sepoid plan includes a *shell* consisting of a thin plate and a very small chambered portion, as well as a head, tentacles, and a mantle that covers the shell.

Notice that the species is a collection of individual animals, and some taxonomists argue therefore that the species is real and the higher categories which are collections of species, or genera, or families, etc. are not real. Just what difference it makes may be beyond the intellect of the nontaxonomist, but the argument undoubtedly develops one's mental muscles.

Although the species may be further subdivided into subspecies, it remains the basic unit since the individuals of a species intergrade with one another in form but are distinct from all other species coexisting in time in one or more characteristics. Genera are composed of similar species, families of similar genera, and so on. This definition of species is a limited one since some (in theory, all) living species can be defined on other grounds that are more useful, but it is the only one strictly applicable to fossil animals and will satisfy the need until a fuller definition is developed in the next chapter.

In the system of classification each species is given a name consisting of two parts and written so: *Diploceraspis burki.* (In print the species name is italicized; in typewritten or long hand manuscript it is underlined.) The first term is the name of the genus in which the species is placed; the second, the specific modifier, tells which one of the species of *Diploceraspis* is being considered. The generic name is applied to this one genus and to no other in the animal kingdom; the specific term is used only once within any genus, but may be reused in many other genera for different species. The whole procedure is like writing Jones, John; Jones, Robert, and Clark, John; Clark, Robert, and so on. The specific name thus is just a modifier for the generic name. A full citation of a species should also include the name of the individual who first described the group and the year the description was published, e.g., *Diploceraspis burki* Romer, 1952. This full statement permits easy reference to the original description. Rules for formation, modification, and suppression of taxonomic names are complex (see Mayr, Linsley, and Usinger, 1952), but are necessary to promote stability, so that *Diploceraspis* will mean just one genus to all paleontologists, and will, at the same time, allow flexibility in accord with new knowledge gathered about the group.

Names at the specific levels are fairly stable, but unfortunately at the generic, family, and order level they jump about wildly. As new information accumulates, the student of *Diploceraspis* may find either that he is dealing with two genera of different families or that he must redefine the recognized orders to show the evolutionary relationships disclosed by study of this genus. Thus, in poorly known groups, names are constantly changed. The tendency of the taxonomist either to split his groups so that individual variation becomes the basis of new species or to lump many individuals or groups so that meaningful differences are obscured under a single name, complicates this difficulty.

TABLE 3–1
THE ANIMAL PHYLA

Unless otherwise noted, the members of each phylum retain the characteristics of the preceding phylum as well as possessing their own unique structures and organization. A question mark before a geologic age implies that the identification of the group in rocks of this age is uncertain.

Phylum	Characteristics	Modern representatives	Mode of life	Geologic range	Importance as fossils
Protozoa	Unicellular animals of various grades of complexity. Some colonial types. Some have skeletons of calcite, of silica, or chitinoid material. Skeleton may show spherical, radial, or bilateral symmetry; may be coiled, or may be asymmetric.	*Euglena, Amoeba, Paramecium, foraminifers, radiolarians,* and so on.	Aquatic, parasitic	(?) Precambrian to Recent.	Types with skeleton, particularly *Foraminifera,* of great importance in stratigraphy of well cuttings.
Porifera	Many celled animals of low grade of complexity. Cells show incipient organization into tissues; lack organs. Most have skeleton of spicules of calcite, or silica or of organic fibers, spongin. Some have radial symmetry; others asymmetric. System of canals and pores.	Sponges. Approximately 3000 recent species.	Aquatic. Attached to bottom. Primarily in waters with little mud. Feed on microorganisms filtered from water.	(?) Precambrian to Recent.	Spicules common; complete skeletons less so. Of relatively small importance except for a few genera.
Mesozoa	Many-celled animals of low grade of complexity. Incipient development of tissues but lack organs. No skeletons. Elongate mass of slightly differentiated cells.	Small number of obscure species.	Parasitic	Recent.	Unknown as fossils, but of interest as possible connection of protozoans to the many celled animals.

Phylum	Characteristics	Modern representatives	Mode of life	Geologic range	Importance as fossils
Coelenterata	Tissues well developed and include three layers of cells, but organs only slightly developed. Middle cell layer develops largely from external layer. Large central body cavity with single opening, the mouth. Mouth encircled by tentacles. Bear "stinging" cells. Some have skeleton of $CaCO_3$. Radial or biradial symmetry; a few with bilateral symmetry. Some colonial.	Jelly fish, hydra, various types of corals. Approximately 10,000 recent species.	Aquatic, predominately marine. Attached to bottom or free swimming and/or floating. Primarily predaceous.	(?) Precambrian to Recent.	Those with calcareous skeletons common and interesting fossils. Soft bodied types rare.
Ctenophora	No skeleton. Lack "stinging" cells. Tentacles do not encircle mouth. Bear plates of cilia for swimming. Biradial symmetry. None colonial. Medial cell layer (mesoderm) developed from internal cell layer.	Comb jellies	Aquatic. Free swimming. Primarily predaceous.	Recent.	Unknown as fossils.
Platyhelminthyes	Tissues developed; some organs differentiated. Body cavity opens only through mouth. Bilateral symmetry; flattened; head slightly differentiated.	Flat worms. Over 6000 recent species.	Aquatic, primarily crawling or swimming over bottom. Parasitic.	Recent.	Unknown as fossils.
Nemertinea	Anus present as well as mouth. Extrusible proboscis.	Nemertine worms. About 500 recent species.	Largely marine. Predaceous.	Recent.	Unknown as fossils.

Phylum	Characteristics	Modern representatives	Mode of life	Geologic range	Importance as fossils
Entoprocta	Cavity between wall of gut and body wall; cavity develops as remnant of hollow in "hollow-ball" stage of development and is not completely lined by medial cell layer (p. 266). Gut looped so that anus is near mouth. Mouth encircled by ciliated tentacles. No proboscis. Most are colonial.	Small number of obscure species.	Fresh water, attached to bottom. Collect microscopic animals with ciliated tentacles.	Recent.	Unknown as fossils.
Aschelminthes	Gut not looped but straight; no ciliated tentacles. Not colonial.	Large number of parasitic and free living "worms." Rotifers.	Aquatic; parasitic.	Recent.	Unknown as fossils.
Bryozoa	Body cavity between wall of gut and body wall; cavity formed within medial cell layer and is lined completely by cells from this layer. Gut looped to bring anus near mouth. Circle or horseshoe of ciliated tentacles about mouth. Skeleton of CaCO$_3$. Colonial.	Moss animals. Approximately 3000 living species.	Aquatic. Attached to bottom. Nearly all are marine. Feed on microscopic animals filtered by ciliated tentacles.	Ordovician to Recent.	Important in numbers and variety. Useful in correlation and study of ancient environments.
Phoronida	Ridge bearing tentacles is horseshoe shaped. Simple circulatory system of closed vessels. Solitary. No skeleton or chitinous tube.	Approximately 15 species.	Aquatic, marine. Burrowers. Feed on microscopic organisms collected by ciliated tentacles.	Recent.	Unknown as fossils.

Phylum	Characteristics	Modern representatives	Mode of life	Geologic range	Importance as fossils
Brachiopoda	Ridge bearing tentacles is drawn into elongate coiled arms. Solitary; bivalve; shell chitinophosphatic or calcareous; valves dorsal and ventral; each valve symmetrical about midline.	Lamp shells. About 120 recent species.	Aquatic, marine or brackish water. Feed on microscopic organisms collected by ciliated tentacles.	Early Cambrian to Recent.	Common; particularly abundant and varied in Paleozoic rocks. Very important in correlation and in studies of fossil environments.
Mollusca	Without ridge bearing tentacles. Most have calcareous shell of one or more pieces. If bivalve, valves are right and left. Muscular foot (in some modified to arms) for locomotion. Head differentiated; well developed circulatory, nervous, respiratory and excretory systems. Spaces of internal body cavity reduced in size. Circulatory system includes spacious cavities about organs. Differentiated dorsal skin, the *mantle*. Body cavities form as splits inside medial cell layer.	Chitons, tusk shell, snails, clams, squids. Approximately 70,000 living species.	Aquatic, marine and fresh water; terrestrial. Attached to bottom, burrowing, crawling, swimming. Predators, scavengers and herbivores. One group (pelecypods, the clams) filters microscopic organisms from water passing over gill system.	Early Cambrian to Recent.	Probably most common and varied group of fossils. Very important in correlation and in studies of fossil environments.
Sipunculoidea	Spaces of body cavity large; without shell or mantle. Proboscis. Anus dorsal.	Small number of obscure species.	Marine	Recent.	Unknown as fossils.
Priapuloidea	Anus terminal. Otherwise similar to siphunculoids.	Small number of obscure species.	Marine	Recent.	Unknown as fossils.
Echiuroidea	Without proboscis. Otherwise similar to Priapuloidea.	Small number of obscure species.	Marine	Recent.	Unknown as fossils.

Phylum	Characteristics	Modern representatives	Mode of life	Geologic range	Importance as fossils
Annelida	Body divided into segments. In some the segments may bear pairs of appendages. Well developed nervous, excretory, circulatory and respiratory systems. Head not strongly differentiated. Internal body cavity relatively large.	Earth worms, leeches, and so on. About 7000 recent species.	Aquatic; some terrestrial. Burrowing, crawling, swimming. Some parasitic. Predators, herbivores, scavengers.	(?) Precambrian. Cambrian to Recent.	Chitinous jaws found occasionally as micro-fossils. Otherwise very rare.
Pararthropoda	Head well differentiated. Body cavity reduced in size. Circulatory system includes large spaces around organs.	Obscure group, about 80 species.	Terrestrial.	(?) Middle Cambrian. Recent.	Impressions in Middle Cambrian Burgess shale.
Arthropoda	Segments typically differentiated into head and one or two other regions. Paired, jointed appendages. External skeleton of chiton; the skeleton in some is impregnated with $CaCO_3$. Circulatory system includes large spaces around organs. Internal body cavity reduced in size.	Insects, shrimp, lobster, spiders, barnacles, and so on. Over one million recent species.	Aquatic; terrestrial. Burrowing, crawling, swimming, flying. Predators, herbivores, scavengers, parasites.	Cambrian to Recent.	Trilobites common and significant in early and middle Paleozoic faunas. Otherwise uncommon.
Chaetognatha	Non-segmented. No paired appendages. No skeleton. Nervous system poorly developed; no definite excretory and circulatory organs. Body cavities developed from pouches on sides of gut. Bilateral symmetry. Anus subterminal on ventral surface.	Arrow worms; about 30 species.	Aquatic, marine. Swimming. Predators.	(?) Middle Cambrian. Recent.	Questionable fossils in Burgess shale.

Phylum	Characteristics	representatives	Mode of life	Geologic range	Importance as fossils
Echinodermata	Secondary radial, typically pentamerous, symmetry. Torsion of viscera in development changes position of mouth and anus. System of radial canals and associated structures called water vascular system. Skeleton of calcareous plates and spines developed in medial cell layer just below skin.	Sea lilies, sea-cucumbers, starfish, brittle stars, sea urchins. Approximately 5000 species	Aquatic, marine. Attached to bottom or crawling. Feed by collecting microorganisms on ciliated tracts or are predators, herbivores, and scavengers.	Cambrian to Recent.	Common and varied in post-Ordovician rocks.
Protochordata	Bilateral symmetry. Some have traces of axial supporting rod, the notochord. No water vascular system. Gill slits between anterior gut and external surface. Nervous, excretory, circulatory systems moderately well developed. Some colonial. Chitinoid skeleton in some. Anus terminal.	Acorn worms.	Aquatic, marine. Burrowing, attached to substrate or floating.	Cambrian to Recent.	Only a group of Paleozoic colonial forms, the graptolites, are common.
Chordata	Notochord and gill slits well developed, at least in embryo. Nervous, excretory, circulatory, and respiratory system well developed. Segmented. Most have internal skeleton of bone and/or cartilage. Anus subterminal.	Sea squirts, fish, amphibians, reptiles, birds, mammals. About 65,000 species.	Aquatic, marine and fresh water; terrestrial. Burrowing, crawling, swimming, flying. Predators, herbivores, scavengers. Some filter microorganisms out of water passing over gills.	Ordovician to Recent.	Rare as fossils but of great interest to their fellow vertebrates.

THE MAJOR ANIMAL GROUPS

Zoologists recognize approximately twenty phyla in the animal kingdom (Table 3–1), the exact number varying with the allocation of certain small groups to the major phyla or to a phylum of their own. The basic plans of these phyla differ in degree of organization, type of symmetry, presence and kinds of spaces within the body, absence or presence of an anus, division of body into segments, possession of limbs of one sort or another, nature of excretory, respiratory, and skeletal systems, and in pattern of development of these features of organization.

Some of these phyla are highly diversified in form and in mode of life; others are very limited in diversity. The phylum Chordata, for example, includes three subphyla and one of these subphyla, the Vertebrata, comprises eight classes. Each class is a variation upon the structural plan of the phylum, and these variations are related to a general adaptation to a major way of life: the birds (Class Aves) to flight; the bony fishes (Class Osteichthyes) to swimming; the frogs, salamanders, and their extinct relatives (Class Amphibia) to existence in transition between aquatic and terrestrial life. Although within a phylum some classes are adapted to a similar mode of life, the adaptations either involve different levels of organization (like the Mammalia and Reptilia) or different approaches to the same adaptations (like the sharks, Chondrichthyes, and the bony fishes, Osteichthyes).

The subclasses and orders, of course, show still finer variation in detail within the structural plan of phylum and class and consequently more limited adaptation. Some of these subdivisions are worth closer attention, but this can best be done in the concluding chapters of the book. Table 3–1 therefore includes only the larger divisions in animal classification.

REFERENCES

Anderson, E. 1957. "An Experimental Investigation of Judgments Concerning Genera and Species," *Evolution*, vol. 11, pp. 260-263. An interesting paper on the psychology of classification.

Buchsbaum, R. 1948. *Animals without Backbones*. 2nd ed. Chicago: University of Chicago Press. A simple, well illustrated book, brief but very excellent, on the invertebrate phyla.

Colbert, E. H. 1955. *Evolution of the Vertebrates*. New York: Wiley.

Gregg, J. R. 1954. *The Language of Taxonomy.* New York: Columbia University Press. A consideration of the logical basis of taxonomy.

Hyman, L. H. 1940. *The Invertebrates.* New York: McGraw-Hill. A series of volumes that will, when finished, cover in some detail all invertebrate groups.

Mayr, E., E. G. Linsley, and R. L. Usinger. 1952. *Methods and Principles of Systematic Zoology.* New York: McGraw-Hill. An extensive description of taxonomic practice that applies to paleontology as well as zoology.

Michener, C. D. and R. R. Sokal. 1957. "A Quantitative Approach to a Problem in Classification," *Evolution,* vol. 11, pp. 130-162.

Moore, R. C., C. G. Lalicker, and A. G. Fisher. 1952. *Invertebrate Fossils.* New York: McGraw-Hill. A relatively detailed text dealing principally with morphology and stratigraphic occurrence.

Newell, N. C. 1948. "Intraspecific Categories in Invertebrate Paleontology," *Jour. of Paleontology,* vol. 22, pp. 225-232.

Nitecki, M. H. 1957. "What is a Paleontological Species?" *Evolution,* vol. 11, pp. 378-380.

Piveteau, J. (ed.). 1952. *Traité de Paleontologie.* 7 vols. Paris: Masson and Cie. An extensive and authoritative treatment of all fossil animal groups.

Romer, A. S. 1945. *Vertebrate Paleontology.* Chicago: University of Chicago Press. The standard textbook on vertebrate fossils.

Shrock, R. R. and W. H. Twenhofel. 1952. *Principles of Invertebrate Paleontology.* New York: McGraw-Hill. A relatively detailed text that deals principally with the morphology of fossil invertebrates.

Simpson, G. G. 1943. "Criteria for Genera, Species, and Subspecies in Zoology and Paleozoology," *N.Y. Acad. Science Annal.,* vol. 44, pp. 145-178.

Swinnerton, H. H. 1947. *Outlines of Palaeontology.* London: Arnold. An interesting although slightly outdated text on invertebrate and vertebrate fossils and on principles of paleontology.

Woodger, J. H. 1945. "On Biological Transformations," in le Gros Clark and P. B. Medawar, *Essays on Growth and Form.* Oxford: Clarendon Press. A stimulating paper on the theory of comparative morphology.

Zittel, K. A. 1913. *Textbook of Paleontology,* 2nd ed., 2 vols. Translated and revised by C. R. Eastman. London: Macmillan. An old, but useful book concerned with fossil morphology.

See also references for Cazier and Bacon (1949), Michener and Sokal (1957), and Weller (1955), in Chapter 4; Arkell and Moy-Thomas (1940), Jeletsky (1955), Simpson (1945), Weller (1949), and Zangerl (1948) in Chapter 7.

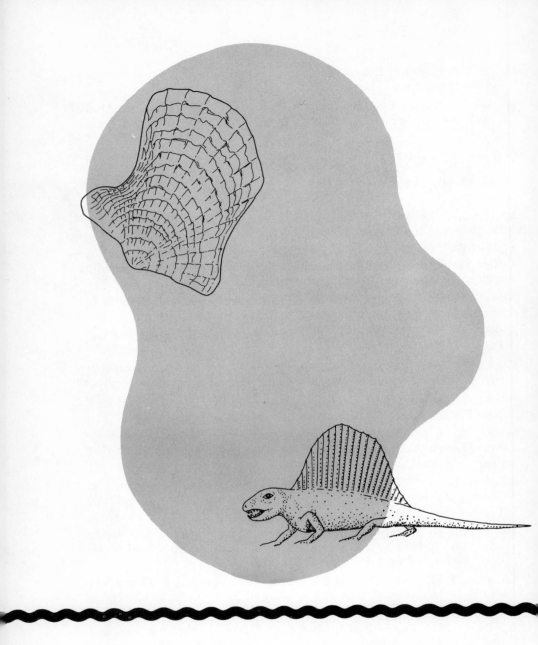

4. The SPECIES

A species is . . . ? I defined it on a preceding page as a group of animals discrete in form (and in other attributes such as physiology and behavior) from other groups of animals. Is this the only possible definition or even the best one for the purpose? Just what is the purpose?

If I can answer the second question, there will be some basis for answering the first. Paleontologists and biologists want a species definition that will include the most information about an animal group in the simplest and most direct way. The definition used in the preceding chapter is direct enough but hardly simple—what is meant by "group" and "discrete?" Further, this definition includes information about the forms of animals but nothing of the biological relation of one animal to another. Thus, when one says that a species consists of a group of animals (or fossils) more like each other than they are like animals in other groups, one raises the question of why they are alike.

One answer might be that these individuals are adapted to similar environments and that the differences in form, physiology, or behavior result from different functions in different environments. This relationship is useful—I'll have a good deal to say about it later on—but not only do individuals, with what seem to be the same functions, fall into different groups on basis of form, but individuals with similar form function differently in different environments. Still more questions!

Let's try another approach then. Form and the other characteristics are the result of development, and development, in turn, is controlled by environment acting on a field of hereditary potentialities (p. 25). Animals growing in similar environments will, in consequence, develop features in common. But if hereditary potentialities are very different, these common features will be but a small part of the animals' total form, and, further, may show little relation to function. Therefore, any classification based on features related to environment of development raises questions rather than answers them.

If, however, animals draw on a common pool of hereditary material through interbreeding (pp. 24-25) they will vary in form only as much as there are different hereditary systems available from this pool (and as the environment of development varies for each). Since the common hereditary pool limits variation in form

51

and consequently in adaption, individuals of this group can survive only in similar environments. This concept synthesizes three different aspects of a species population and states a meaningful biological relation between individuals.

Differences between species must result from differences in available hereditary material, but recombination of genetic material, i.e. interbreeding, in every generation should destroy any particular set of differences. If this recombination is prevented, the species remain distinct. Therefore an inability to exchange genetic material or, simply, inability to interbreed, is a necessary condition for the maintainance of distinct populations. This phenomena of reproductive isolation is so pregnant with evolutionary consequences that biologists have adopted a species definition from it. Thus:

Species are groups of actually (or potentially) interbreeding natural populations which are reproductively isolated from other such groups. (Mayr, Linsley, and Usinger 1952).

This definition does not apply directly to paleontologic species. If, however, the populations of animals from which the fossils were derived were reproductively isolated, there would be a morphological (form) difference related to the genetic differences (or, more correctly, probably would be). The species definition in paleontology is then to be restated as:

Species are groups of morphologically distinct populations within which variation is of the magnitude expected in interbreeding populations, and between which the differences are of the kind and degree expected to result from reproductive isolation of natural populations.

This redefinition solves one problem for the paleontologist but not all. Fossil populations are samples of biological populations. Is the sample a good (large, unbiased, and so forth) one? Fossil populations have duration in time, but this definition says nothing of time. Many modern species show only minor differences in the soft anatomy. Can the paleontologist detect these species limited as he is to the skeleton? To solve these problems the characteristics of species must be considered in greater detail.

GENETIC CHARACTERISTICS OF SPECIES POPULATIONS

Recombination and mutation

Since reproductive isolation and interbreeding are the defining characteristics, I'd best begin with a review of the exchange of hereditary material in reproduction. Even though the hereditary material can be determined only indirectly from the fossil record, it is obviously important in developing a complete concept of a species population (and basic to Chapter 6 on the evolution of species).

Fig. 4–1. *ORDINARY CELL REPRODUCTION.* The rod-shaped chromosomes that bear the genetic material split longitudinally. Each new cell has the same chromosome complement as the original. A_1 and A_2 are a pair of genes occupying a similar position on the chromosomes.

Although the nature of the hereditary material has not been determined with certainty, the behavior of this material in inheritance can be described in terms of series of particles (*genes*) mounted along the length of a number of rodlike bodies (*chromosomes*) which lie in the cell nucleus. These genes may be separate molecules or distinct parts of larger molecules—that's not important in this context—but they do behave as distinct units associated with each other by their location on the chromosome.

During ordinary cell reproduction, duplicate sets of genes are furnished each new cell (Figure 4-1), so that each cell in the organism has an identical complement of hereditary material. But this "normal" process goes astray during the production of egg and sperm. Each egg or sperm carries in its nucleus only half the genetic complement of the ordinary cells. Since the genes and chromosomes occur in pairs, each of these reproductive cells has one of a pair (Figure 4-2).

There are some departures from this pattern where sex determiners are borne on an unpaired chromosome or where three or more chromosomes of one type are found in an ordinary cell, but these exceptions do not change the theoretical picture developed here. The new organism formed when the sperm fertilizes the egg obtains one half of its genes from each parent so a *recombination* of hereditary material takes place.

If all the individuals in the interbreeding population possessed identical sets of genes, recombination would lack significance; it

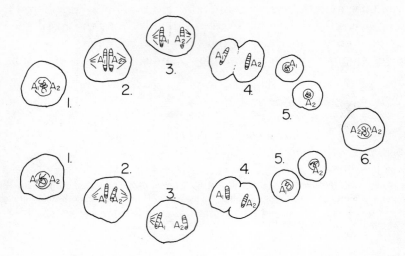

Fig. 4–2. *DIVISION OF CELLS IN SEXUAL REPRODUCTION.* Simple diagram of the reduction of chromosome number and hereditary material. During division, chromosomes pair, and one of each pair goes into sex cell. Stage 6, as a result of recombination of genes, has a different hereditary material than either parent. A_1 and A_2 are a pair of genes, one on either chromosome.

would simply put back together that torn asunder. No such population is known. The complex molecule that is a gene lacks complete stability, and the structure may, very infrequently, change. Since the gene controls some portion of the cellular activity, that activity is changed, and the form of the organism changed. As a result of the mutation, i.e., the change, of genes on one chromosome or the other of a pair, the cells differ in gene complement after division (Figure 4-2). As an example, a particular gene A_1 changes in structure to A_2. In a few generations some individuals will have a complement of $A_1 A_2$; others $A_2 A_2$; and some will still retain the original $A_1 A_1$. Another gene B_1 mutates to B_2. Different individuals in the population can now carry one of nine combinations $A_1 A_1 B_1 B_1$; $A_1 A_2 B_1 B_1$; $A_1 A_2 B_1 B_2$; $A_1 A_2 B_2 B_2$; $A_1 A_1 B_1 B_2$; $A_1 A_1 B_2 B_2$; $A_2 A_2 B_1 B_1$; $A_2 A_2 B_1 B_2$; and $A_2 A_2 B_2 B_2$. Furthermore A_2 might mutate to A_3; A_3 to A_4 and so on.

If each cell contains only two hundred genes (one hundred pairs) and if four variant genes (A_1, A_2, A_3, A_4,) are present in the population for each pair, how many different combinations of hereditary

material are possible? There must be 10^{100} different combinations.*
Since the total number of individual animals that have ever lived
on the earth probably does not greatly exceed 1.5×10^{25} †, much
more genetic variability is available than has ever been used.

Casual observation demonstrates, however, that most individuals
in a species population are quite similar. Either a relatively small
number of gene systems must predominate in the population, or
the differences between gene systems must produce relatively small
changes in the developmental systems. Experimental studies of
gene frequencies in natural population indicate that both of these
alternatives are true, for some genes are much more common than
others and only a very few of the observed differences in gene
systems result in major differences in the individual.

But why do some genes have high frequencies and others low?
To answer that I'll have to go back again to the description of
genetic recombination and exhume some buried assumptions. First
of all, gene frequencies are determined by mutation toward and
away from a particular gene. If one out of every million A_1 genes
mutates to A_2 in every generation and if A_2 does not mutate at all,
the population will eventually loose all of its A_1's, and the frequency
of A_2 will be 1.0, unless something interferes. If A_1 mutates to A_2
at a different rate, the time for A_2 to replace A_1 will change but the
final result won't. In contrast, if A_2 mutates back to A_1 at an equal
rate, the frequencies of A_2 will increase to .5 but go no further. In
a population of one million individuals at this equilibrium point,
there would be one million A_1 genes and one million A_2 genes.
Mutation would produce, on the average, one new A_2 in every generation, but this would be counterbalanced by one mutation from
A_2 to A_1. The frequencies of the different genes therefore are proportional to the mutation rates.

---

* The result is calculated from the Hardy-Weinberg law. This is written most generally as:

$$\prod_{L=1}^{k} \left[\sum_{i=1}^{k} (a_i A_i) \right]^2$$

Where: a_i is the frequency of gene A_i;
$a_1 + a_2 + a_3 \ldots = 1.0$;
and $A_1, A_2, A_3, \ldots A_n$ are the series of mutant genes
at a particular position on a chromosome.

† Two million species $\times$ ten billion individuals in a species during a generation $\times$
two generations a year $\times$ four billion years equals 1.6×10^{25}; this is pretty speculative, but the figure almost surely lies between 10^{23} and 10^{27}.

Selection and population structure

Unless something interferes! Assume that these genes A_1 and A_2 occur in guinea pigs. The genes function in the developmental system by the kind of enzymes they produce (or cause to be produced). When cells containing $A_1 A_1$ are present at the anterior pole of the embryo, they tend to develop by growth and cellular differentiation into a head. When the cells contain $A_1 A_2$ or $A_2 A_2$, an insufficient amount of enzyme necessary to this growth and differentiation is produced. The head fails to develop, and the guinea pig bearing A_2 genes survives only a few hours after birth. The frequency of A_2 in the guinea pig population will equal the net mutation rate to A_2 but will not exceed it since A_2 genes disappear as rapidly as they appear. The effect of A_1 and A_2 varies, of course, with the gene system in which they are placed and with the environment of development. The frequency of different gene systems (and consequently of the genes that compose them) depends on their survival value in the environment of the animals carrying them as well as on the mutation rates of genes in the combinations. The gene frequencies, as a result, are "selected" by the environment (this will be discussed in Chapter 6).

Finally, all these statements assume a very large breeding population and random breeding between individuals bearing different combinations. If the population numbers only 10 and the frequency of A_1 is only .1, the A_1 is likely to be eliminated by (1) the death of the A_1 individual(s) before reproduction, or (2) the failure of eggs or sperm carrying A_1 to reach fertilization. This accidental elimination of genes produces fixation of a small number of gene combinations in small populations.

But small populations are small breeding populations and may be parts of a large species population. If individuals migrate only slowly from one part of the species range to another, the parents of an individual may be drawn from a breeding population of only a few dozen. Local fixation of gene frequencies thus can occur within species populations numbering in the billions. In addition, individuals are likely to mate with close relatives in this population set up; such mating reduces the number of gene combinations occurring in a locality, and the individuals in a local unit display a unity of form that distinguishes them from individuals of other units. Such modifications of local populations do not, however, change the frequency of genes in the population as a whole. As a consequence of these factors, the species population at a particular time consists of individuals similar in most genes but differing in a few.

GENETICS OF FOSSIL POPULATIONS

These, then, are the genetic characteristics of the species population: an array of gene combinations controlled by gene frequencies and modified by gene mutation, by selection, by population size, and amount of inbreeding. But the paleontologist cannot study fossil chromosomes under a microscope nor conduct breeding experiments on dinosaurs. If he is to determine the genetics of fossil populations, he must do so indirectly through morphology. As a further complication, the relation between gene systems and form is neither a straightforward nor a one-to-one relationship, since different gene combinations can produce quite similar morphological characteristics. The correlation between sample measurement (fossil morphology) and the characteristic of the living system (the gene system) is too low for comfortable armchair hypotheses.

In spite of this difficulty, studies of "fossil genetics" are of considerable importance. The genetic characteristics of populations are a critical factor in their evolution (Chapter 6). Two approaches have been tried in order to estimate the gene system from fossils. The first involves study of differences among individuals of a fossil species that can be classified as presence-absence differences, that is, either a spine is present on the third body segment of a trilobite or it is not.

Kurtén (1955), for example, attempted such an explanation for tooth size relationships in recent and Pleistocene bears. In the two species of bears studied, he found that the height of the crown of the first upper molar is relatively greater in longer teeth. Short teeth have relatively low crowns; long teeth relatively high. Figure 4-3 shows this by a plot of crown height against crown length.* The points on the graph fall in two clouds. All those in one cloud belong to the species *Ursus arctos*, the European brown bear. The other cloud includes all specimens of the Pleistocene cave bear, *Ursus spelaeus,* and a very few (four individuals) of *Ursus arctos.* The problem arises from these four variant *U. arctos.*

---

* The graph was constructed in the same way as the relative growth graph on p. 28.

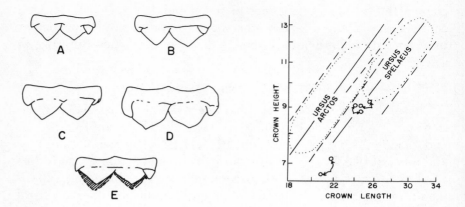

Fig. 4–3. *RELATIVE CROWN HEIGHT IN BEAR TEETH.* Side view of crown of first upper molar. A) and B) Small and large specimens of the European brown bear, *Ursus arctos.* C) and D) Small and large specimens of the cave bear, *Ursus spelaeus.* E) Tooth of *U. arctos* with exceptionally low crown (*U. spelaeus* type). Shaded outline indicates crown height of normal *U. arctos* of the same crown length. Diagram at right summarizes measurements of crown height and length of 96 brown bears and 109 cave bears. Dotted line bounds distribution of points; solid lines are regression lines for each distribution; dashed lines indicated expected range of variation in a sample of 1,000. Circles are measurements on three brown bears that fall in the cave bear range. Specimen E at left is one of these bears. (After Kurtén.)

To quote Kurtén:

But in the height-length relation these specimens may be said to "imitate" the cave bear. The conclusion that these are mutants seems to have much to say for it, . . .

His reasoning is somewhat like this:

1. Most, if not all, the variation among individuals represented within each cloud of points resulted from variation in environment of development.

2. The variation in form represented by the difference between the clouds resulted from a genetic difference between the groups of individuals.

3. Since the difference is of the presence-absence type—the bears have either an *arctos* type or a *spelaeus* type tooth—the genetic difference involves a pair of genes, A_a and A_s. Most *U. arctos* individuals carry either $A_a A_a$ or $A_a A_s$, but some have the pair $A_s A_s$. All cave bears, however, have the latter combination.

Kurtén then attempts to follow these genes into the ancestral population, and to discuss the selective factors and genetic background. I lack space to develop his ideas here, but his analysis is brilliant.

As Kurtén recognizes, the interpretation depends on a large number of untestable assumptions. Therefore the genetic system may have been much more complex than he suggests. I would enter here additional reservations applying to any such study. Interpretation depends on assumptions, derived from biology, about genetic systems. Since it can do no more than illustrate biological theories— the extent of illustration depending upon the brilliance of the paleontologist—is it any more than an interesting exercise?

The other approach is more susceptible to rigorous analysis and begins with the assumption that a high correlation exists between the amount of variation in gene combinations and the amount of morphologic variation between individuals in the species. If this assumption can be verified by study of modern species (and present evidence is against it, Bader, 1956), the paleontologist will possess a useful tool for the study and description of fossil species and their evolutionary development—if certain other conditions can be met.

Method 2

What conditions? If one begins a study of this sort, he needs to know just what kind of population he has sampled. Are these fossils from a single contemporaneous population? Or are part of them from one population, part from another later in time, and a third part from a still later population? If contemporaneous, were they all members of a single small interbreeding unit or of a much larger breeding unit or derived from several partly isolated units? The answers might come from careful field work showing the stratigraphic position of the specimens or their association at a single stratigraphic level (if this "level" represents a very small time interval).

MORPHOLOGICAL CHARACTERISTICS OF SPECIES POPULATIONS

The availability of information on fossil morphology and the modes of analysis of that morphology will, however, always restrict such studies. Common sense and biological observation demonstrate the variation in form from individual to individual of the same species. Description of form (and determination of its significance) depends upon simultaneous recognition of this variation and of the common plan underlying variation. Thus, the paleontologist recognizes a "normal" or "typical" morphology for a given species and also observes that "norm" as an abstraction based on a large number of individuals. Individuals from other species overlap in many characteristics; they do not fall within the defined limits of variation for that set of characteristics peculiar to the species.

In this fashion, the Permian reptile species, *Dimetrodon milleri* consisted of a series of individuals (from which the paleontologist [*] has a number of fossil skeletons as samples) reproductively isolated from co-existing species. Because of that isolation and the consequent difference in gene frequencies, the species was characterized by a unique set of gene combinations. The morphology of the individuals controlled by these combinations varied to the extent that different combinations in this set differed in developmental effects. The paleontologist proceeded to describe *D. milleri* from the limits of variation shown in the fossil sample. Before description he recognized the distinctness of this particular group of fossils (<u>intuitively</u>, I believe) and then sought by formal comparison and description to confirm his original hunch. He noted in his collections a number of reptiles with long spines arising from the vertebra and observed that some had spines with a circular cross-section and other spines with a figure-eight cross-section (Figure 4-4). Two species! But are they? First, are there intergrades between the two spine types? Second, do the individuals with circular spines differ in other ways from those with figure-eight spines?

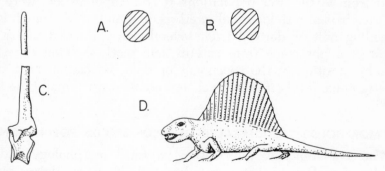

Fig. 4–4. *DIMETRODON MILLERI*, Romer, 1937. A) Cross section of one of spines that arise from vertebrae, *Dimetrodon milleri*. B) Cross section of spine, *Dimetrodon limbatus*. C) Vertebra and spine, side view. D) Restoration of *Dimetrodon milleri*. (After Romer.)

Since he found no intergrades among individuals from the same layers of rock and could associate the difference in spine character

---

[*] With apologies to Dr. A. S. Romer who named and described *D. milleri* (Romer, 1937) for casting him as an unwitting actor in this taxonomic melodrama.

with other differences in the skeletons, he concluded that the two species are real and are samples from genetically isolated populations. Other similar species of long spined reptiles had already been described under the generic name *Dimetrodon* so he grouped the round spined form with those species, and distinguished it from them by the specific adjective, *milleri*. Thus, *Dimetrodon milleri*. Finally he published a description of *D. milleri* consisting of:

1. the name.
2. the designation of a single specimen as the species type—the name bearer. The locality and stratigraphic position was also given.
3. a list of other specimens referred to the species and used in establishing the limits of specific variation.
4. a diagnosis of the features common to individuals of *D. milleri* in which they differ from individuals assigned to the other species of *Dimetrodon*.
5. a general description of the morphology of *D. milleri* and of variations in morphology among the referred specimens.

The statistical study of species morphology

Does this satisfy all the requirements of the species concept? Consider that he had only five specimens of *D. milleri* for study, not the millions that must have composed the species population. These five certainly do not cover the entire limits of variation for the species population nor is the "norm" based on these likely to be the one that would be derived from study of the total population. A paleontologist must, therefore, estimate the characteristics of the populations and compare populations rather than samples. What is the chance of getting two samples, one with circular spines, one with figure-eight from the same species population? This is a little hard to answer, but it must depend to some extent on the size of the samples and depend also on the variation of spine cross-sections within each sample compared with the difference between samples. If some with circular spines show a little pinching or "waist" and some with the figure-eight section have only a small "waist," the difference within samples are nearly as great as difference between samples. If the samples comprise only a few individuals, the chances of getting two such samples from the same population are pretty good.

Using several different characteristics—say the proportions of limb bones, the spine cross section, and over-all size—helps, for the chances of getting differences in all three by accident are much less than for one characteristic. Still the paleontologist (at least this particular paleontologist) would like to know precisely what that chance is.

This concept might be clearer if I manufacture an example. Assume that the *D. milleri* fossil population includes four kinds of individuals, those with extreme figure-eight dorsal spines, those with moderate figure-eight spines, those with slightly pinched spines, and those with circular spines. The paleontologist desires to determine the percentage of individuals with each type of spine. Given a time machine and unlimited budget he recedes to the year X, Permian period, and finds:

> 1,693,748 individuals with extreme figure-eight spines.
> 2,316,190 individuals with moderate figure-eight spines.
>   715,113 individuals with slight figure-eight spines.
> 1,112,643 individuals with round spines.
>
> ─────────
>
> 5,837,694 Total species population.

The desired percentages in the population (technically *parameters* of the statistical *universe*) calculate out to:

> 29.0% individuals with extreme figure-eight spines.
> 39.6% individuals with moderate figure-eight spines.
> 12.3% individuals with slight figure-eight spines.
> 19.1% individuals with round spines.

Without time machine or budget he must find some method for estimating these percentages. If lucky he might collect a fossil sample of ten specimens. He considers this to be one of all possible samples of ten drawn from the total population (statistical universe). Some of these possible samples would contain only individuals with extreme figure-eight spines; some would contain only individuals with moderate figure-eight spines; some only individuals with slight figure-eight spines; some only individuals with round spines; and the remainder various proportions of two, three, or all four types. Obviously the extremes would occur very much less frequently than the values closest to 29.0, 39.6, 12.3, and 19.1 per cent. Conversely, the percentages in any sample are more likely to be near that of the universe than they are to be some distance from it. Because this is true, he or anyone else can estimate the percentages in the total population. This estimate results in a statement that the values are probably (a definite percentage) between two extreme values.

In all the foregoing, I've assumed a random sample. If individuals with round spines had a smaller chance of preservation, the fossil population was not selected at random from the living. If the collector had an aversion to specimens with round spines, the sample was not selected at random from the fossil population. Estimates of population characteristics from this sample would be nearly meaningless. The moral? Complete fossil collections and careful study of the fossil occurrence.

Now let me apply this concept to the *D. milleri* problem, using some (unfortunately) hypothetical data. The statistical universe is the entire population of the species. Two samples are distinguished for comparison, one consisting of the specimens referred to *D. milleri*, the other specimens of similar size referred to *D. natalis*, all the specimens arranged in a series from those with circular spines to those with figure-eight spines. A number is assigned each specimen, corresponding with its position in this series (Table 4–1).

TABLE 4–1

CROSS SECTIONAL SHAPE OF THE DORSAL SPINES IN TWO SPECIES OF *Dimetrodon*
(Ranked from 1, circular, to 16, extreme figure-eight. Data is hypothetical.)

D. milleri	D. natalis
1	4
2	5
3	6
7	9
8	10
	11
	12
	13
	14
	15
	16

The two samples overlap in this characteristic, but most of the *D. milleri* specimens have round spines and none of the *D. natalis* do. The samples are different though they overlap. Is the difference valid? It probably is if the difference between the samples is significantly greater than the difference within the samples. Mathematical analysis * is necessary here (but only as a footnote) and reveals the difference "between" as greater than the difference "within."

But is this significant? "Significant" means that such a ratio would occur in two samples drawn from the same universe only a few times in many cases. I will arbitrarily take five cases in a hundred as my significance level in this problem. Assuming the samples were random and that the distribution of sampling errors is nearly "normal"—sometimes risky assumptions—I go to tables calculated to show the probabilities of obtaining a given ratio from the same universe by chance. Since probabilities are controlled by sample size, this problem requires a table that shows them for a sample of sixteen. Since a ratio this large occurs by chance less than five times in a hundred, I conclude the two samples were drawn from different universes, and, consequently, from different populations, and represent two different species.

The preceding example used some very general observations on dorsal spine characteristics. If two species are quite similar and the samples small, a finer test of difference is necessary.

Measurement of the length of the third upper premolar in a sample of a fossil mammal species *Ptilodus montanus* is shown in Table 4–2. Inspection of the table shows that most of the indi-

---

* Without attempting to justify the method, I use the following formula:

$$H = \frac{12}{N(N+1)} \sum_{i=1}^{k} \frac{R_i{}^2}{n_i} - 3(N+1)$$

Where H is the ratio of variance,
N is total number of observations in all samples;
$R_1, R_2, \ldots, R_k$ are the sums of the ranks for each sample, and
$n_1, n_2, \ldots n_k$ are the size of each sample
and calculate thus:
Sum of ranks for *D. milleri* (R_1) = 21
Sum of ranks for *D. natalis* (R_2) = 115
$n_1 = 5$ $\qquad n_2 = 11$ $\qquad\qquad N = 16$
$R_1{}^2 = 441$ $\qquad R_2{}^2 = 13225$

$$H = \frac{12}{N(N+1)}\left(\frac{R_1{}^2}{n_1} + \frac{R_2{}^2}{n_2}\right) - 3(N+1)$$

$$H = \frac{12}{16 \times 17}\left(\frac{441}{5} + \frac{13225}{11}\right) - 3 \times 17$$

$H = 56.9 - 51$
$H = 5.9$
and arrive at a ratio H that compares the difference between the samples with the difference within samples.

TABLE 4–2

LENGTH OF AN UPPER CHEEK TOOTH IN THE EXTINCT MAMMAL
Ptilodus montanus.

(Data taken from Simpson and Roe, 1939)

Measurements	Measurements
3.0	2.6
2.8	3.3
3.4	2.9
3.2	3.0
3.0	2.8
2.9	2.9
3.1	2.7
2.9	2.9
3.1	2.8
3.0	3.1
3.0	

viduals had teeth close to 2.9 mm. long, but some were considerably larger and others smaller. These measures can be plotted on a graph (Figure 4-5). The curve generated by this plot is a *frequency distribution* and shows graphically the characteristics of the sample. The *mean* value (average) can be determined by inspection to be about 2.95 mm., but a more accurate determination is possible by adding all the values and dividing by the number of values added.*

Variation of the sample can be determined by subtracting the mean from each value, squaring the result for each subtraction, adding the squares and dividing this by the number of values less one.† This calculation yields the square of the *standard deviation*.

The mean length of tooth row works out as 2.97 mm. and standard deviation about this mean as .0406 mm. Mean and standard deviation then serve in comparison of this sample with others.

But comparison doesn't give a precise result unless one can determine whether the difference is "accidental" or is significant.

---

* In symbols:

$$\overline{x} = \frac{x_1 + x_2 + x_3 + \cdots}{N} = \frac{\Sigma x}{N} = 2.97 \text{ mm.}$$

where x = mean; x_1, x_2, and so on are the values for each specimen; and N is the number of specimens.

† $$\sigma^2 = \frac{(x_1 - \overline{x})^2 + (x_2 - \overline{x})^2 + \cdots}{N - 1} = \frac{\Sigma (x - \overline{x})^2}{N - 1} = .0406$$

σ = standard deviation.

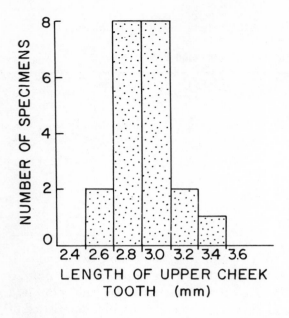

Fig. 4–5. *LENGTH OF UPPER CHEEK TOOTH IN PTILODUS.* Plot of measurements from 21 individuals. Number of specimens *(frequency)* on vertical scale; length on horizontal. Class interval for plot, 0.2 mm. (Information from Simpson and Roe.)

Again variation within the samples must be compared to the difference between samples.

The standard deviation measures variation within the sample. From this value *standard errors* can be calculated. The standard error simply states the limits within which means and standard deviations of samples from the same universe are likely to fall. The sum of the standard errors of the samples is then compared with the difference between samples.* To test the significance of this ratio, random sampling is assumed again, and an assumption is also made about the distribution of values in the universe. This latter concept needs some explanation.

Studies of very large samples of modern organisms and of fossils show a distribution of values that approaches the so-called "normal frequency distribution." As shown in Figure 4-6, this distribution generates a bell-shaped curve with a grouping of values about some center, a rapid decrease away from this central group, and a more

---

* $\sigma_{\bar{x}} = \dfrac{\sigma}{\sqrt{n}}$. $\sigma_{\bar{x}} =$ standard error of the sample mean.

$$t = \frac{\bar{x}_1 - \bar{x}_2}{\sqrt{\sigma_{\bar{x}_1}^2 + \sigma_{\bar{x}_2}^2}}$$

gradual decrease in the tails of the curve. In a universe with such a distribution two-thirds of the values lie within one standard deviation of the mean and 95 per cent within two standard deviations of the mean. If, as seems probable from the studies of large samples, the morphology of populations of most species approaches a normal curve distribution, the biologist and paleontologist are justified in assuming this for populations of which they have only a small sample. Furthermore, the distribution of values for most of the statistics from a series of samples is nearly normal, even if the universe distribution departs considerably from normality.

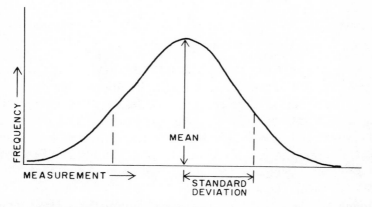

Fig. 4–6. *NORMAL FREQUENCY DISTRIBUTION CURVE.* Values of the variable are plotted on the horizontal axis; the number of individuals with a particular value is plotted on the vertical axis. Two-thirds of the individuals are within a standard deviation of the mean.

The consequence of the assumption is this: 95 per cent of the sample means from such a universe lie within two standard errors of each other. A ratio of *differences of means* to *sum of standard errors* greater than 2 will occur by chance only five times in every hundred trials. This probability statement, however, is true only for samples that approach the size of the population (infinity in this case) so we must use tables of probability that take sample size into account. Table 4–3 shows a small part of such a table for the *t* ratio.

Growth and interpretation of morphology

Comparison of means or of standard deviations of single measurements is useful but limited since it neither expresses the develop-

TABLE 4–3

PARTIAL TABLE OF *t* VALUES

0.05

The value n *is the total number of individuals in the two samples less two. The probability is given in decimals rather than per cent. The probability (0.5) indicates that a* t *value this large or larger would occur five times in every hundred comparisons of samples drawn from the same universe.*

Samples	Probability		
n	.10	.05	.01
1	6.3	12.7	63.7
5	2.0	2.6	4.0
10	1.8	2.2	3.2
15	1.8	2.1	2.9
20	1.7	2.1	2.9
∞	1.6	2.0	2.8

ment of the animal nor shows the interrelation of various parts of an organism. The first defect further limits application of this technique because similar developmental stages must be compared, e.g. young individuals of a brachiopod species will have significantly smaller shells than older individuals of the same species. A sample composed largely of immature brachiopods might thus be mistaken for a separate species. Olson (1957) demonstrated that the frequency of fossils of various sizes is very little dependent upon frequency of these sizes in the living population. He concluded that selective preservation, transportation, and other post-mortem factors outweigh the effects of original size distributions. The ideal solution would result in a comparison of populations of animals at the same stage of development, but the ideal is attained only if the species has an adult form that can be distinguished. The teeth of a mammal do not grow once they erupt and therefore are comparable with other mammal teeth, but if the characteristic measured is modified by wear, measurements can be compared only on teeth showing the same degree of wear.

If proportions of the animals are compared, this difficulty is partly overcome, but only partly, because different parts of animals grow at different rates. Examples of this phenomena were given on p. 29. If, however, both the proportions and the changes in proportion are determined for two samples, and if one can obtain some idea of the factors affecting size frequency distribution or of the life distribution, comparison becomes possible. A plot of one dimension (length of shell in brachiopod species) against another dimension

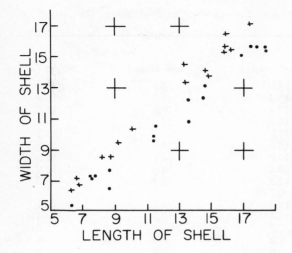

Fig. 4–7. *LENGTH AND WIDTH MEASUREMENTS IN TWO BRACHIOPOD SAMPLES.* Measurements made on two samples (two species?) of the genus *Composita*. Sample A is represented by dots. Crosses indicate sample B. Difference between samples probably not significant.

(width of shell) as done on p. 29 provides a graphic comparison. Each point on the graph (Figure 4-7) represents this pair of measurements taken on an individual brachiopod (Table 4–4).

Plotting points for all the specimens in two samples yields two "clouds" of points, and a line along the trend of each cloud shows the relative growth of width to length. If the two point clouds intermingle indistinguishably, the samples are not to be distinguished—at least by this particular pair of measurements. On the other hand, if the clouds are somewhat separate, the samples obviously differ. A statistical test of significance is necessary; for such a test I refer you to a paper listed in the references (Olson and Miller, 1951).

This method of comparison of pairs of measures suggests a solution to the other defect of single measure comparison, the failure to show the interrelations of various parts. Of course, two measures do not show much about the total interrelationships, but they are useful in analysing simple functions. This sort of thing is shown simply by a plot of the length of the upper segment of the hind limb against the lower segment for two species, the kangaroo rat, which hops on the hind legs, and the related pocket mouse, which runs on all fours (Figure 4-8).

The properties and possibilities of the paired measure technique are not fully exploited, however, by simple comparison of two lines. Although I have no space to describe them here, they are discussed

TABLE 4—4

LENGTH AND WIDTH IN TWO SAMPLES OF THE BRACHIOPOD, *Composita*

Sample A		Sample B	
Length (mm.)	*Width (mm.)*	*Length (mm.)*	*Width (mm.)*
17.9	15.7	16.1	15.5
18.4	15.4	15.8	15.4
14.6	13.1	17.3	17.2
16.9	15.1	15.9	16.6
17.5	15.8	13.2	13.3
18.3	15.5	15.9	15.6
13.6	10.9	14.7	14.2
14.4	12.4	14.8	13.9
13.5	12.3	13.2	14.6
11.4	9.7	9.1	9.4
11.5	10.6	8.8	8.7
7.8	7.4	10.0	10.4
7.6	7.2	8.2	8.5
7.5	7.3	6.6	7.1
11.4	9.9	6.9	6.9
8.7	7.7	6.2	6.3
6.3	5.3		
8.7	6.5		

in statistics books under such names as analysis of covariance, multivariate analysis, correlation, and factor analysis. The references for this section given in the bibliography cover their application to animal morphology.

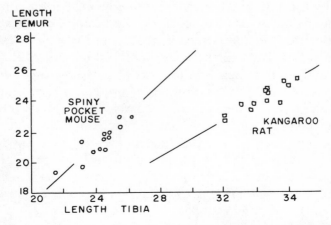

Fig. 4—8. *LENGTH OF LIMB SEGMENTS IN TWO CLOSELY RELATED SPECIES OF RODENT.* The length of the upper bone (femur) of the hind leg plotted against the length of the next lower (tibia). In an ordinary quadrupedal type like the Spiny Pocket Mouse, the tibia is relatively short. In a jumping rodent like the Kangaroo Rat, the tibia is relatively long. The difference between the two regression lines is very great.

General problems in statistical analysis

Measurement of animal form and the statistical analysis of these measurements possess certain advantages as shown in the preceding examples. Measurements can be repeated by another paleontologist; the intuitive analysis, the hunch, can never be repeated exactly by even the same man. If samples are good, minor differences in size or proportion will yield to statistical discrimination though they are imperceptible upon gross inspection. Statistics also provides a method for grouping individual variants that might otherwise be considered different species. Finally, statistical analysis demands rigorous statement of the problem and of the hypotheses, and it results in a statement of the probability that a hypothesis is valid. Even though the data may not be amenable to measurement, statistical formulation of a problem yields valuable and refreshing insight.

Statistics provides a powerful method for solution of geologic problems, but measurement still depends on intuitive perception that the same things are being measured; the necessary "random" sample is often only an assumption; and conclusions as to distribution in the universe are also assumptions. A significant difference between two samples demonstrates just one thing, that, with respect to the chosen measurements, the sampled populations were probably different. It does not demonstrate the existence of two species—that is an inference only partly supported by a significant statistical difference. Subpopulations of a single species often show such differences. Statistical operations are also hampered by the small size of samples in paleontology; intuitive analysis may yield finer discriminations with very small samples. No one has tested this latter hypothesis, however, though a test should be fairly simple. On the other hand, any sort of analysis of morphology, intuitive as well as statistical, depends on assumptions about the amount and kind of variation likely to occur among individuals of the same species and also assumes a "normal" sample, i.e. a random one.

A last objection! Statistical calculation is laborious (and boring and expensive), but some useful statistics, such as the ones used in the *Dimetrodon* example above, are considerably simpler to use.

THE ECOLOGICAL CHARACTERISTICS OF SPECIES

With or without statistics, observation of species morphology is an essential of paleontology, but no species (or paleontologist for that matter) survives on form alone. Somewhere back of the abstractions, back of type specimens, means, and analysis of relative growth, animals must exist. And existence depends upon eating and not being eaten, upon heat and light, upon all the relations of the animal to the world in which it participates. The interpretation of fossil species depends, in great part, upon the discovery of these relations from fossil form, occurrence, abundance, and association.

The study of these relations is subsumed under the name, *ecology*. A sea urchin on the bottom of Puget Sound has a specific ecology, which is described by measurement of the environmental factors acting on it and of its reactions to those factors.

If one measured the ecology of a series of urchins of a single species, e.g., *Strongylocentrotus drobachiensis,* he would find a general similarity though each one differed slightly. One individual might live in 3 meters of water and another in 5 but none in 100 meters or .1 meter. The *action-reaction* systems vary but within definite limits. If the environment of an urchin is manipulated under controlled conditions, the tolerance of the individual to variations in the environment can also be measured. The action-reaction systems of the individual in nature are within these limits of tolerance. One might expect, offhand, that the limits of variation in ecology as shown by the species population would coincide with these tolerance limits. Remember though that no two individuals of a species are identical in form, physiology, and behavior. The population can tolerate a wider environmental range than that of any individual. But the important measure of these tolerances is not the laboratory experiment; it is rather the occurrence of the animal and animal species in nature. A complete analysis of a species population is beyond present methodology, but separate studies of the different aspects of the individual and species ecology provides a framework for analysis. This analysis in turn offers a basis for *paleoecology,* the study of ancient ecology.

Ecology and population structure

Let me set up a hypothetical experiment. Assume a very large number of fertilized sea urchin eggs are sown from an airplane along a stretch of the Pacific coast so that they fall randomly over a five square mile area (Figure 4-9). The experiment uses a sufficient number of eggs to give an average of one per square-yard-sown. The number of these sea urchins in the area is counted at intervals. The results of this census can be stated conveniently as number of individuals per unit area, so the total area is divided into hundred square yard plots for the count. The "density" can then be plotted as a series of contour lines.

A census is made immediately after distribution of the eggs, at

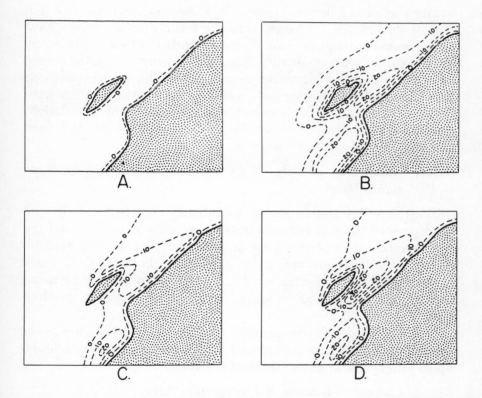

Fig. 4–9. *VARIATION IN SEA URCHIN POPULATION DENSITY.* An illustration of a hypothetical experiment in which urchin eggs would be sown at random over a five-mile area. Land area shaded. Densities indicated by dashed contours. *A)* Population at end of 24 hours. Zero density line along shore lines. Essentially random densities otherwise. *B)* Population at end of one week. Distinct pattern of high and low density shown by contours. *C)* Population at end of one month. Total population has decreased, but pattern of distribution is similar. *D)* Population at end of one year. Reproduction has increased total population and maximum densities. Note that areas of maximum survival and of maximum reproduction do not coincide completely.

the end of twenty four hours (Figure 4-9a), at the end of one week (Figure 4-9b), at the end of one month (Figure 4-9c), and at the end of one year (Figure 4-9d). The numbers in adjacent plots at the first census vary, but the variation is at random so no contour pattern can be drawn. At the end of twenty-four hours, however, a pattern begins to form because all the eggs that fell on land have died. A zero contour can be drawn along the shore line, but the distribution elsewhere remains pretty much at random, though average density has fallen slightly.

Six days later the average number of sea urchins per hundred square yards has fallen still more, but, more important, the distribution of densities is no longer random. Some of the squares have many more individuals than they had earlier; others have many less. Because average density has fallen, many individuals must have died (or moved from the census area). The local populations that increased in density must have done so by immigration from the remaining plots. The number in any one of these populations comprises the original number plus the immigrants less the dead and less the emigrants. Or write it this way:

Rate of Change in Density = Immigration Rate — Death Rate — Emigration Rate

The thirty day census merely accentuates the results of the one week census: the areas of zero density are more extensive, and the concentration of density in a few of the census plots is more marked. Average density is now only a few per cent of the original. The rate of change in density for the whole population continues to be negative and quite high, though some local populations have a positive rate.

At the final census the average density has jumped; obviously some individuals have reproduced. The situation can be summed up in an expansion of the original equation:

Rate of Change in Density = Immigration Rate + Birth Rate — Death Rate — Emigration Rate

The birth rate for areas of zero density must, of course, be zero, so the population of these areas, if it increases, must do so by immigration. On the other hand, some populations of moderate density may have a higher birth rate than those of high density so the pattern of the density map changes.

Numbers and distribution of the sea urchin result from individual survival, from dispersal, and from reproduction. These, in turn, must be the product of interaction between animal and environment. For a population, these processes are summarized as rates; for the individual animal they are living, mating, and dying. By measuring the environment of life, fertilization, and death the ecologist can refer these rates back to the limits of tolerance of the individual and to the range of those limits within the population.

Factors in species ecology

Variation in population density results, then, from variation in environment. "Environment" includes the interaction of the individuals within the species population as well as factors external to that population. Animals respond to the environment as-a-whole, but this environment as-a-whole cannot be adequately measured. An ecologist does measure components of the environment, such as temperature and moisture, and relates these factors to the processes of population increase and decrease. Since any population capable of reproduction can potentially increase in number, these factors can be regarded as limiting, either through limiting reproduction and immigration to a rate below the theoretical maximum or through increasing death and emigration rates. An animal species lives in, has as its *habitat*, the area defined by these *limiting factors*. Finally, these limiting factors act because they influence or because they are part of the three basic requirements of an organism, i.e. sources of energy, utilization of energy, and ability to adjust to, control, or resist changes in the physiochemical world of which it is a part; or else they act because they influence the basic requirement of a species population, i.e. reproduction.

All this is admirably theoretical, one might even say spiritual, but again the animal—what are the components of a sea urchin's environment? How do the urchin and the urchin population react to that environment?

First, the energy source. Urchins of the species, *Strongylocentrotus drobachiensis* eat varying proportions of seaweed, diatoms, tube worms, and hydroids, holding their food with spines and tube feet and chewing it by a complex jaw system called "Aristotle's lantern." Food gathering is accomplished in part by random search and in part by perception of suitable food—probably largely by "smell." Locomotion toward food (or away from enemies) is accomplished by movement of the tube feet and the spines. Survival of the individual urchin depends upon obtaining a certain minimum of food; survival of the species depends upon obtaining a quantity above that minimum sufficient for reproductive activities by a minimum number of individuals. The amount of available food in Puget Sound, for example, will limit the density of the urchin population—a limit set by the total mass of suitable food less the amount used by other species, less the amount not found by the urchins in their search. As the number of urchins increases, the amount of food not found is reduced to that outside the area of search. The increased death of the food species (plants, worms, hydroid) in excess of their reproductive increase reduces the food population density; thus the total amount of food decreases; and the percentage of the amount of food not found (because nonexistent) by the urchins increases. More urchins starve and fewer individuals are able to reproduce; the death rate goes up, the rate of reproduction down, and the population density decreases. In this circumstance, the population of *Strongylocentrotus drobachiensis*, and of its food species constantly adjust to one another.

Probably more often, factors acting on the utilization of food through the limits of tolerance for physio-chemical changes or on

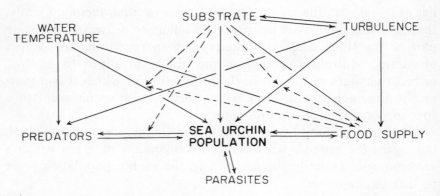

Fig. 4–10. *SOME FACTORS AFFECTING A SEA URCHIN POPULATION.* Interrelation of 6 of the factors that limit density and distribution of sea urchin population. Direct actions are indicated by solid lines. Influences modifying the action of other factors are shown by dashed lines; e.g., the substrate influences the population directly. As shelter, it also modifies the effects of temperature, turbulence, and predation on the population, and it is directly related to turbulence, since the substrate character and turbulence form an interacting system. Cf. p. 79.

reproductive potential limit population density. For example, the temperature of the water about the sea urchin determines the activity rate of the animal, modifies the processes going on in the organism, and may induce new processes. The mechanical disruption of freezing or cessation of necessary protoplasmic activities limits survival at the lower end of the temperature spectrum; at the upper end, the induction of harmful reactions culminates in coagulation of the proteins. Heat, therefore, is a limiting factor, the effects of which vary with different individuals so that the population has a range of tolerance greater than that of the individual. Further, the existence of protected and exposed areas modifies the effects of temperature on species survival. The urchins avoid light and either burrow into the bottom or retreat beneath rocks and shells. In a shallow pool, this behavior protects them—in part—against temperature changes. The number of such protected locations is limited, and the number of suitable rocks and places to burrow sets a population density limit. One might consider competition for hiding places the factor responsible for the limitation, but this does not detract from the limit imposed by the number of hiding places nor from the fact that the temperature changes actually produce death.

The burrowing habits of the urchin also affect survival in storms, since unprotected individuals are broken in the surf. Again the availability of protected burrows sets a maximum density. In this case, other behavior factors might modify survival. If the food species were rare, some urchins would be forced further from protected areas in search of food and exposed to greater risk of wave and turbulence. Several factors interacting in a complex fashion would control the density of the population.

The apparent complexity of the relationship between the species population and the environment increases if the action of one individual on another and the effects of density on reproduction are considered. Ecologists know practically nothing of these factors in sea urchins, but they have been studied in other animal species so I can shift to another example, muskrat populations in the central United States. In a large marsh inhabited by muskrats, low densities reduce the chance of mating and in consequence the birth rate. Each individual, though, has a greater chance of survival because of relative abundance of food and good hiding places. If the death rate for this reason is lower than the birth rate (assuming immigration = emigration), the density will increase; and as it increases, the birth rate will likewise increase; that is, not only will more young be born but the rate of birth per adult individual will increase. But, as the number of individuals increases, a greater percentage of them must occupy less protected places, exposed to attack from owls, hawks, and foxes. Further, fighting among individuals for the available space increases; a greater percentage of individuals entering from outside the marsh are driven away or drive away the original inhabitants, and a greater percentage of the immature or senescent individuals are likewise driven out by vigorous adults. As the population changes in composition by differential loss of non-breeding individuals, the birth rate changes further as a result of changes in physiology and behavior of the individuals affected by crowding and a lesser supply of food. The death rate increases as does the emigration rate until, together, they equal or exceed the rates of birth and immigration. The population density now assumes a steady state or decreases. Changes in the marsh complicate the situation. High water levels result in more food and more dwelling places; densities increase as does the rate of increase. Several years of favorable conditions would result in great numbers and high densities, and the death rate in the succeeding low water years would increase correspondingly. Because of these fluctuations in the environmental factors, most, if not all, natural pop-

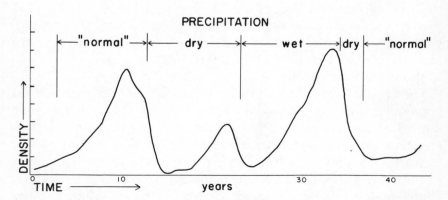

Fig. 4–11. *VARIATION OF MUSKRAT POPULATION DENSITIES IN TIME, IDEALIZED.* The changes in density are relative; the time scale is based in a general way on recorded fluctuations in Canada. Wet years induce high maxima and minima, and dry years induce low maxima and minima, but neither in themselves produce the fluctuations.

ulation densities fluctuate more or less widely about an equilibrium (Figure 4-11).

Probably no species population is limited throughout its existence by any one of these factors; almost surely they fluctuate as the population changes in density and in character of component individuals. The limiting factors must change also as the environment changes. For purpose of analysis, the ecologist isolates certain factors or combinations of factors, but no animal exists in isolation with temperature, with a parasite, or with its siblings. The animal is rather an intersection in the network of environment. The strands of that network may be described and classified in many ways but most conveniently in terms of isolated measurable factors, light, heat, predation, food supply, and so on. (Table 4—5). The effect of variation in any one of these factors on the population is modified by the total combination of ecologic factors, by the flexibility of individuals in adjusting to the variation, and by the range of species tolerance (Figure 4-12). The flexibility of the individuals and the variation in their tolerance define the range of species tolerance.

TABLE 4—5

FACTORS OF THE ENVIRONMENT

1. Primarily Physical or Chemical.
    A. *Solar radiation.* High intensity damages living organisms. Low intensity limits production by photosynthetic plants. Visible light affects perception and, thus, periods and places of activity.
    B. *Heat.* High and low temperatures can damage living organisms. Temperature controls the rate of animal activity by modifying rate of chemical processes.
    C. *Gravity.* This limits the bulk and orientation of animals that live on a land surface or on the sea bottom. It is related to density, bulk, and body form of swimming, floating, and flying animals.
    D. *Pressure.* High pressures in oceanic depths influence marine organisms.
    E. *Currents of air.* This is important in determining climatic patterns. Directly influences animals through winds.
    F. *Currents of water.* Currents in marine and fresh water affect distribution of aquatic animals, modify their activities, and may damage them if intense.
    G. *Substrate.* This is the surface on which animals live or are supported. It includes surface of water, land surface, and surfaces beneath bodies of water. It influences organisms by stability, firmness, roughness, and so on. It is important to paleoecologists because it is related to sedimentary environment.

H. *Physiochemical and chemical phases.* These are viscosity, diffusion, and osmosis. Viscosity affects rates of sinking, of swimming and floating organisms. Osmosis involves the exchange of ions through cell membranes and so influences survival in water of low or high ion concentrations.

I. *Water.* Water is an essential constitutent of protoplasm. The dry environments of the atmosphere and land surface restrict those environments to animals that can store and conserve water.

J. *Atmospheric gases.* Free oxygen is essential to energy utilization in most organisms. Dissolved gases, particularly oxygen, limit the distribution of aquatic organisms.

K. *Dissolved salts.* Some elements are essential to life processes. The concentration of $CaCO_3$ and other shell building materials assumes particular importance to the paleontologist.

L. *Fluctuations in environmental factors.* Regular or irregular variation in any of the above factors is an important modifying influence in itself.

M. *Combinations of environmental factors.* The availability of essential materials and the effects of individual physical and chemical factors are modified by other factors in the environment. Thus, temperature is related to water vapor, and calcium carbonate to pH.

2. Primarily Biological.

A. *Predation.* This is the effect of a predator on a prey species.

B. *Food.* This includes animal food for predators and parasites and plants for herbivores.

C. *Parasitism.* This is the effect of a parasite on the parasitized species.

D. *Modification of physical and chemical factors affecting several species.*

E. *Symbiosis.* This is the interaction of two or more species without injury to either and with benefit to at least one partner.

The fossil species and its environment

Since an animal is an intersection in the biologic net, it can have its fullest meaning only if considered in that net, in the environmental context. A paleontologist must seek beyond fossil form and beyond rock association to this wider meaning and trace out the environmental strands or at least some part of them. In so doing he returns to the concept of sample and universe. Fossils, together with information on location, association with other fossils, and rock association, are samples of a *geological universe* comprising all the fossils of the same species and their relationship to place, other fossils, and rock. From the characteristics of this universe, or, more formally, the universe parameters, he infers the ecology of the biological population. He bases his inference on the identity of some of the fossil parameters with parameters of the biological

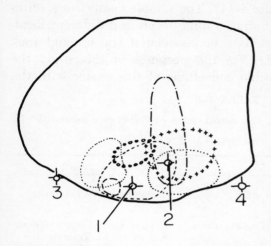

Fig. 4–12. *RELATION OF EN-VIRONMENT AND ADAPTA-TION.* The solid line bounds the total range of environmental tolerance of the species. The various broken lines are the tolerance limits of individual animals. The crosses with circles are the environments at particular localities. The individuals vary both in adaptation (tolerance limits) and in adaptability (range of tolerance). Local environments vary in particular environmental factors and in fluctuation of these factors. Thus in Locality *1*, one individual could survive, but the local population could not reproduce itself. In Locality 2, four individuals could survive. The local population could reproduce and could even contribute new individuals to live at *1*. At Locality 3, some individuals could survive part of the time. At Locality 4, the species could never survive.

population and on the estimation of other biological parameters from those that can be determined directly.

An analysis of the environmental relations of the fossil oyster, *Cubitostrea lisbonensis,* made by H. B. Stenzel, illustrates the development of a paleoecologic study. This species (Figure 4-13) is known from the Weches formation of middle Eocene age and its equivalents on the Gulf Coastal Plain in Alabama, Mississippi,

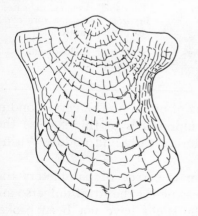 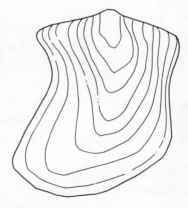

Fig. 4–13. *CUBITOSTREA LISBONENSIS.* Left and right valves of this middle Eocene oyster. (After Stenzel.)

Louisiana, and Texas (Figure 4-14). The sample comprises a series of collections from different stratigraphic levels and different localities in Texas and includes data on associated species and rock characteristics (Table 4–6). For the purposes of this study the "universe" includes all possible collections of this oyster with the

TABLE 4–6

DATA ON FORM, OCCURRENCE, AND ASSOCIATIONS OF *Cubitostrea lisbonensis*

(Information from Stenzel 1945, and 1949)

Parameters	*C. lisbonensis* Type 1	*C. lisbonensis* Type 2
Stratigraphic occurrence	Early Weches only.	Throughout Weches time.
Geographic occurrence	Central Leon County, Texas and eastward.	Central Leon County, Texas, and westward. Transgressive eastward in later Weches time.
Form of *C. lisbonensis*	Large heavy shells heavily ribbed and fairly regular form predominate. Thin and irregular shells rare or absent. Intergrades with Type 2 westward.	Smaller, thin shells, with low ribs and irregular form predominate. Thick and regular shells rare or absent. Intergrades with Type 1 eastward.
Fragmentation, wear, etc.	Some broken shells; many show evidence of abrasion and rolling.	Very few broken shells; no evidence of wear or rolling.
Population characters	Mature individuals predominate; immature specimens rare.	Many very young and immature specimens.
Association with other fossils	?	Thin shelled clams, delicate bryozoa, and some rare corals, sea urchins and crabs.
Character of rock	Limestone boulders, layers of rolled and worn shells, coarse glauconite grains.	Shaly, thin bedded, fine glauconite grains.

association data throughout the area of outcrop. The corresponding biologic population would be all individuals of this species that lived in the present outcrop area during early and middle Weches time.

The paleontologist's first problem is choice of parameters that he can reasonably assume to be the same for the fossil universe and the living species population. If the shells have not been broken before burial, distorted by compaction, nor changed by decay, replacement, and recrystallization, the form and composition of

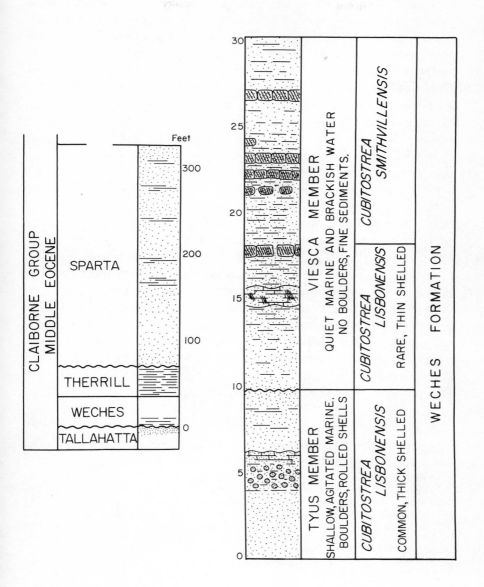

Fig. 4–14. *STRATIGRAPHIC DISTRIBUTION OF CUBITOSTREA LISBONENSIS.* Section at the left shows the general position of the Weches within the Claiborne Group. The section at the right shows the character of the Weches at Hurricane Shoals, western Houston County, Texas. Farther west, the Tyus member becomes finer grained, loses the boulders and rolled shells, and contains rare, thin shelled *Ostrea lisbonenses.* (After Stenzel.)

individual shells must be the same now that they were when they were parts of the living oysters. Decision as to breakage, distortion, and composition change is largely intuitive and based on experience with shape and composition of modern organisms, on imperfect symmetry where perfect would be expected, or on expected effects of mechanical pressure or of recrystallization. Microscopic examination of thin sections of the shell may demonstrate distortion by micro-faulting, warping of structure, or partial recrystallization. Even if the oyster shells have been mangled in some fashion, part of the form and composition characteristics persist without significant change (they must if the specimen is to be recognized as a fossil). These characteristics may then be used in reconstructing (estimating) the original form and/or composition.*

The inorganic composition of unaltered shells is of particular importance since it is influenced by the physio-chemistry of the water surrounding the oyster. The major shell constituent (calcium carbonate in the oyster) is controlled by the availability of the chemical ions necessary to build the shell; the availability is a product of ion concentration and the sensitivity of the animal to concentration in a particular environment. For this reason, many animals living in fresh waters low in $CaCO_3$ have thin shells or ones composed of some other compound, but some species can build heavy $CaCO_3$ shells in waters of very low $CaCO_3$ concentration. The proportion of the trace elements, strontium and magnesium, to calcium and the ratio of oxygen isotopes $\frac{^{16}O}{^{18}O}$ in the shell varies with the temperature at which the material was deposited —at least in some animal groups.†

---

* Organic compounds included in the inorganic shell offer a particular problem since these constituents are chemically unstable and change in different ways under different conditions of temperature and pressure. Although paleontologists can only say at the present time that some organic compounds similar to those in shells of modern animals are found in fossil shells, these compounds may ultimately provide a measure of the animal's biochemistry.

† The reasons for this change in ratio are not important here, but interpretation of the ratio in fossils depends on several assumptions. If the ratio is directly related to the physio-chemical properties (mass, ionic radius, and so on) of the elements or isotopes; if salinity was approximately the same as the recent oceans, and if processes of fossilization do not change the ratio after death without detectable changes in crystal structure of the skeleton, then the paleontologist can determine the absolute temperature at time of shell formation. If the second and third assumptions are valid and the first isn't, a statement of relative temperatures is possible—that is, time A was colder than time B—but absolute temperatures cannot be determined. The immediate problem in applying these techniques is to test these assumptions.

Once the paleontologist establishes the identity of form (and, if possible, composition of individual specimens), he must demonstrate the relationship of average form and variation in form of the fossil population to that of the living population. Again he faces a difficult problem for which no absolute answer seems possible. Wear, breakage, separation of valves in bivalve animals, orientation of specimens, and sorting, all indicate selective transportation of different sizes and shapes. If transported samples are to be compared, he should compare samples showing a similar amount of transportation, or, better, compare features of shape and structure not affected by speed of current. Thus, the average and variation in shape of the muscle scars in oyster shells might be independent of selective transportation. But, again, if larger oysters had relatively longer muscle scars, transportation would bias the sample. Very probably the oysters found in eastern Leon County were transported—at least wear and breakage indicate this—but, since transportation indicates strong currents where the oysters lived, the evidence of transportation tells something of the life environment.

Selective preservation is probably more common and certainly more subtle. A larval oyster before shell formation has as little chance of preservation as the proverbial snowball in hell. Try, then, to compare similar growth stages of two oysters—one with a thick shell; one with a thin—the thick shelled form is more likely to be preserved than the thin. Some individuals of the species grow attached to other shells or rocks; others, after early shell growth, lie unattached on the bottom. In this situation, individuals with different behavior might well be differentially preserved, and if there were a corresponding morphologic difference, a false conception of the species morphology would develop.

Most paleontologists, recognizing these sampling difficulties, have attempted to offset them by working at a gross level—estimating the species morphology very broadly; they estimate it, let us say, generally as "oyster-form," and distinguish between environmental relations of "oyster-form" and "razor-clam" species. This particular approach helps in interpreting fossil environments, but to accept it as the sole approach is to abandon the ecologically significant differences between local populations of a species and, often, the differences between species of the same genus. Utilization of these minor differences requires that the samples be taken randomly with respect to the character in question or that the amount of bias be estimated in a precise way.

Unfortunately, there seems to be no general method to establish compliance of the sample with these requirements. In this example, some of the variation in shell thickness among local samples of *Cubitostrea lisbonensis* probably corresponds to differences among local populations, since the heavy shelled individuals, the most likely to be preserved, are not found in association with the thin shelled fossils. Transportation and/or sorting might be shown by a study of size distribution (Tasch, 1957, for example) as well as by wear and breakage, but selective preservation in a broad sense requires much more data on modern occurrences. The absence of the thin shelled types in a sample does not demonstrate, however, that such individuals were absent from the living population. They may have been removed or destroyed by wave action or never fossilized. The difference in percentage of immature oysters likewise could be attributed to their differential preservation. One might test by comparison of thickness and size of the broken and/or leached shells with intact shells from the same sample. These two portions of the sample should be similar in these characteristics if no bias exists. For this example, you will have to assume that randomness has been established by this or some other test, but the need for such tests limits the applicability of statistical techniques, restricts the conclusions that may be drawn from the samples, and demands careful problem design and interpretation for any such study of intraspecific differences. The importance of complete and unbiased collecting is obvious. Large, well-preserved specimens attract the collector, but small broken ones do not. Methods include collection of all specimens from a randomly chosen area or at least observation and identification in the field of such complete samples.

Other parameters might include the number of *Cubitostrea lisbonensis* relative to other fossil species associated with it; spatial association with individuals of the same species and with individuals of other species; sediment size and composition, and sedimentary structures such as cross bedding and particle orientation. For each of these parameters the data must also come from a random sample, and there must be some assurance, either intuitive or from modern environmental studies, that the parameters of the geologic universe correspond with measures of the species environment.

The second step in this paleoecologic analysis is the estimation of further measures of the environment from the established ones. The characteristics of the individual oysters and the variations among individuals correspond to particular sets of functions and variations in function. Mechanical analysis of structure, analogy from function in modern animals of similar structure, and inference from functions in related living species contribute to this reconstruction of function. Emiliani (1950) has suggested that a study of the amount of variation might be a useful parameter. From adaptations to particular functions, the paleontologist reconstructs the environment, for a particular set of functions must have been mated to a particular range of environmental factors. The association of other species and the characteristics of the rocks contributed also to his image of the environment. Because estimation of function, and, consequently, of environment, and estimation of environment from sediment involve imperfect correlations, the statement of environmental peculiarities involves uncertainty, a degree of probability. If several parameters can be used in estimating a factor, however, the probability increases. So one must seek such joint estimates.

For example, comparison of samples of *C. lisbonensis* shows a gradual change from thick shell to thin shell forms along an east-west trend in the lower Weches strata of Texas (Table 4–6).

If the samples are random, i.e. there is no selective preservation or collection with respect to this character, and since the differences are large compared with variation within each local collection, the samples presumably came from distinct local populations.

Shell thickness in many species of living pelecypods is correlated with turbulence of water, the vigor of wave action or strength of currents, but the correlation is imperfect. Stenzel infers turbulence to be greater in the eastern portion of the "Weches Sea" than in the western, but the inference is not very firmly established; other explanations are equally probable.

His field observations, however, include information on sediment size, a parameter rather highly correlated with strength of current or wave action. An estimate of turbulence on the basis of sediment size agrees with the estimate derived from a study of shell thickness.

In addition, because turbulence is often associated with the oxygen content of the water, relative oxygen concentration may be estimated as well.

Note the terms *greater; relative*. This analysis, then, expresses relative differences among local areas in the Weches Sea, not the absolute values of current velocity or of oxygen concentration. Sometimes such absolute values can be determined; studies of size, shape, and specific gravity of the sedimentary particles might yield a precise quantitive estimate of turbulence. Such determinations are rare, however, and the paleontologist must be satisfied with relative values, with perhaps some vague idea of the magnitude of the difference. This limitation, though unfortunate, is not as fearsome as it first seems, for animal populations are limited by relative values as well. Since the distribution of oysters is controlled by the salinity of the water (among many other controlling factors), their occurrence or non-occurrence therefore expresses relative salinity.

In using the word *controlled,* I imply a causal relationship between distribution and salinity and imply, moreover, that causation can be determined in paleoecology as well as in ecology. Examine this proposition in terms of the distribution of *C. lisbonensis*. In the westernmost outcrops of the Weches formation, this species is absent or limited to a few horizons and a few localities. Obviously, some change or group of changes in the environment limited the occurrence of this oyster in the western part of Weches Sea. Studies of sediment size and shell thickness indicate lower turbulence. Possibly this reduction results from protection by bars and from shallower water. Other sedimentary features demonstrate that the western outcrops were near the shore line of the Weches Sea. Stenzel concluded that the local environments in the west consisted of broad shallow lagoons. The physical environment of these lagoons probably differed significantly from that of the open sea in temperature, light, substrate, gas concentrations, and salinity in addition to turbulence. If the limits of *Cubitostrea lisbonensis* distribution coincide with changes in one of these environmental characters, conclusions can be drawn about the limiting factor for the species population. Coincidence of distribution with two or more changes is likely; such coincidence would not change the method of analysis but would make it more difficult and too lengthy to discuss here.

The animals collected with specimens of this oyster include other pelecypods (pectins), bryozoans, corals, and sea urchins. Their closest modern relatives are marine and cannot tolerate *brackish* (low salinity) waters for any prolonged period, nor are closely related species known to have existed in ancient freshwater or brackish water environments. Further, the oyster beds formed by *Cubitostrea lisbonensis* always include several other animal species in fairly large numbers. This variety contrasts with modern brackish water oyster beds which contain few organisms and few species of organisms other than oysters. Because of this correlation of distribution with species sensitive to low salinity, Stenzel concluded that lowered salinity limited the westward distribution of this oyster species. A further test of this conclusion would be possible if one knew the precise degree of association of the oysters with those species that are sensitive to salinity, or if one knew the percentage of immature oysters. An unusually high death rate among immature organisms would argue recurrent unfavorable environments. The proportion of immatures is, of course, higher in the west, but the data in Stenzel's paper does not show the association of this change with changes in the salinity indicators.

Notice, however, that I have not said that lower salinity causes the excess of deaths over births and immigration. The effect might in fact be much more subtle and, for example, be related to effects of salinity changes on food sources or parasites. Bearing this in mind, we can say that salinity changes limited, either directly or indirectly, the distribution of *Cubitostrea lisbonensis*.

Significance of paleoecologic studies

These few fossil oysters represent the inhabitants of a warm sea that covered eastern Texas some fifty million years ago. Though a paleontologist cannot measure, except in some dim and inaccurate way, the numbers or the density of the oyster population in this ancient sea, he can determine in part the limits of the environments, observe the differences between oyster banks as the environments differ, and observe those local populations grow or diminish as the sea bottom world changes through time. He is triply rewarded for his efforts, for not only does he attain the simple satisfaction of reconstructing the ancient world, but he finds that the reconstruction also helps him to interpret paleogeography (and aids him, consequently, in the search for oil) and to place the evolution of *Cubito-*

strea lisbonensis in a context of adaptation to environment (see further pages 98 to 110 and 131 to 136).

THE SPECIES IN PALEONTOLOGY

But let me return to my questions on the validity of the species concept and its significance to paleontologists. Admittedly, the correspondence between morphological and genetic species cannot be complete, nor can the paleontologist find those fine distinctions that the zoologist sometimes makes or requires to be made. The paleontologic species, however, has its basis in the genetic species, and the paleontologist can draw worthwhile conclusions about its morphology, ecology, and, finally, on its evolution.

REFERENCES

Allee, W. C.; A. E. Emerson; O. Park; T. Park, and K. P. Schmidt. 1949. *Principles of Animal Ecology.* Philadelphia: Saunders. A comprehensive treatment of ecology with many examples.

Andrewartha, H. G., and L. C. Birch. 1954. *The Distribution and Abundance of Animals.* Chicago: University of Chicago Press. A stimulating treatment of the ecology of animal populations in relation to their abundance and distribution.

Bader, R. S. 1956. "Variability in Wild and Inbred Mammalian Populations," *Quart. Jour. of the Florida Acad. of Sci.,* vol. 19, pp. 14-34.

Burma, B. H. 1948. "Studies in Quantitative Paleontology. I. Some Aspects of the Theory and Practice of Quantitative Invertebrate Paleontology," *Jour. of Paleontology,* vol. 22, pp. 725-761.

————. 1949. "Studies in Quantitative Paleontology. II. Multivariate Analysis—a New Analytical Tool for Paleontology and Geology," *Jour. of Paleontology,* vol. 23, pp. 95-103.

Cazier, M. A., and A. L. Bacon. 1949. "Introduction to Quantitative Systematics," *Bulletin American Mus. of Nat. History,* vol. 93, pp. 343-388. The application of statistics to problems of taxonomic discrimination.

Chave, K. E. 1954. "Aspects of the Biogeochemistry of Magnesium. 1. Calcareous Marine Organisms," *Jour. of Geology,* vol. 62, pp. 266-283. Deals principally with environmental factors controlling deposition of Mg in carbonate skeletons.

Emiliani, C. 1950. "Introduction to a Method for Determining the Physical Characters of Fossil Environments," *Jour. of Paleontology,* vol. 24, pp. 485-491.

Errington, P. L. 1946. "Predation and Vertebrate Population," *Quart. Rev. of Biology,* vol. 21, pp. 144-177; 221-245. A review paper of great importance and of significance in invertebrate ecology as well as vertebrate.

Hedgpeth, J. W., and H. S. Ladd, (eds.). 1957. "Treatise on Marine Ecology and Paleoecology," 2 vols. *Geol. Soc. of America, Memoir 67.* Many research and review papers plus extensive annotated bibliographies on ecology and paleoecology.

Kurten, B. 1954. "Population Dynamics—a New Method in Paleontology," *Jour. of Paleontology,* vol. 28, pp. 286-292.

————. 1955. "Contribution to the History of a Mutation during 1,000,-000 Years," *Evolution,* vol. 9, pp. 107-118.

Lowenstam, H. A. 1954. "Factors Affecting the Aragonite: Calcite Ratios in Carbonate-Secreting Marine Organisms," *Jour. of Geology,* vol. 62, pp. 284-323. Part of the pioneering work being done in biogeochemistry and on its relation to paleoecology.

————, and S. Epstein. 1954. "Paleotemperatures of the Post-Aptian Cretaceous as Determined by the Oxygen Isotope Method," *Jour. of Geology,,* vol. 62, pp. 207-248. One of the more recent papers in a series dealing with the oygen isotope method.

Mayr, E., E. G. Linsley, and R. L. Usinger. 1952. See Chapter 3.

Moore, R. C. 1957. "Modern Methods of Paleoecology," *American Assoc. of Petr. Geologists, Bulletin,* vol. 41, pp. 1775-1801. A review of work now being done in this field.

Odum, E. P. 1953. *Fundamentals of Ecology.* Philadelphia: Saunders. An excellent introductory text on ecology.

Olson, E. C. 1957. "Size-Frequency Distributions in Samples of Extinct Organisms," *Jour. of Geology,* vol. 65, pp. 309-333. A study of the relation between fossil sample and living population.

————, and R. L. Miller. 1951. "Relative Growth in Paleontological Studies," *Jour. of Paleontology,* vol. 25, pp. 212-223.

Parkinson, D. 1954. "Quantitative Studies of Brachiopods from the Lower Carboniferous Reef Limestones of England. III. *Pugnax Acuminatus* (J. Sowerby) and *P. Mesogonus* (Phillips)," *Jour. of Paleontology,* vol. 28, pp. 668-676. A good example of problems and results in this type of study.

Romer, A. S. 1937. "New Genera and Species of Pelycosaurian Reptiles," *New England Zool. Club, Proc.,* vol. 16, pp. 89-96.

Scott, C. 1940. "Paleoecological Factors Controlling the Distribution and Mode of Life of Cretaceous Ammonoids in the Texas Area," *Jour. of Paleontology,* vol. 14, pp. 299-323.

Shaw, A. B. 1956. "Quantitative Trilobite Studies. I. The Statistical Description of Trilobites," *Jour. of Paleontology,* vol. 30, pp. 1209-1224. An example of current research in this field.

Simpson, G. G. and A. Roe. 1939. *Quantitative Zoology*. New York: Mc-Graw-Hill. Partly out of date but still valuable. A revised edition has been announced.

Soloman, M. E. 1949. "The Natural Control of Animal Populations," *Jour. of Anim. Ecology*, vol. 18, pp. 1-35. A significant review paper.

Stenzel, H. B. 1945. "Paleoecology of Some Oysters," *National Research Council, Report of the Committee on Marine Ecology as Related to Paleontology*, No. 5, pp. 37-46.

————. 1949. "Successional Speciation in Paleontology: The Case of the Oysters of the *Sellaeformis* Stock," *Evolution*, vol. 3, pp. 34-50.

Sylvester-Bradley, P. C. 1958. "The Description of Fossil Populations, *Jour. of Paleontology*, vol. 32, pp. 214-235.

Tasch, P. 1957. See references for Chapter 5.

Thorson, G. 1950. "Reproductive and Larval Ecology of Marine Bottom Invertebrates," *Biol. Review*, vol. 25, pp. 1-45. A problem neglected in most paleoecologic studies.

Trueman, A. E. 1930. "Results of Some Recent Statistical Investigations of Invertebrate Fossils," *Biol. Review*, pp. 296-308. Part of the pioneer work in this field.

Weller, J. M. 1955. "Fatuous Species and Hybrid Populations," *Jour. of Paleontology*. vol. 29, pp. 1066-1069. A review dissecting a taxonomic paper that failed to use the population concept of species.

See also the references for Chapter 5, particularly Ekman (1953), MacGinitie and MacGinitie (1949), and Hesse, Allee, and Schmidt (1951), and for Chapter 3, Olson and Miller, 1957.

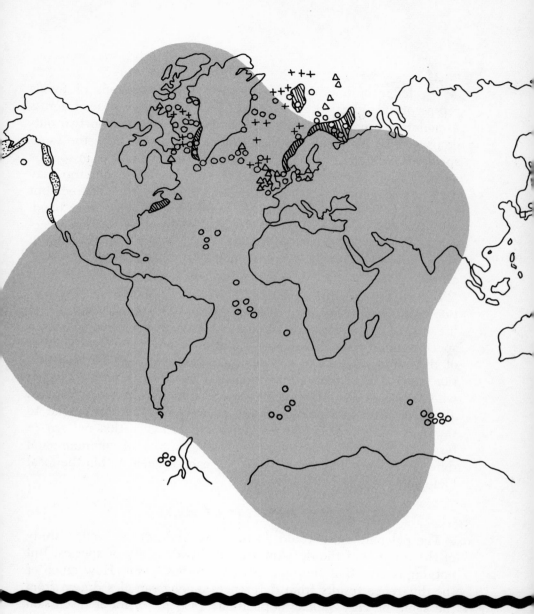

5. The DIVERSITY of SPECIES

A ledge of limestone may contain some hundreds of fossils representing several dozen species. This rock layer, traced across a mountain range, will yield thousands of fossils, but no two outcrops will be identical in fossil content. Some will have the same species but different proportions of each; others will differ in species as well as in proportions. The several species in an outcrop may display common adaptations to the environment they shared, but they will surely differ in some characteristics. On the other hand, different species from different locations will share some characteristics though adapted to different environments. The paleontologist, therefore, deals both with diversity of fossils from different areas and the diversity of fossils in the same area.

But all this is to be expected. The limited adaptation of a particular species population restricts the distribution and mode of life of the population. An individual animal can survive only a specific range of environmental variation. Conversely, two animals of different species, distinct environments, and separate distribution need similar adaptations to similar modes of life. A zoologist, whether he studies adjacent beach and dune habitats or compares alpine meadow and Arctic tundra, encounters a pattern similar to that observed by the paleontologist. He analyzes this pattern in terms of geographic distribution (zoogeography), of environmental differences, and of the part played by each species within the local biological system.

THE PERVERSITY OF ROCKS

The paleontologist would do the same and add, as well, a study of the origin and the development of this diversity of species. But nothing is ever that simple when one studies fossils. How much of the difference results from differences among samples drawn from the same or very similar populations (see p. 62 for a discussion of sampling error)? Did the species live where fossilized? Were the skeletons of a trilobite species preserved on the mud flats and destroyed on the sand bars though far more common in the latter environment? Or are the outcropping rocks of different age, and, therefore, is the difference one of time as well as environment and space?

The last question will be discussed at length in Chapter 8. Here

I will assume that time differences between the fossil samples compared are insignificant—a dangerous but necessary assumption. The other questions were raised in the preceding chapter and answers were attempted there. These questions concern not only the geographic differences among fossil samples but also the diversity within samples. Therefore, I will re-examine the solutions proposed earlier.

Paleontologists could analyze differences between samples by statistical methods, but have done little along this line. In many problems statistics are unnecessary—if fossils are numerous and the differences between samples large. But what of subtle differences among small samples? Perhaps problems of this second sort deserve more study. They do if the data can be placed in proper form and adequate statistical methods can be employed.

Paleontologists must also recognize the effects of transportation on a fossil sample and recognize that transportation may be vertical as well as horizontal. The indicators of transportation are wear, breakage, sorting, separation of articulated elements, orientation, and, of course, fossil size relative to sediment size. The extreme of much abraided and well sorted fossil fragments stands distinct from the extreme of delicate specimens of varied sizes fossilized without prior wear or breakage. The intermediates are, unhappily, less distinct. The studies of shell transportation (Menard and Boucot, 1951; Martin-Kaye, 1951, and Johnson, 1958) help in interpretation, but as yet do not suffice for any close distinction.

Vertical movement of animal skeletons provides an equal problem. At the start, one must recognize that swimming and floating animals after death fall to the bottom and their remains collect with those of the bottom dwellers. Further, if sedimentation is slow or temporarily interrupted, a single layer of shells will represent successive generations of life. But even entombment does not ensure rest. Currents may remove sediment without moving the shells and skeletons (Johnson, 1957). They therefore remain as a lag deposit, a shell pavement, assembled from a considerable thickness of sediment. Finally, slump and flow or the churning of the sediments by burrowing animals or by wave action may disturb and intermingle remains of animals that did not—even could not—live together.

Selective preservation is a two-headed monster in a paleontologic nightmare. First, large numbers of species disappear without trace.

+ Study of pecten shells in Trinidad; found only one valve although the 2 are similar.

If these were minor performers in the local biological system one could let them go without regret, but among them are many of the most numerous and ecologically significant species. All other threats to paleoecologic interpretation can, at least in theory, be eliminated, but this one remains. Correspondingly, interpretation remains uncertain and limited in reach.

But selective preservation is not satisfied with destroying a major part of the living system; it produces subtle or gross differences in species composition and proportions as it eliminates more or fewer of a particular species in different areas. Fortunately, the paleontologist can estimate and allow for these discrepancies. Evidence of differential leaching, breakage and crushing will be evident upon careful observation. If thin and delicate calcareous skeletons occur intact, then little loss has occurred in species provided with calcareous structures. If calcareous skeletons are poorly preserved and chitinous ones well preserved, then changes in proportion almost certainly occurred.

Obviously, many, if not most, assemblages of fossils collected from a single bed at a single locality represent a subtle mixture, modified by selective preservation, of several distinct assemblages of living animals. The death assemblage fails to correspond to a life assemblage. The prospect is discouraging, but the very act of unraveling the intricacy of a fossil assemblage reveals significant episodes in the local biological history and important characteristics of the local environment.

THE PERVERSITY OF ANIMALS

One more difficulty remains. Can we attribute all differences among living assemblages to differences in environment or to limited dispersal? This question arises particularly in the study of modern marine bottom associations. Two different assemblages may live side by side on the same muddy bottom exposed to the same water temperatures, the same depth, the same amount of light—in all measurable characters, the same environment. The difference between the assemblages may indicate some undetected environmental difference, but the majority of marine ecologists believe not. The difference may reflect minor and perhaps undetectable differences in the history of organisms at two different spots. Or the cause may be some process of random colonization accentuated by some unexplained tendency of many species to form localized clusters.

In either case, a paleoecologist must sort such nonenvironmental differences from those that are environmentally controlled. Some paleoecologists find the problem a desperate, destructive one, but others regard it as a minor difficulty. My own inclination is toward the latter group, though my optimism may rest more on hope than reason. There is reason to hope, however. Most collections of fossils, however carefully done, mingle several living assemblages, and thereby encompass several of adjacent and different associations. Collecting, therefore, may average out these local nonenvironmental differences.

If collecting does not do the work for us by its very imprecision, then a comparison of differences among a number of collections from the same outcrop or adjacent outcrops with the differences among more distant localities should help. Defined formally, the universe of this comparison consists of all possible local collections, and the sample of a number of these collections from the same outcrop or locality. If the differences among localities are significant, they should considerably exceed (by 2 σ if statistics are used) the differences within a locality. Table 5–1 illustrates this technique.

TABLE 5–1

DISTRIBUTION OF *Foraminifera* OFF THE MISSISSIPPI DELTA

(Data abstracted from Phleger, 1955)

Locality number	Abundance of species A in %	Abundance of species B in %
70	39	29
71	42	23
69	39	54
204	33	38
67	3	47
211	38	26
65	4	18
66	0	40

The abundance in the first four samples of Species *A* was compared with that in the second four by the technique of rank analysis of variance (p. 64). Differences of this size or larger occur less than six times in a hundred among samples drawn from the same universe. Comparison of Species *B* in the two groups of samples indicates that the difference would occur less than eighty times in a hundred—obviously not a significant difference.

Phleger (1955) identified the *Foraminifera* from a series of bottom samples off the delta of the Mississippi and calculated the percentage of individuals belonging to each species. The table includes data from his study, data on eight samples from a clay-silt bottom. Estimates of environment based on the character of the sediment would be about the same for all eight samples. Are the differences in percentages of Species A and of Species B "accidental," or do they indicate some real difference in environments not shown in the sediment? Samples 67, 211, 65, 66 were taken close to one another off the mouth of Main Pass; 70, 71, 69, 204 were also close to each other but were collected about ten miles east of the first group of samples (Figure 5-1). The two groups are compared with each other by treating each group as a local collection and comparing the difference between groups to the difference within groups. Pretty obviously Species A is less common near Main Pass than it is further east. Variation in Species B, however, does not appear to be significant in this problem.

THE DISTRIBUTION OF ANIMALS IN SPACE

I have established a significant difference between the fossils collected in two areas. What can be done with this observation? Two paths of analysis are open; I can study the relationship of the several species in a single sample; I can interpret the environmental and/or geographic factors that induced the difference between samples. The two alternatives are not really this distinct, as a later discussion will show, but they can (or must) be considered so for initial exposition. So first, the interpretation of spatial differences.

If, as was suggested earlier, an individual from a species population is an intersection in the environmental net, the distribution of each species population can be considered in terms of the strands, the factors, that are knotted together. Each species differs in temperature tolerance, food requirements, salinity tolerance, parasitism, and so forth. Therefore variation in temperature, availability of food, salinity, parasites, and so forth limit a particular species population to those portions of the earth where tolerance limits and environment coincide. All this, of course, is a repetition of the comments in the preceding chapter, but in a new and extended context. Thus the sea urchin, *Strongylocentrotus drobachiensis,* is limited in distribution by strength of wave action and is absent on exposed marine headlands. Other urchins, however, are

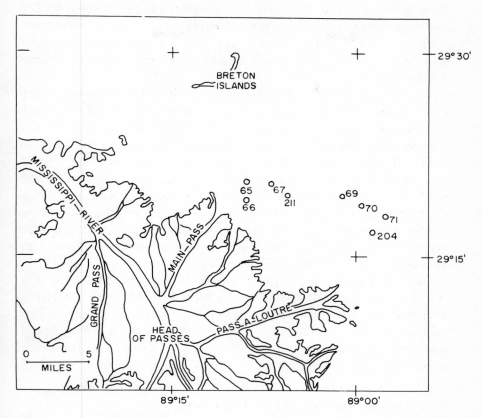

Fig. 5–1. *LOCATION OF SAMPLES OF FORAMINIFERA OFF MISSISSIPPI DELTA.*
Location of samples indicated by circles and accompanying numbers. (From Phleger, 1955.)

rock borers and can survive intense wave action. The species of the headland and the species of the protected inlet differ as a consequence of this environmental difference. The ecologists can speak then of a headland habitat and of an inlet habitat, distinguished by differences in turbulence and probably also in temperature, oxygenation, and bottom character.

Habitat classification

If the distribution of animals is treated as a result of differences in habitat, species may be grouped according to habitat preference, or, to go back to the net analogy, may be grouped on the basis of similarity of certain strands leading into the knots. Habitat classifications now in use are based on differences in environmental factors that appear most important in determining animal distributions ("most important" factors meaning those which affect the most species). Cross-classifications involving several different factors are also made.

In this way, the ecologist distinguishes the terrestrial and aquatic environments by the character of the medium; classifies habitats within the aquatic environment as fresh, brackish and marine according to salinity; further subdivides the marine habitats by depth of water (which is correlated with turbulence and light); and might base a further classification on type of bottom (substrate) or on variation in turbulence or light intensity. A cross-classification on temperature yields even finer subdivision, for example, temperate, aquatic, marine, shallow, rocky, and a further cross-classification on geographic location as North Atlantic temperate, aquatic, marine, shallow, rocky.

Neither the classification of habitats used here (Table 5–2; Figure 5-2) nor any classification I know of is completely consistent within itself. Moreover, the division between habitats is, in part, arbitrary. This classification (and others) are, however, pragmatically consistent since they yield a useful visualization of habitat differences and establish a standard terminology.

Habitats and environments of deposition

In the fossil record, loss of diagnostic criteria such as depth and temperature, difficulties in distinguishing features of the life environment, and admixture of foreign species by transportation, handicap recognition of these habitats. Otherwise interpretation proceeds much as in the case of single species populations with the use of the adaptations of the organisms, the taxonomic affiliations of the fossils to modern animals, and the sedimentary characteristics to establish critical parameters. In the sedimentary rocks deposited in a single sedimentary basin, a paleontologist can typically recognize several distinct animal associations. These different associations presumably occupied distinct habitats, and any one association occupied the same habitat throughout the basin. The Permian rocks in the basins of west Texas contain several such habitats (sometimes called *biotopes*) as shown in Table 5–3 and Figure 5-3 (Newell, 1957). The basin floors were low in oxygen.

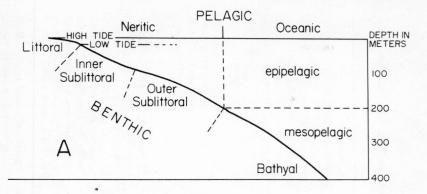

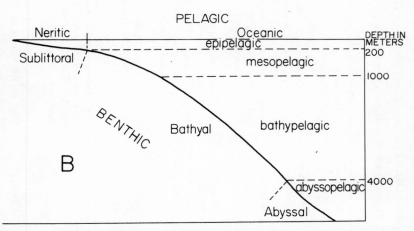

Fig. 5–2. *CLASSIFICATION OF MARINE ENVIRONMENTS.* **A)** Shallow water zones. **B)** Deep water zones. The pelagic environment and its subdivisions are water zones. The benthic environment and its subdivisions are bottom zones. The upper portion of the epipelagic and the inner sublittoral and littoral environments are lighted; the others receive no effective amount of sunlight. (Based on Hedgpeth, 1957.)

The high organic content of the sediment and the small numbers and slight variety of bottom dwelling (*benthonic*) organisms indicate this. The fine grain size of the sediments and their even bedding demonstrate that they must have been deposited in quiet water, probably at considerable depth. In addition to the scattered fossils of benthonic animals, the basin floor deposits contain numbers of radiolaria, calcareous algae (simple plants), and cephalopods. In structure and in mechanics of structure these resemble recent floating (*planktonic*) and swimming (*nektonic*) organisms. Presumably, they lived in the well aerated water near the surface. Here a single

TABLE 5–2

CLASSIFICATION AND CHARACTERISTICS OF THE MORE IMPORTANT HABITATS

Classification of marine habitats follows Hedgpeth, 1957. Classification of sedimentary environments is based on Krumbein and Sloss, 1951. Description is not intended to be exhaustive.

Habitat, biome or biotope	Primary ecologic factors	Sedimentary environments	Sedimentary characteristics	Organic characteristics
1. Terrestrial A. Forest	Light intense to moderate; moisture, high to moderate; substrate, soft to firm; succulent vegetation; abundant O_2.	Fluvial—alluvial plain, channel.	Rapid fluctuations – coarse to fine; oxidation; laterization; channeling; structureless shales; interlensing beds of different rock types; interbedded swamp and lacustrine lithotopes.	Terrestrial adapted; arboreal animals; browsing herbivores; vertebrates – tetrapods; fluvial, swamp, and lacustrine associates.
B. Grasslands	Light intense; moisture moderate to low except on river borders; substrate firm; abundant O_2.	Fluvial. Eolian. Lacustrine—ephemeral.	As above except more oxidation; caliches; some laterization; pond ls. and playa facies. Eolian deposits with well sorted and rounded, frosted grains.	Terrestrial adapted; cursorial vertebrates; grazing herbivores; tetrapod vertebrates; fluvial and lacustrine associates.
C. Deserts	Light intense; moisture low; substrate firm or rocky; scrub-grass vegetation; abundant O_2.	Eolian. Fluvial. Playa.	Fanglomerates; eolian sands and silts; evaporite facies.	Terrestrial adapted; cursorial vertebrates; few fish or snails.
D. Swamps, marshes, tundra	Light intense to moderate; moisture abundant; substrate soft; succulent vegetation; bottoms acidic, anaerobic.	Swamp.	Fine sediments; high amount of carbonaceous material; reducing; usually lensing into lacustrine and fluvial beds.	Aquatic and semiaquatic animals; fish, amphibians, snails, small pelecypods, arthropods of various types. Admixture of terrestrial adapted types.
E. Caves	Little or no light; generally abundant moisture; no vegetation; O_2 variable.	Cave.	Clay or silt fillings in fissures or pockets.	Mixture of animal types washed in or seeking shelter in caves, plus few specially adapted types—blind fish, ambibians, in-

Habitat, biome or biotope	Primary ecologic factors	Sedimentary environments	Sedimentary characteristics	Organic characteristics
F. Polar	Low temperatures; H_2O difficult to obtain; tundra vegetation; abundant O_2.	Glacial.	Till and outwash; solufluction.	Terrestrial adapted animals; some insects, homiothermal vertebrates.
G. Alpine	Low to moderate temperatures; moisture high to low; substrate firm, irregular; intense light; O_2 partial pressure reduced.	Glacial. Fluvial.	Till and outwash; fanglomerates.	Terrestrial adapted animals; some insects, homiothermal vertebrates.
2. Aquatic A. Fresh water (1) Running waters	Salinity low; abundant oxygen; high turbulence; substrate variable—usually firm to moderate; light intense to low (controlled by turbidity); turbidity variable; vegetation slight.	Fluvial–channel. Deltaic–distributaries.	Channel fills in fluvial facies; relatively coarse; fossils commonly broken or worn.	Fish, amphibians; crustacea and other aquatic arthropods; snails, pelecypods; intrusive terrestrial animals.
(2) Standing waters a) Lakes	Turbidity moderate to low; salinity low to low; substrate firm to soft; low turbulence; O_2 abundant to anerobic; abundant plant life.	Lacustrine.	Fine-grained silts and shales; laminated; interfingering with delta swamp, and alluvial deposits.	Fish; amphibians on margins; aquatic arthropods; snails and pelecypods; intrusive terrestrial animals on margins.
b) Ephemeral ponds	Turbidity moderate to high; light intense to moderate; substrate firm to soft; low turbulence; O_2 abundant; salinity low except in playas.	Lacustrine. Swamp.	Restricted extent; mudcracks; lime mud breccias; occasionally playa facies. Lenses in alluvial and/or swamp.	Some fish, amphibia, crustacea snails, pelecypods; intrusive terrestrial animals.
c) Swamps and marshes	See above.	Swamp.	See above.	See above.
B. Brackish	Low salinity, otherwise as in running waters (estuaries), lakes (lagoons), and swamps and marsh (lagoons).	Deltaic. Lagoonal. Littoral.	As in Fluvial (channel), Lacustrine and Swamp.	Few species—fish, gastropods, pelecypods, few brachiopods.

Habitat, biome or biotope	Primary ecologic factors	Sedimentary environments	Sedimentary characteristics	Organic characteristics
C. Marine (1) Benthic a) Supra-littoral	Light intense; moisture slight to moderate; vegetation varied—grasses, forest, swamp; substrate firm to soft; above high tide but may be affected by storm waves; much O_2.	Supralittoral intergrades with Fluvial and Deltaic. In many cases Eolian.	Fluvial and deltaic sediments and associations. Dune structures with well sorted, rounded grains of sand.	Variety of terrestrial invertebrates and vertebrates.
b) Littoral	Between high and low tides; O_2 typically high; moisture and light fluctuate. Algae. Water saline; substrate moderate to soft. Wave action strong except in estuaries and lagoons.	Lagoonal. Littoral. Deltaic.	Beach structures—ripple marks, cross-bedding, rain drop prints, beach cusps. Mud flats—ripple marks, mud cracks; swamp sediments. Sediments typically well sorted.	Burrowing and crawling invertebrates; some echinoderms. A few types of sessile animals with external shells.
c) Sub-littoral 1. Inner	Depths to 350'; light moderate to low intensity; wave action moderate to slight; O_2 typically moderate. Saline—occasionally hypersaline; substrate firm to soft; algae; turbidity moderate to high.	Epineritic. Infraneritic.	Moderate to fine-grained sediments; sorting moderate to poor. Typically reduced. Ripple marks; even bedded, some cross-bedded; "sheet" deposits. Carbonates. Evaporites.	Many types of attached invertebrates; brachiopods, corals, bryozoans, pelecypods. Burrowing and crawling echinoderms, molluscs, and arthropods.
2. Outer	Depths to 600'; light low to absent; wave action slight to none; O_2 moderate to low; saline—occasionally hyper-saline; substrate soft; a few algae; turbidity moderate to high.	Infraneritic.	Fine-grained sediments. Sorting moderate to poor. Typically reduced. Graded beds from turbidity currents. Even bedded—"sheet" deposits. Many carbonates. Evaporites.	As in inner sublittoral.
d) Bathyal	Depths between 600 and 6000'; light and wave action absent; O_2 moderate to low; substrate soft; temperatures low; low velocity currents.	Bathyal.	Very fine sediments—carbonates subordinate to clastic, glauconitic, and siliceous. Evidences of turbidity currents. Even bedded—"sheet" deposits; re-duced.	Organisms rare with increasing depth—mostly scavengers and predators. Sessile types limited.

Habitat, biome or biotope	Primary ecologic factors	Sedimentary environments	Sedimentary characteristics	Organic characteristics
e) Abyssal	Depths between 6000 and 15,000'. No light or wave action; O_2 moderate to low; substrate soft, temperatures quite low; low velocity currents.	Abyssal	Very fine sediments—calcareous and siliceous oozes and red and blue muds. Possibly some coarser sediments brought by turbidity currents.	Organisms relatively rare—mostly scavengers and predators. Sessile types limited.
f) Hadal	Depths below 15,000'. Otherwise similar to abyssal.	Abyssal	Very fine sediments. No calcareous deposits.	Organisms as in abyssal.
(2) Pelagic a) Neritic	Waters above sublittoral benthic; characteristics the same except lack of substrate; turbidity moderate to low.	Epineritic. Infraneritic.	As given above for these sedimentary environments.	Floating and swimming organisms. Abundant microscopic plants and animals.
b) Oceanic 1. Epipelagic	Depths to 350' ±. Characteristics as in inner sublittoral except lack of substrate; low turbidity.	Bathyal Abyssal	Same as above.	Same as above.
2. Mesopelagic	Depths between 350 and 3000'. Characteristics as in outer sublittoral and bathyal except lack of substrate; low turbidity.	Bathyal	Same as preceding.	Floating and swimming organisms. Few plants; animals primarily larger scavengers and predators.
3. Bathypelagic	Depths 3000'-6000' ±. Characteristics as in bathyal except lack of substrate.	Bathyal	Same as preceding.	Floating and swimming organisms. No photosynthetic plants; animals primarily larger scavengers and predators.
4. Abyssopelagic	Depths below 6000'. Characteristics as in abyssal except lack of substrate.	Abyssal	Same as preceding.	Same as preceding.

TABLE 5–3

INTERPRETATION OF MARINE HABITATS IN PERMIAN ROCKS OF WEST TEXAS

(Data and interpretations based on Newell, 1957)

General environment of deposition	*Rocks*	*Organisms*	*Probable habitats*
1. Basin Phase — infraneritic and bathyal.	1. Fine-grained quartz sandstones; black, bituminous limestones; black bituminous, platy siltstones. Thin uniform beds.	1. a. Brachiopods, pelecypods, small gastropods, (?) sponges. b. Pelagic protozoans, algae, ammonoid cephalopods.	1. *a*) Outer sublittoral, bathyal. Environment probably anerobic at times. *b*) neritic, epipelagic, mesopelagic.
2. Reef and Bank Phases—epineritic and littoral.	2. Limestone composed chiefly of fossils and fossil fragments. Typically dolomitized, some detrital sand and mud.	2. Calcareous algae, calcareous sponges, benthic foraminifers, corals, bryozoans, brachiopods, a few ammonoid cephalopods.	2. Inner sublittoral, (?) littoral, neritic.
3. Shelf Phase—epineritic and littoral.	3. Thin dolomitic limestones, many pisolithic; thin wedges of quartz sandstone; limestones arenaceous. Some anhydrite and red sandstones.	3. Calcareous algae, benthic foraminifera. A few species of brachiopods, pelecypods, and gastropods.	3. Inner sublittoral, (?) littoral, neritic. Environment probably hypersaline.

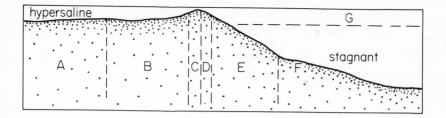

Fig. 5–3. *MARINE ENVIRONMENTS IN THE WEST TEXAS PERMIAN BASIN.* A section from the open basin across the barrier reef and back reef lagoon. *A)* Lagoons behind barrier reef, sublittoral (inner) and neritic environments. Salt concentrated by evaporation. Fossils very rare; a few brachiopods, pelecypods, and gastropods occur. *B)* Bank behind reef; inner sublittoral and neritic Foraminifera, crinoids, some brachiopods, Bryozoa, and algae are characteristically found. *C)* Reef top, sublittoral and possibly littoral. The fossils include massive calcareous sponges, bryozoans, and algae, as well as cemented brachiopods. *D)* Reef front, inner sublittoral. Brachiopods and Bryozoa of more delicate structure than those in (C). Calcareous algae. *E)* Upper talus slope, sublittoral and upper bathyal environments. Water intermittently stagnant with high concentration of hydrogen sulphide. Sponges with siliceous skeletons are most common fossils. *F)* Basin floor, upper bathyal. Water stagnant. Very few fossils other than pelagic types are found in rocks representing this environment. *G)* Epipelagic and neritic environments. Radiolaria, calcareous planktonic algae, and ammonoids are the most common fossils. (Information from Newell, 1957.)

sedimentary environment contains fossils from two distinct habitats.

On the margins of the basins are reefs built largely by calcareous algae, but also containing masses of calcareous sponges, bryozoans, and hydrocoralines. The accumulation of such an abundance of calcareous deposits and of animals and plants with calcareous skeletons could occur only in relatively warm, well-aerated waters. The breakage of the fossils indicates that the upper part of the reef was subject to intense wave action. Delicate Bryozoa, protected from wave action by the massive skeletons of the upper reef organisms, lived on the lower parts of the reef. The basinward side and shoreward side of the reef also contain different species. Thus, the reef consists of several different but related habitats, each with characteristic animal species, most of them benthonic.

The sediments and fossils of the lagoons behind the reefs are those characteristic of shallow, well-aerated waters. Apparently the reefs prevented free circulation of water into the lagoons from the basins, and evaporation produced highly saline conditions. The fauna was limited to those animals that could tolerate high salt concentrations. Since soft calcareous muds floored the lagoons, the

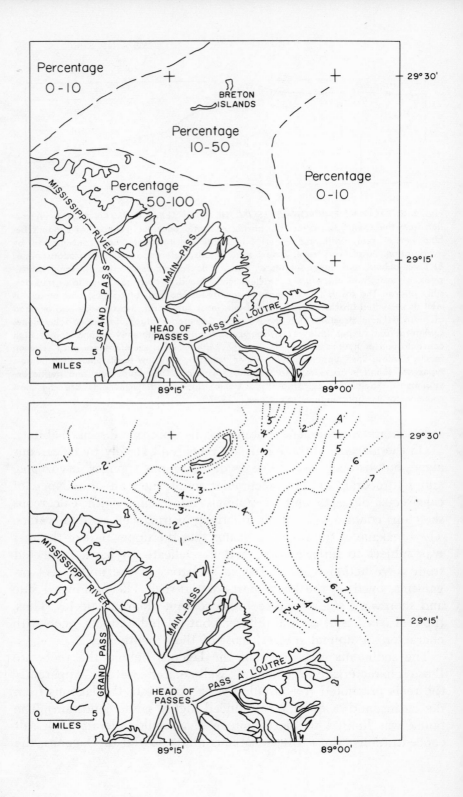

benthonic animals were types adapted to prevent sinking into the mud.

Some of these habitat associations occur in several different sedimentary environments; some sedimentary environments include several different habitat associations. These occurrences confuse the paleoecologist since identification of habitat depends, in part, on identification of sedimentary environment (or environment of deposition). They also confuse the stratigrapher since interpretation of sedimentary environment rests, in large measure, on interpretation of habitat. A stratigrapher-paleoecologist must therefore make constant cross reference from rock to fossil and back. He joins the fossil assemblage to a critical suite of sedimentary environments; the sedimentary environment to a critical suite of fossil assemblages.

method

This interplay sometimes yields more detailed interpretations of ecology (Figure 5-4, adapted from Phleger). The foraminifer assemblages cross the boundaries between different environments of deposition. They do not, however, live in all the sedimentary environments of the area, nor do they inhabit all of any one sedimentary environment. Obviously, the sedimentary characteristics (turbidity and substrate) do not limit their distribution because they occur on both mud and sand bottoms. On the other hand, depth is not the critical factor; they are always found in relatively shallow water but not on all shallow bottoms. They live near shore but not in all near-shore environments.

Inspection of the map suggests a relation to the main distributary channels of the Mississippi. The water in these channels freshens the ocean water near the point of discharge, and also bears a load of suspended and dissolved organic nutrients. Almost surely the distribution of this foraminifer assemblage is related to one or the other of these factors. The ecologist can now explain the anomalies of distribution. Both sand and mud bottoms occur off the distributary mouth; therefore this assemblage lives in both, but only at the distributary. The depths at the distributary mouth are shallow,

---

Fig. 5–4. *DISTRIBUTION OF A FORAMINIFER SPECIES AND RELATION TO ENVIRONMENT.* The upper map shows relative abundance of the species Ammobaculites salsus in per cent. The lower map shows depth of water in fathoms. The sediments, not shown here, display a rather complex pattern across abundance trends and, in part, across water depth. Note relation of distribution to distributaries (passes) of Mississippi. (Data from Phleger, 1955.)

but shallow waters elsewhere are too saline or lack the necessary organic nutrients.

But how would a paleoecologist recognize the control of the river distributary on animal distribution? The sedimentary environments are not unique in this particular point; sands are found elsewhere and so are muds.

The configuration of environments, the interrelation of sand in channel fills and bar fingers and of silts and clays in the natural levees and delta front deposits, establishes the presence of the distributary mouth. Once the relation of the assemblage to this brackish habitat is demonstrated, the assemblage becomes an environmental index for other deposits. A lagoon deposit might be brackish, normal, or hypersaline without any indication in the sediments or their interrelation. If a paleoecologist found this assemblage of foraminifers, he would logically conclude the lagoon was brackish.

A first summation

To recapitulate, the paleontologist recognizes differences between fossil samples of the same age collected in different localities. He must first determine what part of these differences corresponds to differences between the living populations and what results from transportation and selective preservation. Once he reaches this determination, he attempts to discover the environmental factors that controlled the distribution of the animals. Typically, he observes distinct fossil associations whose occurrence correlated in part with differences in rock type. By study of the adaptations of the fossils and the characteristics of the rocks, he comes to recognize ancient habitats and their characteristic species. The course of this analysis does not differ from that of a single species population (see pp. 80-89) except in the variety of animal types.

ANIMAL GEOGRAPHY

Barriers to dispersion

But this interpretation of ancient habitations falls short of a complete explanation of all differences between fossil samples. For example, early Pleistocene fossil mammals collected in Australia differ radically from those in southeastern Asia, although they possessed adaptations to similar environments and, further, are found associated with other fossils and rocks that indicate similar en-

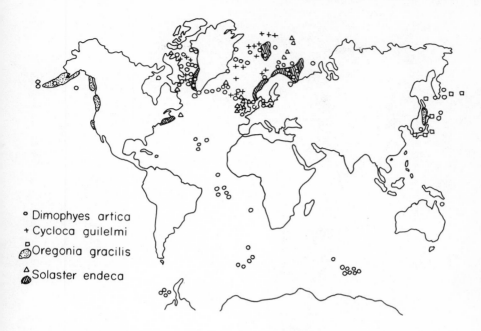

Fig. 5–5. *GEOGRAPHIC DISTRIBUTION OF FOUR SPECIES OF MODERN MARINE ANIMALS.* Two of the species, the coelenterate, *Dimophyes artica,* and the arthropod, *Cycloca guilelmi,* are pelagic. *D. Artica* has a world-wide distribution, but *C. guilelmi* is restricted to the North Atlantic. The crab, *Oregonia gracilis,* is a benthonic species limited to the North Pacific; the starfish, *Solaster endeca,* is similarly benthonic but occurs only in the North Atlantic. (Based on Ekman, 1953.)

vironments, similar habitats. Just the same they differ in species, genera, families, and orders. The answer to the puzzle is simple enough. The two areas were separated by seaways that the terrestrial mammals could not cross.

One can only conclude from this and similar examples that animals are limited in distribution by their ability to cross geographic barriers. Species distributions have a definite geographic pattern dictated by this adaptation (Figure 5-5). For example, some birds and strong flying insects overleap barriers of sea and mountain to populate new areas, but the Isthmus of Panama bars a clam species on the Gulf coast from favorable habitats on the Pacific coast a few miles away. The probability of a species dispersing across any part of the earth's surface is the product of inherent powers of dispersion of the species, of the specific effect of the environment in the intervening area on the power of dis-

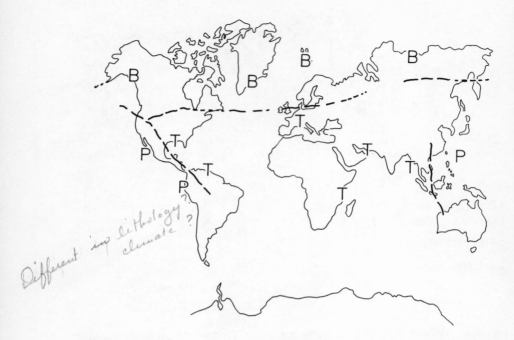

Different in lithology?
climate?

Fig. 5–6. *DISTRIBUTION OF JURASSIC MARINE FAUNAL REALMS.* The three realms, Boreal (B), Teythan (T), and Pacific (P), are defined by distinct groups of animals. Boundaries between realms are approximate and shifted from time to time. (Based on Arkell, 1956b.)

persal, and of the distance. The establishment in a new area depends, of course, on its ecological suitability. Many birds have great inherent power of dispersal consequent from their own flight and from the likelihood that storms will carry individuals from their home area. Further, the environment of the intervening area has little influence on that power. As a result the probability of dispersal is great, even across considerable distances. All they need, then, is a suitable place to land at the end of their flight.

The dispersal of the clam species is much more restricted because of the clam's limited powers of locomotion, because of the slight chance of accidental transportation, and because of the great effect of environment on that innate ability. The clam population thus will live along the Gulf shore in favorable habitats—distributed there because the environment does not greatly restrict movement, but restricted to that coast because thirty miles of dry land reduce that ability to nothing.

The barriers to dispersal can be more complex than this how-ever, for the environments across which the animals move and the ones they might expect to populate are complex. If the new habitats contain a predator, competitor, or parasite, the entering species may not survive the predation, competition, or parasitism. This invasion and defense may be passive and free of alarms, excursions, and direct bloodshed, but it is none the less deadly to invader or invaded. These biological barriers to dispersal probably have a complex history and may not be as permanent as the oceanic deeps or the stable continental interiors but serve equally well while they stand.

It is not difficult to observe differences between fossil samples that correspond to existing or ancient geographic barriers. The case of the Australian Pleistocene mammals has already been described. The paleontologist may be satisfied to treat the observation de-scriptively and distinguish, as does the animal geographer, realms, biotic provinces, and subprovinces. These geographic units are characterized by particular assemblages of species or higher taxonomic groups. Similar habitats occur in several provinces, but the species which inhabit them are, in large part, different. By this method, Arkell (1956) distinguishes in the Jurassic three major marine biological realms, the Tethyan, Pacific, and Boreal (Figure 5-6). He defines these realms primarily from the distribution of the ammonite cephalopods but finds that the distribution agrees, in general, with that of the other fossil groups.

Reconstruction of the crime

Arkell's interpretation reveals a successive increase in the differ-ences between these Jurassic biotic realms and lateral shifts in their boundaries. Clearly this is an historical problem. The paleon-tologist, therefore, typically goes beyond observation to interpre-tation. He must ask how the realms developed and the precise geographic and ecologic conditions that produced this develop-ment. Once that is done he has gone far toward the reconstruction of ancient geography.

Let me describe a fairly simple case. The middle Permian dry delta of north-central Texas resembled, so far as the ecology of large reptiles is concerned, the middle Permian deltas of Russia. The reptiles, however, are different, that is, different in the sense of not including the same genera or families (Olson, 1955). Therefore, some sort of barrier to dispersion existed. The early Permian dry delta of north-central Texas differed ecologically from the humid early Permian delta of the Allegheny plateau region. The faunas, however, are quite similar, except that the species were adapted to the environmental differences. The conclusion: there was no important barrier to dispersion. Apparently no land bridge existed between Eurasia and North America in the middle Permian, but one connected Texas and West Virginia at the beginning of Permian time.

In making such an analysis of faunal differences in rocks of approximately the same age, the paleontologist partitions the differences. That is, he attempts to associate part of the difference with those environmental differences that seem pertinent, and he tosses the remainder into a wastebasket called evolutionary relationship. If the ratio of environmental to evolutionary differences is large, he takes that to mean absence of barriers; if the ratio is small, that is taken to demonstrate major barriers. In the example just described, the evolutionary differences between reptiles in Texas and Russia are large as indicated by separation into distinct genera and families. On the other hand, they are both adapted to similar environments. If the two areas were connected, some species could move to occupy both Texas and Russia, though many or most were excluded by biological barriers—competition or predation. Environmental differences are small and evolutionary differences large; a barrier to migration must have existed.

My facile conclusion about land bridges or their absence in the Permian goes beyond these premises, for the low ratio says "barrier"—not what kind of barrier. If one can deduce or induce from existing animal distributions the types of barriers that restrict certain types of animals, inference as to the character of the barrier is possible. Or, if additional geologic or paleontologic evidence is available, some conclusion is possible. I'll amend my statement then and say "no land bridge suitable for reptile dispersion." This does not rule out the possibility of land connections across the Arctic circle with a temperature barrier for reptiles.

Comparison of the mammalian faunas, both recent and fossil, from North and South America (Simpson, 1950) demonstrates a complex pattern of migration between the two continents (Table 5–4. The dispersive powers of the various species, the environment of the intervening area, and the suitability of the environment in

TABLE 5–4

EFFECTS OF MIGRATION ON CENOZOIC MAMMALIAN FAUNAS OF NORTH AND SOUTH AMERICA

(Information taken from Simpson, 1950)

Time of Migration	Mode of migration	Animals invading South America from North America	Animals invading North America from South America
Late Miocene to Recent.	Along Isthmus of Panama and/or along island chains.	Deer, Camels, Peccaries, Tapirs, †Horses, †Mastodons, Cats, Weasels, Raccoons, Bears, Dogs, Mice, Squirrels, Rabbits, Shrew.	Porcupine, Armadillos, †Ground sloths, †Glyptodonts, (?) Oppossum.
Late Eocene to Oligocene.	Probably along island chains—"island hoppers."	Primitive rodents ancestral to porcupines, cavies, chinchilla, etc. Advanced lemuroid primates ancestral to New World monkeys.	(?) None
Early Paleocene.	Along land bridge connection.	Primitive herbivores ancestral to varied South American ungulates (4 orders all now extinct).	(?) None
		Primitive edentates ancestral to sloths, armadillos, anteaters, and glyptodonts.	
		Opossums—ancestral to marsupial carnivores (now extinct) and caenolestoids.	

† Group now extinct in area.

either continent determined these migrations. Since Simpson could estimate the first and last of these from the characteristics of the species and direct knowledge of the environment, he could reconstruct the environment of the intervening area during the Cenozoic. The high degree of divergence between the North and South American faunas suggests that strong barriers to migration existed during most of the Cenozoic—particularly in view of the considerable dispersive powers of the mammals and the relative similarity of many environments in the two continents. The inevitable conclusion is that the Panamanian land bridge was submerged. By study of the faunas at successive time levels during the Cenozoic, the times of dispersion between the continents can be established.

The geographic distribution of fossil assemblages also bears on the interpretation of the extent of ancient epicontinental seas. Rocks of a particular age generally outcrop in only a few isolated areas. Were they deposited as a continuous sheet and later reduced by erosion? If so, the difference between fossil collections should be the difference between local environments. If not, similar environments in different areas should contain different (distantly related) faunas. But how are their relative ages determined if the faunas are different? This complicated problem has not been made easier by the tendency of some paleontologists to ascribe any faunal difference to a "land barrier" without regard to differences in environments.

NATURAL SOCIETIES

Diversity and natural societies

As shown in the preceding paragraphs, the diversity of animals in different areas arises from diversity of adaptation and the heterogeneity of environment. The diversity of species in the same area with similar general environment, must also be a product of diversity in adaptation but in quite a different way. A few local animal populations comprise but a single species, but the rarity of single species populations emphasizes the more typical diversity.

The easy explanation, based on observation of species adaptations in a single habitat, would be that animals can adapt in different ways to the same environment. But isn't this really an observation, not an explanation? Even if the historical (evolutionary) causes for different adaptations to similar environments are left aside for the moment, an explanation must still be sought and sought in the face of a contradiction. For the adaptations of two species are not equally fit to any particular environment.

A re-examination of the concept of environment, as I used the term before, yields a glimmering of enlightenment. The environment is the same only in the sense that temperature, light, currents, and so on are the same, but these differ in effect with the adaptations of the species, i.e., the environment is similar but the ecologies of the individuals and of the species differ. Thus a whale shark lives in the same environment as a dolphin, but their ecologies are quite different in at least one aspect, the food source, for the whale shark is adapted to feed on microscopic plants and animals, the dolphin on rather large fish.

Quite apparently no species can exploit all the different ecologic possibilities of its environment equally well just as no species can occupy different environments equally well. For this reason a "division of labor" exists among species in a natural society, as I shall hereafter call these species associations. The position, the "job," of a species in a natural society is its *niche*. A particular species is adapted to a particular niche. Moreover, some of the species form part of each other's environment, either directly as prey, predator, competitor, or parasite, or indirectly as the activities of one species change the characteristics of the habitat.

The concern here is not with the individual intersections of the ecologic net but with the whole net. A coral reef is such a net of interrelated species. It is dominated by those coral species and algae that build massive wave-resistant skeletons; in a different sense, dominated by fish adapted to feed on living corals, and in still a different way by the sharks that eat the fish. Bound into the system are the algae that feed the corals and depend on the living breakwater of the reef for survival, and the parasites in the shark's gut and the sea urchin that scavenges the reef floor. All this is within the limits of the South Pacific, tropical, shallow, marine aquatic.

When the species are bound one to another in a natural society that is relatively independent of other associations, it is convenient to distinguish these as communities. Thus a community is defined as:

". . . a natural assemblage of organisms which, together with its habitat, has reached a survival level such that it is relatively

[margin annotation: community defined]

independent of adjacent assemblages of equal rank; to this extent, given radiant energy, it is self sustaining." (Allee, Emerson, Park, and Schmidt, 1949, p. 436).

In this sense, a coral reef is a community,* and a chance association of clam and brachiopod populations on a sandy bottom is not a community. In the variety of modern natural societies, all intergrades between these extremes exist. In turn, zoologists classify these societies on the degree and kind of integration of the component species and on the relative independence of the society from others.

The various types of natural societies can be further classified by reference to the type of habitat—a shallow, north temperate pond association—or to dominating or striking species in the association—an oak forest community. In turn, the species composing a natural society can be classified on the basis of function within the society structure so that the lynx is a medium-sized predator in the Canadian coniferous forest community.

Fossils and natural societies

The discussion has progressed from individual adaptation and function to species ecology and now to the ecology of natural societies. To the extent possible in paleontology, the analysis of fossil associations, extending the interpretations, and reweaving the ecologic net, proceeds in the same manner. The extension involves also a testing of earlier inferences, modification of interpretation, and increased precision of estimates as more and more parameters are determined.

The treatment of faunal associations as samples from natural societies involves no new methods but simply the recognition that the ecological relations between species are two-way. The sea weed that serves as food for the sea urchin is no longer just a factor in the urchin's environment; rather echinoid and plant are two species related by the feeding behavior of the urchin.

The paleontologist infers species interrelation by analogy with the relation between similarly adapted modern species or with similar modern associations and/or by correlation in occurrence between two or more species populations. Since reef formation re-

---

* The coral reef falls somewhat short of the definition since a considerable supply of food, algae and small animals, is added from outside the geographic limits of the reef.

duces strength of wave action, a reef coral species and the delicate bryozoan occurring within the reef are interrelated by the modification of wave action by the corals. The two species may, however, occur separately, the bryozoan in a protected lagoon, the coral in waters where the temperature exceeds the tolerance limits of the bryozoan. The paleoecologist would infer an interaction from the adaptations of species but not from correlation of occurrence. On the other hand, he might find an echinoid species always in association with the corals and infer an interrelation, though its nature could not be determined (predation of urchin on coral?). In theory, all interrelated species should show correlation in occurrence, even if they can survive independently. I doubt, though, whether paleontologists can determine these correlations unless they are very large.

The paleontologist can use statistical measures of association if requirements of random samples are met; these measures may be more sensitive than intuitive conclusions, but the analogies to modern inter-species adaptations are difficult to place in statistical form, if it can be done at all. Statistical analysis of association is advisable only when the analogy technique fails to deliver.

Vertebrate fossils in the lower Permian of Texas represent several different natural societies interrelated by occurrence in the same general environment and by occurrence of some species in more than one society (Olson, 1952). The structural adaptations of the different species tell something of the society they belonged to and of their ecologic position in that society. The association with different lithologies also indicates their affiliations with different communities (Table 5–5 and Figure 5-7). Figure 5-8 summarizes a similar analysis of Silurian coral reefs—based on data from a paper by Lowenstam (1957).

Since most marine animal associations are only loosely bound—more often by similar limiting factors than by direct interaction—interpretation becomes more difficult. Certain species occur together, and changes in their abundance show significant statistical correlation. Thus, in the Centerfield coral zone (mid-Devonian) of eastern Pennsylvania, three associations, one consisting largely of corals, and the other two of brachiopods, occur. Since they are all sessile animals, they competed for space and probably also for food. The available evidence does not indicate this competition limited the abundance of any species. Indeed, animals that might seem to

TABLE 5–5

ANALYSIS OF NATURAL SOCIETIES IN EARLY PERMIAN VERTEBRATES OF TEXAS (ARROYO TIME)

(Information in large part from Olson, 1952)

Habitat— Natural Society	Rock-environment Associations	Animals	General niche
Upland	Alluvial—floodplain, red clay-stones.	Reptiles Dimetrodon Diadectes Captorhinus	Large carnivore. Moderately large herbivore. Small carnivore-insectivore.
Pond margin	Interfingering of floodplain and pond deposits and in pond deposits.	Amphibians Seymouria Broiliellus Eryops Trematops	Moderate sized predator—small vertebrates and invertebrates. Small (?) predator on small invertebrates and vertebrates. Moderately large carnivore—predator on amphibians, small reptiles, and fish. Moderate size—predator on amphibians and fish.
		Reptiles Labidosaurus Edaphosaurus	Moderate sized predator. Large herbivore.
Pond	Pond—thin, even-bedded shales.	Amphibians Diplocaulus magnicornis Euryodus Lysorophus Trimerorhachis	Moderate to small size. (?) Mudgrubber-scavenger. Small—probably predator on small invertebrates. Small—probably predator on small invertebrates. Moderate sized predator—fish and smaller amphibians.
		Bony fish Gnathorhiza	Moderate-small lung-fish. Predator on small,

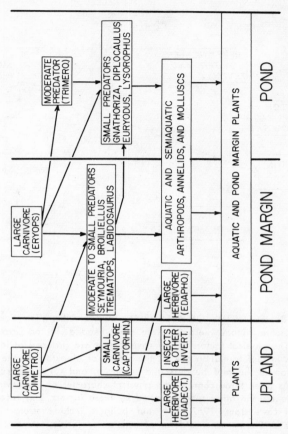

Fig. 5–7. *ANALYSIS OF THE EARLY PERMIAN FAUNA OF NORTH-CENTRAL TEXAS.* Arrows indicate probable predation. Species in any one block in part competitive. The plants, though poorly known as fossils, must have furnished the ultimate food source for whole society. The herbivores included two large reptile genera, *Diadectes* and *Edaphosaurus*, and, less well-known from fossils, a variety of small invertebrates. The latter were consumed by the small to moderate sized predators, including a variety of amphibians and reptiles. The master predators were a reptile, *Dimetrodon*, and an amphibian, *Eryops*. Three distinct habitats—upland, pond margin, and pond—are included in this area, and the probable life occurrence of the various genera in these habitats is indicated. Abbreviations: Captorhin., *Captorhinus*; Diadect., *Diadectes*; Dimetro., *Dimetrodon*; Edapho., *Edaphosaurus*; Trimero., *Trimerorhachis*. (Based, in part, on Olson, 1952.)

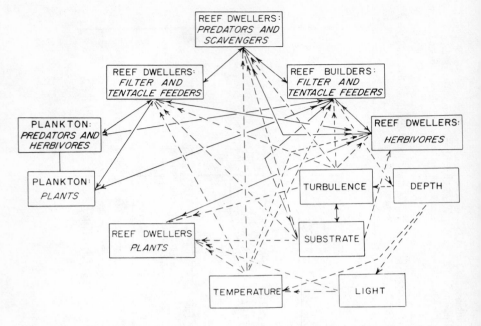

Fig. 5–8. *ECONOMY OF A SILURIAN CORAL REEF.* The double-headed, solid arrows indicate mutual interaction; the single-headed dashed arrows indicate unilateral action. The physical factors of the environment are grouped at lower right. The critical relations in reef formation are (1) the supply of plankton for the reef builders, (2) the interaction of the reef builders and substrate, and (3) the effect of reef building on depth. As these three change, the physical character of the environment changes and, consequently, the other species limited by these factors. This reconstruction is based in part on Lowenstam, 1957. The reef builders include stromatoporoid and tabulate corals and *Stromatactis*, a form of unknown affinities. Among the herbivorous reef dwellers are the gastropods, possibly some of the trilobites, and a variety of "worms" unrepresented as fossils. The filter and tentacle feeders include crinoids, cystoids, brachiopods, bryozoans, and pelecypods. The scavengers and predators comprise trilobites, cephalopods, and possibly annelid worms. The other components of the society were not preserved

be the closest competitors, like the various horn corals, occur together. In this example, the corals occur in the siltier beds. Possibly they required a firm substrate for support. The brachiopods, on the other hand, are most abundant in layers that show short periods of non-deposition. They apparently thrived only when deposition was very slow. The species (or in this case genera) are united in an association by similar response to factors of the external environment—the character of the substrate and the rate of deposition.

Transportation and selective preservation must modify many fossil associations. Tasch (1957) has shown that several faunas thought to be composed of individuals dwarfed by unfavorable environments are almost certainly the results of sorting. He found in the Dry shale in Kansas a clear-cut grading of sizes in a typical sedimentary pattern. In the example of the Centerfield coral zone just discussed, transportation was not an effective factor, for the delicate skeletons of bryozoans were buried unbroken, but large elements of the society are missing. We can find no trace of those important scavengers and predators, the annelid worms, nor of the primary food source, the algae. Analysis can proceed so far but no farther.

Animals, natural societies, and stratigraphers

The interpretation of natural societies provides a final synthesis of what I like to call two-dimensional paleontology. The first step in this sort of paleontology is the observation of the form of the individual fossil. Next, the paleontologist can interpret growth and development of form and the relation of form and function. He proceeds to a classification of animals based primarily on their form; from this classification arises the concept of the fundamental unit, the species. Each species has genetic, morphologic, and ecologic characteristics. As a consequence of these characteristics, the distribution of any particular species is restricted, and fossil assemblages from separate localities differ to the extent of these restrictions. Also, as a consequence of these characteristics, each species occupies a separate niche in a local assemblage of animals. Analysis of the relations of the assembled species integrates all the prior observations and inferences.

Since paleontologists and stratigraphers, whether they interpret evolutionary patterns, draw paleogeographic maps, or correlate rocks, deal with animals once part of natural societies, they must also deal with such societies. If each fossil bore a convenient label, "I was a scavenger on the bottom of a 30 meter deep sea from 231,612,907 B.C. to 231,612,906 B.C," there would be no need for paleoecologic studies of fossil assemblages. So long as they are not so labeled or until a satisfactory time machine is available, paleontologists are limited in their study of fossils by their restricted knowledge of the paleoecologic framework.

REFERENCES

Allee, W. C.; A. E. Emerson; O. Park; T. Park, and K. P. Schmidt, 1949. See references for Chapter 5.

Arkell, W. J. 1956. *Jurassic Geology of the World*. New York: Hafner.

Boucot, A. J. 1953. "Life and Death Assemblages among Fossils," *Amer. Jour. of Science*, vol. 251, pp. 25-40. A discussion of the factors controlling fossil assemblages.

Bradley, W. H. 1948. "Limnology and the Eocene Lakes of the Rocky Mountain Region," *Geol. Soc. of America, Bulletin*, vol. 59, pp. 635-648. A classical paleoecologic study.

Craig, Gordon Younger. 1953. "Fossil Communities and Assemblages," *Amer. Jour. of Science*, vol. 251, pp. 547-548. Discussion of factors controlling the sample called the fossil assemblage.

Ekman, S. 1953. *Zoogeography of the Sea*. London: Sidgwick and Jackson. Extensive work on the distribution of marine animals.

Ellison, S. P., Jr. 1951. "Microfossils as Environment Indicators in Marine Shales," *Jour. of Sed. Petrology*, vol. 21, pp. 214-225.

Fisher, D. W. 1951. "Marcasite Fauna in the Ludlowville Formation of Western New York," *Jour. of Paleontology*, vol. 25, pp. 365-371. A paleoecologic study of a peculiar assemblage of fossils.

Hedgpeth, J. W. 1957. "Classification of Marine Environments," in: "Treatise on Marine Ecology and Paleoecology," vol. 2, *Geol. Soc. America, Memoir 67*, pp. 93-100.

Hesse, R., W. C. Allee, and K. P. Schmidt. 1951. *Ecological Animal Geography*, 2nd ed. New York: Wiley. A text on environmental controls of animal distribution.

Imbrie, J. 1955. "Quantitative Lithofacies and Biofacies Study of Florena Shale (Permian) of Kansas," *Amer. Assoc. of Petr. Geologists, Bulletin*, vol. 39, pp. 649-670. A pioneer quantitative paleoecologic study of a fossil assemblage.

Johnson, R. C. 1957. "Experiments on the Burial of Shells," *Jour. of Geol.*, vol. 65, pp. 527-539. Work on transportation and burial of shells by currents.

Joleaud, L. 1939. *Atlas de Paleobiogeographie*. Paris: Lechevalier. An atlas of fossil distributions, summarizing knowledge of time.

Jones, N. S. 1950. "Marine Bottom Communities," *Biol. Review*, vol. 25, pp. 283-313. A significant review paper on the character of benthic marine natural societies.

Jorgensen, C. B. 1955. "Quantitative Aspects of Filter Feeding in Invertebrates," *Biol. Review*, vol. 30, pp. 391-454. Since most invertebrate fossils were filter feeders this paper has much pertinence to paleoecology.

Krumbein, W. C., and L. L. Sloss. 1951. *Stratigraphy and Sedimentation.* San Francisco: Freeman. A text that emphasizes recognition of depositional environments and their concomitants.

Lowenstam, H. 1957. "Niagaran Reefs in the Great Lakes," in: "Treatise on Marine Ecology and Paleoecology," vol. 2, *Geol. Soc. of America, Memoir 67,* pp. 215-248.

Lowman, S. W. 1951. "The Relationship of Biotic and Lithic Facies in Recent Gulf Coast Sedimentation," *Jour. of Sed. Petrology,* vol. 21, pp. 233-237. An important study of the relation between animal assemblage and sediment.

MacGinitie, G. E. and N. MacGinitie. 1949. *Natural History of Marine Animals.* New York: McGraw-Hill. A good general discussion of marine ecology.

Martin-Kaye, P. 1951. "Sorting of Lamellibranch Valves on Beaches in Trinidad, B. W. I.," *Geol. Magazine,* vol. 88, pp. 432-435.

Menard, H. W., Jr., and A. J. Boucot. 1951. "Experiments on the Movement of Shells by Water," *Amer. Jour. of Science,* vol. 249, pp. 131-151.

Newell, N. D. 1957. "Paleoecology of Permian reefs in the Guadalupe Mountains Area," in: "Treatise on Marine Ecology and Paleoecology," vol. 2. *Geol. Soc. of America, Memoir 67,* pp. 407-436.

Olson, E. C. 1952. "The Evolution of a Permian Vertebrate Chronofauna," *Evolution,* vol. 6, pp. 181-196.

————. 1955. "Parallelism in the Evolution of the Permian Reptilian Faunas of the Old and New Worlds," *Fieldiana: Zoology,* vol. 37, pp. 385-401.

Parker, R. H. 1955. Macro-invertebrate Assemblages as Indicators of Sedimentary Environments in East Mississippi Delta Region," *Jour. of Sed. Petrology,* vol. 25, pp. 216-221.

Parkinson, D. 1957. Lower Carboniferous Reefs of Northern England," *Amer. Assoc. of Petr. Geologists, Bulletin,* vol. 41, pp. 511-537.

Phleger, F. B. 1955. "Ecology of Foraminifera in Southeastern Mississippi Delta Area," *Amer. Assoc. of Petr. Geologists, Bulletin,* vol. 39, pp. 712-752.

Simpson, G. G. 1950. "History of the Fauna of Latin America," *Amer. Scientist,* vol. 38, pp. 361-389.

Sloan, R. E. 1955. "Paleoecology of the Pennsylvanian Marine Shales of Palo Pinto County, Texas," *Jour. of Geology,* vol. 63, pp. 412-428.

Tasch, Paul. 1957. "Fauna and Paleoecology of Pennsylvania Dry Shale of Kansas," in: "Treatise on Marine Ecology and Paleoecology," vol. 2, *Geol. Soc. of America, Memoir 67,* pp. 365-406.

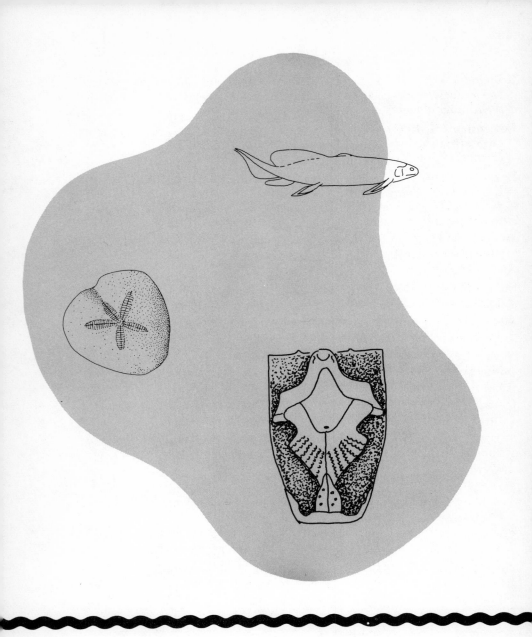

6. EVOLUTION

$\mathcal{A}$ s noted in the last chapter, the book has, to this point, been concerned with "two dimensional" paleontology—the study of contemporaneous samples or simply of fossils abstracted from their occurrence in time. I have mentioned—and then avoided—the problems of evolution and of correlation, but few real paleontologic problems are free of such problems, nor would many paleontologists care to have them so.

Evolution appears in the fossil record in several guises. Obviously it is related to the succession of fossil assemblages in the stratigraphic column. Less obviously it is related to the similarities and differences between contemporaneous species, to the geographic diversity of species, and to the diversity within natural societies. This and the succeeding chapter will deal with these relationships and with the mechanics of evolution; Chapter 8 will consider the significance of evolution to the stratigrapher.

ORGANIC CHANGE IN THE GEOLOGIC RECORD

In any considerable thickness of sedimentary rocks, successive layers contain different species. If the oldest beds were deposited in a marine environment and later ones on a floodplain, a fauna of terrestrial vertebrates, insects, and snails succeeded a fauna of clams, fish, and crabs. The change in environment controlled the change in species. When the sea again encroached on the floodplain, the original species reappeared (Figure 6-1). The succession of faunas resulted from the same limiting factors that determine the distribution of a species at any particular time.

Most fossil species, however, disappear for good as the environment changes—disappear from the local area and indeed from the face of the earth. Their places are taken by new species, unknown in older rocks, so that the total number of species does not change greatly. This succession of faunas is, in some examples, correlated with environmental change, but the early species do not recur if the environment switches back (Figure 6-2).

Occasionally a paleontologist finds a third type of faunal succession. He discovers distinct species populations from the top and bottom of the sequence but finds that intermediate beds contain populations intermediate in character, some of which might be logically placed in either species (Figure 6-3). Again, if fortunate,

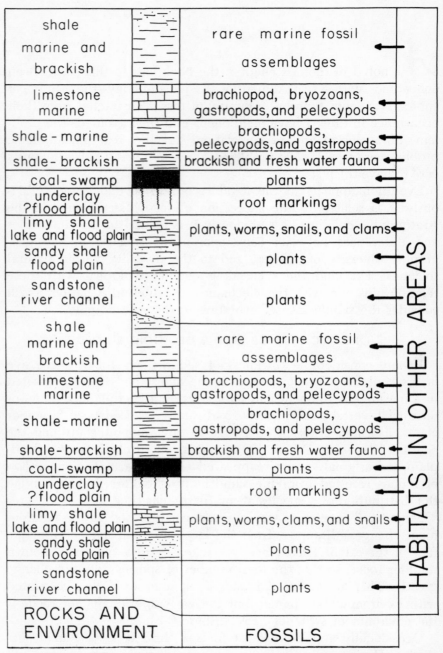

Fig. 6–1. *SUCCESSION OF FOSSILS IN A LOCAL STRATIGRAPHIC SEQUENCE.* Here species disappear and reappear as the environment fluctuates. The variation in time here is exactly comparable to geographic variation at any one time. The succession is one typical of the cyclic deposits in the Pennsylvanian rocks of Illinois. (Weller, 1957.)

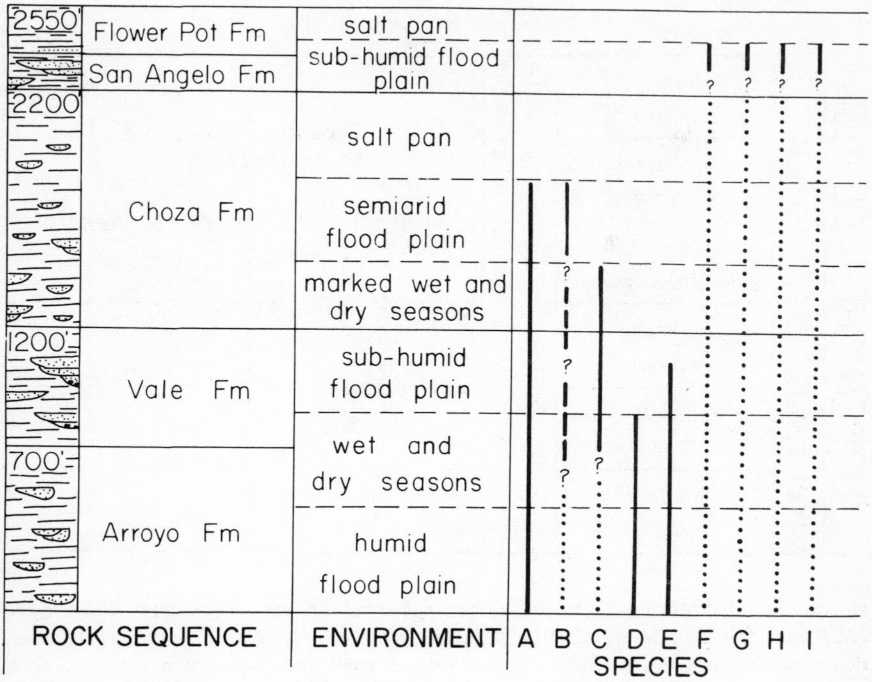

ROCK SEQUENCE		ENVIRONMENT	SPECIES A B C D E F G H I
2550'	Flower Pot Fm	salt pan	? ? ? ?
	San Angelo Fm	sub-humid flood plain	
2200'		salt pan	
	Choza Fm	semiarid flood plain	
		marked wet and dry seasons	?
1200'	Vale Fm	sub-humid flood plain	?
700'		wet and dry seasons	? ?
	Arroyo Fm	humid flood plain	

Fig. 6–2. *SUCCESSION OF FOSSILS IN A LOCAL STRATIGRAPHIC SEQUENCE.* The faunal and lithologic sequence in the early and middle Permian, north-central Texas. As the environment changes, species disappear from the local sequence. When the environment changed back to a more favorable type in San Angelo time, none of the old species reappeared. In place of them appeared several new but ecologically similar species. A and F are large carnivorous reptiles; B, C, G, H, and I are moderate sized to large herbivores reptiles. The two amphibians, D and E apparently had no ecological successors. (After Olson, 1952, and Olson and Beerbower, 1953.)

the paleontologist can relate the change in morphology of successive populations to environment changes. The only reasonable conclusion seems that of a gradual change in genetic composition of an interbreeding (species) population through time, a change related in some way to the environment change.

Obviously, he forces the term *species* on this population succession through time, for the populations were never reproductively isolated in the same sense contemporaneous populations are. Nor are the populations distinct morphologically. If he groups these populations into species, he must give arbitrary assignments (this practical problem is discussed at greater length on page 147) so that the differences in "average morphology" between temporal

ZONE

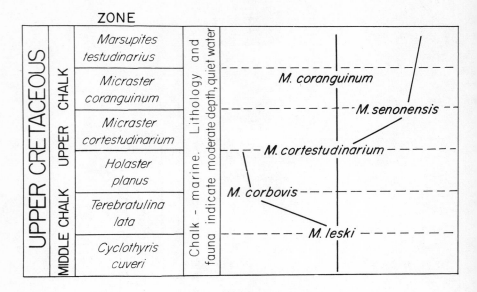

Fig. 6–3. *SUCCESSION OF INTERGRADING SPECIES OF MICRASTER, LATE CRE-TACEOUS OF SOUTHERN ENGLAND.* The *Micraster leski-M. coranguinum* succession comprises a series of fossil samples from a continuous population sequence. The samples from any two successive beds overlap in morphology. The "distinct" species are connected by a series of transitional forms. (After Kermack, 1954.)

species is about the same as that between similar contemporaneous species. A few rock sequences, representing nearly continuous deposition through a considerable period of time, include long successions of "temporal species," successions sufficiently long so that the extremes can be classified in different genera.

These three modes of faunal succession are characteristic not only of species but also of the higher categories of classification. Genera, families, and so on may succeed each other temporarily or permanently and, if permanently, either abruptly or by gradual transformation. Since the species are the basic units in the construction of these categories, this should be expected; arguments for special origins for these categories will be considered later.

Abrupt faunal changes

The first mode of faunal succession—a direct consequence of environmental change—has been disposed of; the second and third, which are, in any definition, evolution, require extended discussion.

The sudden appearance of new species, families, orders, and so on in a fossil succession might ensue either *a*) from the sudden origin of these groups, *b*) from their migration into the area after slow evolution elsewhere, or *c*) from an extended period of local nonpreservation during which gradual change took place. The second and third possibilities are just special cases of the gradual succession described above and can be shown to be valid explanations for some sudden faunal changes. For example, cats, deer, elephants (mastodons), dogs, horses, peccaries, camels, and several other mammal groups are unknown from the Cenozoic rocks of South America until the very top of the sequence (see p. 115; Table 5–4). Then these groups appear without any intermediate links to the earlier mammalian fauna. The antecedents of these mammals, however, exist in older rocks of North America and Eurasia. Similarly, the Cenozoic mammalian faunas in the deposits of the intermontane valleys of Montana change abruptly with no transitions between genera and families. But the transitional species and genera are known from rocks in South Dakota, Colorado, Wyoming, and Nebraska. Although these transitional forms almost certainly lived in Montana, the deposition of sediments was spasmodic (as can be shown by physical geologic evidence), and the fossil sequence lacks continuity.

Because some abrupt faunal changes can be shown to be the results of migration or gaps in preservation, because the fossil record is discontinuous, and because the sedimentary rocks of any one geologic age cover only a small part of the earth's surface, most paleontologists argue that all examples of evolutionary "jumps" have the same origin. Some disagree, however, and the magnitude and nature of some of these "jumps" are admittedly puzzling. Since a general theory of evolution cannot depend on a lack of data, I'll postpone discussion of abrupt evolutionary changes to a later page.

Gradual changes

Let me return to an example of gradual transformation of populations and examine the details of this phenomena. A fossil sea urchin, *Micraster* (Figure 6-4) occurs through several hundred feet of a section in the Cretaceous of southern England. Specimens from the top of the section differ notably from those at the base; transitional forms are found in intermediate layers (Rowe, 1899, Kermack, 1953). Urchins from any one level vary considerably; this

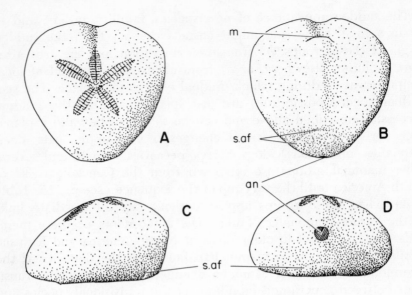

Fig. 6–4. *SEA URCHIN, MICRASTER CORANGUINUM.* A) View of upper surface. B) View of lower surface. C) Side view. D) Rear view. Test was covered with numerous small spines in life. Length of specimen approximately 39 mm. Abbreviations: *an*, anus; *m*, mouth; *s. af*, subanal fasiole.

variation represents differences within the interbreeding species populations during a relatively short interval. Successive samples overlap in morphology so that part of the individuals in the later samples display characteristics like some of those in the earlier. I've expressed this in Figure 6-5 by frequency curves showing variation in a particular characteristic for successive populations. If one had quantitative data, he could estimate means and standard deviations for these characters in each population from the sample distribution.

The change in the subanal fasciole (Figure 6-6) is one of the more striking modifications. This structure consists of a shallow groove forming an irregular circle immediately below the anus. Among modern sea urchins, the groove bears numerous hair-like cilia. The cilia beat constantly and maintain a strong backward current of water. I think it reasonable that the fasciole functioned in the same way in *Micraster*. Modern urchins living on the sea floor lack a fasciole; grains of sediment and small organisms are removed either by gravity or by the downward currents produced by cilia on the upper surface of the animal. Burrowing species, how-

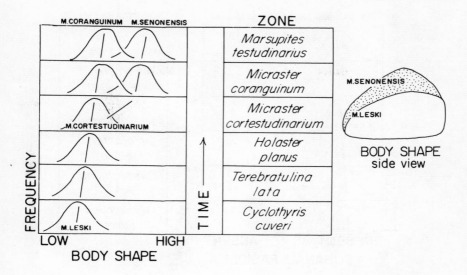

Fig. 6–5. *EVOLUTION OF MICRASTER: BODY FORM.* The frequency curves show population variation on relative body height for successive populations. Drawing at right shows difference between high and low forms. (Information from Kermack.)

ever, cannot rid themselves of the nuisance in such a simple way, for they require a constant current of water to remove wastes and provide for respiration. The ciliary tract of the subanal fasciole provides this current.

The change in body shape (Figure 6-5) in the *Micraster* populations indicates a change from burrowing (flattened body) to surface living (high body).* The change in the subanal fasciole, therefore, is correlated with a change in environment. Since the change in function of the part is also related to the environmental change, i.e., results in an adaptation to the new environment, the environmental change in some sense directs the morphologic change.

The environmental change directs—but how? To answer this, we must re-examine the effects of the environment on organisms. Environment acts on the individual through modification of the genetic material (by inducing mutation or change of chromosome structure), through its influence on the processes of growth and development, and through limitation of survival and reproduction of that individual. Further, environment affects the interbreeding

---

* Why the change from burrowing to surface? Was it directed by a change in the external environment? This question is as yet unanswerable.

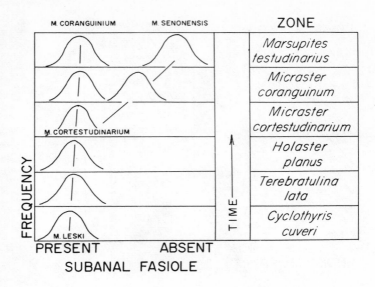

Fig. 6–6. *EVOLUTION OF MICRASTER: SUBANAL FASIOLE.* The frequency curves show population variation in the subanal fasiole for successive samples. (Information from Kermack.)

population not only by action on the individuals but also through control of reproduction and dispersal. The environment, if it causes morphologic change, must operate through one or more of these processes.

The mutations or chromosomal modifications produced by the environment (cosmic rays, heat, and so forth) result in the change of developmental processes and, consequently, in morphology, physiology, and behavior. The changes are, however, random with respect to the causal factor. For example, a gene mutation produced by cosmic rays might induce the development of purple hair in a cow, or it might induce greater or less resistance to hard radiation, i.e., cosmic rays. The point is, it's just as likely to do one as the other. An individual in which greater resistance to cosmic rays existed would be better adapted, but the species population would not, for there would be an equal chance of producing an individual with lower resistance.

On the other hand, the second cause of environmental modification of morphology, influence on development (or on behavior for that matter), affects all individuals of the population equally and in the same direction although effects differ with different developmental potentialities. Thus a man with high hereditary potential for resisting sunburn would be better adjusted to intense sunlight than an individual with low potential, though the result might be equally dark protective tans.

Further, some environment factors may induce a modification related directly to the factor, such as tanning of the skins in humans. The result is modification of the population with direct adaptation to environment. If the environment modifies cytoplasm of the cell as it is known to do, these modifications may be carried through many generations. If, however, the environment resumes the earlier condition, the adaptation is immediately or gradually reversed since the hereditary material was not changed. Moreover, potential pathways of development limit such environmentally produced changes. Obviously, these modifications of species morphology are not evolution in the normal sense of that term, and do not explain the observations of the fossil record. By elimination of other possibilities, environmental control of survival, reproduction, and dispersal is left as the directive force in this evolutionary sequence.

The mechanism of direction is perhaps clearer if you consider the species population divided into subpopulations of morphologically similar individuals. Using *Micraster*, the earliest population is conveniently divided into five subpopulations (Figure 6-7), the most abundant morphologic type in III, less abundant in II and IV, and a few individuals in I and V. Each subpopulation has a birth rate and a death rate, and if the species population is changing neither in number nor in morphologic characteristics, the birth rate in each subpopulation must equal the death rate. If the birth rates exceed the death rates, the total population will increase in number and will also change in average morphology if the excess of births is unequal in the subpopulations. The reverse would, of course, be true if the net rate (birth rate less death rate) were negative.

On the other hand, if *Micrasters* with relatively large subanal fascioles (subpopulations IV and V) have the lowest net rate, the morphological characteristics of the species will change, the average shifting from "large subanal fasciole" toward "small subanal fasciole." These rates also determine the range of variation within the population, for morphologic types with negative net rates will diminish and disappear. If the net rate of increase for small subanal fascioles is much higher than for other types, the distribution curve will have a very sharp peak (Figure 6-8); if only a little higher, the

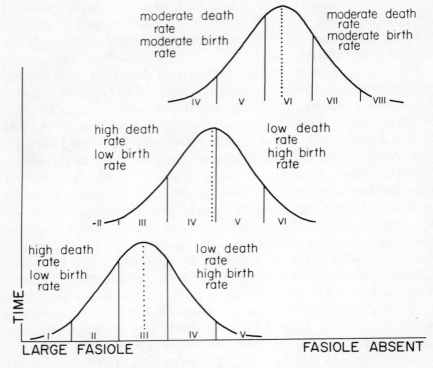

Fig. 6–7. *TRANSFORMATION OF A MICRASTER POPULATION SUCCESSION.* The early population has a large number of individuals with large subanal fasiole (Groups *I, II, III*). The other groups, however, have higher survival and reproduction rates so that the population frequency distribution shifts, in time, to the right.

curve will be flattened. In statistical terminology, these rates determine the mean, range, and standard deviation. Finally, the rate of change in morphology is the product of absolute values of the net rates.

THE MECHANISM OF EVOLUTION

It has seemed simple enough, but I have hidden complexity beneath this simplicity. A set of genes produces enzymes that manifest themselves in the development of the characteristic, "subanal fasciole." These enzymes also enter into the development of other features of the animal. A number of different gene sets probably gave rise to a similar "large subanal fasciole" but produced different results in other parts of the body. Gene set *A*, then, might reduce the death rate by improving the "subanal fasciole," but,

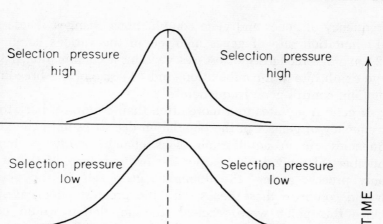

Fig. 6–8. *RELATION OF POPULATION VARIATION AND SELECTION.* The upper frequency curve shows a narrow range of variation as the extremes are removed by selection. In the other situation (lower curve) the more extreme variants survive under lower selective pressure.

at the same time, might decrease the birth rate by adverse effects on the reproductive organs. The recombination of genes complicates the matter further, for crossing a male with gene set *A* and a female also with *A* might yield only a few offspring with set *A* and many with other gene sets. On the other hand, a male with set *B* and a female with set *C* might produce 90 per cent set *A* young.

If anyone attempted analysis in terms of specific matings, he soon would bog down in millions of computations, but he can, however, lump all these specific matings and individual deaths in terms of averages. The geneticist prefers to do this with respect to single genes.

Mutation and selection

The Hardy-Weinberg Law (page 55) predicts the chances of getting a particular gene set in any generation. Because morphology is correlated with the gene system, the law also predicts the chance of getting an animal with a particular morphology if the animal develops in a particular environment. As shown in the section on genetics of populations (page 55), the frequency of occurrence of a gene or a set of genes is constant for a population in equilibrium. If the factors acting on the population are not in equilibrium, the frequency of genes and gene combinations changes. These factors, (1) mutation rate of genes involved in the various combinations, (2) average fecundity of crosses yielding a combination, (3) average death rate of a combination, and (4) size of the breeding population, control gene frequencies.

If gene A mutates to a more often than a mutates back to A, the frequency of gene A in the population decreases until the gene frequencies are in equilibrium. This change results in increasing numbers of individuals bearing the favored gene. If this were the only process acting, the dominant gene sets in the population would comprise those genes with the greatest chemical stability. Once this point were reached, the population would cease to change—if no other factor acted.

Differential fecundity between various crosses likewise will change the frequency of gene combinations. If the various crosses yielding "small subanal fasciole" averaged 100 offspring in each mating and those producing "large subanal fasciole" 85 offspring in each, most of the population would bear gene combinations for "small subanal fasciole."

On the other hand, if "large subanal fasciole" increases the average length of survival of the animal, this advantage might outweigh the disadvantage in average fecundity. The sum of rates of fecundity and of survivorship can be stated as an adaptive or selective value. In theory, one could determine the average selective value of each gene and each gene combination in a living natural population at any time. Since no research man or combination of research men could measure fast enough to actually do this, biologists must accept the theoretic results supported by limited experiments and careful mathematical deduction.

An evolving population would shift in the direction of the gene combination or combinations possessing the highest selective value and would shift at a rate determined in part by this value. In the *Micraster* example, each of the variant subpopulations (the products of different gene combinations) presumably had different selective values. The direction of evolution indicates the "small subanal fasciole" subpopulation had the highest selective value. As the population changed, the probability of getting a particular gene combination decreased (gene sets for "large subanal fasciole") or increased (gene sets for "small subanal fasciole"). Individuals with "no subanal fasciole" appeared in the population; individuals with very "large subanal fasciole" began to disappear. Since the new subpopulation, "no subanal fasciole," had a higher survival value than the "small subanal fasciole," the population average continued to shift. Note that this does not change the variety of recombinants but rather the chances of getting a particular recombinant. In the earliest population, individuals carrying a gene combination for "no subanal fasciole" had a chance of occurrence of, perhaps, 10^{-12}, but, with the shift of the population mean, the probability jumps to about 10^{-1}. In practice "no subanal fasciole" individuals would not appear in the original population but would turn up fairly often in the later one. In this way evolution generates new variation without new gene mutation, but it also deprives the population of other variants.

Population distribution and evolution

I have buried two assumptions in the preceding discussion that now must be dug up. Those assumptions are, first, completely random breeding among individuals in a large species population and, second, a homogeneous environment throughout the limits of species distribution. To this extent, the evolutionary model depends on a hypothetical situation never realized in nature. Therefore, I had best describe the effects of breeding structure of the population and of environmental heterogeneity.

All natural species populations are conveniently thought of as being divided into local, freely interbreeding units. The genetic variation (and possibly the morphologic) within these local populations will be somewhat less than that of the species population because no single local population is likely to include all the less frequent gene combinations. As long as each local population breeds freely with adjacent populations, the genes circulate freely among these local units, and the probability of a particular gene combination in a local population is the same as that for the entire population. If, however, no breeding occurs between local populations, the gene frequencies within the local population determine the probability of that combination. Since these gene frequencies differ from those in the species as a whole, each local population will differ from all the others in morphology, behavior, and so on. Most species populations probably fall between these extremes of fully interbreeding or of completely isolated local populations and consist of partly isolated units. This change in population breeding structure is of particular importance if there exist in the population certain rare gene combinations with potential high selective value. In freely interbreeding populations, these combinations tend to be swamped by accidents of recombination. In a partly isolated local population, however, the combination is much more likely to survive because inbreeding will maintain the frequencies of the necessary genes above those in the total population and give the potential selective value an opportunity to function.

If the effective size of the local populations is quite small and immigration very slow, another factor is likely to come into play. Genes (and therefore the gene combinations) are eliminated from such populations by accidents of sampling. The gene frequencies will drift even against rather strong selection; the local population will lose its genetic variance; and many of these populations will become extinct because fixation of gene combinations with low fecundity and/or high death rates. Species populations with such a structure are likely to lose variability with fixation of a relatively few gene combinations. Such trends are likely to be unfavorable for the species—extinction is hardly favorable—but might, on rare occasions, be of advantage if they, by accident, resulted in a favorable combination. The population would make an evolutionary change not related to selection on the initial population, and genetic drift would start off a novel evolutionary trend.*

The effects of population structure are thus largely concerned with control of the amount of variability and of its availability for evolution. Population structure does not, however, exist in isolation but is rather an expression of the environmental matrix and of the intrinsic powers of dispersal of the local populations. Ecological barriers reduce dispersal between local populations and partially isolate them. The ability of gene combinations to sweep through a population is, therefore, determined by the intrinsic powers of dispersal of their bearers and the nature of barriers to dispersal as well as by their selective advantage.

Finally, different local populations seldom, if ever, have identical environments. For this reason, the selective value for a gene combination varies from population to population. In a freely inter-

---

* Genetic drift would account for the sudden appearance of new animal groups, since the ancestral populations might be so small that they do not appear in the fossil record. For this reason, paleontologists have found the concept tempting—but dangerous, since conclusions are based on the lack of evidence, the lack of fossils.

breeding species population, recombination overcomes this tendency to local population differentiation, and the frequency of a combination remains the same everywhere. On the other hand, if the possibilities of interbreeding are restricted, the local populations evolve in different directions. In species consisting of local units that interbreed freely only with adjacent units, the adjacent populations, inhabiting somewhat similar environments, resemble each other more than they do non-adjacent populations. Each local population has its "average morphology" in that set of combinations most favored in the local environment. Some local populations have a higher rate of increase and thus tend to swamp adjacent localities. The averages then fall at an equilibrium point between the set favored by immigration and that favored by local fecundity and survival. The average changes gradually among different areas as local differentials in selection overcome immigration from neighboring areas.

In defense of Neo-Darwinism

The ideas set forth in the preceding paragraphs form the basic concepts of evolution. We can be reasonably certain that some evolution occurred in this fashion, for this theory accords with some, if not all, paleontologic evidence, agrees with the properties of modern species populations, and can be demonstrated experimentally. Some paleontologists and biologists argue for other evolutionary "models" or for major revisions in the Neo-Darwinian "model." I'll describe some of these suggested mutant concepts in the following chapter, but most workers in the fields of evolution believe that the primary mode of organic change is by selection of variant individuals within a species population. The variation is supplied by mutation and recombination; the structure of the population modifies the effects of recombination and of selection.

ISOLATION AND THE DIVERSITY OF SPECIES

The transformation of one species into another accounts in some part for the succession of fossil species in the geologic column. This transformation, however, does not, in itself, explain the diversity of contemporaneous species nor the apparent family resemblances among these species. A further inquiry is necessary.

Obviously, if partial ecologic barriers reduce immigration among local populations, differentiation among them is likely to be greater and more sharply defined than in freely interbreeding populations. Complete isolation ends gene flow and permits divergence of the local populations under the influence of environmental differences. If isolation is sufficiently long, the diverging populations lose their interbreeding potentialities and form new species. When and if the ecological or spatial barrier disappears, the two may intermingle without any flow of genes between populations. Since the environments were initially different, the "daughter species" evolve differently, each adapted to its local environment. In plain, the two species differ in form (and mode of life) but resemble each other in characters retained from their common ancestor. This answers the initial question of this chapter as to source of similarity and diversity between species. But is the answer complete?

The divergence of isolated populations provides a mechanism for the origin of diversity of species in different areas. Does it also account in some fashion for the origin of diversity in a single area? To answer, I must review the consequences of population divergence. Isolation permits finer adjustment of each local population to the peculiarities of the local environments. The rate of increase for the morphologic subpopulations in each will differ to the extent that the environments are different. As diagrammed in Figure 6-9, subpopulation III has the highest rate of increase in local population M, and subpopulation VII in local population N. The means of the local populations shift toward the local optimum, and, given time, the two will develop completely different gene systems (they may still have many genes in common though with different frequencies). These differences in gene systems result, to a varying extent, in differences in behavior, morphology, physiology—particularly with the reproductive aspects of these three. If the two populations are brought back into contact, few, if any, of the individuals in the two populations can interbreed.*

Formally, the populations are reproductively isolated and behave as good species toward one another. As the two populations intermingle the environment of each changes because of the presence of

---

* In some groups, plants particularly, interspecific crosses are fairly common, and, in some cases, the recombinants are adaptively superior to the original populations. Since this process, evolution by introgression, is only a particular case of the general evolutionary model, there is no point in discussing it at length in a short treatment of evolution.

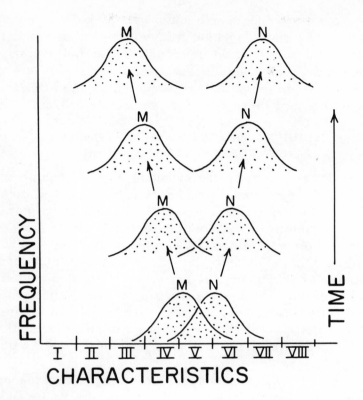

Fig. 6–9. *EVOLUTIONARY DIVERGENCE OF ISOLATED POPULATION.* M and N represent different local populations of a single species. Though subject to divergent selective pressure, they are held together initially by the flow of genes in interbreeding. When the two are isolated and gene flow ended, they diverge under local selection, ultimately to form two new species.

the other. If, as is probable, the two still overlap in mode of life, they will have somewhat similar ecological requirements and limitations. The total population size of the two species in the overlap cannot exceed that of one of the species alone. In these circumstances, one or the other of the species will be forced toward extinction because of inherent inferiority in this local environment. Those individuals most different from the other species in requirements will be those most likely to survive. In fact, if both species survive in the same area, selection will force continued divergence. The ultimate result will be a diversity of species in the same area with diverse adaptation.

This forced divergence of species must have occurred frequently in the geologic past. Species split and resplit, each division carrying the species form and adaptation further from the ancestral type. Given time, the results could be as different as tapeworms, ants, and elephants. Each daughter species adjusts to an individual mode of life, and those species that occupy the same habitat do so because they occupy different niches (see further p. 175ff.).

EVOLUTION, PHYLOGENY, AND TAXONOMY: PHYLOGENETIC CLASSIFICATION

To this point, I have treated evolution as a mechanism whose essential parts are mutation, recombination, selection, and isolation. The evidence for this mechanism is partly from observation of fossil and recent organisms, and partly from studies of genetics and selection in laboratory populations. If accepted, what is its significance to paleontology? And, I might also ask, what is the significance of paleontology to studies of that mechanism? These questions are not really different, for they are two aspects of the same problem. Any study of fossils from a geologically significant span of time involves interpretation of the evolutionary mechanism, and, conversely, these interpretations modify, extend, or delimit the picture of that mechanism.

For his first step the paleontologist must arrange his fundamental observations or, less pedantically, classify the fossils he collects. All modern classifications arise from an interpretation of phylogeny, i.e., the evolutionary relationship of the species involved in the classification. As a paleontologist conceives the mechanism of evolution, so will he classify.* This causes an initial problem; how can his observation of animal form be related to his interpretation of probable evolutionary events? Once he decides on a phylogeny, he then must translate that to a classification. This is the second problem and, since it is one of procedure, is easier to discuss; hence, I'll deal with it first.

Evolution is a continuous process, but the categories of classification are discontinuous. Divergence can be shown by placement in separate taxonomic categories; descent or common ancestry by allocation to the same category. The difficulty is to do both. The hierarchic system unfortunately is not ideal and must compromise between showing the occurrence of animals along a single line of

---

* And as he classifies so will he conceive the evolutionary mechanism!

descent and the degree of divergence between related lines at a single time. For example, a primitive family of carnivorous mammals, the miacids, is probably ancestral to all the recent carnivores, and should, therefore, logically be grouped with them in the suborder *Fissipeda*. The miacids, however, are quite closely related, as shown by the lack of morphologic divergence, to contemporaneous carnivores grouped as suborder *Creodonta,* and with equal logic could be placed in this group. Either classification is correct, but each emphasizes a different aspect of miacid relationships (Figure 6-10). A specialist on late Cenozoic carnivores might prefer the first classification because it expresses the ancestry of those carnivores, and a specialist on early Cenozoic stratigraphy would employ the second because it particularizes a difference between early and late Cenozoic faunas.

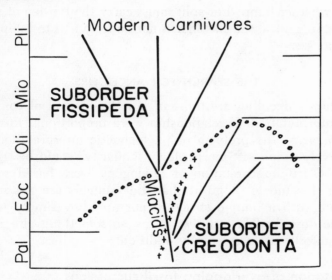

Fig. 6–10. *PROBLEM IN CLASSIFICATION.* The miacid carnivores may be classified with contemporaneous and similarily primitive carnivores in the suborder Creodonta (boundary set by circles). Or they may be placed with their descendents, the modern carnivores, in the suborder Fissipeda (boundary indicated by crosses). The first is a "horizontal" classification; the second, a "vertical."

Similarly, the rank given a related group of species and the amount of subdivision of a category varies with the purpose (and the psychology) of the classifier. The recent cats, for example, are often placed in three genera, one for the hunting leopard, one for the large cats, lion, tiger, and so on, and one for the smaller cats, wildcats, ocelot, and others (Simpson, 1945). Such a grouping emphasizes the similarities of most cat species. Some mammalogists, however, wishing to emphasize the differences, distinguish twenty genera. In the latter classification, the relationship of these genera must be shown by grouping them into subfamilies. I can only give a personal reaction to lumping vs. splitting of categories: that it is better to lump than split. Splitting helps those few paleontologists who specialize in a particular group but injures the majority who are not specialists. An effective compromise might be to use the chief steps, in the classification (genus, family, and so on), to group animals and the intermediate steps to divide them. Thus, one could recognize three cat genera (which all could know) divided into twenty subgenera (which only the specialists need know). Of course the arrangement of these supraspecific taxonomic groups, whether lumped or split, must carry the burden of phyletic relationship, and so the classifier is not entirely free to lump or split as he chooses.

THE SEARCH FOR ANCESTORS

But these difficulties are those of practicality and of convention, not of interpretation. If relationship were proportional to morphologic similarity, the problem of phylogenetic interpretation would be relatively simple—if "morphologic similarity" could be rigorously defined. Or, if interpretation of phylogeny were based solely on intuition, I could let it go at that; but animals are not minerals, each type with a unique structure nor are they simply works of art to be described in intuitive terms, so something else must be added—unfortunately a lengthy addition.

Interpretation of overlapping fossil successions

The paleontologist usually finds the simplest case of phylogenetic interpretation to be that of successive overlapping populations. He groups individuals collected from a single bed or another stratigraphic unit into species. This grouping is intuitive and based on a feeling for the limits of morphologic variation. After the initial groupings are made, he can test statistically the unity of the group and the degree of distinctness from other groups and derive, in this way, a fairly rigorous definition of species. When fossil species samples from successive layers of rock overlap, i.e., some individuals in one sample fall within the range of a morphologic subpopulation of the other, the paleontologist usually concludes that the overlapping of morphologic subpopulations means overlapping of genetic systems. Although in theory similar genetic systems could arise in two different species populations, this is most improbable if not impossible. The two samples are then regarded as segments of an evolving population, and the differences in populations, if significant, are regarded as the consequence of that evolution. Note that morphologic similarity here means near identity; some specimens from sample 1 can hardly be distinguished from some specimens of sample 2. The *Micraster* population sequence described on p. 130 exemplifies this sort of relationship.

A continuous series of samples from an evolving population produces taxonomic complications because the species concept covers only contemporaneous, reproductively isolated populations. The complications are, however, in our intellectual habits rather than in practice. Most such series have some gaps which separate statistically distinct samples. The species boundary is simply placed at such a gap (Figure 6-11). If the series is truly continuous, species boundaries are set arbitrarily so that any "species" includes about the same range of variation as a good contemporaneous species. This is the rule-of-thumb, but it works.

Interpretation of discontinuous fossil successions

If evolution ran on railway tracks, directly from fish to man or worm to trilobite, interpretation of phylogeny would be simple. The paleontologist could finish his business and leave the geologist to fit any new forms into a neatly drawn chart.

Fortunately for the careers of paleontologists, though not so fortunately for their ease of mind, nature lacks rails, cross-ties, and block signals. A species population may evolve in one direction for a while under the impetus of a single selective factor, but few if any such simple trends can be long continued. If a paleontologist has but a few fossils from isolated spots along this cow-path of evolution, how is he to tell that they are segments of a single phyletic lineage?

I have implied an answer (page 142), ". . . two species differ in form (and mode of life) but resemble each other in characteristics retained from their common ancestor." I will try to illustrate this answer by discussing the relationships of the lungfish, the lobe-fin

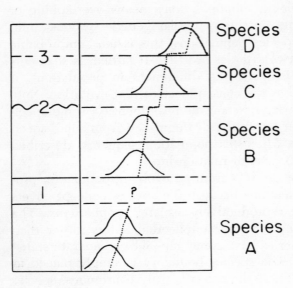

Fig. 6–11. FOSSIL SPE-
CIES AND INTERRUPTIONS
IN THE FOSSIL RECORD.
The transformation from species A to D was continuous
and gradual. The fossil record of that evolution, however, is neither continuous
nor gradual. Thus, during
time *1*, the species lineage
is excluded from the area by
a change in the environment,
but it continues to evolve
elsewhere and reappears as
a distinct population, species
B. At time *2*, the fossil evidence of evolution has been
removed by erosion. At *3*, a
period of nondeposition prevented accumulation of fossils. Each interruption divides
preceding and succeeding
populations into distinct species.

Species D

Species C

Species B

Species A

fish, and the early amphibians; and, for the sake of brevity and
simplicity, I will limit the example to two middle Devonian fish
genera, *Dipterus* and *Osteolepis* (Figure 6-12), and to three late
Devonian genera, the fishes *Scaumenacia* and *Eusthenopteron* (Figure 6-13), and the amphibian, *Ichthyostega* (Figure 6-14).

Dipterus and *Scaumenacia* are fairly similar in character. Their
bodies are relatively slender, compressed from side to side, and
elongate, and are covered by thick bony scales. Two dorsal median
fins are present, and the tail is heterocercal, i.e., the vertebrae extend into the upper half of the tail fin. As in all more advanced
fish, there are two sets of paired fins, one pair just behind the head,
the other just in front of the anus. Each fin is a leaf-shaped structure
with a slender bony central axis of many segments and numerous,
short, side branches. The inner end of the bony axis articulates with
a small bony plate in the body wall. The backbone is well ossified,
although the individual vertebrae are not tightly articulated. The
ribs were apparently cartilaginous. The skull is moderately short
with a particularly short cheek region. The skull comprises a large

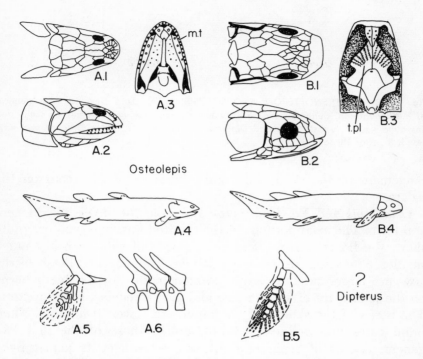

A.I

A.3 — m.t

A.2

Osteolepis

B.I

B.3

t.pl

B.2

A.4

B.4

A.5 A.6

? Dipterus

B.5

Fig. 6–12. *OSTEOLEPIS AND DIPTERUS.* Characteristics of two middle Devonian fish genera. A) Osteolepis; A.1) skull roof; A.2) side view of skull; A.3) palate; A.4) general body form; A.5) one of anterior paired fins and bony plate in body wall on which base of fin articulates; A.6) three vertebrae. Structure of fin and palate based in part on later genera. B) Dipterus; various views as in Osteolepis; vertebrae probably similar to Osteolepis but not known certainly. Abbreviations: *mt*, marginal tooth; *tpl*, tooth plate. (A.1–3. After various sources. A.4 After Traguair. B.1–3. After Westol. B.4. After Traguair.)

number of small plates in the skull roof, a well-ossified brain case, several large bony elements in the roof of the mouth, and a lower jaw that consists of several unfused bones. The bones in the roof of the mouth bear radial rows of large teeth, but marginal teeth are either absent (*Dipterus*), or rudimentary (*Scaumenacia*). The bones of the upper and lower jaws that bear the marginal teeth in other vertebrates are also lacking or very small.

The two genera differ in only a few characteristics. The first dorsal fin of *Scaumenacia* is smaller and the second dorsal larger than that of *Dipterus*. The paired fins of *Scaumenacia* are somewhat more slender. Finally, there are small differences in the ar-

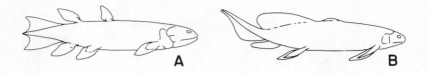

Fig. 6–13. *EUSTHENOPTERON AND SCAUMENACIA.* Late Devonian fish genera. A) *Eusthenopteron,* general view. B) *Scaumenacia,* general view. Details of skulls and fins quite similar to *Osteolepis* and *Dipterus,* respectively. (A. After Gregory and Raymond. B. After Hussakof.)

rangement of the skull bones and character of the teeth on the palate.

Osteolepis and *Eusthenopteron* resemble the preceding in general form. The axial portions of their paired fins, however, are quite short, the bones heavier, and the number of side branches much smaller. The skulls are relatively longer. The marginal bones of the jaws are large and bear large, pointed teeth, but the teeth borne on the palate are of smaller size and lack a regular, radial pattern. The bones of the skull roof are larger and fewer in number. Their brain cases are well ossified but, unlike those of the first two genera, consist of separate front and rear elements joined by a movable articulation. The two genera differ from each other chiefly in the structure of the tail—the vertebrae in *Osteolepis* turn into the upper lobe, in *Eusthenopteron* they extend straight backward to form a central lobe of the tail—and in minor details of proportion and bone arrangement.

The amphibian, *Ichthyostega,* is quite different from any of these middle or late Devonian fish genera. The body is flattened from top to bottom rather than from side to side. The tail is long and slender and bears long, low fins above and below rather than the broadly expanded fin characteristic of the fish. The vertebrae are large, heavy, and closely articulated, and, except for those in the tail, each one bears a pair of ribs. In place of the paired fins are ordinary tetrapod limbs articulated with broad plates, the pelvic and pectoral girdles, on the sides of the body. The skull resembles those of *Osteolepis* and *Eusthenopteron* to some extent and comprises a number of large elements in the skull roof, a well-ossified brain case, a series of marginal plates on both upper and lower jaws bearing large teeth, and several bones in the roof of the mouth. Some of the palatal bones bear rather large teeth but these are never

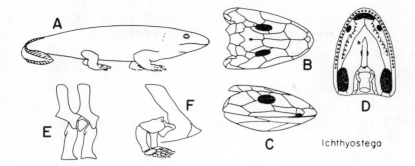

Fig. 6–14. *ICHTHYOSTEGA.* Late Devonian amphibian, *Ichthyostega.* A) General form. B) Skull roof. C) Side view of skull. D) Palatal view. E) Vertebrae. F) Forelimb and bony plates (pectoral limb girdle) with which it articulates. Compare with Fig. 6–12. (After Jarvik.)

in closely oppressed radial rows as they are in the lungfish. As in the fish, the nostrils open internally into the mouth.

What sort of pattern can be made of these observations? What are the evolutionary relationships of the five genera? Some have already been implied by the description, but more are needed. I could now attempt a formal analysis of similarities and differences, but discussion may be clearer with a hypothetical and, for the moment, arbitrary reconstruction of the evolutionary changes.

Imagine that two local populations of a fish species live in the rivers of two different but adjacent drainage basins. The two populations differ slightly in average form and physiology. The differences would either accord with local differences in environment or else result from local genetic drift (p. 139). A barrier arises between basins; the local populations diverge in isolation; two species appear where there was one before. The relationship of these species is obvious for the differences are slight (recognized by placing them in the same genus), and their relationship to the ancestral species is equally obvious. Each species retains most of the characteristics of ancestors; the morphologic differences are consequent upon minor variations in the same general type of environment, the same basic mode of life.

The species, however, continue to diverge.* The original species

---

* If the two subsequently occupied the same rivers, their competition may have forced greater divergence.

may have eaten other fish and occasionally varied its diet with cray-fish. One of the new species sticks to this diet, but the other for some reason shifts entirely to crayfish and other small shelled invertebrates. Selection acts on the first species to produce large marginal teeth (and perhaps a joint in the brain case that takes up some of the shock of a bite). Selection acts on the second species to enlarge the teeth on the palatal bones and to arrange them in closely spaced radial rows suitable for crushing hard shells. In consequence of this adaptation, the marginal teeth and the bones that bear them are reduced and finally lost.

The resultant species differ chiefly in the structure of the skull, in the adaptations to different diets. They retain generally similar characters of fins, body, and skull so far as these are not affected by this adaptation. We can recognize in these two, *Dipterus* and *Osteolepis,* the middle Devonian fish genera. They differ in form to the extent that they have different modes of life, but they retain many characteristics of their common ancestral species. One can-not be certain that the fish-eating habit was the ancestral type, but our knowledge of early Devonian fish suggests it was.

The analysis, however, has hardly begun, for the paleontologist must connect the three late Devonian genera to the middle Devonian forms. *Scaumenacia* resembles *Dipterus* most closely. *Dipterus* (or a very similar genus) must have given rise to *Scaumenacia.* But did it? The modification of the palatal teeth occurred once in response to selection. Why could it not occur again by modification of an isolated local population of *Osteolepis?* If it did, several seemingly improbable events must have happened. First, the new adaptive line arising from *Osteolepis* must have recreated the precise form of tooth and jaw structure. It might produce a similar set of structures to fit similar needs, but production of identical structure seems far less likely. Second, the new line must have developed paired fins and other characteristics like those of *Dipterus,* although these are not adaptations to the same selection pressures as the evolution of the jaws and teeth. It seems ex-tremely improbable that the same set of selective factors that acted on the ancestor of *Dipterus* would again be combined in the same way and that it would find the same genetic systems among which to select. Finally, if *Scaumenacia* evolved from *Osteolepis,* the truncated axis of the paired fins, the regular arrangement of skull roof bones, and the jointed brain case, all so distinctive in the latter genus, were lost without trace in *Scaumenacia*. Because of these improbabilities, the paleontologist returns to the initial interpretation and makes *Scaumenacia* a descendant of *Dipterus*.

Now for *Eusthenopteron*. Purely on degree of resemblance this genus, or rather the species that compose it, descended from *Osteolepis*. But one must ask if it could have arisen from *Dipterus*. Again it depends on probabilities. Evolution from *Dipterus* would require that the truncated axis of the paired fins, the arrangement of the skull bones, and the jointed brain case evolved twice to almost identical structure—a double coincidence of selection and available variation. Also, the peculiarly adapted dentition of *Dipterus* would be lost and marginal teeth regained—a clear and minute reversal of an evolutionary trend. The probabilities, therefore, indicate the *Eusthenopteron-Osteolepis* connection to be the correct one.

These cases are not too difficult since the ancestor and descendant are quite similar, but the interpretation of the amphibian's origin poses greater demands. The paleontologist has now a much wider channel to bridge between the ancestral fish and its descendant. The evolution of amphibian morphology rests on the structures available in the fish; one should be able to perceive some remnant of those structures. Since the chief adaptation is for life on land, the major changes should show in the limbs, the limb girdles, the tail, and the vertebrae. The modifications of the skull should be less marked.

Could *Ichthyostega* have evolved from *Dipterus?* The bony axis of the paired fins might change to the bones of a foot and leg, although the change might be troublesome. The plates supporting the paired fins become the limb girdles. The vertebrae need only firmer articulation—not a major change. The ribs change to bone from cartilage. The tail, no longer used for a scull, becomes relatively slender and narrow. The small plates of the skull roof either fuse or are lost to leave a series of large regular plates. The bones covering the gills are reduced or lost. The brain case and the internal openings of the nostrils require no modification. The teeth and jaws— there's the difficulty. The amphibian has large marginal teeth and jaw plates; *Dipterus* has few or none. Either the trend exhibited by *Dipterus* must have reversed or the connection of *Dipterus* and *Ichthyostega* is impossible.

Let me try *Osteolepis* as an ancestor. The tail and vertebrae would need no more modification than for *Dipterus*. The change in paired fins is quite a lot simpler—and thus more probable. The skull roof plates are already large and display an orderly pattern. Close observation shows the pattern is much the same in *Osteolepis* and *Ichthyostega*. They resemble each other in number and in their relation to eyes, nostrils, jaw articulation, openings for nerves and blood vessels, and each other. Both have similar palatal bones and lateral jaw plates and teeth. The only major discrepancy comes in the structure of the brain case, divided and articulated in one, a unit in the other. This could disbar *Osteolepis* from its job as ancestor or it could be a change that occurred during the evolution of *Ichthyostega*. Since modern amphibians have a stage in their larval development during which distinct elements can be discerned in the front and rear parts of the brain case and since some Paleozoic amphibians have unossified gaps between the two parts, the latter seems reasonable. Of the two choices, *Osteolepis* is the more probable ancestor.

The paleontologist in his imagination has stripped away the terrestrial adaptations of the amphibian and restored the pristine piscine form. Since the restored form agrees with that of the middle Devonian fish, he has found the ancestor—maybe. Actually, he may have as fossils a species off the direct evolutionary line. Reconstruction seldom can be so precise as to pick an ancestoral population from among similar species, or, if the gap reconstructed is large, from among similar genera.

One final point, the taxonomic expression of the amphibian—fish relationship. The morphologic difference between the primitive amphibian and its ancestor are not much greater than those between orders of fish in the same subclass. Should the paleoichthyologist establish a new order in the same subclass to receive the amphibian? Certainly a logical step. But he displays illogic for the amphibian becomes representative of a new class. His reasoning must have been like this: "this animal (he should have thought 'population') opens new prospects in evolution; if given a chance he will evolve into something as remarkable as a frog or even a dinosaur or a monkey. The differences between frog and fish are great; therefore, I will begin a new class with this animal. I'll classify him not for what he is but for what he'll become."

I'll end my piscatorial research here. But you may say: "I'm not interested in fish except as food. Trilobites (or brachiopods) are what excite me. How do I work out their phylogeny?" Even if you don't ask this, I'll give some general rules anyway.

(1) The common structural plan must be seen. Before morphologic details can be compared, the paleontologist must have some assurance he's compared the right things—tail with tail, paired fin with leg. Since evolution acts either by building on or by reshaping the ancestral structure, ancestor and descendant should have a common plan, and two descendant lineages should likewise share a basic organization of parts. Studies of development, of the embryo, assist here since the organization is laid out in simpler form in the embryo.* Thus the primordal gill arches can be compared in fish and human embryo though the adult fish gill bars and the human hyoid bones would seem to have little in common.

Parts occupying the same position in the structural plan are termed _homologes;_ the individual bones of the _Osteolepis_ skulls are homologous and are given the same names.†

(2) The differences and similarities of elements in the structural plan and of additions to that plan must be weighed. Similarly adapted characteristics are least important because they may evolve independently in separate lines. On the other hand, similarities in structures that serve different functions indicate relationship. The similarity between the leg of the amphibian and the paired fin of the fish cannot be laid to similar selective pressures; it can be found in a common ancestry. Several characteristics are better than one in establishing relationship—unless they are adaptations to similar modes of life or features related to a single adaptation. The paleontologist gives most weight to the "conservative" features held in common by diversely adapted species.

(3) He must reconstruct the phylogeny, i.e., strip the new adap-

---

* The biogenetic law—ontogeny (development of an individual) recapitulates phylogeny (evolution of a population lineage)—is good material for a lengthy, pedantic footnote. Sometimes ontogeny does so, because new structures may be added or old ones reformed near the end of development. But, on the contrary, embryonic structures may be retained into the adult. Or the embryo (or better, larva) may have evolved its own peculiar adaptations. It might be better said that phylogeny recapitulates ontogeny. It adopts the possibility inherent in development not vice versa. Since it adopts this possibility, developmental stages of ancestor and descendent or of descendents of a common ancestor will resemble each, though the resemblance may be between different stages of immaturity or between immaturity and maturity.

† The definition of homology has been disputed in recent years. The use here is that suggested by Zangerl (1948), and encompasses the embryological and phylogenetic definitions suggested by others.

tations from the descendant population or add them to the ancestral. He constructs a hypothetical ancestor or descendant and matches hypothesis with fossil record. Ideally, this reconstruction should be based on four considerations: *a*) the form of the reconstructed structure should be compatible with its probable function in the ancestor; *b*) the modification of the structure to its present form should be logical in terms of continued adaptation during the period of evolution; *c*) the modifications should be compatible with what is known of the developmental patterns that produce the structure, and *d*) the modifications should involve the fewest possible changes between ancestor and descendant.

(4) If the presumed ancestor reversed its evolutionary trend to produce the descendant, it couldn't have been the ancestor. This bars two-toed horse species from evolving into three-toed horses or a species of large elephant from producing a species of small elephant. In detail, structures lost will not be regained; complex structures will not become simple; large forms will not give rise to small. Unfortunately, this law (Dollo's) only works a six-day week—on Sunday anything can happen. Certainly selection can be reversed, and, thus, an evolutionary trend can also be reversed. This reversal probably will not retrieve the lost genetic combinations and the precise form of the ancestor but it can produce a close facsimile of that form. Paleontologists take it, then, only as a working principle to be disregarded on the basis of other evidence.

(5) The evolutionary relationships should be compatible with geographic distribution. The connection of South American and Old World porcupines was suspect for this reason. One couldn't have given rise to the other without a ferry between South America and Africa. Restudy of morphology suggests that the similarities are due to similar adaptations developed in two lineages that were closely related to begin with.

(6) The smaller the morphologic differences across which the paleontologist must extrapolate, the smaller is the chance of error. Missing links, when found, serve not only to confirm a hypothesis but also to render it more precise.

(7) Conservative groups—those that change slowly—provide knowledge of ancestoral types not available directly as fossils. The paleontologist depends on certain Permian amphibians for evidence of reptile origins, since the true, late Mississippian and early Pennsylvanian ancestry is not preserved in the fossil record.

THE FLUX OF PHYLOGENY

Fossils are found; phylogenies established; classifications published. Truth is graven eternally into the literature of fossil fishes, trilobites or brachiopods. And then someone turns a slab of rock and finds a new species that fits into a phyletic sequence—but not the accepted one—or new evidence accrues from studies of adaptive significance, or embryos, or comparison of proteins in the blood serum of lions and antelope, or a classification of the parasites of kangaroos and South American monkeys. Or stratigraphic research on relative age discloses that the "ancestor" was really the descendant. The remarkable thing is not that phylogenies and the classifications based on them are often found in error, but that they frequently have been confirmed by new evidence. This is of importance not only to the reputation of the phylogenist but also to the soft-rock geologist who would rely on interpretation of evolutionary trends to establish relative age and on degree of divergence to determine paleogeography.

This discussion has touched but superficially on the methods of phylogenetic interpretation. I have omitted much and simplified the remainder. It is, however, sufficiently detailed to permit a description of the patterns of evolution as they show in the phyletic reconstructions.

REFERENCES

Arkell, W. J. and J. A. Moy-Thomas. 1940. "Paleontology and the Taxonomic Problem," in: *The New Systematics*. Oxford: Oxford University Press, pp. 395-410. The classification of fossil groups.

DeBeer, G. R. 1951. *Embryos and Ancestors,* revised ed. Oxford: Oxford University Press. A discussion of developmental phenomena and their relation to evolution.

Dobzhansky, I. 1951. *Genetics and the Origin of Species,* 3rd ed. New York: Columbia University Press. Evolution from the viewpoint of a geneticist.

Goldschmidt, R. 1940. *The Material Basis of Evolution.* New Haven, Conn.: Yale University Press. Statement of a theory of sudden origin of major animal groups by a single major mutation. Goldschmidt, until his death, was the leading opponent of the Neo-Darwinian theory of evolution. The book is primarily genetics.

Huxley, J. 1942. *Evolution: the Modern Synthesis.* New York: Harper. A study of evolution in various aspects—very little paleontology.

Jeletzky, J. A. 1955. "Evolution of Santonian and Campanian *Belemnitella* and Paleontologic Systematics: Exemplified by *Belemnitella Praecursor* Stolley," *Jour. of Paleontology*, vol. 29, pp. 478-509.

Jepsen, G. L., Mayr, E., and G. G. Simpson, eds. 1949. *Genetics, Paleontology, and Evolution*. Princeton, N. J.: Princeton University Press. A series of papers by specialists in various fields that deal with evolutionary problems.

Kermack, K. A. 1954. "A Biometric Study of *Micraster Coranguinum* and *M. (Isomicraster) Senonensis*," *Roy. Soc. of London, Philos. Trans.*, Ser. B, vol. 237, pp. 375-428.

Mayr, E. 1942. *Systematics and the Origin of Species*. New York: Columbia University Press. A discussion of evolution from the viewpoint of the taxonomist.

Olson, E. C. 1952. See references for Chapter 5.

————, and J. R. Beerbower. 1953. "The San Angelo Formation, Permian of Texas, and its Vertebrates," *Jour. of Geology*, vol. 61, pp. 389-423.

Petrunkevitch, A. 1952. "Macroevolution and the Fossil Record of the Arachnids," *Amer. Scientist*, vol. 40, pp. 99-122. A non-Neo-Darwinian view of evolution as displayed in the fossil record.

Rowe, A. W. 1899. "An Analysis of the Genus *Micraster*, as Determined by Rigid Zonal Collecting from the Zone of *Rhynchonella Cuvieri* to that of *Micraster Cor-anguinum*," *Quart. Jour. Geol. Society of London*, vol. 55, pp. 494-547.

Simpson, G. G. 1945. "The Principles of Classification and a Classification of Mammals," *Amer. Mus. of Nat. History, Bulletin*, vol. 85.

————. 1952. *The Major Features of Evolution*. New York: Columbia University Press. A broad discussion of evolution—mechanism and phenomena—primarily from the paleontologic viewpoint.

Weller, J. M. 1949. "Paleontologic Classification," *Jour. of Paleontology*, vol. 23, pp. 680-690. The approach of a stratigrapher-paleontologist to a pragmatic view of classification.

————. 1957. "Paleoecology of the Pennsylvanian Period in Illinois and Adjacent States," in: "Treatise on Marine Ecology and Paleocology," vol. 2. *Geol. Soc. of America, Memoir 67*, pp. 325-364.

Zangerl, R. 1948. "The Methods of Comparative Anatomy and its Contribution to the Study of Evolution," *Evolution*, vol. 2, pp. 351-374. One of the best papers in English on the philosophy of comparative anatomy.

See also the references for Chapter 7.

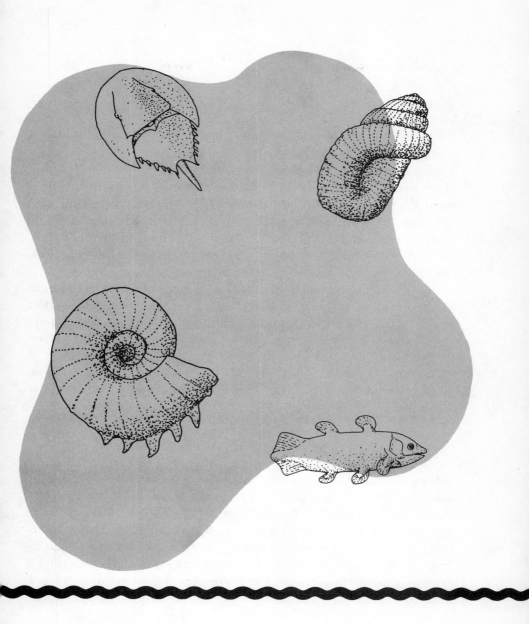

7. PATTERNS of EVOLUTION

J could have titled this chapter, "What Happened in Evolution," for this is the unique contribution of paleontology to the study of evolution. In an ideal world, the fossil record would provide a continuous motion picture of evolution, each frame in the sequence a successive layer of fossil-bearing rock. Since this world is not ideal, the evolutionary record consists of scraps left on the cutting-room floor. Some of the scraps are single frames, still-pictures in fact, the actors frozen in silence. A few are continuous strips in which the principles scurry into motion—and then the lights go up; the reel is changed, and we have a new strip with a different plot, old actors disguised, and new ones on the scene.

Continuing this figure a little further, I can say the paleontologist has two tasks in restoring this ancient movie, to discover the actors in their disguises and to work out the vagaries of plot that require the disguise. He has a third task as a critic examining the reconstructed film; he must discern the unifying or common features of the various subplots. The preceding chapter dealt with the reconstruction of the actors' parts. This one must analyze and criticize the story.

FOSSILS AND EVOLUTIONARY MECHANISMS

I set the rhetorical, opening question like this: "Can paleontologists measure in any precise way the various evolutionary processes and factors from the fossil record?" The parameters of an evolving population are (1) the genetic variation of that population, (2) the morphologic variation, (3) the reproductive structure, and (4) the selection values (rates of subpopulation change) for various genetic systems or the corresponding morphological systems. To the extent paleontologists measure these, they can explain the course of evolution illustrated in the various phyletic lines.

A warning is necessary, however; since the paleontologist uses particular evolutionary theories to work out phylogeny, he may devour his own intellectual flesh. Thus, a theory of linear evolution yields linear phylogenies which support a linear theory of evolution. Some major works on evolutionary theory should bear the sign *cave canem*.

160

Genetic variation

Genes and gene variation are beyond the paleontologist's grasp. At best, he may perceive their action on morphology, but without certainty that a particular characteristic results from any particular gene or that a given amount of morphologic variation corresponds to a particular amount of genetic variation (p. 58). Kurten (1955, see p. 59 this book) followed a particular tooth character through Pleistocene to recent bears and interpreted these morphologic changes as the result of a specific change in gene frequencies. Two different genes occurred at the same position on the chomosome and controlled or modified the development of the first molar. The ancestoral population had both genes. One descendant line lost one gene altogether; the other line retained this gene but had the other reduced to a very low frequency. He adopted, just as a geneticist does with recent animals, the simplest possible genetic interpretation for an observation of morphologic evolution. Unlike the geneticist, however, he cannot conduct breeding experiments to test his hypothesis. He did not demonstrate that evolution occurred by change in gene frequency (not that he intended to), but rather that some observed morphologic changes are consistent with a theory of genetic change.

Morphologic variation

Paleontologists must, therefore, treat the second parameter, morphologic variation, without being able to resolve its genetic basis. They may make qualitative observations of variation, or, since the fossils form a sample, they can estimate the species population (or local population) characteristics in the normal fashion (p. 65), and describe the change in range and average morphology through time. Sounds simple enough, doesn't it? But, as usual, there is a booby trap buried with the bones.

Paleontologist Doakes collects a sample from a single stratigraphic horizon at a single locality and concludes the average and standard deviation of the population to be thus and so. Paleontologist Smith collects from twelve horizons over a ten thousand square mile area. A third man, Jones, compares their data and says: "Aha! Smith's species was more variable than its descendant species (Doakes'). This proves something." What it probably proves is that Doakes sampled a local population at a single time and Smith several different local populations at different times. It's not much use comparing unless one compares commensurates. Morphologic variation can be used (must be, of course) in evolutionary studies but used with due caution and precaution.

Population structure

The paleontologist finds determination of population structure and of local variation in morphology related to that structure very difficult. In some cases he may be sufficiently certain of the ecological limits of the species to draw conclusions about distribution patterns, ecologic barriers, and the resulting effects on that population. For example, an aquatic amphibian species will consist of small to medium-size populations distributed linearly along water courses and nearly isolated within single drainage basins, whereas a single active carnivorous mammal (a mountain lion, perhaps) will range over an area wider than that same watershed. If, as in a very few cases, he can establish the synchroneity of rocks in different areas, he can measure directly the variation between local populations in a species. These occasions are most rare, and, even then, he cannot be certain how much of the variation is a result of relative isolation and how much of different local selection values.

Selection

Measurement of selection consists really of two measurements, the direction of selection (subpopulation with the highest selective value) and the selection pressure (the difference between selective values for the various subpopulations). Direction, of course, is established by comparison of characteristics of succeeding populations. Usually, it is desirable to establish causes for the superiority or inferiority of a given subpopulation. This is done either on the basis of presumed advantages of a subpopulation in terms of the species environment (as in the interpretation of *Micraster,* p. 135), or by observation of correlation of morphological and environmental changes. The common factor yielding the correlation may be difficult to determine—a "change in rainfall affects the vegetation which affects the herbivores which affects the carnivores" sort of thing—but one can sometimes relate adaptive change directly or indirectly to the environmental change.

The amount of difference between successive populations relative to the time elapsed should give a measure of selection pressure, but the relation is not a simple, direct one. Mutation rates and population structure also control evolutionary rates; measurement of elapsed time is difficult, and the size of a morphologic change may not correspond with its evolutionary significance.

THE PAST RECAPTURED

But, in spite of this pessimistic view, paleontology can make—and has made—worthwhile contributions to the study of the dynamics of evolution. Remember, it deals with a very large number of examples and very long periods of time. The individual interpretations may be incorrect or, at best, dubious, but taken in bulk they suggest questions and some conclusions. The paleontologist, therefore, must, perforce, test the concepts of modern theories of evolution by applying them to patterns observed in the fossils.

The patterns themselves are varied. The brachiopod *Lingula* persists, unchanged, for several hundred million years; the mammalian evolutionary line has passed through six classes since the Ordovician. What combination of factors produced this extraordinary difference in rate of evolution? The Ordovician fish resemble some arthropods remarkably, though the respective ancestral species must have been quite different. What chance of mutation, recombination, or selection brought about this resemblance?

Or does it matter? One would like to know out of sheer alarm-clock-tinkering curiosity. One needs to know to fulfill those central functions of paleontology, to date rocks and to interpret their environment of deposition. Not all, or even most, studies of evolutionary patterns have this practical significance, but all fossil correlations and paleoecologic interpretations need the background of such studies.

The tempo

Measurement of evolutionary rates. Obviously, animals have evolved at different rates. There would seem to be nearly as many ways of measuring those rates as there are different kinds of animals. The first problem is that of a time scale. If a close estimate can be made from radioactive dates, the researcher can use an absolute scale of years (Figure 7-1). Otherwise he must employ relative time units. Many studies include something of both, i.e., general-

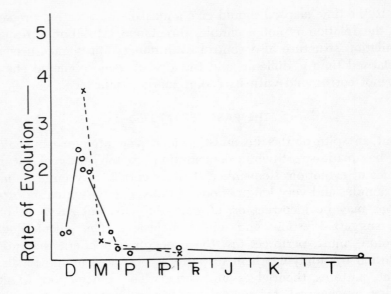

Fig. 7–1. *RATES OF EVOLUTION.* The rates of evolution of the lung fish (circles and solid line) and of the coelacanth fish (crosses and dashed line) plotted against time. The ordinate scale is in number of character changes per million years; the abscissa is divided into segments proportional to approximate duration of geological periods. Abbreviations: D, Devonian; M, Mississippian; P, Pennsylvanian; *P*, Permian; *R*, Triassic; J, Jurassic; K, Cretaceous; T, Tertiary.

ized and, therefore, crude absolute time scale *and* the comparison of contemporaneous evolutionary lines in that time span (Figure 7-1). If he uses the latter method, the several lines may be plotted against each other on an arbitrary scale (Figure 7-2), or the change may be plotted against the thickness of the fossil-bearing rocks.

The second, and more difficult, problem is what to plot against the time scale? A single morphologic characteristic like the height of a snail's spire, Or some *group* of characteristics? The second is more desirable, but is convenient with present techniques only if rates of taxonomic change are used (Figure 7-3). The time for one species to change into another is, of course, based on over-all morphologic change. Unfortunately, the differences between species of clams and between species of mammals are not the same qualitatively or quantitatively. Single characteristics can be set in absolute values to avoid this difficulty. But does doubling the height of the snail's spire have the same significance as doubling the relative length of a horse's leg?

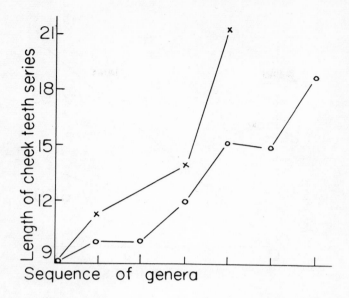

Fig. 7–2. *RELATIVE EVOLUTION OF TWO HORSE LINEAGES.* The *Miohippus-Mega-hippus* line is indicated by crosses; the *Miohippus-Equus* line by circles. Ordinate, length of cheek tooth series in centimeters (means of generic samples); abscissa, arbitrary scale for two contemporaneous evolutionary sequences. The amount and rate of change is obviously greater in the *Megahippus* line. (Data from Romer, 1949.)

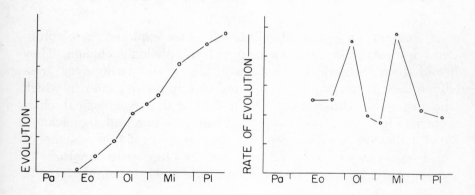

Fig. 7–3. *EVOLUTION IN HORSES.* Graph at left shows amount of evolution. The ordinate scale is purely relative and partly subjective—it indicates Simpson's (1952) estimate of the relative amount of difference between successive genera. The abscissa shows relative duration of the Cenozoic epochs. The graph at right indicates the rate of change per million years and therefore is a plot of the slope for each segment of the other graph. The peaks in early Oligocene and mid-Miocene are striking. Abbreviations: *Pa*, Paleocene; *Eo*, Eocene; *Ol*, Oligocene; *Mi*, Miocene; *Pl*, Pliocene.

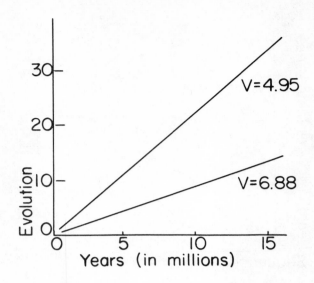

Fig. 7–4. *EVOLUTION IN TWO MIOCENE OREODONT LINEAGES.* The upper line represents the subfamily, Merycochoerinae, the lower the subfamily, Merychyinae. The ordinate scale indicates the difference between the natural logarithms of the mean width of the third molar in the initial and in the final populations of a lineage. The slope of the lines (2.11 and .90 respectively) indicates rate of evolution. The V-value is the average amount of variation within species populations of a lineage. Note that the more rapidly evolving line varies less at any one time. (Data from Bader, 1955.)

At present, most paleontologists who have explored "rate" problems use either or both measures of morphologic change. They avoid these theoretical difficulties either by comparing very gross differences in rates or by comparing closely related lines in which the taxonomic categories (Figure 7-2) and morphological characters (Figures 7-1 and 7-4) have similar scope and significance. As I indicated in the preceding chapter (p. 145), the scope of taxonomic categories varies from one investigator to another; in consequence, taxonomic rates of evolution must be considered with caution.

Paleontologists have worked out the precise lineages in only a few fossil groups, although the broader relationships of genera or families may be evident. Simpson has suggested an approach to determining evolutionary rates based on average "longevity" of genera (Figure 7-5). A rapidly evolving group will have genera with brief "life spans" as they appear by evolutionary transforma-

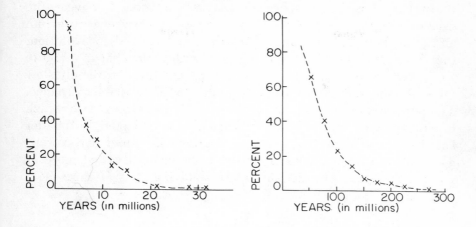

Fig. 7–5. *SURVIVAL OF PELECYPOD AND MAMMALIAN CARNIVORE GENERA.* Graph on left shows length of survival of carnivore genera. Less than 20 per cent survived more than 10 million years. Over 20 per cent of the pelecypod genera (graph on right) persisted 100 million years or more. If the genera in the two groups are of similar morphologic scope, the rate of transformation of the carnivore genera was many times as rapid. (From Simpson, 1952.)

tion and disappear by further transformation or by extinction; a slowly evolving group includes genera with long life spans.

Kinds of rates. In spite of the frustrations in measuring rates of evolution precisely, paleontologists can at least distinguish between the very slow, the moderate, and the very fast. Before I discuss each kind let me first post warnings.

Slow rates or moderate rates are averages taken over a long span of time with relatively few examples in which the record is continuous. These rates may actually be slow through the full period or they may fluctuate from fast to very slow. With only two or three samples in a line, extrapolation between samples is questionable.

Slow and moderate rates are slow or moderate rates of morphologic change and changes in only a small part of the animals' morphology. Physiological changes or changes in soft anatomy appear only to the extent they modify the skeleton.

Most examples of rapid change are associated with known or probable stratigraphic gaps. Since the time involved in these gaps is unknown, the magnitude of the rate remains unknown. Further, the sedimentary record is so spotty that a particular line may be unknown for much of its existence.

THE LAGGARDS. The brachiopod, *Lingula*, mentioned above is the classic example of extremely slow evolution. Nearly every phylum and class, however, contains forms that have lagged in evolution; that have persisted over long periods with little change (Figure 7-6). Some paleontologists have theorized that such extremely slow rates of evolution result from a limitation of available variance. The population does not change because it has nothing with which to change. Very little reliable data have been collected, but Bader has shown recently (1955) that, in a group of extinct herbivorous mammals, the populations in slowly evolving lines varied more at a particular time than did the rapidly evolving lines (Figure 7-4).

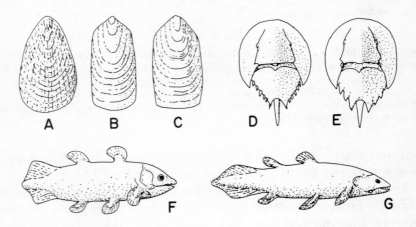

Fig. 7–6. *SLOWLY EVOLVING ANIMAL GROUPS.* A) *Linguella*, a Cambrian brachiopod, B) *Lingula münsteri*, Silurian; C) *Lingula anatina*, Recent. D) and E) Jurassic and Recent representatives of the horseshoe crab, *Limulus*. F) *Macropoma*, a Cretaceous coelacanth fish; G) *Latimeria*, a Recent coelacanth fish. (A. After Walcott. B. After Piveteau, ed. *Traité de Paléontologie*. Copyright, Masson et Cie, Paris. Used with permission. D. After Størmer. F. and G. After Schaeffer.)

An immediate thought would be that slowly evolving populations were large, freely interbreeding units. As was stated in the preceding chapter (p. 140) such populations have great evolutionary inertia. Unfortunately, recent species of conservative lines appear to have about the same sorts of population structure as representatives of progressive lines. Was population structure effective in some cases? If it was, the information is not now available, but then very little precise information is.

If variability was normal or even relatively great and population structure no factor, slow rates of evolution imply little differential in selective values for the different gene combinations, or, said in another way, they imply low selection pressure. You should immediately ask why these low differentials remain in spite of a constantly changing environment.

Some paleontologists have suggested that these conservative lines had some sort of "generalized adaptation" that permitted them to survive in different and changing environments. The concept is interesting, but I find it difficult to imagine any sort of rigorous test. On *a priori* grounds, one might suspect that the line achieved a maximum adaptation to a particular environmental niche which persisted over a long period of time. This hypothesis sounds good but is also difficult to test.

The problem may be purely verbal; perhaps each example has a different explanation. Certainly, the problem of conservative groups requires some radical thinking.

THE MODERATES. If the tortoise and the hare pose refractory questions, the horse does not. The horse lineage indeed provides a classical example of moderate evolutionary change (Figure 7-3). So far as detailed quantitative studies have been made, such lines had moderate to low variance at any one time. Selection pressures, then, must have chopped off the extremes, and new, favorable, genetic combinations appeared as the population mean shifted. Presumably, selection pressures were moderate. Though population structure may have influenced—either accelerated or decelerated— the rate of evolution, there would seem to be no reason to think it a controlling factor.

THE IMPETUOUS. I approach the subject of rapid evolution rather gingerly. Many of the major animal types, the phyla, classes, and orders, pop abruptly into the fossil record. Their ancestry, if known at all, is vague, and they are much more advanced than the presumed ancestral types. So far as the fossil record goes, their evolution was extremely fast (Figure 7-7).

One faction, now the minority, claims some special sort of mutation, or extremely rapid mutation rates are necessary to account for these saltations in evolution. Some of the members of this school hold what seems an extreme view about the nature and origin of taxonomic categories. I have no wish to bog down here in philosophical or semantic problems, but briefly they hold that the major categories (phyla, classes, and so on) are separated by unbridge-

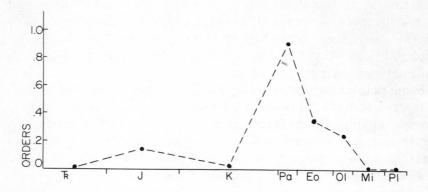

Fig. 7–7. *RATE OF APPEARANCE OF MAMMALIAN ORDERS.* Values on the ordinate scale derived by dividing the number of orders first appearing during a period or epoch by the approximate duration of the period in millions of years or, more concisely, number of new genera per million years. Abscissa shows approximate duration of periods and epochs. Note burst of diversification in Paleocene. For abbreviations see Figs. 7–1 and 7–3. (Data from Simpson, 1952.)

able gaps, and, therefore, that they did not arise by gradual transformation and diversification of a population succession but in a sudden "macromutation" in a single individual, a "hopeful monster."

Such mutations have not yet been surely identified in recent populations. If they do occur, most would not be viable without commensurate, buffering changes in the gene systems. If they do occur in viable form, they must be selected in the normal fashion from the gene combinations in an interbreeding species population. Even if selection pressures are very high, the macromutation will change in frequency at a finite rate. A "mutant" coral with six-fold radial symmetry would still belong to a species with four-fold symmetry. Is a man with six fingers on each hand a "macromutant"?

The other major party to this controversy holds that these major evolutionary steps occurred through high selection pressures on a population with favorable reproductive structure. Since the initial steps (usually hypothetical through lack of fossils) seem to be inadaptive, Simpson suggested they were the result of drift in very small populations, a drift that moved against selection until a new adaptive significance was established. This latter idea is interesting but no one has yet demonstrated positively that it happened or even that it is likely to happen.

As this is written, the controversy has quieted—principally from lack of data to substantiate various theories. A decisive series of observations must be sought, but there seems no good reason to accept a theory of special origin or to dispute over definitions of macromutation or taxonomic category. Studies of evolutionary rates mean little unless they can be shown to be free of sampling difficulties, can be referred to the biology of the animals, and can be placed in an environmental context. Paleontologists have made only a few such complete studies.

The trends

Adaptation. I have discussed the tempo of the evolutionary drama; now what of the story line itself, the trends in evolution? Many of the well known examples of evolution, the reduction of toes in the horse lineage for one, have obvious adaptive significance. They improve the fit of the population to a particular environment. Other recognized evolutionary sequences lack any obvious adaptive significance. These include nonadaptive trends that neither help nor injure the animals that bear them and inadaptive trends that are injurious to the evolving population sequence.

Some workers in the field of evolution have offered the initial evolution of rhino horns as an example of nonadaptive. They argue that the horns had no selective value until they were of considerable length. Therefore, they did not evolve by selection of short-horned variants in an otherwise hornless population. Since short horns were of no value, their appearance was nonadaptive. Only after they became long did adaptive evolution begin.

Simpson (1945, 1952) demolished a sufficient number of such interpretations to cast doubt on all. Some are simply the result of arbitrary selection of morphologic characters. The configuration of bones in the skull roof of early lungfish may have been a developmental adaptation, but whether a particular bone is large or small had little to do with protection of the skull. The character, the size and shape of a bone, has in itself no adaptive significance (Westoll, 1949).

Other "nonadaptive trends" reflect *preadaptations.* Some scallops swim by clapping the two valves of the shell. The form of shell and musculature are adaptive to this life, but how could a primitive burrowing clam with different form and musculature develop this adaptation? The answer would seem to be that the scallop ancestors attached to the bottom by a thread-like structure. The musculature

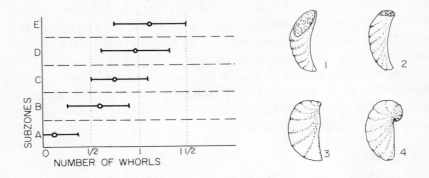

Fig. 7–8. *INADAPTIVE EVOLUTION.* Evolution of coiling in the Cretaceous pelecypod, Gryphaea. The shift of the population in time is shown at left; length of the heavy lines indicates range of variation in sample; circle indicates average. Drawings at right show change from non-coiled (1) to strongly coiled (4). A few of the strongly coiled individuals in the later populations may not have been able to open their shells at the end of their life. (After Trueman.)

and shell form adapted to this mode of life and proved preadaptive to swimming.

Finally, many examples of nonadaptive evolution are based on a lack of imagination. The person making the study cannot conceive of any adaptive significance. Such conclusions will not support any new and drastic theories of evolution.

The fossil record demonstrates some apparent inadaptive (deleterious) trends (Figure 7-8). For example, a pelecypod lineage developed a coiled shell. Late populations in this line had the shell so coiled that old individuals may not have been able to open their shell and perforce died of starvation. The trend is deleterious, but, as Simpson pointed out, only to old individuals. These individuals lived to this excessive age because they were successful. Other inadaptive changes like the great size of horns and antlers in some mammal lines are shaky interpretations because no one can demonstrate, or at least has demonstrated, that they were disadvantageous in the particular species ecology.

Until otherwise shown, all evolutionary changes should be considered adaptive or correlated with adaptive changes. If you doubt this abrupt conclusion, then prove it wrong.

Orthogenesis. One mode of evolution that has been a source of much controversy is the apparent linearity of some phyletic lines, or, more particularly, of the evolution of some characteristics. The horse line, *Hyracotherium-Equus*, has been taken as an example of this sort of evolution, and many of the cases of nonadaptive evolution mentioned in a preceding paragraph are cited also. I find linear evolution difficult to define, but, in use, it refers to phyletic lines that change in a regular manner from the ancestor, e.g., a small, three-toed horse with simple teeth, to the descendant, a large, single-toed horse with complex teeth, and change without temporary reversal or divergence. Such linearity, particularly in nonadaptive and inadaptive evolution, has been taken as a demonstration of some sort of special evolutionary mechanism. Some hypotheses involve a metaphysic of purpose either in the organism, or in the organic world as a whole. Such explanations may rest on valid metaphysic grounds, but they have no scientific value. Purpose may be a characteristic of the organic world, but the scientist wants to know how purpose acts in producing evolution. Once the operation of the evolutionary mechanism is defined, purpose becomes a superfluous hypothesis.

Other theories suppose some inherent tendency of the genetic material to change (mutate) in one direction. Disregarding the difficulty of associating a "linear" evolution of morphology with linearity of mutation, such theories are perfectly valid; populations, in the absence of selection for or against a series of genes, will evolve toward the most stable gene. "In the absence of selection" is the key; nonadaptive modifications could arise in this way and adaptive modifications be assisted in evolution, but mutation rates sufficient to push the population very far against selection are not known to occur. The inadaptive and nonadaptive trends placed in evidence by some orthogeneticists were kicked around thoroughly in the preceding section. In their weakened condition, they are not of much use in validating any theory.

Any serious discussion of linear evolution must include consideration of what is meant by linearity, for a basic principle used in determining phylogeny is an assumption of linear evolution. Further, I, for one, find it much easier to find linearity of trend, in absence of knowledge of causal factors in a particular evolutionary sequence; the *Hyracotherium-Equus* line looks straight (Figure 7-9) until one recognizes that the *Hyracotherium-Miohippus* portion of the line evolved in response to the limitations of a forest environment and the *Miohippus-Equus* portion in response to limitations of a grasslands environment. However artificial some

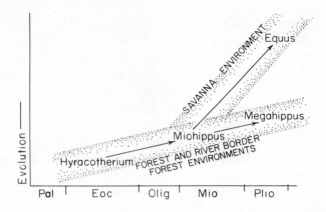

Fig. 7–9. *LINEAR AND DIVERGENT EVOLUTION.* The *Hyracothesium-Equus* lineage has been considered by some to be an example of straight line evolution. More careful study reveals that *Equus* is the terminus of a divergent stock that evolved in a grassland environment. Abbreviations: *Pal,* Paleocene; *Eoc,* Eocene; *Olig,* Oligocene; *Mio,* Miocene; *Plio,* Pliocene.

examples of linear evolution may be (as a consequence of straight thinking, perhaps), others seem perfectly valid and can readily be explained as a consequence of continued selection in one direction. The extrabiotic environment supplied this direction in some; in others, it was done by a feed-back relationship such as prey-predator. Further, the available variation in the population and the inherent structural limitations restrict the possible direction of change, for a leg can become shorter or longer but it can't do much much else.

Specialization. Linear evolution modifies the individuals and the population to perform a special set of functions. This process, specialization, limits the ecology of the species in many, if not all, ways. The cause is simple; animals which have only to run can be much better adapted to running than those that must both run and climb. The ultimate animal would do only a very few things but do those exceedingly well.

Specialization limits structural diversity within a species population, and thus limits possible directions of selective pressure. Evolution is further restricted by the mechanical limits of a particular structural plan; bone or shell can only be so strong or a muscle so effective. Since the structural plan results from prior and current adaptations, it, too, is limited by specialization. In this sense, evolution is self-limiting.

Preadaptation. From this postulate some people have argued that evolution is actually a downhill process and will cease as all of the potential variants in the different species populations are either used or eliminated by continued adaptive modification. A different view of evolution is possible, however, for each modification of form creates potential new adaptations. In this sense, a population or the variants in it are at all times *preadapted* to environments differing from the one to which the population is currently adapted. Birds, for example, probably first evolved as climbing reptiles and, in response to the requirement for activity and coordination of activity, adapted with a highly developed central nervous system and excellent eyes and with constant temperature mechanisms (four-chambered heart and feathers). These specializations are for climbing and thus limit the potentialities of the old reptilian morphologic plan, but they are also preadaptations for flight and transcend the possibilities of that same reptilian plan. Paleontologists must study the preadaptive possibilities of a specializing line as well as the course of the adaptation itself. Evolution both limits possibilities and creates new potentialities.

Adaptive radiation. Those happy few that strike upon new possibilities renew the vigor of evolution. Rather than dwindle to the spindly shoot of specialization, they root and branch (Figure 7-10).

Conceive, if you will, a continent populated by species specialized variously for running, climbing, or swimming; specialized also for eating leaves, fish, or each other. Conceive also that a few species are present, generalized with respect to these adaptations though specialized in other ways; among these is a constant body temperature. Then, for some reason, this continent is denuded of most of the specialized species. What happens? Theorizing is unnecessary, for this happened in the early Cenozoic. The remaining generalized species are adapted to do any one of these things and can conceivably evolve specializations in any one of these directions if given a chance. "Given a chance" is rather personalizing the matter though. Actually the process must involve: first, isolation and divergence into separate though similar species in response to local environment differences, e.g., for tree climbing on a forested island and running on a desert plain; second, breaking down of the isolating barrier with contact and with ecologic interaction between the new species—the climbers may be better adapted for eating the runners than they are for eating cactus, and the runners better

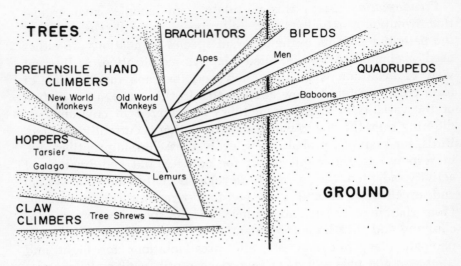

Fig. 7–10. *ADAPTIVE RADIATION.* The radiation of the major groups of primates as shown in their mode of locomotion.

adapted for eating leaves than for capturing climbers, and, third, continuous selection of the subpopulations best fitted for running and eating leaves or for climbing and eating runners. The ultimate results, of course, are horses and mountain lions.

This process of diversification is called radial evolution or adaptive radiation. Since the generalized species has certain specializations (like hair, a four-chambered heart, and mammary glands) not present in contemporaneous species, the subsequent evolution of the generalized to the specialized produces new forms unlike their adaptive antecedents. In this way, the hippo is quite different from a brontosaur although both have (or had) semiaquatic herbivorous adaptations.

Paleontologists sometimes desire to measure the rate of adaptive radiation. Commonly, they do this by determining the rate of occurrence of new genera (or other taxonomic categories) per unit of relative or absolute time. Unfortunately, this measure is not completely satisfactory since the scope of genus varies in different taxonomic groups, since it measures geographic diversity as well as ecologic, and since it is dependent on the completeness of the geologic record at any particular time.

When these rates of taxonomic diversification are plotted for various groups through time (Figure 7-11), two phenomena strike the eye; rates vary within the different groups at different times and some groups have higher average rates than others. If these differences are real, they deserve careful interpretation—but are they real? High taxonomic rates may represent the special interest of some paleontologists in the group and, therefore, reflect the number of papers published, or they may simply represent a group locally diversified in a thoroughly studied rock sequence. Because of the theoretical importance of determining these rates in their relation to each other and to major geologic events, an unambiguous method of measuring diversification deserves more general interest.

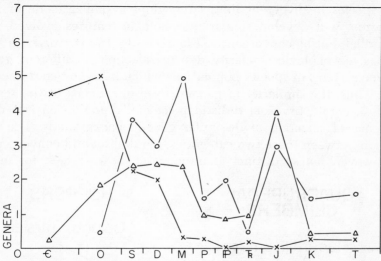

Fig. 7–11. *RATES OF EVOLUTIONARY DIVERSIFICATION.* The value (rate for each period is calculated by dividing the number of genera that appear for the first time in the period by the length of the period in millions of years. Triangles represent articulate brachiopods; crosses show inarticulate brachiopods; and circles indicate corals. Note alternate periods of rapid and slow diversification, the initial bursts, the late Paleozoic decline, and the high rates again attained in the Jurassic. Some of the differences may result from the relative amount of work done on different groups at different ages; the Triassic decline may represent our slight knowledge of Triassic marine environments. Abbreviations: C, Cambrian; O, Ordovician; S, Silurian; for other abbreviations see Fig. 7–1. (Based on Newell, 1952.)

Parallelism and convergence. After a group begins its radiation, several of the new species may adopt or maintain a similar mode of life, i.e., fall into the same adaptive channels. Some of these species are eliminated by their peers who evolved a better way of doing things; isolation protects others; and still others survive together by adopting variant niches of the same general adaptation.

Similar environmental factors select similar individuals in the different populations. The lines evolve in parallel (Figure 7-12); thus, the mammoth and mastodon lineages in the elephant stock paralleled each other in development of great size, tusks, and other features. In an extreme form, the concept of parallelism implies selection of the same genes or gene systems in two species populations which had diverged from their common ancestry in only a few genes. Since it is nearly impossible to measure genetic similarity in fossil populations, the term parallelism is best used for the similarities in adaptive trends in related lines.

If species in divergent lines later adopt a similar mode of life, they, too, will develop similar morphologic features evolved, not in parallel, but by convergence (Figure 7-13). In extreme form, this implies morphologic similarity due to selection of different genes or gene systems in species populations which have no genes in common. Thus, the similarity in general form of animals of the sessile benthos, corals, bryozoa, rudistid pelecypods, and so on is a consequence of selection of dissimilar genetic backgrounds. The distinction between these two categories, parallelism and convergence, is, however, not so distinct as implied by the extremes, for many

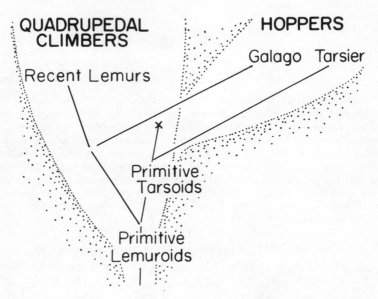

Fig. 7–12. *PARALLEL EVOLUTION.* The recent galagos and tarsiers evolved their arboreal, hopping adaptations independently but in parallel from a primitive lemuroid ancestry.

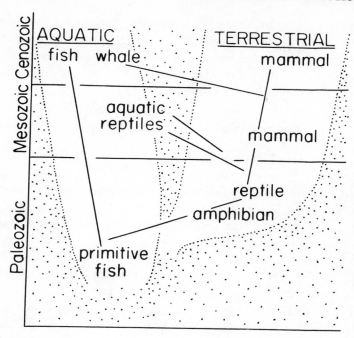

Fig. 7–13. *CONVERGENT EVOLUTION.* The amphibian-reptile-mammal line adapted to the terrestrial environment and diverged from the fish groups that remained in the aquatic environment. Some of the terrestrial vertebrates later readopted an aquatic habit, readapted to that environment, and converged on the fish in evolution.

cases of morphologic similarity probably involve both convergence and parallelism. In the example of the elephants used before, the two lines initially diverged in type of tusk development as the mastodons evolved tusks in both lower and upper jaws. Later they reduced the lower tusks, and the line converged on the mammoths.

Although the numerous examples of parallelism and/or convergence are of evolutionary interest, they are often a confounded nuisance in paleontology. For example, the dating of rocks may depend on interpretation of phylogeny; phylogenies are erected on evaluation of similarity and difference in form; similarity of form can result from parallelism or convergence as well as from common ancestry; therefore . . . paleontologists get confused. The weighing of characteristics in interpreting evolutionary relationships (p. 155) is an attempt to overcome this problem by considering the function of various structures. In this scheme, similarity in structures of similar function is given relatively little weight in determining relationship. I should note, however, that detailed similarity even in similarly adapted structures implies relationship. In this way the "coral-like" rudistid pelecypods resemble each other more in structures adapted for sessile bottom life than they resemble similarly adapted corals.

EVOLUTION OF NATURAL SOCIETIES

The interrelated radial evolution of one or more groups of organisms yields a number of contemporaneous natural societies. Because the species populations composing any one of these societies are mutually interrelated, the society itself can be said to evolve as the populations and their ecologic relationships change in character. Just as treatment of a natural society as an ecologic unit is a higher synthesis than study of a single species in that society, so the treatment of evolving natural societies or better, *evolving ecosystems,* is a higher synthesis than the study of evolution of "isolated" populations. The initial act of synthesis is more complex than the interpretation of single population evolution, but, because it involves simultaneous approaches to the same fundamental measures of a biological system, it permits a closer estimate of characteristics of that system.

Analysis of ecosystem evolution requires the determination of association between species and environmental factors in contemporaneous ecosystems, and of association of evolutionary trends between species and with environmental changes. Association may be measured statistically through correlation coefficients or similar techniques, and the nature and extent of ecological interaction estimated from contemporaneous association, from association of evolutionary trends, from association of species with environment, and from interpretation of ecology based on adaptations of form. Figure 7-14 is a partial analysis of a fossil faunal assemblage of lower Permian vertebrates from Texas (see also p. 119, Figure 5-7, Table 5–5). In this case, the data do not permit statistical measures of association, nor are evolutionary trends sufficiently pronounced to tell us much about association of such trends. The change in faunal composition with time does indicate, however, response to a changing environment.

At the time I write this, only two complete analyses have been made of evolving societies, both of terrestrial vertebrate faunas.

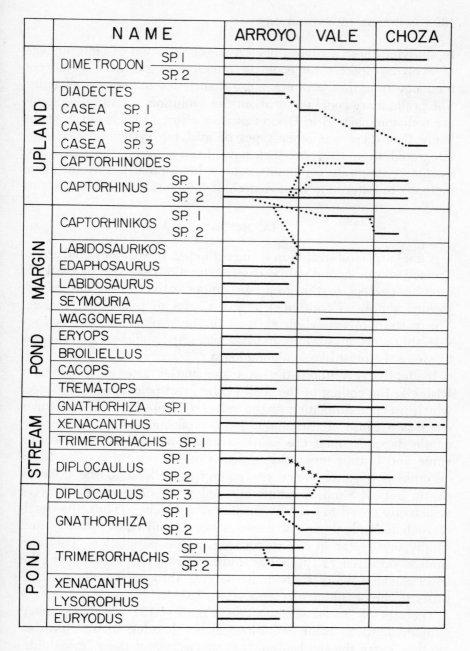

	NAME		ARROYO	VALE	CHOZA
UPLAND	DIMETRODON	SP. 1			
		SP. 2			
	DIADECTES				
	CASEA SP. 1				
	CASEA SP. 2				
	CASEA SP. 3				
	CAPTORHINOIDES				
	CAPTORHINUS	SP. 1			
		SP. 2			
MARGIN	CAPTORHINIKOS	SP. 1			
		SP. 2			
	LABIDOSAURIKOS				
	EDAPHOSAURUS				
	LABIDOSAURUS				
	SEYMOURIA				
POND	WAGGONERIA				
	ERYOPS				
	BROILIELLUS				
	CACOPS				
	TREMATOPS				
STREAM	GNATHORHIZA SP. 1				
	XENACANTHUS				
	TRIMERORHACHIS SP. 1				
	DIPLOCAULUS	SP. 1			
		SP. 2			
POND	DIPLOCAULUS SP. 3				
	GNATHORHIZA	SP. 1			
		SP. 2			
	TRIMERORHACHIS	SP. 1			
		SP. 2			
	XENACANTHUS				
	LYSOROPHUS				
	EURYODUS				

Fig. 7–14. *EVOLUTION OF A PERMIAN VERTEBRATE SOCIETY.* Arroyo, Vale, and Choza are successive formations in the Clear Fork Group, late early Permian of Texas. Solid lines indicate the stratigraphic distribution of various genera. Dotted lines indicate evolutionary connections; crosses, ecological replacement. For an analysis of ecologic relations within the society, see Figure 5–7 and Table 5–5. The faunal and lithologic evidence indicates increasing aridity and consequent evolution and attrition of the fauna. (See Olson, 1952, for discussion.)

In studying these analyses, one has the impression of close linkage of evolving species by ecologic interaction and of a persistent tendency of rather complex natural societies to behave as units. The preliminary conclusions about the evolution of natural societies are well summarized in Olson's pioneer effort (1952), but it seems likely that there are other types of evolving systems less closely integrated than the two that have been studied. In particular, marine invertebrate communities must be approached by the same methods to determine their degree of integration in evolution.

DOOMSDAY

A final aspect of evolution is the extinction of species populations. Treated simply as individual cases, extinctions are not particularly exciting (except to the group becoming extinct) and can be explained simply as continued negative rates of population change. The pattern of extinction as seen in the geologic record is considerably more mysterious and has generated sufficient controversy to excite the most blasé paleontologist.

Inadaptive evolution—the excessive antler size in the extinct Irish elk; the coiling of the shell in the fossil pelecypod, *Gryphaea*, which prevented opening of the valves (Figure 7-8)—is sometimes cited as a cause of extinction. The significance of the former example depends upon the word *excessive* which has no objective value and is thus unworthy of scientific consideration. The latter example is objective since the coiling must lead to the animal's death, but, as Simpson points out, only very old individuals were sufficiently coiled to prevent opening of the valves. Thus, the death of such individuals was a consequence of individual senility and simply one factor in the death rate of the population. This and similar occurrences probably indicate relative success of the species, since many individuals survive through youth and maturity to die of "old age" (see Kurtén, 1954).

Theories of "racial senescence" (Figure 7-15) are often linked with inadaptive, linear evolution. These theories, in one form or another, carry the implication that species populations "grow old;" that the old age is likely to be associated with "excessive" ornamentation and other nonadaptive features, and that it ultimately ends in racial death (extinction). As a metaphoric or metaphysic concept, these theories are not without interest. But species popula-

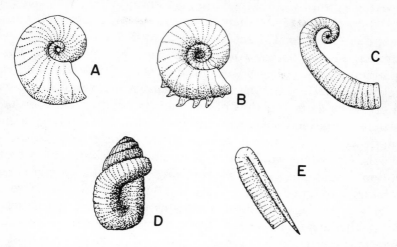

Fig. 7–15. *RACIAL SENESCENCE.* The aberrant cephalopod shells drawn here have been interpreted as examples of "racial senescence." *A)* "Normal" type. *B)* Normal coiling but shell spinose. *C)* Adult part of shell not coiled. *D)* Initial part of shell coiled like snail shell, later part bent into tight U-shape. *E)* Shell not coiled but bent into tight U-shape. These variant forms probably represent adaptation to new habitats or habits rather than "racial senescence." (A. After Pavlow and Lamplugh. B. After Mazenot. C. After Collignon. D. After Stephenson. E. After Orbigny.)

tions are not metaphors, and using metaphoric terms does not make them so. The real question is something like this: Adaptive radiations, taken as a whole, tend to run out in very specialized lines. Are these lines so closely adapted to particular environmental limits that they cannot survive environmental change? There are still some undefined terms in question (very specialized, closely adapted, and so on), but this is a little closer to an operational scientific question.

If, as seems possible, adaptive radiations are the result of complex ecosystem evolution, the species produced by the radiation are in rather delicate ecologic adjustment to one another. If someone upsets the applecart by becoming extinct— due, say, to climatic change—the whole system is likely to be unfavorably affected. What paleontologists need is precise analysis of faunal assemblages before and during a wave of extinction—not metaphors.

CATACLYSMS

Some "waves of extinction" and "explosive evolution" of new groups seem to be real. Some abundant and diversified groups disappeared abruptly, and, with equal abruptness, their heirs appeared to dominate the new communities. The plots of rates of generic origin on p. 177 reflect this, even if one discounts possible sampling errors. Some workers theorize that the restriction or expansion of the epicontinental seas accelerated or damped rates of evolution and extinction. But do extensive seas result in a greater variety of habitats and thus of possibilities for diversification or do restricted seas increase opportunities for isolation and consequent divergence? Some people think that shrinking seas crowd the animals. Crowding would increase competition. More intense competition would raise selective pressures and result in more rapid evolution and greater diversification. But I would like to see an oyster shouldering aside brachiopods as they all hurried along the bed of the dwindling ocean. Even for those animals capable of migration, one may doubt whether the advance or retreat of the sea was sufficiently rapid to prevent normal adjustment of population size. For a contrary view see a paper written by Moore (1955).

These bursts of extinctions and radial evolution are among the major markers in the geologic time scale. Therefore, it is of extreme importance that they be understood. Theories are plentiful; the hard facts of large collections, careful field studies of the geology, and informed synthesis of these collections and studies are excessively rare. We may find that the term *abrupt* is very relative; certainly many dinosaur lineages became extinct at various times before the close of the Cretaceous, and those species whose disappearance marks the end of that period are few in number and almost surely did not become extinct at one time or in all places at the same time.

REFERENCES

Bader, R. S. 1955. "Variability and Evolutionary Rate in the Oreodonts," *Evolution*, vol. 9, pp. 119-140.

Kurtén, B. 1954. "Population Dynamics and Evolution," *Evolution*, vol. 8, pp. 75-81.

————. 1955. See references, Chapter 4.

Newell, N. D. 1952. "Periodicity in Invertebrate Paleontology," *Jour. of Paleontology*, vol. 26, pp. 371-385.

Olson, E. C. 1952. See references for Chapter 5.

Romer, A. S. 1949. "Time Series and Trends in Animal Evolution," in:

Genetics, Paleontology, and Evolution. (See in Chapter 6, Jepsen, Mayr, and Simpson, 1949.)

Schaeffer, B. 1952. "Rates of Evolution in the Coelacanth and Dipnoan Fishes, *Evolution,* vol. 6, pp. 101-111.

Simpson, G. G. 1945; 1952. See references for Chapter 6.

Westoll, T. S. 1949. "On the Evolution of the Dipnoi," in: *Genetics, Paleontology and Evolution,* pp. 121-184. (See in Chapter 6, Jepsen, Mayr, and Simpson, 1949.)

See also references for Chapter 6.

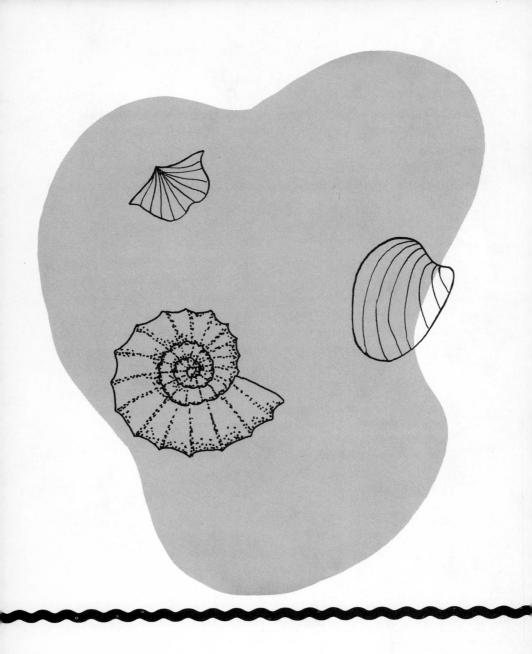

8. FOSSILS *and* STRATIGRAPHERS

$\mathcal{T}$he succession * of organisms in time forms the keystone of stratigraphic correlation. The restriction of particular animals to particular environments permits interpretation of ancient environments and geography. Conversely, correlation presents the necessary data for phylogenetic interpretation, and paleoecology and paleogeography are essential in the determination of the causes of evolution. The historical development of paleontology reflects these interrelations, for correlation was rudimentary until faunal succession was recognized, and the significance of fossils to evolutionary theory was not clear until the succession of various forms was determined.

To recognize the significance of paleontology to stratigraphy, you need only examine the difficulties of geologists working in areas of Precambrian rocks. Some of the most brilliant physical stratigraphy has been done in the Precambrian series, partly because the geologists lack the crutch of paleontology there, yet Precambrian historical geology is still poorly known. To recognize the significance of stratigraphy to paleontology, you need only examine disputed datings of fossil men and "proto-men" in Africa. The morphologic studies have been careful and ingenious, but their significance to the interpretation of human evolution is clouded by inadequate stratigraphic background.

ADVENTURES IN TIME

If animals had not evolved, correlation of rocks within a sedimentary basin would be difficult, and correlation between basins almost impossible. To the extent that evolution is simultaneous over a wide area and is recorded by fossils in the rock sequence, so evolutionary events serve as time markers (Figure 8-1).

"To the extent that evolution is simultaneous" and "is recorded" —these are the jokers in the deck. If you will remember that interpretation of evolutionary relationships is always tentative and is based on small samples limited in time and geographic extent, the problems in making paleontologic correlation become obvious.

---

* I have used the term *succession* in this chapter to indicate the sequence of different animal populations as determined by superposition of the beds in which they are found. I do not imply, by the term, phyletic (evolutionary) sequence, although such sequences presumably hide behind the directly observed succession of faunas.

187

The stratigrapher so rarely possesses a phyletic sequence for correlation that he must regard it as an ideal, almost as a concept to be relegated to paleontology textbooks. As a rough generalization, similarity of faunas from rocks in different areas indicates a similar time of deposition for the rocks. In preliminary work, particularly in the field, this generalization is good enough. But similarity of faunas also indicates similarity of environment, and dissimilarity of faunas may indicate a difference in environment or geographic isolation as well as difference in time (Figure 8-2).

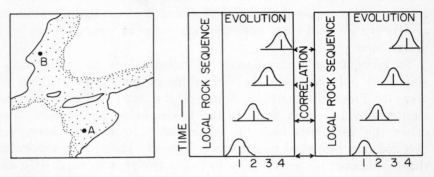

Fig. 8–1. *EVOLUTION AND CORRELATION.* The evolution of a sequence of populations should be nearly simultaneous everywhere the populations occur. The stippled area in the map at left indicates the geographic occurrence of a species population. Thus, similar stages in the evolutionary sequence at locations A and B indicate similar age as shown in the stratigraphic columns at the right.

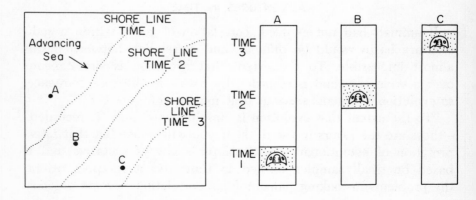

Fig. 8–2. *PROBLEMS IN CORRELATION: ENVIRONMENTAL SUCCESSION.* As the sea advances (map at left) the same species occurs at successively later times in the three localities. The first occurrence of the species is not a time boundary but transgresses time (columns at right).

The basis of correlation

The stratigrapher-paleontologist can actually observe age relationships only in a local stratigraphic section. Direct evidence of superposition permits him to determine a succession of species in such a section. This succession forms the central supporting pier of correlation; all else is deduction and hypothesis. Each species has a definable stratigraphic range within the local section. That range, of course, is a segment of the total duration of the morphologic group classified as a species. The stratigrapher has, in addition to this assemblage of species, information on the association with rock characters, on the occurrence of species with each other, and on the numbers, condition, orientation, and distribution of the fossils.

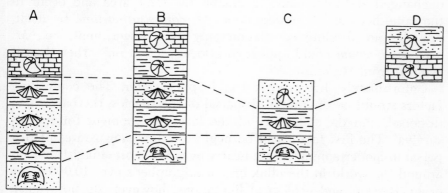

Fig. 8–3. *LOCAL FOSSIL SEQUENCE AND CORRELATION.* A similar sequence of fossils occurs in each of four different local sections. The occurrence of a particular type or association of fossils thus provides the basis of correlation between local sections.

He next compares adjacent local sections (Figure 8-3). Similarities of rock type and rock sequence establish rock unit equivalence. Similarities of species occurrence and sequence establish biological equivalence. Here, however, difficulties, both practical and theoretical, appear. Each local section contains somewhat different species assemblages. Some species occur in one and not the other, and the stratigraphic ranges of species relative to each other and to the rock units vary. The explanation is simple enough—local environmental differences control the occurrence—but what can be done to make the problem of correlation equally simple?

Correlations on evolutionary sequence. The answer to the problem above may be "nothing," for even stratigraphers disagree on the validity of interpretations, but let's examine some of the alternatives. The most direct and only "absolute" method is that of phylogenetic correlation (Figure 8-1). In the evolution of *Micraster* discussed on page 131, the species succeed each other by gradual transformation. The events of that transformation should be essentially simultaneous throughout the geographic range of the interbreeding species population. The change from *Micraster leski* to *M. cortestudinarium* marks, in any local section, the same time horizon; the change from *M. cortestudinarium* to *M. coranguinum* another such horizon.

Notice that the transformation, not the species, is the key marker. Thus, an isolated population of *M. cortestudinarium* might persist unchanged and later come to inhabit the same area and occur in the same beds as *M. coranguinum*. *M. cortestudinarium*, by itself, provides an absolute correlation only as a lower limit, i.e., *M. cortestudinarium* could appear in a local section no earlier than it evolved from *M. leski*.

Unfortunately, however, it could appear later. The controlling factors would be the rate of dispersal of the species, the barriers to dispersal, and the suitability of the local environment for species survival. The first factor can be neglected, for known rates of dispersal in modern animals could carry even the most sluggish species around the world in the blink of a stratigrapher's eye—10,000 years or so. Barriers and ecological limitations, however, do not vanish so easily, and here the stratigrapher leaves the realm of "absolute" correlations and enters that of probability and of the empiric guide fossils.

Correlations from dispersal. If similarity of environment among local sections can be established—by a study of the rocks and of the fauna as a whole—then the appearance (or, possibly, the disappearance) of a species in those sections forms a time marker. If a clam species migrated into or evolved in the local area in a specific habitat, then it should appear everywhere that habitat occurs, but the stratigrapher can establish only a general similarity, not a specific identity of habitat. For some animals, and for some habitats, he can be reasonably certain of his interpretations; for most invertebrates and most marine habitats, he cannot be. Nor can he overlook the possibility of undetected local barriers to migration.

In practice, he is usually satisfied with an inverse statement: if difference in habitat is demonstrated, different species will occur, even though the deposits are contemporaneous. I warn therefore that the following example represents an ideal, not a typical case.

The lower Oligocene beds of Montana contain a forest fauna. Comparable fossil animals in the lower Oligocene of South Dakota appear only in local outcrops that represent a river border forest. The greater part of the South Dakota deposits were formed in a semi-tropic grassland and scrub forest environment and contain quite different animals (Figure 8-4). The only justified comparison

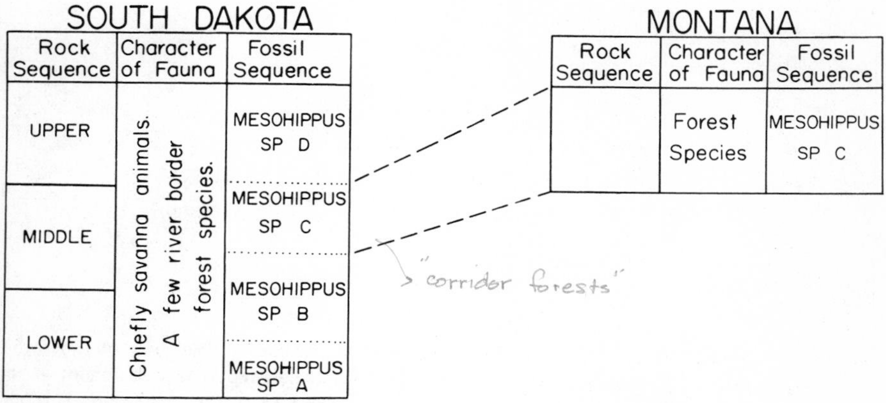

Fig. 8–4. *PROBLEMS IN CORRELATION.* Mesohippus, an inhabitant of the early Oligocene river border forest in South Dakota, provides a basis of correlation with the forest fauna of the Pipestone Springs formation in Montana. The other species, savanna and forest, are not diagnostic.

is between the forest animals. Among these occurs a horse, *Mesohippus.* The Montana horse is closest to a species that occurs toward the top of the South Dakota section. In South Dakota this species was preceded and succeeded by other *Mesohippus* species in a phyletic sequence. Since these are not found in Montana, the stratigrapher correlates the Montana local section with a small part of the South Dakota local section. Since he compares similar environments and since he believes with some evidence that there were no geographic barriers between them, he expects the same species to appear in the two areas simultaneously.

The probability is difficult to estimate, but he can and does increase it by looking at other species to see if they coincide. The local extinction of species and genera, however, is a less reliable guide. A primitive camel occurs in the Montana section. The same species has been found in South Dakota, but only in the lower part of the lower Oligocene section. On this comparison the Montana deposits would be much earlier—before the key horse species had evolved. Since the latter deduction contradicts observation, the correlation must be incorrect, and the camel survived to a later time in the Montana forests.

Correlations from guide fossils. The stratigrapher may also find in his comparison of local sections that some species occur in more than one fossil and rock association. Either they lived in several

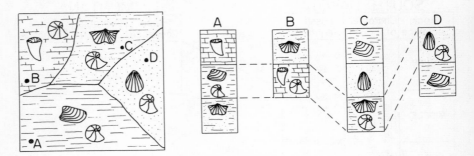

Fig. 8–5. *RELATION OF GUIDE FOSSIL AND ENVIRONMENT.* The map at left indicates the distribution of animals at a single time. Thus a pelecypod association at A, a coral at B, a brachiopod at C, and a different brachiopod at D. The cephalopod, however, ranges widely and occurs in all four associations. The sections at right indicate fossil sequence at each of the four locations. The animals limited to localized environments occur or disappear in the sections as the environment changes. Only the cephalopod provides a guide for correlation.

habitats or else occupied one like the pelagic that was widely distributed. In either case, they provide a tie between local sections of otherwise diverse faunas (Figure 8-5). The same limitations of distribution apply, however, and the species may well deceive the stratigrapher, either by disappearance from some habitats before others or with a change of the widely distributed habitat—a change unrecognized by the stratigrapher. They are not infallible guide fossils.

Finally, the stratigrapher sometimes finds long, invariable successions of genera or species in the local sections. Thus, in the Jurassic of Europe, a particular succession of ammonites is found wherever these occur (Figure 8-6). In any particular section, some of the genera may be missing but those present are never out of sequence—*Arnioceras* never occurs with or below *Arietites* or with or above *Euasteroceras*. Where these successions show gradual evolutionary transformations, they are of the same absolute type as discussed before. Where they are not evolutionary sequences, they

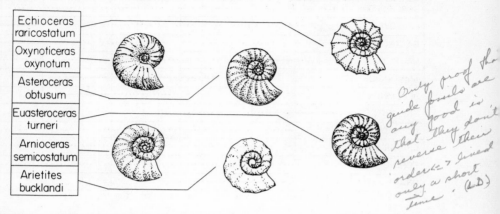

| Echioceras raricostatum |
| Oxynoticeras oxynotum |
| Asteroceras obtusum |
| Euasteroceras turneri |
| Arnioceras semicostatum |
| Arietites bucklandi |

Only proof tha[t] guide fossils are any good is that they don't reverse their order & lived only a short time. (L.D.)

Fig. 8–6. *FOSSIL ZONES AND ZONAL FOSSILS.* The sequence of these six species of Jurassic ammonites provides a guide for correlation wherever they occur. The succession appears invariable, and the species have never been found to overlap in stratigraphic distribution. (Based on Arkell, 1956b.)

depend upon a succession of genera that disperse quickly into many habitats or across a few widespread ones. In this latter case, the correlations are again probable, not absolute; and the choice of guide fossils is based upon experience. If *Arnioceras* were some day found to occur in rocks below *Arietites*, it would no longer serve its function. Similarly, one would not choose as guides genera known to overlap in time. As the transformation is the critical marker in evolutionary sequences, so the invariable succession is essential to the guide fossil concept. Transgressive or regressive seas might produce a short succession but long sequences could only result from rapid dispersal of newly evolving genera or species— each dispersal nearly instantaneous—for otherwise they would overlap. Please observe, however, that these guide fossils are empiric, subject to revision, that not many qualify, and that their time of appearance in local sections will differ even though their total period of existence may be so short as to make these differences unimportant. A relatively few groups of organisms provide most of the index fossils and do so for only part of their history (Figure 8-7).

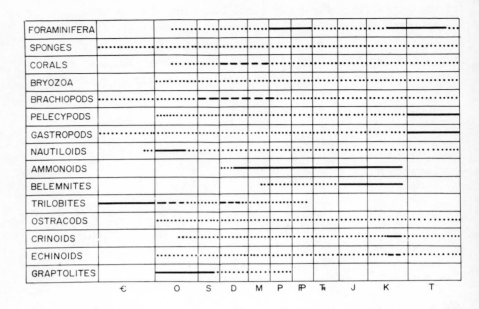

Fig. 8—7. *STRATIGRAPHIC SIGNIFICANCE OF FOSSIL GROUPS.* The solid line indicates the group was important for world-wide zoning and correlation; the dashed line, important in regional correlation; the dotted line, occasional or rare use as zonal fossils. (After Teichert, 1958.)

Correlation of faunas. Correlations generally improve if more than one species is considered. Ideally, whole assemblages are compared and analyzed. Overlapping times of first appearance are used to subdivide the succession and to provide closer correlation. As diagrammed in Figure 8-8, species A_1 occurs first in a section along with B_1 and C_1. B_2 then replaces B_1, and C_2 still later replaces C_1. Another local section with A_1, B_2, C_1 correlates with the middle of the first, although A_1, by itself, does not provide that precise an interpretation. Use of several species does not, however, free the stratigrapher from the obligation of studying the environmental controls of dispersal for each.

Interpretation of faunas as units poses refractory problems. In some studies, the percentage of genera or species in common between sections serves as a measure of relative age. If each species comes and goes independent of the others, then the reliability of the correlation is high. But most species occurrences are not independent for they depend upon common factors of the environment

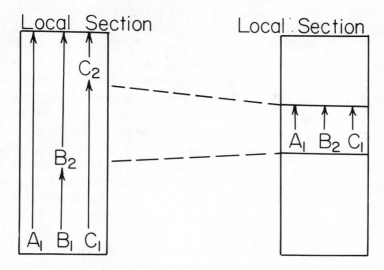

Fig. 8–8. *USE OF OVERLAPPING FOSSIL SEQUENCES IN CORRELATION.* In one local section, species A_1 continues through the section; B_1 is replaced by B_2; and, somewhat higher in the section, C_1 by C_2. In another local section, the occurrence of A_1, B_2, and C_1 in a unit implies a correlation with the middle of the first local section.

or upon each other. As many stratigraphers have pointed out, these differences in percentage are more likely to indicate an environmental difference rather than a chronologic.

Equally, the comparison of relative abundance of various species indicates more of environment and preservation than of time. The fossil sample size is so sensitive to selective preservation that variations may mean little or nothing. Attempts to use successional change in abundance in the same way that species successions are used have largely broken down. The paleontologist studying fossils in well cuttings is forced to percentage analyses by mixture of specimens within the well, but the change in percentage is properly taken as a result of mixing, not as a consequence of orderly stratigraphic change.

In spite of these objections to correlation by total fauna, some worthwhile work has been done. If the similarity of habitat is assured, then variation between local sections results from difference in time. This variation may be simply of occurrence or nonoccurrence or may involve subtler factors of abundance and association. The latter have been too little studied for discussion here.

Regional and interregional correlations. Within a basin of deposition, the species distributions depend principally upon local environmental controls. Extension of correlation from adjacent sections to more distant ones, therefore, follows the same pattern already outlined. The dangers, however, are greater and the probabilities of valid interpretation somewhat less since the possible range of environmental differences is greater. Similar habitats in the northern and southern ends of a geosyncline may have quite different faunas, the difference being related to temperature. For this reason, the stratigrapher analyzes the environmental controls of dispersal more carefully and places more reliance on a few widely distributed species. He must also be wary of seas which, encroaching on the continents, carry particular habitats and faunas slowly from the lower parts of the basin to the higher parts.

Even so, he builds up a reliable system of correlations throughout the basin, or even across several interconnected basins. Where he tries, however, to correlate between distant deposits formed in distinct biologic provinces or realms, correlation inevitably becomes more uncertain. He, in fact, depends on a very few species that range widely, most of which are active pelagic or terrestrial animals like the cephalopods and vertebrates. He further depends upon brief periods of mixing and migration between provinces and realms or, in other words, for breaks in the geographic barriers to dispersal. For example, the South American terrestrial faunal succession is distinct from that of North America throughout most of the Cenozoic. Only near the beginning of the era and near the end do the same or closely related genera and species occur in both areas. In some correlations, stratigraphers have been forced to compare the relative amount of evolution of lineages in the two areas—a dangerous and unreliable procedure.

Summary. Let me summarize and conclude. Local sections are the basis of all stratigraphic inferences. Correlation begins with comparison of local sections and is based primarily on fossil similarities. Evolutionary events provide the most accurate correlations; comparison of faunal sequences in similar environments can be used where evolutionary sequences are not available. Genera and species with widespread geographic and/or environmental distributions are the most useful in correlation, and rapidly evolving groups provide a succession of "guide fossils" that have only a limited stratigraphic range. These latter groups, if they can be identified, have so short a duration that local ecological controls and geographic barriers do not affect their range in the local section significantly. Correlation based on the total fauna, or at least several species within that fauna, can be more precise and more probable than those derived from single "guide fossils." Regional and interregional correlations depend on these same methods, but geographic barriers pose increasing difficulties as distances become greater.

Units of correlation

The founders of biostratigraphy, impressed by the limited time range of most fossil types, attempted to divide the geologic column into a series of zones characterized by one or more genera or species. These characteristic genera and species were variously *marker, guide,* or *index* fossils. Subsequent workers have had somewhat divergent conceptions of the zone, and subsequent research disclosed that some of the diagnostic fossils were not restricted to "their" zone, that most had quite limited geographic ranges, and that all were confined to a relatively few environments of deposition. For some areas and some periods however, the zone with its guide fossils provides the most practical and accurate method of correlation.

European stratigraphers have tended to hold closely to the zone as the basic unit of correlation, to disregard rock units, and, consequently, to neglect the distinctions between rock-stratigraphic, time-stratigraphic, biostratigraphic, and time units. Work in North America has centered more on rock and rock-time problems—perhaps because of a relative lack of such superb zonal sequences as occur in the European Mesozoic. In any case, stratigraphers now use a variety of different terms for different stratigraphic units. This unhappy situation is still "in court," awaiting the decision of usage.

Zones and subzones. Not only do the advocates of faunal zones and rock-time units disagree, but supporters of the former view have their internal heresies. Is a zone a segment of "pure" physical time (Schindewolf, 1957)? Is it a segment of the stratigraphic column? Or is it sort of a combination of the two (Arkell, 1956a)?

Regardless of this dispute, zones are characterized by zonal guide fossils, and these guide genera or species are chosen because of their constant succession, their wide distribution, and apparent short ranges in time. The Jurassic of northwestern Europe is thereby divided into fifty-eight ammonite (cephalopod) zones. The zone represents the practical limit of regional correlation, although, locally, subzones may be useful. In theory, stratigraphers should find the same zone every place at which rocks of that age occur. But, since the zone is a practical unit, this "onionskin" concept has to be disregarded. Therefore, each faunal province or realm requires a separate zonal sequence. Further, many local sections lack the critical guide fossils, and correlations are built up as fossils of local stratigraphic significance are tied into the sections that contain zonal guide fossils. Taken broadly, then, the definition of a particular zone is, itself, built up by comparing the stratigraphic ranges in the local sections (teilzones) of the various genera and species and by selectiing those which seem to have the shortest total duration (biozones).

Biostratigraphic, time-stratigraphic, and rock-stratigraphic units. Zones, of course, are biostratigraphic units, that is, they express the stratigraphic ranges of one or more species or genera. Time-stratigraphic units comprise the rocks deposited during a particular time. Rock-stratigraphic units are simply mappable lithologic units, and the same rock may have been deposited at different times in different places.

The definition of a particular time-stratigraphic unit (Table 8–1), the Permian system or the Paleocene series, is built up, like the zone, by correlation between local sections, or, where possible, by designation of a single continuous section covering the full time interval. These particular local sections then become *standard sections* and provide, particularly in their fossil asemblages, a reference for further correlation. Typically, stages have one or more corresponding biostratigraphic zones. However, a stage represents all the rocks deposited during a time interval, not just those containing zonal fossils. In consequence, a stage (or the larger units) represents inference about relative time and is less objective and more abstract than a zone.

As I indicated before, zones have regional significance, but only rarely do zonal guide species or genera occur widely enough to permit extension of the zones over great distances. This limited distribution restricts comparisons between regions to larger taxonomic units, e.g., broad genera or subfamilies. The finest interregional correlations, therefore, come between stages or even series.

Geologic-time units. Each time-stratigraphic unit has a corresponding unit in physical time, the geologic-time unit. Ideally,

TABLE 8–1

CLASSIFICATION OF STRATIGRAPHIC UNITS

Geologic-time units	Time-stratigraphic units
Era	
Period	System
Epoch	Series
Age	Stage
Biostratigraphic units	Rock-stratigraphic units
	(Do not correspond to time-strati-graphic or geologic-time units.)
Zone	Group
	Formation
	Member, lentil, tongue
	Bed

the same geologic-time units should be recognized everywhere, but, typically, ages are limited to particular areas, and only epochs have world-wide recognition.

AND IN SPACE

Sections in the preceding chapters dealt with the methods of paleoecology and paleogeography. The two are closely related to correlation because an analysis of geographic and environmental changes helps in correlation. If a geologist establishes a particular bed to be of continental origin and traces it basinward, he anticipates finding marine rocks of the same age. The character of environment or geographic position helps to determine the correlative bed in the marine sequence.

Conversely, paleogeographic maps or paleoclimatic interpretations are no better than the correlations between various areas. Was the sea continuous across the Cincinnati Arch at a particular time in the Ordovician? One can know only if the age equivalency of rocks on and about the Arch are determined.

Valid paleogeographic interpretation depends also on interpretation of phylogeny. If species are closely related, they cannot have been long isolated; if distantly, then they must have been separated by geographic barriers for some time. But phylogeny depends on the sequence of forms; if reversed by poor stratigraphy, the phylogenetic sequence will yield quite different and erroneous ideas on the paleogeography.

REFERENCES

Allen, R. S. 1948. "Geological Correlation and Paleoecology," *Geol. Soc. of America, Bulletin*, vol. 59, pp. 1-10. A discussion of the importance of paleoecologic studies in correlation.

Arkell, W. J. 1956a. "Comments on Stratigraphic Procedure and Terminology," *Amer. Jour. of Science*, vol. 254, pp. 457-467.

————. 1956b. See references for Chapter 5.

Clark, B. L. 1945. "Problems of Speciation and Correlation as Applied to Mollusks of the Marine Cenozoic," *Jour. of Paleontology*, vol. 19, pp. 158-172. An example of applied stratigraphic paleontology.

Dunbar, C. O. and J. Rodgers. 1958. *Principles of Stratigraphy.* New York: Wiley. A general text emphasizing physical stratigraphy.

Fiege, K. 1951. "The Zone, Base of Biostratigraphy," *Amer. Assoc. of Petr. Geologists, Bulletin*, vol. 35, pp. 2582-2596. A discussion of the philosophy of practice of biostratigraphy.

Gignoux, M. 1955. *Stratigraphic Geology.* San Francisco: Freeman. A survey of world stratigraphy.

Hedberg, H. D. 1951. "Nature of Time-stratigraphic Units and Geological Time Units," *Amer. Assoc. of Petr. Geologists, Bulletin*, vol. 35, pp. 1077-1081.

Jeletsky, J. A. 1955. "Paleontology, Basis of Practical Geochronology," *Amer. Assoc. of Petr. Geologists, Bulletin*, vol. 40, no. 4.

Krumbein, W. C. and L. L. Sloss. 1951. See references for Chapter 5.

Moore, R. C. 1952. "Stratigraphic Viewpoints in Measurement of Geologic Time," *Amer. Geophysical Union, Transcript*, vol. 33, 150-156.

Payne, T. G. 1942. "Stratigraphical Analysis and Environmental Reconstruction," *Amer. Assoc. of Petr. Geologists, Bulletin*, vol. 26, pp. 1697-1770. A general review of methods of stratigraphic interpretation.

Schindewolf, O. H. 1950. *Grundlagen und Methoden der Paläontologischen Chronologie.* Berlin: Borntraeger. A general text on paleontologic correlation.

————. 1957. "Comments on Some Stratigraphic Terms," *Amer. Jour. of Science*, vol. 55, pp. 394-399. A formalistic approach to correlation.

Shimer, H. W. and R. R. Shrock. 1944. *Index Fossils of North America.* New York: Wiley. A "dictionary" of American guide fossils.

Teichert, C. 1958. "Some Biostratigraphical Concepts," *Geol. Soc. of America, Bulletin*, vol. 69, pp. 99-120. A review of correlation concepts and philosophy—an emphasis on pragmatic stratigraphy.

Wilson, J. L. 1957. "Geographic of Olenid Trilobite Distribution and Its Influence on Cambro-Ordovician Correlation," *Amer. Jour. of Science,* vol. 255, pp. 321-340. An example of the relation of paleogeography and correlation.

Zeuner, F. E. 1946. *Dating the Past.* London: Methuen. A text covering all aspects of geochronology.

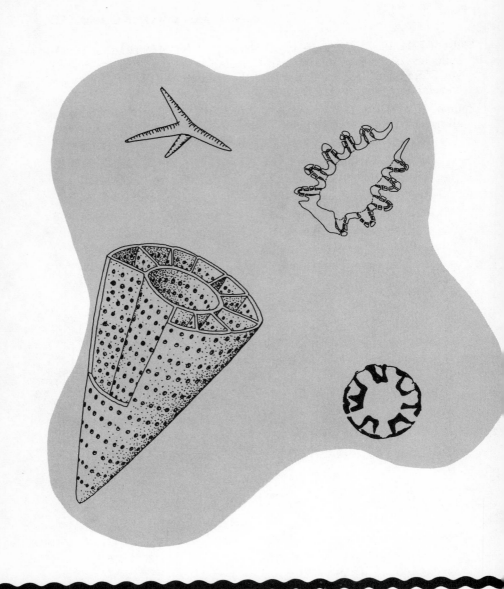

9. The TWILIGHT WORLD

$\mathcal{T}$he preceding pages describe briefly the methods, principles, and conclusions of paleontology. The succeeding ones apply these generalities to specific groups of fossil animals. Unfortunately, many important events in the history of life are unrecorded. These gaps must be bridged by inference from the most nearly related fossil and recent animals. Really very little is known of the adaptations, ecology, and evolution of most fossil species. These areas of ignorance must be brought into perspective with that which is known.

Frankly, this is too much for a few hundred pages of text and illustrations. It is too much for the six volumes of the *Traite de Paleontologie* and even for the twenty-four parts of the *Treatise on Invertebrate Paleontology*. The best to be done in the confines of this book is to cover the most important things; to mention some of the most interesting (interesting to me at least), and to illustrate further some of the methods, principles, and conclusions.

REMEMBRANCES OF TIMES LOST

Paleontologists view the origin of earth and its early history dimly through a murky twilight. The first evidence of life may be the Archean graphites and carbonaceous slates where the naked organic molecules were burnt to carbon and streaked out as a black smudge in marble or slate (Table 9–1). The thick carbonaceous, coal-like beds of Huronian age in the Canadian and Scandinavian shields offer more definite evidence of early life. Tyler and Barghoorn (1954) have found primitive plants in the middle Huronian of Ontario. The early Precambrian rocks also yield some slight evidence on the environment in which life originated. This evidence is padded by inferences on mode of origin of the earth and on the physiochemical conditions that would follow such an origin. The interpretation of this evidence, sketchy and uncertain as it is, gives a picture of early Precambrian environment not inconsistent with that demanded by the biochemist for the origin of life.

The picture is of a world that would seem as strange and hostile to us as the surface of the moon, a world without free oxygen in the atmosphere, penetrated by intense ultra-violet radiation from an unshielded sky, with abundant metallic carbides on the surface. In such a world the puddles and streams and oceans must have

TABLE 9–1

EARLY EVIDENCES OF LIFE

Observation	Probable age (years)
1. Possible hydrocarbons from Thomson slate (Knife Lake series) of Minnesota.	(1) 2.0×10^9
2. Algae from chert in Gunflint iron formation, Ontario. (? Middle Huronian.)	(2) 1.5×10^9
3. Calcareous algae from Belt Group (Montana) and other late Precambrian rocks.	(3) .75 to 1.1×10^9
4. Anthracitic coal from upper Huronian black shales in northern Michigan.	(4) 7.0×10^8

been weak solutions of simple organic compounds. Somewhere in this broth, after a long period of preliminary, pre-organic evolution (Oparin, 1938; Blum, 1951; Madison, 1953; Barghoorn, 1957, and many others), things that we would call organisms appeared—some billions of years before the beginning of the Cambrian.

Until the descendants of these first organisms began to build skeletons of sufficient form for recognition of their organization and of sufficient durability for fossilization, they would leave no trace but streaks of carbon. The oldest recognizable fossils, the middle Huronian algae, though of relatively simple structure, are much advanced over the primordial organism. Calcareous algae appeared in abundance in late Precambrian (Algonkian) time, but animal fossils, collected from a few scattered localities, include only questionable specimens of protozoans, jellyfish, "worms", sponges, brachiopods, and arthropods (Figure 9-1). Even if these are correctly identified, they reveal very little of the early evolution of animals, for the simplest of them are organisms more complex than some animals living now.

THE BEGINNING OF THE CAMBRIAN

The obscurity of the fossil record ends rather suddenly at the Precambrian-Cambrian boundry. For example, the late Precambrian rocks of the Belt Mountains, Montana, include a variety of sedimentary rocks deposited in shallow seas and on deltas (Fenton and Fenton, 1957). Masses of calcareous algae occur in some beds, but animal fossils include only "worm" trails and burrows (possibly annelid) and some doubtful brachiopods. Adjacent to these Precambrian rocks are Cambrian deposits, some of them representing comparable environments of deposition, but the lower

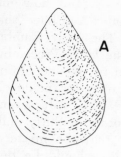

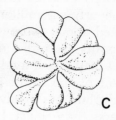

Fig. 9–1. *SOME PRECAMBRIAN FOSSILS.* A) Brachiopod, *Linguella,* from Belt series of Montana. B) *Xenusion,* a possible onychoporan from probable Precambrian of Scandinavia. C) Jellyfish, *Brooksella canyonensis,* from Grand Canyon series, Arizona. (A. After Fenton and Fenton. B. After Heymans. C. After Bassler.)

Cambrian includes fossils representing seven or eight phyla (Table 9–2), highly differentiated and highly organized animals.

TABLE 9–2

LIST OF EARLY CAMBRIAN FOSSILS

(?) Phylum Protozoa	Phylum Arthropoda
Phylum Porifera	Phylum Mollusca
Phylum Coelenterata	(Class Gastropoda)
Phylum Brachiopoda	Phylum Echinodermata

This sudden appearance of fossils has been one of the major mysteries of paleontology and called forth voluminous speculation. One theory states that the late Precambrian rocks are all continental in origin; another that there was little $CaCO_3$ in Precambrian seas; still another that the late Precambrian atmosphere was reducing and inhibited skeleton formation. Unfortunately, these theories and variations on them lack substantiating evidence—indeed the evidence seems to be against them (Raymond, 1935).

Are we left, then, with the benevolent little green men from Mars who taught sponges, corals, brachiopods, snails, trilobites, and echinoderms to build stony houses? If so, they must have repeated their lessons later on to the clams, the cephalopods, the bryozoa, the foraminifera, and the vertebrates.

This absurdity emphasizes one point—that some animal groups had long evolutionary histories before they evolved preservable skeletons. The uniqueness of the Cambrian fauna, then, is in the number of groups that did this simultaneously. But how many lineages actually evolved a skeleton at this time? And how "simultaneously"—a million years or ten million? The early Cambrian lasted about twenty-five million years, and the latest Precambrian deposits are rare and more often represented by an unconformity that may give a total of thirty million years or more for the development of the lower Cambrian fauna. If there were only seven or eight lineages involved over a period in the order of thirty million years, there must be a definite probability that the mystery is simply a coincidence—the order of probability should be determined before one goes to wonderland for new hypotheses. Preston Cloud (1948) argued that although preservation of soft-bodied animals is rare, it is sufficiently frequent to yield some such animals from the Precambrian. He inferred from the lack of such occurrences that all multicellular animals evolved in a short period of time near the end of the Precambrian. He also pointed out that arthropods and brachiopods must have had skeletons very early in their evolution. If this began well back in the Precambrian, these skeletons should have been fossilized.

His conclusions are tentative, and some are questionable. On the other hand, they emphasize the need for further investigation of late Precambrian and earliest Cambrian rocks and their fossil potentialities. They also make clear the importance of study of skeletal evolution and the biochemistry of skeletal formation. Could arthropods evolve their jointed appendages without a rigid external skeleton? What factors of the environment could control the deposition of skeletal material besides the concentration of calcium ions? If a change in the environment released a supply of skeletal material, would this have set off rapid adaptive radiation?

ANCESTORS AND COUSINS: THE PROTOZOA

Although the fossil record is of little help, the early evolution of life can be reconstructed with some certainty from a study of recent organisms. One or more—probably several—lineages passed through the stages of organization represented by the bacteria to that of the Protozoa. This latter group consists of aquatic or parasitic unicellular organisms that lack tissues or organs and exist singly or in colonies. In the simplest members of the group, the structure is differentiated only into cytoplasm and nucleus, but generally the cytoplasm has further differentiated into *organelles* that serve special functions (Figure 9-2).

One class of protozoans, the flagellates, probably includes the ancestors of both plants and animals and, thereby, defies placement in a hierarchic taxonomy unless one makes a separate kingdom for Phylum Protozoa. The remaining classes (Table 9–3) are generally

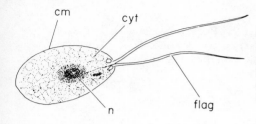

Fig. 9–2. *GENERAL FORM OF THE PROTOZOA.* A relatively simple flagellate protozoan, much enlarged. Abbreviations: *cm.*, cell membrane; *cyt.*, cytoplasm; *flag.*, flagellum; *n.*, nucleus. (After Entz.)

TABLE 9–3

Classification of the Protozoa

Precambrian to Recent. Unicellular animals of various grades of complexity. Some colonial types. Marine, fresh water, parasitic. Benthonic and pelagic.

CLASS FLAGELLATA

(?) Late Cambrian to Recent. Moderate to high complexity in cell. Locomotion by long whiplike threads, the flagella. Marine, fresh water, parasitic. Benthonic and pelagic. Some with skeletons.

Order *Chrysomonadina*

(?) Late Cambrian to Recent. Simple, some amoeboid. One or two flagella. Two groups recognized as fossils, the Silicoflagellidae with a skeleton of siliceous rings and spines and Coccolithidae with a skeleton of tiny calcareous disks. Both groups marine, typically planktonic. Silicoflagellates, Cretaceous to Recent. Coccoliths, Late Cambrian to Recent, common in Cretaceous and Cenozoic rocks.

Order *Dinoflagellata*

Late Jurassic to Recent. Skeleton of cellulose. Marine, planktonic. Other orders of class unknown as fossils.

CLASS SARCODINA

(?) Precambrian, Cambrian to Recent. Amoeboid. Locomotion and food capture by extensions of body, the psuedopodia.

Order *Testacea*

Eocene to Recent. Skeleton of sedimentary particles and siliceous plates. Rare fossils. Fresh water.

Order *Foraminifera*

(?) Cambrian, Ordovician to Recent. Skeleton of chitin, sedimentary particles and/or calcium carbonate. Most species marine. Predominately vagrant benthos but some sessile benthos and planktonic. Includes approximately fifty families.

Order *Radiolaria*

(?) Precambrian, Cambrian to Recent. Skeleton is lattice work of silica; typically spherical symmetry. Marine, most planktonic.

Four other orders of class not certainly known as fossils.

CLASS SPOROZOA

Parasitic; unknown as fossils.

CLASS SUCTORIA

Complex protozoans, sessile adults somewhat resemble coelenterate polyp. Unknown as fossils.

CLASS CILIATA

Jurassic to Recent. Complex protozoans. Locomotion by many short hairlike processes, the cilia. One family, the Tintinnidae, have gelatinous or chitinoid skeleton and incorporate mineral grains in skeleton. Tintinnidae typically planktonic marine forms; some fresh water.

---

considered more animal-like, and, on this ground, the phylum is usually placed in the animal kingdom. Considered from the protozoan viewpoint, the evolution of a multicellular organization is merely one of several possible advances in organizational complexity; the other possibilities are represented within the flagellates and in the remaining classes (Figure 9-3). These more complex protozoans have organelles, some of which function as muscles and others as nerves. Indeed, some have an equivalent of an intestinal tract and a highly developed sensory system of tactile bristles and complex photoreceptors. The diversity of organization within the Protozoa as well as apparent affinities of some Protozoa to plants has lead some zoologists and paleontologists to recognize a Kingdom Protista. The use of this concept in the *Treatise on Inverte-*

brate Paleontology has resulted in a vigorous controversy. As an old guard conservative, I retain the phylum Protozoa with the recognition that it is not strictly the same kind of group as the other animal phyla.

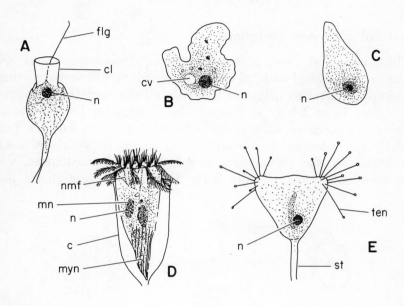

Fig. 9–3. *VARIETIES OF PROTOZOA. A)* Class Flagellata. Attached flagellate with collar (*cl*) about base of flagellum. *B)* Class Sarcodina. Amoeboid cell with lobate pseudopods and contractile vacuole (*cv*) to dispose of excess water. *C)* Class Sporozoa. *D)* Class Ciliata. Attached ciliated with cilia modified into bristles about upper end of protozoan. Quite complex with case (*c*), muscular fibrils (*myn*), micronuclei (*mn*), and neuromuscular fibrils (*nmf*). *E)* Class Suctoria. Attached protozoan with long slender tentacles (*ten*). Abbreviations: *c*, case; *cl*, collar; *cv*, contractile vacuole; *flg*, flagellum; *mn*, micronucleus; *myn*, muscular fibrils; *n*, nucleus; *nmf*, neuro-muscular fibrils; *st*, stalk; *ten*, tentacle. (*A.* After Lapage. *B.* and *C.* After Hyman, *The Invertebrates.* Copyright, McGraw-Hill, New York. Used with permission. *D.* After Campbell. *E.* After Kent.)

Protozoans belong almost entirely to a microworld, the fairyland that Leeuwenhoek found with his primitive lenses, and are as varied within that world as the megascopic inhabitants of a coral reef or a jungle. Among their various adaptations have been resistant skeletons of calcium carbonate and silica. Groups bearing these skeletons have, alone among the multiplicity of protozoans, been preserved as fossils, and tell what little is known directly of the history of this antique group.

THE FORAMINIFERA

Structural plan and variations

The commonest fossil protozoans, the Foraminifera, stand low in the organizational scale of the phylum—more differentiated than the simplest flagellates, less so than the ciliates and the advanced flagellates. They have, of course, the fundamental elements of nucleus (sometimes several nuclei) and cytoplasm but are particularly characterized by irregular body shape, by slender thread-like extensions, the *pseudopods,* that branch and anastomose, and by a skeleton or *test* (Figure 9-4). The bulk of protoplasm lies

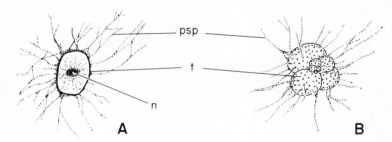

Fig. 9–4. *MORPHOLOGY OF THE FORAMINIFERA. A) Gromia. B) Globigerina.* (See glossary for abbreviations.) *(A. After Hyman, The Invertebrates.* Copyright, McGraw-Hill, New York. Used with permission. *B. After Jepps.)*

GLOSSARY FOR THE FORAMINIFERA

(Numbers in parentheses refer to figure illustrating structure.)

Agglutinated. Test composed of grains of foreign material—sand, sponge spicules, etc.—cemented together. (9–5A; 9–6B, C.)

Apertural face (ap. f). Flattened surface of chamber adjacent to aperture. (9–6F, G; 9–7F, G.)

Aperture (ap). Relatively large opening to exterior in last-formed chamber. (9–6F, G; 9–7F, G.)

Biserial. Test with two rows of chambers. Chambers alternate on either side of the plane between the rows. (9–6D; 9–7C.)

Cell membrane (cm).   Indistinct layer forming periphery of an animal cell. (9–2, 9–3, 9–4.)

Chamber (ch).   The space within the test as well as the enclosing walls. Test may be divided into several chambers separated by partitions. (9–6G, *et al.*)

Cilia.   Numerous short, hair-like processes on surface of cell. Occur in many animals besides protozoans. (9–3D.)

Convolute.   Coiled test in which inner portion of the last whorl extends to the center of the spiral and covers the inner whorls. (9–5C; 9–6G; 9–7A, B, G.)

Costae (cos).   Ridges on external surface of test. They may run along sutures or be transverse to them. (9–7B.)

Cytoplasm (cyt).   Semi-fluid, living portion of cell surrounding the nucleus. (9–2, 9–3, 9–4.)

Flagellum (flag).   Long, slender, whip-like process extending from cell. (9–2, 9–3A.)

Foramina.   Opening connecting adjacent chambers in test. Typically formed as aperture(s) and enclosed by development of additional chambers.

Fusiform.   Spindle-shaped. (9–6J.)

Involute.   Coiled test in which inner portion of last whorl extends to cover part of the adjacent inner whorl. (9–5B.)

Keel (keel).   Keel-like ridge along outer margin of the test. (9–7B.)

Megalospheric.   Test with relatively large initial chamber. Constructed by individual formed from asexual division of parent. (9–8.)

Microspheric.   Test with relatively small initial chamber. Constructed by individual formed from sexual union of two cells. (9–8.)

Nucleus (n).   Dense body suspended in interior of living cell. Bears most of hereditary material and controls most of cellular activity. (9–2, 9–3, 9–4.)

Perforate.   Test with many small openings in chamber walls. (9–7D, E.)

Periphery (per).   Outer margin of coiled test. (9–6G, *et al.*)

Planispiral.   Coiled test with whorls of coil in single plane. (9–6G; 9–7A, B, G.)

Proloculum (prl).   Initial chamber of test. Typically at small end of series or at center of coil. (9–6C, *et al.*)

Pseudopod (psp).   Lobate or thread-like extension of cell periphery that changes in shape, character, and position with activity of cell. (9–4A, B.)

Punctae (pun).   Small to large holes in external walls of chambers. (9–7D, E.)

Spiral suture (sp. sut).   Line of contact between whorls in coiled test. (9–6F.)

Suture (sut).   Line of contact between adjacent chambers of test. (9–6G, *et al.*)

Tentacle (ten).   Slender arm-like extension of cell periphery of variable length and shape like a pseudopod but of fixed position. (9–3E.)

Test (t).   Skeleton of protozoan. Also refers to skeleton of some other kinds of animals. (9–4A, B, *et al.*)

Trochoid.   Coiled test in which whorls form a spiral on the surface of a cone. (9–6F, H; 9–7D, F.)

Uniserial.   Test in which chambers form a single linear or curved series. (9–6C; 9–7E.)

Umbilical plug (umb. p).   Deposit of skeletal material in axis of coiled test. (9–7A, B.)

Umbilicus (umb).   Depression in axis of coiled test. (9–6G.)

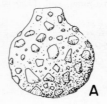 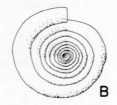 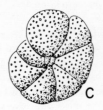

Fig. 9–5. *CHARACTERISTICS OF THE FORAMINIFER TEST.* A) *Saccammina sphaerica;* Recent; magnification about 8 times. Test comprises grains of sand cemented together (agglutinated) and a chitinous base. Form globular; single chamber. B) *Cornuspira involvens;* Recent; magnification about 20 times. Test of calcium carbonate, imperforate, spirally coiled; single chamber. C) *Anomalina grosserugosa;* Recent; magnification about 25 times. Test of calcium carbonate, perforate, spirally coiled; many chambers. (After Brady.)

within the chamber or chambers of the test, but some extends through openings to form a layer over the exterior.

On this basic plan of the Foraminifera has evolved a diversity of species with variation in test composition, structure, and form—variation that can be correlated in part with variation in ecology. Tests are composed either of chitin (thought to be the most primitive type), of foreign particles such as sand grains cemented together, *agglutinated,* or of calcite (Figure 9-5). The microstructure of the calcareous test may be either *granular* or *crystalline,* and, if crystalline, the crystal axes may be ordered or more or less at random. The form of the shell varies in size and over-all shape; in number, shape, and arrangement of the *chambers;* in openings in the test (the *aperture* and *pores*); and in characteristics of the test surface (Figures 9-6, 9-7).

Form and function

The foraminifer uses its pseudopods for locomotion and to capture other microorganisms for food. The food particles are engulfed and digested within the cytoplasm. Oxygen for metabolism diffuses directly through the cell periphery, and carbon dioxide and other metabolic wastes diffuse back into the surrounding water. Some organelles are present; their significance is little understood; but they may function in digestion, food storage, or excretion. The animal as-a-whole perceives changes in light intensity and in the physiochemistry of the water and responds with a limited behavior

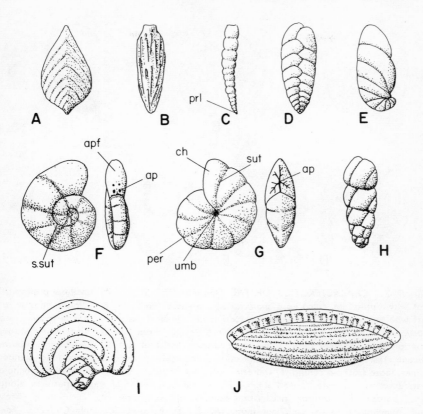

Fig. 9–6. *CHARACTERISTICS OF THE FORAMINIFER TEST.* A) *Frondicularia gold-fussi;* Cretaceous; magnified 8 times. Calcareous test; single row of chambers (uniserial), each of inverted v-shape. B) *Technitella legumen;* Recent; magnified 50 times. Aggluti-nated test (of sponge spicules and sand); single chamber. C) *Nodosinella glennensis;* Pennsylvanian; magnified 40 times. Agglutinated (of fine sand); uniserial. D) *Bolivina incrassata;* Cretaceous; magnified 50 times. Two rows of chambers (biserial); test cal-careous and finely perforate. E) *Polymorphinoides spiralis;* Pleistocene; magnified 35 times. Test calcareous; coiled in immature portion but straight in mature. F) *Entzia tetrastomella;* Recent. Coiled on surface of cone (trochoid) but cone very flat; chitinous test. G) *Dendritina arbuscula;* Miocene. Tightly coiled in a single plane (planispiral) so that outer coil covers inner ones (involute); test calcareous, imperforate; aperture dendritic. H) *Turrilina andreaei;* Oligocene; magnified 40 times. Coiled on elongate cone; test calcareous, finely perforate. I) *Pavonina flabelliformis;* Recent; magnified 40 times. Biserial in early stages, uniserial in later; fan-shaped calcareous test. J) *Schwag-erina huecoensis;* Permian; magnified 5 times. Coiled, fusiform; septa between chambers folded. Abbreviations: *ap,* aperture; *ap. f,* apertural face; *ch,* chamber; *keel,* keel; *per,* periphery; *prl,* proloculum; *sp. sut,* spiral suture; *sut,* suture; *umb,* umbilicus. (A. After Cushman, *Foraminifera.* Copyright, Harvard University Press, Cambridge. Used with per-mission. B. After Norman. C. After Cushman and Waters. D. After Cushman. E. After Cushman and Hanzawa. F. After Daday. G. After d'Orbigny. H. After Andreae. I. After Parr. J. After Dunbar and Skinner.)

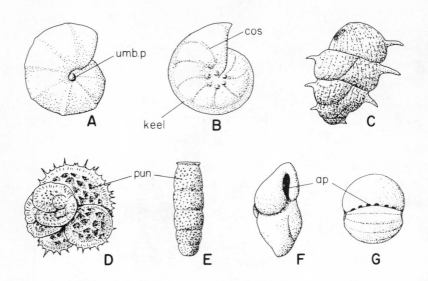

Fig. 9–7. *CHARACTERISTICS OF THE FORAMINIFER TEST. A)* Involute planispiral test with "plug" of calcareous material in umbilicus (umb. p). *B)* Involute planispiral test with raised radial ribs or costae (cos) a narrow keel (keel) on the periphery, and bosses at inner ends of costae. *C) Mimosina;* Recent; magnified 50 times. Later stages biserial; each chamber bears spine; a calcareous, vesicular test. *D) Globigerina triloba;* Recent. Test calcareous; surface cancellated, coarsely perforate, bears long slender spines; loose trochoid coiling. *E)* Uniserial, coarsely perforate (punctuate) test. *F)* Trochoid test; aperture elongate vertical slit. *G)* Planispiral test; series of small apertures along inner border of apertural face. Abbreviations: *ap,* aperture; *cos,* costa; *keel,* keel; *pun,* punctum; *umb. p,* umbilical plug. (A., B., E., F., and G., after Cushman, *Foraminifera.* Copyright, Harvard University Press, Cambridge. Used with permission. C. After Millett. D. After Rumbler.)

pattern. Apparently, there are no specialized parts for perception and coordination.

The specialization for reproduction and development in the Foraminifera consists primarily of provision for alternate sexual and asexual generations. The sexual and asexual individuals are distinct morphologically; those produced by fusion of sex cells have a small initial chamber, the *proloculus*, and those resulting from asexual division have a large proloculus. The individuals with a small proloculus (a *microspheric* test) become multinucleate by continued division of the nucleus without corresponding cell division. The adult microspheric form then divides into many daughter cells, each with a single nucleus. These begin formation of a test with a large proloculus (a *megalospheric* test) before leaving the parent cell (Figure 9-8). The megalospheric individuals remain uninucleate until maturity. After reorganization of the nuclear material, the sex cells are formed; each cell pairs with a similar cell from another megalospheric individual; the cells fuse; and the new individual begins formation of a microspheric test. Microspheric tests are typically much larger than the megalospheric. The different forms of the sexual and asexual generations have caused paleontologists to mistake them for different species, but careful comparison based on study of the entire development through both generations prevents or reduces such errors.

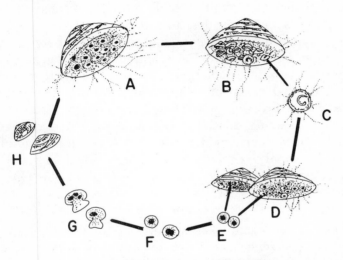

Fig. 9–8. *ALTERNATION OF GENERATIONS IN FORAMINIFERA.* The recent genus *Patellina.* A) A microspheric individual in process of reproduction. Nucleus has divided repeatedly. B) Each nucleus serves as center for development of new foraminifers, each forming its own shell. C) The juvenile foraminifer formed by asexual division of parent. The test has a large initial chamber, is therefore megalospheric. D) The adult megalospheric individual produces a large number of gametes by division of nucleus and cytoplasm. E) Gametes escape and cells from different adults pair. F) Paired gametes fuse to produce new individuals. G) New foraminifers begin to form test with small initial chamber (microspheric). H) Individuals continue growth to adult size. (After Myers.)

Ecology and paleoecology

Most foraminifer species seem sensitive to minor environmental differences, particularly of salinity, temperature, and substrate. A few recent types occur in brackish or hypersaline waters, but none is known from fresh water. An abundant and varied foraminifer fossil assemblage presumably indicates marine water of normal salinity—at least no exceptions have yet been shown. Some aberrant assemblages have been interpreted as brackish water faunas.

Foraminifer species with calcareous tests are most common at present in warmer waters, e.g., near the ocean's surface or in the tropics. This phenomena probably is related to the lesser solubility of $CaCO_3$ in warm water, and fossil faunas with a high percentage of calcareous forms were probably warm-water faunas. Modern tropical faunas also include a large proportion of large Foraminifera with diameters between five and twenty millimeters—this is also a useful measure of fossil environments. Cold water faunas contain a high proportion of species that build a test from siliceous particles (quartz grains, sponge spicules, and so on).

Recent foraminifer faunas show high correlation between generic distribution and temperature. For example, on the Pacific coast several different generic associations can be distinguished, each related to a distinct range of temperature. Because temperature of the water varies inversely with depth, the generic associations are also characteristic of depth zones, although these change with latitude. Cenozoic faunas which contain a high proportion of living genera can be analyzed in terms of these associations and an estimate made of temperature and depth (Table 9–4). One would

TABLE 9–4

CONTROL OF FORAMINIFER ASSEMBLAGES BY TEMPERATURE, CENOZOIC, WEST COAST OF NORTH AMERICA
(Information from Natland, 1957)

Association I.   Lagoonal. 0–20 feet; 24°–5°C.
  Rotalia beccarii, Buliminella elegantissima, Trochammina inflata.
Association II.   Inner sublittoral. 0–125 feet; 21°–13°C.
  Elphidium poeyanum, E. articulatum, E. hannai, Eponides frigidus.
Association III.   Inner sublittoral to upper bathyal; 125–900 feet; 13°–8.5°C.
  Cassidulina limbata, C. tortuosa, C. californica Eponides repandus, Polymorphina charlottensis.
Association IV.   Upper bathyal. 900–2000 feet. 8.5°–5°C.
  Uvigerina peregrina, Epistominella pacifica, Bolivina argentea, B. interjuncta, B. spissa.
Association V.   Lower bathyal. 2000–4000 feet, 5°–3°C.
  Buliminella subacuminata, Uvigerina pygmea.
Association VI.   Lower bathyal to upper abyssal. 4000–7500 feet; 3°–2°C.
  Buliminella rostrata, Nonion pompilioides, Pullenia bulloides, Uvigerina senticosa.

expect the accuracy of these estimates to decrease in progressively older faunas.

The Foraminifera are both benthonic and planktonic—the latter usually have globose, inflated tests (Figure 9-9). The benthonic foraminifers, which crawl along the bottom on their pseudopods, are limited by substrate, light, physiochemistry of the water, and food supply as well as by temperature. Analysis of fossil foraminiferal assemblages shows associations of genera with sedimentary types, but it is difficult to be certain whether this is a direct response to the sediment composing the substrate, or is, rather, the indirect result of a common response of animals and sediment to variation in another factor such as depth.

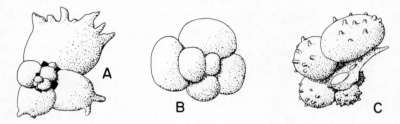

Fig. 9–9. *PELAGIC FORAMINIFERA. A) Globigerinoides sacculifera; Recent. B) Globigerina bulloides; Recent. C) Hastigerina pelagica; Recent. All three magnified about 40 times. Note inflated, loosely packed chambers characteristic of this pelagic group. (A. and C. After Brady. B. After d'Orbigny.)*

Adaptation, evolution, and classification

Although there is clearly some relationship between the foraminifer's morphology and environment, the adaptive significance of most of the test characteristics is unknown. Because of the difficulty of distinguishing adaptive similarities from conservative features inherited from a common ancestry, specialists on the Foraminifera disagree on the phylogenetic relationships of the various lineages (some fifty families are recognized). The consensus holds that the chitinous forms are the most primitive; that the agglutinated tests represent the next evolutionary step, and that the calcareous tests evolved from the agglutinated by an increase in the proportion of calcareous cement to the proportion of foreign particles. Most of the earliest foraminifers had agglutinated tests—some with a chitinous lining—and calcareous types did not become common until the Devonian. The ontogeny of some foraminifers suggests a similar evolutionary pattern; the first chambers of the test are agglutinated; subsequent chambers have an increasing calcite component, and the last chambers are entirely calcareous.

It seems likely that a number of groups evolved calcareous tests independently of one another; at least this is suggested by the occurrence of similar shell forms in agglutinated and calcareous genera. The inferred phylogeny (and classification) depends, therefore, on the relative weight given composition as against form. The interpretation of test form itself is heavily weighted by the pattern of development. In some phyletic lines, individuals of the later species retain in their ontogeny the adult characteristics of the ancestral species. Development has been accelerated so that these adult features appear in the immature foraminifer, and new characteristics are added in subsequent stages. In other lines, however, development was retarded, and the characteristics of the immature preserved in the adult. In these lineages, the adults of the later species resemble the immature of the earlier. These interpretations of phylogeny from development are made with the recognition that morphologic features may shift back and forth in time of development; that the early stages are adaptive as well as the later, and that new features may appear by alteration of developmental patterns which obscure developmental similarities (see p. 155).

Stratigraphic significance

Although the phylogeny of the Foraminifera as a whole has not yet been firmly established, the group is of great importance in stratigraphy. Many of the genera and species have short stratigraphic ranges, and the sequence of species, and in some cases genera, in an evolutionary lineage is well established. On the other hand, the sensitivity of foraminifers to environment changes and the extensive knowledge of the ecology of recent genera provide a delicate tool for the interpretation of past environments. Since foraminifers are one of the few groups of fossils common and identifiable in well cuttings, they have attracted intensive study, perhaps more than any other fossils. In some sedimentary sequences, such as the late Paleozoic of the Midcontinent area, foraminifers are the principal zonal fossils, and correlation of both surface outcrops and subsurface units rests on analysis of extensive foraminifer assemblages (Figure 9-10.

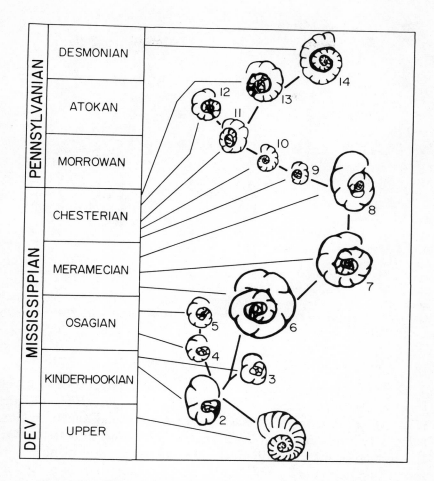

Fig. 9–10. *STRATIGRAPHIC SEQUENCE OF THE FORAMINIFER PLECTOGYRA.* The sequence of *Plectogyra* from the ancestral, late Devonian, *Endothyra* (1) through the Mississippian to the middle Pennsylvanian (14) as shown by more or less "typical" specimens for each stratigraphic level. (After Zeller, 1950.)

Geologic record of the protozoa

The remaining groups of protozoans are less significant to the geologist, but some, the Radiolaria, the Silicoflagellata, the Coccolithophoridae, the Dinoflagellata, and the Tintinnidae, are sufficiently common as fossils to require mention here (see also Figure 9-11).

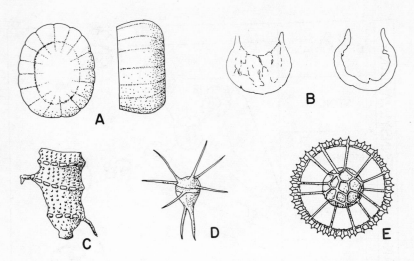

Fig. 9–11. *FOSSIL PROTOZOANS.* A) Coccolithophorid *Calyptrolithus;* Miocene. B) Tintinnid *Calpionella;* Jurassic; sections; enlarged approximately 300 times. C) Dinoflagellate *Wetzelodinium;* Oligocene. D) Dinoflagellate *Raphidodinium;* Cretaceous. E) Radiolarian *Rhodosphaera;* Devonian. (A. After Kamptner. B., C., and D. After Deflandre. E. After Rüst.)

AN ORGANIZATION OF CELLS: THE PHYLUM PORIFERA

Among the recent flagellate protozoans are colonial species which form a gelatinous mass including numerous individuals (Figure 9-12). Typically, these masses are spheroidal, and the individual cells "face" outward with their flagella projecting into the water. In many species, the individual cells in a mass are all alike and form, therefore, a colony of nearly independent protozoans. Among other species, however, the cells are somewhat differentiated; those near the "anterior" pole serve vegetative functions, i.e., locomotion, food-getting, respiration, and so forth, and those near the "posterior" pole are specialized for reproduction. In addition, the beat of flagella is coordinated throughout the colony.

The organization of this colonial form exemplifies quite a different evolutionary trend than that in most protozoans. Rather than organizing within the cell numerous specialized structures, different cells are adapted to different functions and are organized with respect to one another in a definite way. This trend should result in a colony of many different kinds of cells, and an even more com-

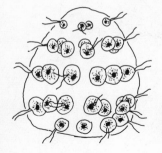

Fig. 9–12. *COLONIAL PROTOZOAN.* The colonial flagellate *Pleodorin.* Note difference in cell size at upper and lower poles. (After Merton.)

plex colonial organization to take advantage of their different specializations. One could, in fact, predict the existence of the phylum Porifera from characteristics of the colonial Protozoa.

General character and mode of life

Any discussion of the Porifera, that is the sponges, must begin with a series of negatives; no other animal group evolved from this phylum, and the individual sponge is neither a real individual nor a colony. The body is roughly globular or sac-like, and most have an internal skeleton of one sort or another. Some sponges show radial symmetry—usually quite imperfect, but many have irregular form that varies greatly among individuals of the same species. Three distinct types of cells are recognized in the sponges. These are organized about a network of canals, the flattened *epithelial cells* covering the external surface of the individual (or the colony as you please), the flagellate *collar cells* lining the canals, and *amoeboid cells* wandering through the gelatinous material between canals (Figure 9-13).

The beat of the flagella of the collar cells maintains a current through canals where food particles are removed by adhesion to the collar. The amoeboid cells serve as jacks-of-all-trades in digesting food, in passing it from cell to cell, in constructing the skeleton, and in forming the epithelial and sex cells. Each cell is responsible for respiration and excretion much as are the single protozoan cells. The skeleton itself is composed either of *spicules* (Figure 9-13), consisting of a set of spines radiating from a point with an organic axis and inorganic walls (calcite of opaline silica), or of organic

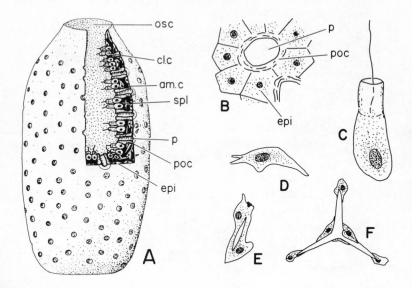

Fig. 9–13. *MORPHOLOGY OF THE PORIFERA.* A) General body form, diagrammatic with section cut out of body wall. B) View of body surface much enlarged. C) Collar cell. D) Amoeboid cell. E) and F) Amoeboid cells constructing spicules. (E. and F. After Woodland.)

GLOSSARY FOR PORIFERA

Amoeboid cell (am. c). Cell with irregular and changing shape. Characterized by lobose pseudopods which may be extended from body surface. Lies between epidermal and collar cells in body well. (9–13A, D, E. F.)

Canal. Tube leading from external pore to cloaca and serving for water flow. May lead into small chambers.

Cloaca. Central cavity of individual sponge into which pores and/or canals empty and which opens externally through the osculum. (9–13A; 9–15A, B, C.)

Collar cell (cl. c). Cell with a distinct tubular collar about the base of a long, slender whip-like extension, the flagellum. Collar cells line inner surface of canals and/or cloaca. (9–13A, C.)

Desma. Spicule of irregular form bearing knotty growths. (9–14D.)

Epidermal cell (epi). Brick-like cell on external surface of sponge. (9–13A, B.)

Monaxon. Spicule with single axis of growth. May be curved or straight and may bear expansions at one or both ends. (9–15E; 9–14A, D.)

Osculum (osc). Large opening from internal cavity of sponge to exterior. Serves for outward (excurrent) flow of water. (9–13A; 9–15A, B, C.)

Polyaxon. Spicule which has several rays diverging from a point.

Pores (p). Numerous small openings from exterior of sponge into canal or cloaca. Serve for inward (incurrent) flow of water. (9–13A, B; 9–15A, B, C.)

Porocyte (poc). Cell which surrounds each pore. Expansion or contraction serves to open or close pore. (9–13A, B.)

Spicule (spl). Skeletal element of sponge. Typically small needle-like rod or fused cluster of such rods.

Tetraxon. Spicule having four axes of development. (9–14B.)

Triaxon. Spicule having three axes of development. (9–14C.)

---

fibers called *spongin.* The fertilized eggs develop into free-swimming ovoid larvae; * after a brief period, they settle to the bottom. Some attach to rocks, plants, and shells; others rest directly on the substrate anchored by their flattened shape or root-like spicules. Once attached or anchored, they remain fixed as sessile benthos. Small pieces broken from the individual (and/or colony) will regenerate a new individual, and some form irregular colonies by some such asexual process.

Ancestry

Almost certainly the sponges evolved from flagellate protozoans. Unlike adult sponges, the larva has simple flagellate cells and lacks collar cells. This may be a primitive characteristic, a recapitulation of evolutionary history, or it may be a larval specialization. If the former interpretation is correct, the sponges developed from some unknown, primitive flagellate; if the latter, the ancestry of the sponge lies in the group of flagellates that is characterized by collar cells.

The Porifera themselves represent one of the two (or more) shoots from the protozoan stock that lead to multicellular animals (Metazoa)—or, if I can switch metaphors, they are one of the railway lines leading from the protozoan terminus. They failed, however, to be more than a narrow-gage branch line along which ran an evolutionary local. Why was this the local? The slick answer would be that the structural plan and its realized and potential variation lacked the necessary stuff to go further than an organization of canals and spicules. But that isn't very satisfactory as an answer. Fossils probably will never be found to supply the solution —still speculation is interesting.

---

* The development of the larval sponge parallels, in a general way, that of the coral described on p. 24, although differing in important details (Hyman, 1940). The mode of development is a primary reason for considering the "sponge" an individual and not a colony.

Trends in adaptation

Canal system. Regardless of sponge ancestry, the subsequent evolution was an elaboration of the structural plan of canals, collar cells, epithelial cells, and amoeboid cells. The simplest sponge structure consists of a simple tube, closed and attached at the base; open at the other end, and pierced by many minute pores (Figure 9-14). The inner surface of the tube is lined by collar cells; the outer by epithelial cells. The beat of the flagella forces water out the open end of the tube, and fresh water flows in through the

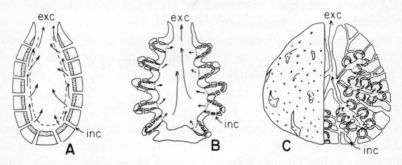

Fig. 9–14. *TYPES OF CANAL SYSTEMS IN THE PORIFERA.* Location of collar cells indicated by stippling. A) Simple type; collar cells line entire surface of cloaca. B) More complex system. Pores open into side canals and these in turn into the cloaca. Collar cells limited to lining of canals. C) Highly complex system. Pores open through small canals into circular chambers lined by collar cells. Chambers empty into canals leading ultimately to osculum. Abbreviations: *exc,* excurrent; *inc,* incurrent.

pores. The food-getting, respiratory, and excretory functions depend on flow of water through this system. The rate of flow is a product of the current flow about the sponge and the current induced by the flagella. Any structural modification which increases the efficiency of the internal "pump" would increase the ability of the animal to survive in different external currents. For reasons related to the size of the flagella and to their beat, they are most efficient in small chambers; evolution, therefore, consists of subdivision of the tube into small bore canals (Figure 9-14B), and the development of an elaborate system of chambers in these canals (Figure 9-14C).

General form. As one might expect, the secondary evolutionary trends are adjustments to the external current and to the sediment carried by that current. The over-all form of the sponge (Figure 9-15) varies with the current character—species with low, encrusting

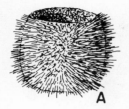 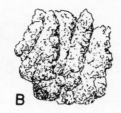 

Fig. 9–15. *VARIATION IN SPONGE FORM.* A) Bowl-shaped with long, slender spicules on external surface. B) Massive, irregular form. C) Slender, tubular sponges.

form grow in turbulent water; species with erect form in calm water. Within a species, the form of "individuals" also varies in response to environmental differences. If the current is constant in direction, the incurrent openings are on the current side; the excurrent openings on the lee side of the sponge. The sponge form is also adapted to sedimentation—which clogs the pores and openings—by erect or elevated form that carries the body above the zone of maximum sedimentary movement and by reduction of sediment collecting surfaces.

Skeleton. The different species of sponges are also adapted to turbulence and to support of the canal system through elaborate skeletal structures. The spicules take various forms as *monaxons, tetraxons, triaxons,* and *polyaxons,* and these, in turn, are woven into rigid skeletons (Figure 9-16). The siliceous and calcareous sponges are more common in cold waters; those with spongin skeletons predominate in tropical and semitropical seas. The adaptive significance of spicule composition is not clear, although the deep water sponges have siliceous skeletons that are less soluble at low temperatures than calcite.

Paleoecology

The sensitivity of sponges to current and sediment load makes them fairly good indicators of fossil environments. At present, they (as most animal groups) are most abundant in shallow waters although some are characteristically deep water. The phylum is predominately marine, but some genera occur in fresh waters. Most modern sponges inhabit relatively quite clear waters, but some Paleozoic types apparently thrived in muddy environments. A few environmental analyses based on sponge adaptations have been made and some efforts to associate particular species with par-

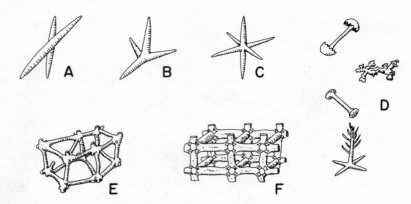

Fig. 9–16. *SPONGE SPICULES A)* Monaxons. *B)* Tetraxon. *C)* Triaxon. *D)* Variety of modified spicules. *E)* and *F)* Spicules fused in tight latticework.

ticular environments of deposition (for summary, see Table 9–5, also Okulitch and Nelson, 1957; de Laubenfels, 1957). As I will report in most of the succeeding chapters, much remains to be done in this field.

TABLE 9-5

PALEOECOLOGY OF SPONGES

Taxonomic group	Paleozoic occurrences (Okulitch and Nelson, 1957)	Post-Paleozoic occurrence (Laubenfels, 1957 a, b)
Calcispongea	Permian reef associations —warm, turbulent, low turbidity environments.	Low turbidity, normal marine salinity, depths less than 100 m.
Hyalospongea		Recent species deep, cold waters, 1000 + m.
Demospongia	Inhabited wide range of environments — turbid to clear. Devonian *Hindia* particularly associated with shaly beds.	Most recent genera occur at moderate depth, 10-300 m., require water of normal salinity, low turbidity.
Archaeocyatha	Reef formers. Probably limited to low turbidity, shallow water environments.	

Classification and distribution in time

Since most sponges that build rigid skeletons (the kind preserved as identifiable fossils) are relatively advanced types, the study of fossil sponges helps little in determining the relationships of the major groups of sponges; the study of recent sponges helps no more. Three classes (Table 9–6) are recognized on the basis of

TABLE 9-6

CLASSIFICATION OF THE PORIFERA

Precambrian to Recent. Multicellular units. Cells not organized into tissues, but three distinct types of cell present. Canal system. Skeleton of calcite, silica, or spongin. Radial symmetry or asymmetric. Marine or fresh water; sessile benthonic.

CLASS CALCISPONGEA

Devonian to Recent. Skeleton formed of spicules of calcium carbonate. Canal system simple to complex.

CLASS HYALOSPONGEA

Cambrian to Recent. Skeleton formed of siliceous spicules of triaxon type.

CLASS DEMOSPONGIA

(?) Precambrian, Cambrian to Recent. Skeleton of siliceous spicules or fibers of spongin. Spicules monaxial or tetraxial.

Simple fossil types with some spongelike features. May represent distinct phyla.

CLASS ARCHAEOCYATHA

Early and middle Cambrian. Skeleton of closely united calcareous spicules. Cup or cone shaped with outer and inner wall. Walls perforate. Sessile benthos, probably all marine.

CLASS RECEPTACULITIDA

Ordovician to Devonian. Skeleton discoid, of closely joined calcareous spicules arranged in double spiral. Sessile benthos, probably all marine.

spicule composition and structure, the Calcispongia with calcareous spicules, the Hyalospongea with siliceous spicules of triaxon type, and the Demospongia with siliceous or spongin spicules, not triaxons. Sponge spicules, probably of a Demospongia, have been reported from the Precambrian. The Cambrian, Ordovician, and Silurian sponges all had siliceous skeletons, but in Devonian time some species with calcareous spicules appeared (Figure 9-17). Since both siliceous and calcareous sponges are locally abundant, some species and genera with short geologic ranges serve as guide fossils. Although isolated spicules are common microfossils, they have been little used because of the variety of types that can be found in a single sponge.

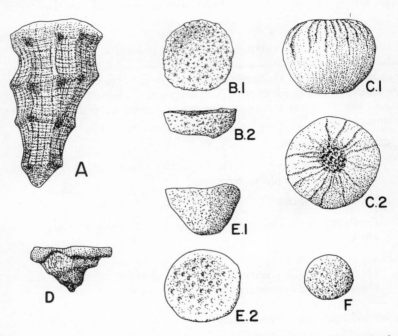

Fig. 9–17. *SOME FOSSIL SPONGES.* Specimens A and B are Hyalospongia; the remainder are Demospongae. A) *Hydnoceras;* Devonian to Mississippian; length 13.5 cm. B) *Astraeospongia;* Silurian to Devonian; diameter 5.9 cm. B.1) top, B.2) side view. C) *Astylospongia;* Ordovician to Silurian; diameter 3.0 cm. C.1) side view; C.2) top. D) *Hyalotragos;* Jurassic; side view; height 3.2 cm. E) *Palaeomanon;* Silurian; diameter 3.1 cm. E.1) side view; E. 2) top view. F) *Microspongia;* Ordovician to Permian; diameter 1.1 cm.

COUSINS OR IN-LAWS?

Several groups of fossils show no clear affinities to any of the recognized phyla. Some have very simple skeletons; others have relatively complex ones, but their general and/or detailed form structure differs sharply from that known in other groups. In none of these fossil scraps-and-tag-ends does the skeleton give sufficient information about the organization of soft parts to help much in identification. Some of them may represent distinct and now extinct phyla, and others may be atypical branches from the known phyla. Paleontologists customarily arrange these as appendices to the recognized phyla on the basis of real or fancied resemblances or on their apparent level of organization. Those with simplest form are usually placed among the sponges or coelenterates.

The Archaeocyatha

One of these, the Archaeocyatha, comprises about sixty-five genera from lower and middle Cambrian rocks. They are somewhat like a coral in form (Figure 9-18), rather cone or cup shaped, and are calcareous. Most consist of two cones, one inside of the other, with various types of plates between. Typically, the walls of the cones and the plates are perforated. The skeleton is radially symmetrical about the axis of the cones. The soft anatomy is entirely unknown. Though they resemble corals superficially, they are quite different in detail. They have a few sponge characteristics, but lack the typical spicules, and the arrangement of cones and plates is unlike the skeleton of the typical sponges. Okulitch, in the *Treatise on Invertebrate Paleontology* (1955), classifies them as a separate phylum; others have placed them among the coelenterates and even as algae or protozoa. If their assignment to a separate phylum is correct, they presumably represent an independent shoot from the Protozoa or from one of the primitive metazoan (many-celled animals) stocks.

The archaeocyathids are useful guide fossils in Cambrian rocks.

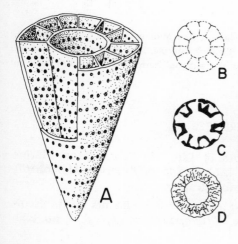

Fig. 9–18. *ARCHAEOCYATHIDS.* A) Diagrammatic view of archeocyathid. Note double wall with radial plates (parieties) in space (intervallum) between inner and outer walls. Note also pores in walls and parieties. B) *Archaeocyathellus;* Early Cambrian; cross section; diameter 8 mm. C) *Ajacicyathus;* Early Cambrian; cross section; diameter 5 mm. D) *Archaeocyathus;* Early Cambrian cross section. diameter 2.5 cm. (B. After Bedford and Bedford. C. and D. After Okulitch.)

Apparently they were world wide in the early Cambrian but restricted to Eurasia by middle Cambrian. They occur in some abundance in some calcareous beds.

The Receptaculitids

The fossils placed in the family Receptaculidae are somewhat more sponge-like. They are ovid or discoid and formed of closely joined calcareous spicules. The spicules are perpendicular to the external surface and are typically arranged in a pattern of double spirals (Figure 9-19). The wall formed by the spicules encloses a central cavity. No pores or canals have been surely identified. The absence of these and the peculiar structure and arrangement of spicules distinguishes the receptaculids from the typical sponges.

Only ten genera are known at present, all from Ordovician, Silurian, and Devonian rocks, but several, particularly *Receptaculites* and *Ischadites* are common fossils.

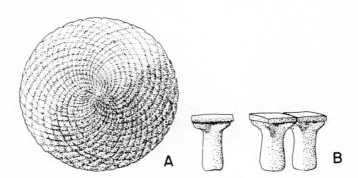

Fig. 9–19. *THE RECEPTACULIDAE. A) Receptaculites, Middle Ordovician to Devonian, view from above, diameter 4.5 cm. B) Individual "spicules" of Receptaculites; lateral views. The rectangular plates which form the external surface of the fossil rest on circular pillars.*

REFERENCES

Barghoorn, E. S. 1957. "The Origin of Life," in "Treatise on Marine Ecology and Paleoecology," vol. 2, *Geol. Soc. of America, Memoir 67,* pp. 75-86. A review paper with bibliography.

Bradshaw, J. S. 1955. "Preliminary Laboratory Experiments on the Ecology of Foraminiferal Populations," *Micropaleontology,* vol. 1, pp. 359-

364. This and the following paper are examples of recent work in a neglected field.

————. 1957. "Laboratory Studies on the Rate of Growth of the Foraminifer, *Streblus beccarii* (Linné) var. *Tepida* (Cushman)," *Jour. of Paleontology,* vol. 31, pp. 1138-1147.

Blum, H. F. 1951. *Time's Arrow and Evolution.* Princeton, N. J.: Princeton University Press. A discussion of evolution from the biochemical viewpoint with a section on the origin of life.

Cloud, P. E. 1948. "Some Problems and Patterns of Evolution Exemplified by Fossil Invertebrates," *Evolution,* vol. 2, pp. 322-350. A consideration of a number of evolutionary phenomena among the invertebrates including a discussion of the sudden appearance of Cambrian fossils.

Cushman, J. A. 1948. *Foraminifera,* 4th ed. Cambridge, Mass.: Harvard University Press. One of the standard texts on this subject.

Laubenfels, L. W. de. 1957a. "Sponges of the Post-Paleozoic" (annotated bibliography), in: "Treatise on Marine Ecology and Paleocology," vol. 2, *Geol. Soc. of America, Memoir 67,* pp. 771-772.

————. 1957b. "Marine Sponges (annotated bibliography)," in: "Treatise on Marine Ecology and Paleocology," vol. 1, *Geol. Soc. America, Memoir 67,* pp. 1083-1086.

Fenton, C. L. and M. A. Fenton. 1957. "Paleoecology of the Precambrian of Northwestern North America," in: "Treatise on Marine Ecology and Paleoecology," vol. 2 *Geol. Soc. America, Memoir 67,* pp. 103-116.

Flower, R. H. 1956. "Some Paradoxes in Taxonomy with Reference to the Protista," *Jour. of Paleontology,* vol. 30, pp. 700-706. One viewpoint on the place of the protozoans in the classification of organisms.

Galloway, J. J. 1933. *A Manual of Foraminifera.* Bloomington, Ind.: Principia Press.

Glaessner, M. F. 1947. *Principles of Micropaleontology.* New York: Wiley. A good general text on microfossils with much material on foraminifers.

————. 1955. "Taxonomic, Stratigraphic and Ecologic Studies of Foraminifera, and their Interrelations," *Micropaleontology,* vol. 1, pp. 3-8.

Hyman, L. H. 1940. *The Invertebrates,* vol. 1, *Protozoa through Ctenophora.* New York: McGraw-Hill. Principally on recent members of three phyla—Protozoa, Porifera, and Coelenterata.

Jones, D. J. 1956. *Introduction to Microfossils.* New York: Harper. A profusely illustrated text on all types of microfossils.

Madison, K. M. 1953. "The Organism and Its Origin," *Evolution,* vol. 7, pp. 211-227.

Moore, R. C. 1953. *Treatise on Invertebrate Paleontology.* New York: Geol. Soc. of America. Parts B, C, and D on Protozoa; D published and

C on press at time of writing. Part E on Porifera and Archaeocyatha published.

————. 1954. "Kingdom of Organisms Named Protista," *Jour. of Paleontology*, vol. 28, pp. 588-598. Argument for the protistans as a kingdom coordinate with plants and animals.

Myers, E. H. 1936. "The Life-Cycle of *Spirillina Vivipara Ehrenberg*, with Notes on Morphogenesis, Systematics, and Distribution of the Foraminifera," *Jour. Roy. Micr. Society*, vol. 56, pp. 120-146. A fundamental contribution on foraminiferal biology.

Natland, M. L. 1957. "Paleoecology at West Coast Tertiary Sediments," in: "Treatise on Marine Ecology and Paleoecology," vol. 2, *Geol. Soc. of America, Memoir 67*, pp. 543-572.

Okulitch. V. J. and S. J. Nelson. 1957. "Sponges of the Paleozoic" (annotated bibliography), in: "Treatise on Marine Ecology and Paleocology," vol. 2, *Geol. Soc. of America, Memoir 67*, pp. 763-770.

Oparin, A. J. 1938. *The Origin of Life* (Transl. by S. Morgulis), New York: Macmillan. A pioneer study of the biochemical problems in the origin of life.

Rankama, K. 1948. "New Evidence of the Origin of Pre-Cambrian Carbon," *Geol. Soc. of America Bulletin*, vol. 46, pp. 375-392. The possible organic origin of carbon in some Precambrian rocks.

Raymond, P. E. 1935. "Precambrian Life," *Geol. Soc. of America, Bulletin*, vol. 46, pp. 375-392. A review of Precambrian fossils and pseudo-fossils.

Swain, F. M., A. Blumentals, and N. Prokopovich. 1958. "Bituminous and Other Organic Substances in Precambrian of Minnesota," *Amer. Assoc. of Petr. Geologists, Bulletin*, vol. 42, pp. 173-189.

Tyler, S. A., E. S. Barghoorn, and L. P. Barrett. 1957. "Anthracitic Coal from Precambrian Upper Huronian Black Shale of the Iron River District, Northern Michigan," *Geol. Soc. of America, Bulletin*, vol. 68, pp. 1293-1304.

Tyler, S. A. and E. S. Barghoorn. 1954. "Occurrence of Structurally Preserved Plants in Pre-Cambrian Rocks of the Canadian Shield," *Science*, vol. 119, pp. 606-608.

Weller, J. M. 1955. "Protista: Non-plants, Non-animals?" *Jour. of Paleontology*, vol. 29, pp. 707-710. An argument against the Protista as a separate organic kingdom.

Zeller, E. J. 1950. "Stratigraphic Significance of Mississippian Endothyroid Foraminifera," *Univ. Kansas Paleon. Contributions*, Art. 4, pp. 1-23.

See also Hedgpeth and Ladd, 1957, in reference list for Chapter 4 and general references for invertebrates in Chapter 3.

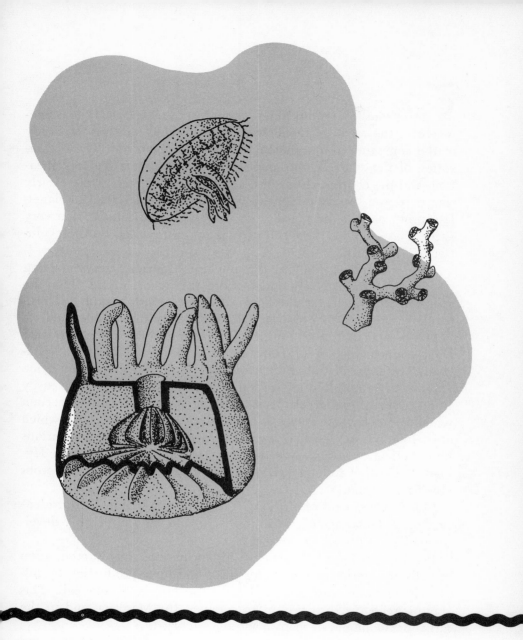

10. *The* **JELLYFISH** *and the* **CORAL**

$\mathcal{T}$he origins of multicellular animals (the Metazoa) lie somewhere in the murk of the Precambrian, lighted only by the study of the comparative morphology of modern organisms. The organization of the sponges, the mode of development of that organization, and the characteristics of constituent cells demonstrate clearly that poriferan lineage either evolved independently from the flagellate protozoans or diverged from the other multicellular line very early. The sponges, then, can give us no information on the evolutionary "mainline."

With a single exception, the phylum Mesozoa, the remaining multicellular animals are much more highly organized than the sponges and much more difficult to connect with a primeval protozoan colony. The Mesozoa, although structurally intermediate between unicellular and multicellular animals, may have regressed from a more complex organization as a result of parasitic adaptations. The larva of the multicellular phyla presumably retain some features of primitive organization, but these features are not easily distinguished from larval specializations. Nor can anyone be certain which are embryonic stages of the primitive organization and which are adult features pushed back into development. Of the various hypothetical evolutionary sequences, the one (modified from Hyman, 1940) that follows (also Figure 10-1) seems at least as probable as any other:

(1) Development of a colony consisting of a hollow ball of identical cells. This stage occurs in protistan colonies and in early development of multicellular animals.

(2) Adaptation of the colony for locomotion by differentiation of cells at anterior and posterior poles and for reproduction by migration of undifferentiated cells into the hollow of the ball. This stage is recognized in protozoan colonies, the Mesozoa, and in the larval development of many (not all) Metazoa.

(3) Some of the cells in the interior, freed from locomotor and food-getting requirements, specialize for food digestion and for circulation of digested food from cell to cell in the colony. Some colonial protozoans and the larva of many Metazoa are at this level of organization.

The third stage in this sequence is about that attained independently (probably) by the sponges. The next most primitive

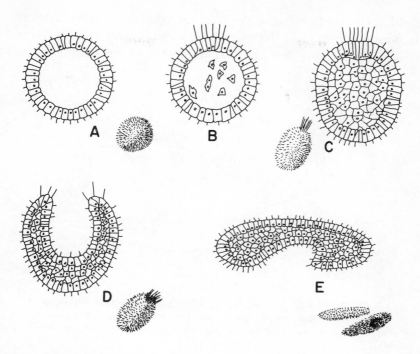

Fig. 10–1. *ORIGIN OF THE METAZOA.* *A)* Spherical colonial protozoan, vertical section and external view. Individual cells are nearly identical, and each bears slender hair-like cilia. *B)* Primitive metazoan; vertical section. Cells at one pole differentiated; ameboid sex cells within hollow sphere. *C)* Primitive metazoan; vertical section and external view. Cells at one pole highly differentiated; cells in interior serve digestive and reproductive functions. *D)* Vertical section and lateral view of proto-coelenterate. A blind gut is formed by the infolding of one side of sphere. The lining of this gut forms a new cell layer concerned with absorption and digestion. The polarity of this figure is reversed with respect to B and C; aboral end corresponds to upper pole of C with specialized sensory and locomotor cells. *E)* Vertical section and dorsal and ventral views of proto-flatworm. Blind gut formed by infolding on ventral surface. Polarity of this animal with respect to C is uncertain.

Metazoa, the coelenterates and flat worms, elaborate this structure by the formation of a primitive gut which brings food into direct contact with the digestive cells, by further differentiation and specialization of cells for special functions, and by formation of a medial cell layer, the *mesoglea* between the external, *epidermal,* and the internal, *gastrodermal* layers. The difference in the development of these elaborations in the coelenterate larva as compared with the other Metazoa larva suggests the coelenterates evolved most, if not all, of these features independently. This divergence may be the result of an early adaptive radiation, the coelenterate stock adapting to a free-swimming life with emphasis on polarity in a globular form, and the other to a creeping bottom-life with flattening of the body and bilateral symmetry as well as polarity (Figure 10-2).

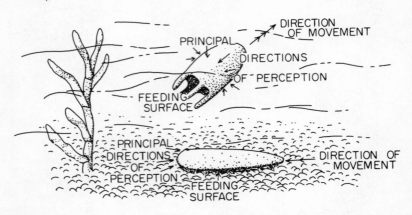

Fig. 10–2. *ORIGIN OF THE METAZOA.* The proto-coelenterate is shown as a jellyfish. An active swimmer, it had polarity and radial symmetry. The proto-flatworm lived on the bottom and was flattened so that the symmetry was reduced from radial to bilateral.

AN ALTERNATIVE METAZOAN ORGANIZATION

Regardless of the evolution of the Metazoa and speculation on that evolution, coelenterate radiation has a basic structural plan, a communal substrate in animals as diverse as jellyfish and corals. This plan stands out in both adult organization and larval development (Figure 10-3).

This structural plan encompasses *radial symmetry* about an axis between the *mouth* (oral pole) and *base* (aboral pole). The body possesses a central cavity, the *coelenteron,* that develops either within the larva or by invagination of the "hollow ball" stage (Figure 2-5 and p. 24). The cavity opens to the surface at the mouth but ends blindly at the aboral end. The mouth is surrounded by *tentacles* (possibly the primitive number is four). Food is grasped by the tentacles, passed through the mouth into the coelenteron, and partly digested there before absorption. Respiration and excretion occur by diffusion from the individual cells.

The body wall consists of two distinct and specialized layers, the *epidermis* and *gastrodermis,* conjoined by a middle layer,

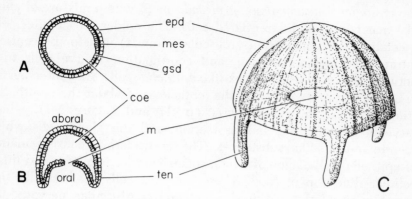

Fig. 10–3. *BASIC COELENTERATE PLAN.* All coelenterates show in development or in adult form a mouth, a central cavity (coelenteron), three layers of the body wall (epidermis, mesodermis or mesoglea, and gastrodermis) and also radially arranged tentacles. *A)* Transverse section at right angles to oral-aboral axis. *B)* Longitudinal section parallel to oral-aboral axis. *C)* Perspective drawing. The primitive form may have been less jellyfish-like; but to produce a polyp from this medusoid, one needs only to invert the drawing.

GLOSSARY FOR COELENTERATA

Coelenteron (coe). Spacious cavity, enclosed by body wall of coelenterate and opening externally through mouth. (2–1E, B; 10–3A, B, C; 10–14A.)

Epidermis (epd). External layer of cells in body wall. Typically the cells are brick-like in form if they are not interconnected to form continuous multinucleat sheet. (2–3A, B; 10–3A, B, C.)

Gastrodermis (gsd). Layer of cells lining body cavity. Forms the inner layer of the body wall. (2–3A, B; 10–3A, B.)

Medusoid. Type of coelenterate of free-living, jellyfish form. Inverted bowl-like form with mouth and tentacles downward. (10–3A, B, C; 10–4.)

Mesentary (ms). One of several radial sheets of soft tissue that partition the internal body cavity. (2–1B, E; 10–14A.)

Mesoglea, mesenchyme, or mesoderm (mes). Layer of cells and gelatinous connective material between inner and outer layers of body wall. (2–3A, B; 10–3A, B.)

Mouth (m). External opening of body cavity. Serves in coelenterates for discharge of indigestible material as well as intake of food. (10–3B, C; 10–14A.)

Polyp. Type of coelenterate of hydra-like form. Columnar body with base attached to bottom and with tentacles and mouth directed upward. (10–4; 10–14A.)

Tentacles (ten). Arm-like extensions around mouth that serve primarily for food-getting. (2–1A, B; 10–14A.)

the *mesoglea* (*mesenchyme* or *mesoderm*),* with a mixture of jelly-like matrix and undifferentiated cells. The epidermis includes cells specialized for contraction (muscular strands) and for perception, intracellular communication, and coordination (nerve cells in a network), as well as the brick-like *epithelial* cells. Also interspersed in epidermis, particularly on the tentacles and about the mouth, are stinging cells, the *nematocysts* (p. 17 and Figure 2-3), which serve in food getting and protection, and the gland cells which secrete mucous-like substances. The gastrodermis consists mainly of epithelial cells, some of which specialized for ingestion and intra-cellular digestion of food. These nutritive cells bear flagella that maintain circulation within the coelenteron. Muscular, nervous, and mucous gland cells also occur in the gastrodermis. Other gland cells produce enzymes that initiate digestion before the food particles are ingested by the nutritive cells.

THE ADAPTIVE RADIATION OF THE COELENTERATES

The abundance and variety of coelenterates from the early and middle Cambrian indicate a long period of radial evolution, extending well down into the Precambrian. The phylum displays a fundamental trichotomy † based on reproductive and developmental adaptations (Table 10–1, Figure 10-4). The primitive coelenterate stock may have consisted of simple jellyfish-like *medusoid* forms, with larvae that spent some time attached to the bottom before they developed into a free-swimming adult. These larvae possessed or evolved powers of asexual reproduction—the initial larval individual budding into a colony whose members then continued development of medusoid stage.‡

---

* Not all zoologists agree that this middle layer is comparable to the mesoderm of other metazoa and prefer the noncommittal term, *mesoglea.*

† Two obscure fossil groups are considered by some paleontologists to constitute two additional classes. One of these has assigned to it a jellyfish-like fossil from the Precambrian Grand Canyon Series. Since little is known of their anatomy and their mode of reproduction and since they are very rare, I have omitted them from this discussion.

Some authorities classify the "comb-jellies," the *ctenophores,* in the Phylum Coelenterata; others place them in a phylum of their own. When ranged in the coelenterates, they are recognized as a separate subphylum, and the three classes described here are grouped in the subphylum Cnidaria. No fossil ctenophores are known certainly.

‡ A number of zoologists believe that the proto-coelenterate was a sessile benthonic species and that the medusoid form evolved later. All of these phylogenies are speculative and may be regarded as an intellectual game, but are useful also to organize the discussion of morphology and ecology.

TABLE 10-1

CLASSIFICATION OF THE COELENTERATA

(Based on the *Treatise on Invertebrate Paleontology*, Part F.)

Precambrian to Recent. Cells organized into tissues but not into distinct organs. Central digestive cavity with single opening. No head. Radial or biradial symmetry. Many have calcareous or horny skeleton. All aquatic; marine and fresh water; sessile benthos and pelagic, either planktonic or nektonic.

CLASS PROTOMEDUSAE

Precambrian to Ordovician and possibly Silurian and Pennsylvanian. Subellipsoidal bodies with lobate radial segments. Some appear to have tentacles. Probably marine pelagic.

CLASS DIPLEUROZOA

Lower Devonian. Biradial, discoid. Many radial segments. Marginal tentacles.

CLASS HYDROZOA

Cambrian to Recent. Radial symmetry. Most species have both medusoid and polypoid stages. Coelenteron not partitioned; mesoglea gelatinous, noncellular. Solitary or colonial; mostly marine; pelagic and sessile benthonic.

Order *Stromatoporoidea*

Cambrian to Cretaceous. Colonial; colony comprising calcareous lamellae and vertical pillars. Sessile benthonic; reef builders.

Order *Trachylinida*

Late Jurassic to Recent, possible Cambrian fossils. Medusoid; polypoid stage reduced or absent. Predominately pelagic.

Order *Hydroida*

Cambrian to Recent. Polypoid well developed, colonial or solitary. Marine and fresh water; pelagic and sessile benthonic.

Order *Spongiomorphida*

Triassic to Jurassic. Colonial. Massive calcareous skeleton with horizontal plates and vertical pillars; pillars may be grouped to form vertical tubules. Probably marine; sessile benthonic.

Order *Milleporina*

Late Cretaceous to Recent. Polypoid colony with massive to encrusting calcareous skeleton with pores through which polyps protude. Medusoid generation reduced. Marine, predominately sessile benthos.

Order *Stylasterina*

Late Cretaceous to Recent. Massive to encrusting skeletons with pores for polyps. Non-medusoid. Marine, sessile benthos.

Order *Siphonophorida*

Ordovician to Recent. Colonial. Polyps and medusae attached to stem or disk. Supported by swimming bell or float. Marine; pelagic. Rare as fossils.

CLASS SCYPHOZOA

Cambrian to Recent. Solitary. Coelenteron divided in some by mesentaries. Radial symmetry. Polyp much reduced, highly modified or lost. Mesoglea cellular. Entirely marine, predominately pelagic.

Subclass *Scyphomedusae*

Late Jurassic to Recent. True jellyfish. Marine, predominately pelagic. Rare as fossils.

Subclass *Conulata*

Middle Cambrian to early Triassic. Skeleton of chitin and calcium phosphate; form, elongate pyramidal. Attached by apex of pyramid or free. Traces of tentacles preserved as well as evidence of tentacular muscle attachments. Probably marine, sessile or planktonic.

CLASS ANTHOZOA

Middle Ordovician to Recent. Biradial or bilateral symmetry. Medusoid stage never present. Coelenteron partitioned by mesentaries. Marine; sessile or sluggish vagrant benthonic.

Subclass *Ceriantipatharia*

Miocene to Recent. Colonial or solitary. Mesentaries unpaired with weak musculature; new mesentaries develop in dorsal intermesenteric space. May have skeleton of horny material. Very rare as fossils.

Subclass *Octocorallia*

Permian to Recent. Eight tentacles and mesentaries. Skeleton of horny or calcareous spicules, separate or closely united. Position of polyp in colony marked by pit, but not divided by radial septa.

Subclass *Zoantharia*

Ordovician to Recent. Mesentaries paired and coupled, typically in cycles of six, six pairs in initial set.

Order *Rugosa*

Ordovician to Permian. Solitary or colonial. Calcareous skeleton with calcareous wall, the epitheca, septa, and typically, tabulae and dissepiments. Six primary septa, others develop in ventrolateral and lateral spaces but none in dorsolateral. Sessile benthos. Some, particularly colonial types, important as reef builders.

Order *Heterocorallia*

Carboniferous. Solitary. Four primary septa split in two near periphery, and additional septa develop between the split portions. Epitheca may be reduced or absent. Edges of tabulae may be inflected to replace epitheca.

Order *Scleractinia*

Middle Triassic to Recent. Solitary or colonial. Calcareous skeleton with epitheca, septa, tabulae, and dissepiments. Six primary septa; others develop in all interseptal spaces. Edge zone of trunk deposits skeletal material on outer surface of skeleton. Some important as reef builders.

Order *Tabulata*

Middle Ordovician to Permian. Colonial. Calcareous skeleton with epitheca and tabulae; septa typically small or absent, most common number, 12. Order of development unknown. Some important reef formers.

(Three other orders not recognized as fossils.)

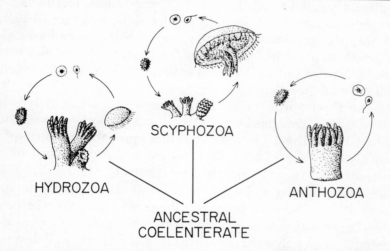

Fig. 10–4. *RADIATION OF THE COELENTERATES.* The relative importance of the attached polypid stage and the free-swimming medusoid stage are shown by the size of drawing. The hydrozoans have a large polyp (often colonial) that produces medusoids by budding. The medusoid stage is relatively insignificant except in production of egg and sperm. The scyphozoans have an insignificant polyp and a large medusoid stage. The anthozoans have lost the medusoid stage, and the polyp itself produces egg and sperm.

The evolution of one class, the *Hydrozoa,* emphasized the elaboration and adaptation of this larval *polypoid* stage so that the medusoid stage became almost an afterthought. The distinctive polyp develops and reaches maturity (of form not sexual maturity) with quite different morphology and adaptations than the medusa. The budding of the medusoid individuals from the polyp (or from specialized polyps in a colony) ordinarily does not end the existence of the polyp, and the larval stage continues to live beside the adult into which it developed. For this reason the polyp and medusa are considered to be separate individuals and the whole cycle, fertilized egg → free-swimming larva → polyp → larval medusoids → adult medusoids → fertilized eggs, is considered an alternation of sexual and asexual generations.

A second class of coelenterates, the *Scyphozoa*, evolved elaborate medusoid adults and a polyp stage highly adapted for asexual budding but with little individuality otherwise. The third class, the *Anthozoa*, lacks a medusoid stage, and the individual animal retains larval characteristics (the polypoid form) to sexual maturity.

Upon this fundamental division are imposed a series of trends, adaptively parallel in all three, but, in some cases, morphologically divergent. These trends include greater differentiation of cells to perform specialized duties, modification of tentacles and area about the mouth to assist in food getting, and subdivision of the coelenteron to increase surface area and to improve circulation of nutrients to all parts of an enlarging body.

Among the Hydrozoa and the Anthozoa, the sessile polyps have evolved a hard skeleton for protection and support in several independent lines. The hydrozoan skeletons, probably because of the relatively small size of the individual polyp and the lack of internal structures that need support, are relatively simple, laminated, vesicular or tubular networks with supporting pillars or spines (Figure 10-7). The anthozoans, on the other hand, average considerably larger and possess an internally divided coelenteron, so the skeleton of each polyp characteristically has distinct, well-developed walls, and many have septa to support the polyp and its internal partitions (Figures 10-10, 10-14).

THE SCYPHOZOA

The true jellyfishes, the *scyphozoans*, are primarily animals of the nekton or plankton where they float or swim by rhythmic contractions of their body. Those incapable of active swimming attach to seaweed for support. They are important and diversified members of the modern marine faunas but, as one would expect, rare as fossils. Four of the five recent orders are known as fossils, plus some genera not easily assigned to those orders. This is a relatively high percentage of preservation for a group lacking an inorganic skeleton, but is based on a very few specimens preserved as carbonized films or as molds and casts of a relatively resistant mesoglea (Figure 10-5).

A small group of Paleozoic and early Mesozoic fossils, the *conularids,* long driven from pillar to post in classification, are currently (Moore and Harrington, 1956) set among the Scyphozoa as a distinct subclass. Typically, they have an elongate, pyramidal skeleton composed of chitin, a chitinophosphatic compound, and calcium phosphate (Figure 10-6). A few specimens show traces of tentacles at the open, lower end of the pyramid, and internal ridges and thickened portions of the shell margin seem to mark attachment of longitudinal and tentacular musculature. Only twenty genera have been described, though a few are fairly common fossils.

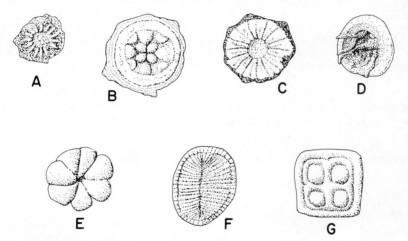

A   B   C   D

E   F   G

Fig. 10–5. *EXAMPLES OF FOSSIL COELENTERATE.* A) *Lorenzinia apenninica;* Eocene; aboral view; 25 mm diameter. B) *Rhizostomites admirandus;* Late Jurassic; oral view; diameter 70 mm. C) *Rhizostomites admirandus;* Late Jurassic; aboral view; diameter 25 cm. D) *Leptobrachites trigonobrachium;* Late Jurassic; oral view; diameter 16 cm. Specimens B through D are from the Solenhofen lithographic limestone. E) *Brooksella alternata;* Middle Cambrian; diameter 25 mm. A jellyfish-like form that may represent a distinct class, Protomedusae. F) *Dickinsonia costata;* Early Cambrian; aboral view; length 50 mm. Another unusual jellyfish placed in a distinct class, Dipleurozoa. Note the strong biradial symmetry. G) *Quadrimedusina quadrata;* Jurassic; aboral view; breadth 70 mm. A scyphozoan. (A. After Gortani. B. After Brandt. C. After Von Ammon. D. After Brandt. E. After Walcott. F. After Sprigg. G. After Haeckel.)

THE HYDROZOA

All five modern hydrozoan orders are known as fossils, and two extinct orders, the *Spongiomorphida* and the *Stromatoporida,* are

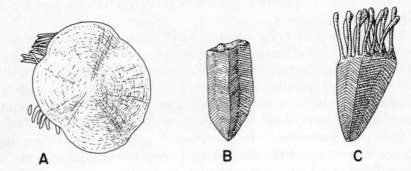

Fig. 10–6. *CONULATA.* A) *Conchopeltis alternata;* Middle Ordivician; aboral view; diameter 50 mm. The ends of the tentacles project from beneath the skeleton along one edge. *Conchopeltis* may have been a free-swimming form. Note biradial symmetry. B) Conularid sp; lateral view; 10 cm. high. C) Reconstruction of conularid showing tentacles. Presumably this type was attached by its base. (A. After photograph by Wells. From *Treatise on Invertebrate Paleontology,* courtesy of Geological Society of America and University of Kansas Press. C. Based on restorations by Kiderlen.)

commonly assigned to this class. The latter order, common only in the early and middle Paleozoic, comprises genera with laminated and vesicular skeletons (Figure 10-7) that might well have been produced by either algae, sponges, bryozoa, or protozoans.

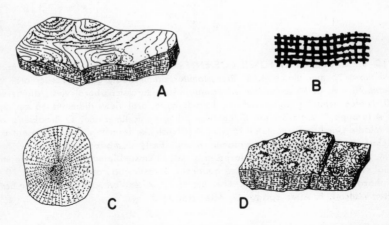

Fig. 10–7. *HYDROZOA.* A) *Actinostroma* sp; Cambrian to Mississippian; oblique view, length 8.5 cm. B) *Actinostroma* sp; thin section; 2.0 mm x 6.9 mm. Vertical elements are *pillars;* the horizontal are *laminae.* C) *Discophyllum;* Middle Ordovician; aboral view; about 7.5 cm in length. D) *Stromatopora;* Ordovician to Permian; oblique view, 5.8 cm long. (C. After Walcott.)

Species of the orders Milleporida and Stylasterida are major components of recent and Cenozoic coral reefs; the stromatoporoid species, of Paleozoic reefs. As such they are important in interpreting the ecology of the reef community. Some fossils of hydrozoan genera are widely distributed and have short geologic ranges; these, of course, serve as guide fossils. Identification is based primarily on variation in microscopic detail as shown in polished or thin section. Because of the relatively simple organization and low grade of developmental integration, the form of hydrozoans (and of the other coelenterates) is quite plastic under different environments of development. The "ecospecies" produced by this plasticity prove valuable environmental indicators—if they are properly distinguished from genetic species.

THE ANTHOZOA

Generalities

The anthozoans are dominant elements of fossil marine assemblage as they are of modern sea floor communities. Of the fifteen or so orders of anthozoans, eleven are known as fossils, and three of these are known only as fossils. The form, the color, the actual existence of many coral reefs depend in large part upon anthozoans, and, although most recent members of the class are warmwater forms, the sea anemones, some solitary corals, and some other anthozoans occur far from the tropics. The variety of anthozoans (and their conspicuous appearance) is demonstrated by their common names, organ pipe coral, soft corals, sea whips, sea fans, blue coral, sea pens, stony corals, thorny corals.

The basic anthozoan plan is much the same as that given in a preceding chapter (p. 15) for a coral. The body is a hollow cylinder, closed below by the *base,* above by the *oral disk* through which the mouth opens, and divided internally by vertical partitions, the *mesentaries.* The oral disk bears one or more circles of tentacles. The body wall consists of two distinct layers, the epidermis and gastrodermis, separated by a mesenchyme containing many undifferentiated cells. A layer of soft tissue connects the polyps in colonial forms. The anthozoans have diverged during evolution in the number and arrangement of tentacles and mesentaries, in the details of mouth structure, in the form and mode of formation of the skeleton, and in symmetry. Unfortunately, paleontologists know little of the adaptive significance of these divergences.

Ceriantipatharia

Of the three anthozoan subclasses, the Ceriantipatharia are least important to paleontologists, for they have so far identified only a single fossil genus, that Miocene in age. The skeleton, in those members of the subclass which possess one, consists of an axial rod of horny material bearing short spines (Figure 10-8). A fleshy layer surrounds the skeleton; from this arise small polyps. Some ceriantipatharians have six mesentaries, apparently a primitive character (see below and Figure 10-8).

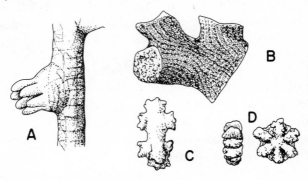

Fig. 10–8. *CERIANTIPATHARIA AND OCTOCORALLA.* A) Polyp of ceriantipatharian, *Antipathella.* Central horny axis shown. B) Octocorallan *Trachypsammia,* fragment of colony; Permian; length 2 cm. C) Octocorallan *Corallium borneense,* spicule; Recent; length 1 mm. D) Octocorallan *Verrucella delicatula,* spicule; Recent; length 0.6 mm. (B., C. and D. After *Treatise on Invertebrate Paleontology.* Courtesy of Geological Society of America and University of Kansas Press.)

Octocoralla

The Octocoralla are distinguished by the possession of eight mesentaries and eight tentacles. Their skeleton consists of calcareous spicules variously arranged in the polyps and in the fleshy layer that connects the polyps in a colony. Some also have a calcified axial structure. The spicules may be closely packed to produce a rigid (and preservable) structure or may be scattered as isolated units in the body wall (Figure 10-8).

Fossil octocorals are relatively rare and include only a few genera. They have not been certainly identified before the Cretaceous, though some doubtful octocorals are known from rocks as old as Silurian. They are important members of recent coral reef associations, and, presumably, played a similar role in the formation of Cenozoic reefs.

Zoantharia

The class *Zoantharia* includes the greatest number of recent and fossil anthozoans—Wells and Hill (1956) record a total of 831 fossil genera. They are distinguished by the number and arrangement of the mesentaries; in addition to the primitive six they have two or more additional pairs. The sea anemones (three orders, Zoanthiniaria, Corallimorpharia, and Actiniaria) lack skeletons, and only a few fossil genera of doubtful affinities have been collected. The other four orders have calcareous skeletons and, of course, were more often fossilized. They are important components of modern and fossil coral reefs, but many also occur in nonreef habitats.

Origins. The arrangement and ontogeny of the mesentaries in recent zoantharians indicate a common ancestry in a species with twelve mesentaries (Figure 10-9). These would include the primitive six found in the ceriantipatharians and in the early development stages of the zoantharians. In the next stage of evolution, a pair of mesentaries occurs in the space between two of the original six. This is the general octocoral plan and occurs also in zoantharian development. For the sake of description, these two new mesentaries are termed the *dorsal;* the pair on the opposite side, the *ventral;* and the pairs between the dorsal and ventral, the *lateral.* In the third stage, two additional mesentaries develop on each side, one between the lateral mesentaries, one between the ventral and the adjacent lateral. This produced six pairs of mesentaries, a *dorsal* pair, a *ventral* pair, two *dorso-lateral* pairs, and two *ventro-lateral* pairs.

This sequence occurs in the development of recent zoantharians and provides a phylogeny that seems to be in general agreement with other morphologic features. In theory, it should be possible to find fossils to test this hypothesis, since skeletal plates, the *septa,* are located between the pairs of mesentaries. Unfortunately, the oldest fossil zoantharians are not much help. The Rugosa apparently had already acquired the basic pattern before they evolved a skeleton in the middle Ordovician. The Tabulata, which appeared at about the same time, have twelve rudimentary septa and very little is known of their pattern of development.

The Rugosa. In the middle Ordovician, Black River strata, ap-

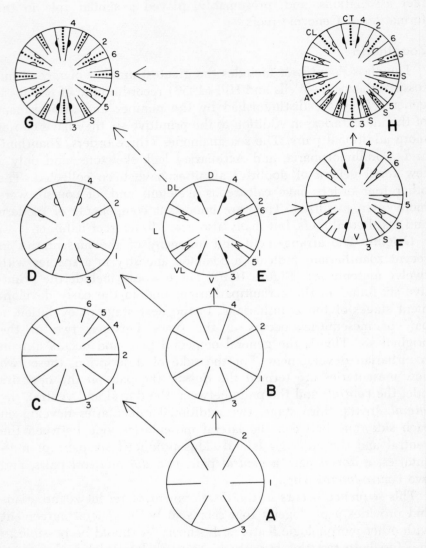

Fig. 10–9. *EVOLUTION OF ANTHOZOAN MESENTARY ARRANGEMENT.* **Cross section of body; body wall and mesentaries shown by solid lines, septa by circles. A)** Anthozoan stem, hypothetical. *B)* Common ancestor of octocorallans and zoantharians, hypothetical. *C)* Ceriantipatharian. *D)* Octocorallan. *E)* Zoantharian stem, hypothetical. *F)* Zoanthinarian. A sea anemone. *G)* Scleractinarian. *H)* Rugosan, reconstructed from septal pattern. Code and abbreviations: *1, 2, 3, 4, 5,* and *6,* primary mesentaries; *A,* alar septum; *C,* cardinal septum; *CL,* counter-lateral septum; *CT,* counter septum; *D,* dorsal; *DL,* dorso-lateral; *L,* lateral; *S,* secondary; *V,* ventral; *VL,* ventro-lateral. (From *Treatise on Invertebrate Paleontology,* courtesy of Geological Society of America and University of Kansas Press.)

pear several genera of corals characterized by a conical calcareous skeleton, a *corallite* (Figure 10-10), comprising a wall, the *epitheca*, septa, and horizontal partitions (*tabulae* and *dissepiments*). Thin sections of the initial part of the skeleton reveal six primary septa that presumably correspond to six pairs of mesentaries. Additional

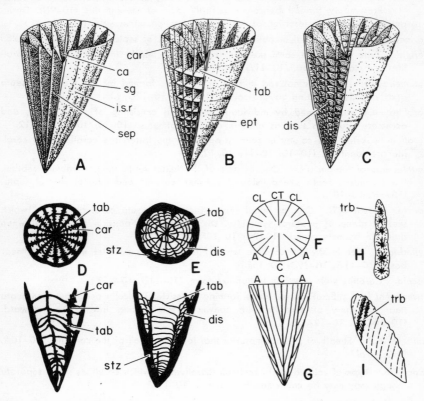

Fig. 10–10. *MORPHOLOGY OF THE RUGOSA. A)* Lateral view, a part of the epitheca and the distal ends of several septa removed. *B)* Lateral view, tabulae shown in open section. *C)* Lateral view, dissepiments shown in open section. *D)* Transverse and longitudinal thin sections. *E)* Transverse and longitudinal thin sections. *E)* Diagrammatic view looking down on calice. *G)* Diagrammatic view from side showing relation of grooves and ridges of cardinal, alar, and secondary septa. *H)* Transverse section of septum. *I)* Longitudinal section of septum.

GLOSSARY FOR RUGOSA
(Numbers following definitions refer to figures which show structure.)

Alar septum (A) One of a pair of the initial septa (protosepta). Located about midway between cardinal and counter septa. Secondary septa may insert pinnately on side away from cardinal. (10–9H; 10–10F, G.)

Axial vortex (ax. v.). Longitudinal structure in axis of corallite formed by twisting together of inner ends of septa. (10–11A.)

Basal disk. Fleshy wall closing off lower (aboral) end of the polyp. (2–1A, B; 10–14A.)

Calice (cal). Upper (oral) end of corallite on which basal disk of polyp rests. Typically bowl-shaped. (10–10A, B, C; 10–11A, B, C.)

Cardinal septum (c). One of initial septa. Lies in plane of bilateral symmetry of corallite. Presumably formed between "ventral" pair of mesenteries (10–9H). Distinguished by pinnate insertion of secondary septa on either side. (10–10F, G.)

Carinae (car). Longitudinal or oblique flanges on sides of septa. (10–10B, D; 10–12E.)

Cerioid. Type of colonial coral skeleton (corallum) in which walls of individual corallites are closely united. (10–11J; 10–12E, G.)

Columella (col). Longitudinal rod in axis of corallite, formed by inner ends of septa and typically projecting up into calice. (10–11B; 10–12G, I.)

Corallite. Skeleton formed by individual polyp and consisting of walls, septa, and accessory structures such as tabulae and dissepiments. (10–10; 10–11; 10–12.)

Corallum. Skeleton of colony or solitary polyp—in the latter, the corallum and corallite are identical. (10–10; 10–11; 10–12.)

Counter lateral septum (CL). One of pair of the initial septa next to counter septum. No secondary septa are developed between counter and counter lateral septa. (10–9H; 10–10F.)

Counter septum (CT). One of initial septa. Directly opposite cardinal septum (which see) in plane of bilateral symmetry. Distinguished by position of cardinal when that can be determined. (10–9H; 10–10F.)

Cylindrical. Nearly straight corallite which has essentially parallel sides except near base. (10–11G; 10–12D; 10–15F.)

Discoid. Corallite with very flat, button-like form. (10–11D; 10–15B.)

Dissepiment (dis). Small curved plate forming a vesicle. Typically occur between septa near periphery of corallite with convex surface facing inward and upward. (10–10C, E; 10–12A, B, E, H.)

Epitheca (ep). Sheath of skeletal material that forms the wall of the corallite. (10–10A, B, C; et al.)

Fasiculate. Type of colonial coral skeleton (corallum) in which corallites stand separate though they may be connected by tubules. (10–11I.)

Fossula (fos). Unusually wide space between septa caused by failure of one or more septa to develop as rapidly as others. Most commonly due to abortion of cardinal septum and therefore a cardinal fossula. (10–11C; 10–12F.)

Interseptal ridge (is. r.). Longitudinal ridge on outer surface of corallite wall. Occurs between position of septa on inner surface. (10–10A.)

Major septum. One of initial or secondary septa. Typically the major septa are of subequal length and extend most of distance from wall to axis.

Minor septum. One of a third cycle of septa formed between the initial and secondary septa and much shorter than they.

Oral disk. Fleshy wall closing off upper end of the cylindrical column that forms the polyp's sides. (10–14A.)

Septum (sep). One of several longitudinal plates arranged radially between axis and wall of corallite. Presumably alternated in position with mesenteries (glossary for

Fig. 10–3) and supported basal disk and lower wall of polyp. (2–1B, D, E; 10–10A, I; 10–14A; et al.)

Septal groove (s. g). Longitudinal groove on outer surface of corallite wall. Corresponds to position of septum on inner surface. (10–10A.)

Stereozone (stz). Zone of dense skeletal deposits—typically along or near wall of corallite. (10–10E; 10–12 A, B, I.)

Tabellae. Small horizontal plates near axis of corallite. In essence, incomplete tabulae.

Tabulae (tab). Transverse partitions in corallite. Either flat or convex upward. May extend from axis to wall or be limited to area near axis. (10–10B, D, E; et al.)

Tabularium. Axial portion of corallite in which tabulae occur (10–10E.)

Theca (wall). Skeletal deposit enclosing corallite and, presumably, sides of polyp. (2–1B, C, D, E; 10–14A.)

Trabeculae (trb). Rod of radiating calcite fibers that forms an element of the coral skeleton. (10–10H, I; 10–14B.)

Trochoid. Corallite with angle of about 40° between sides expanding from apex. (10–11F.)

Turbinate. Corallite with angle of about 70° between sides expanding from apex. (10–11E.)

---

septa developed between the ventral septum, the *cardinal,* and the ventral lateral septa, the *alars;* and between the alar septa and the dorsal lateral, the *counter lateral,* septa. No septa appear between the counter laterals and the dorsal (*counter*). The development of secondary septa in just four of the six interseptal spaces produces a general four-fold symmetry and accounts for a name often used for the order, Tetracoralla. Presumably, the base of the polyp rested on the open end, the *calyx,* of the corallite.

Evolutionary trends (Figures 10-10 and 10-11) within the order include: variation of general shape; modification of the tabulae and dissepiments; reduction of septa so they fail to reach the axis of the coral; complete reduction of one or more of the primary septa, usually the cardinal; appearance of axial rods of one sort or another; development of a *marginal zone* of thickened septa or closely spaced dissepiments; and the derivation of colonial species from solitary types. Unfortunately, little is known of the adaptive significance of these changes.

Rugosans are not common in Ordovician rocks, but become increasingly abundant in Silurian and Devonian. Toward the end of the Paleozoic, they decrease in variety and numbers and are unknown from post-Permian beds. Many genera are important guide fossils; Figure 10-10 gives a few examples.

The ecology of the rugosans has had some attention but, un-

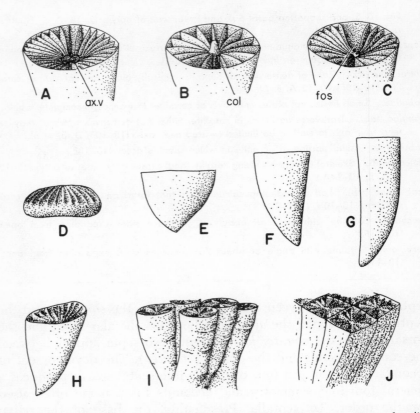

Fig. 10–11. *MODIFICATIONS OF RUGOSAN MORPHOLOGY.* A) View of calice with axial vortex (ax. v). B) view of calice with columella (col). C). View of calice with fossula (fos). D) Discoidal corallite. E) Turbinate corallite. F) Trochoidal corallite. G) Cylindrical corallite. H) Solitary coral, corallite and corallum identical. I) Colonial coral, corallum formed by loosely attached corallites (fasiculate). J) Colonial coral, corallum formed by tightly joined corallites (ceroid). For definitions see glossary for Fig. 10–10. Abbreviations: ax. v, axial vortex; col, columella; fos, fossula.

happily, not enough. They were of course benthonic. The solitary corals had a very small area of attachment and commonly toppled over or sank into the bottom sediments. The growth of a curved or twisted skeleton reflects these minor disasters. The colonial rugosans were supported by their undersurface; very few were attached or encrusting. Few rugosans, either solitary or colony, occurred on the upper part of reefs in the zone of wave action, but they thrived on the reef flanks. Most seem to have lived on shallow bottoms (below wave base) in warm, well oxygenated waters of normal marine salinity. They apparently did best in environments of slow deposition, and, therefore, are more typical of limestone beds than of clastics.

The Rugosa-Scleractinia problem. The Rugosa are unknown after the end of the Permian; the Scleractinia before the beginning of the Triassic. As evidenced by skeletal similarities, the two orders had many similar adaptive trends, and presumably the Rugosa occupied many of the same ecological niches in the Paleozoic benthonic communities that the Scleractinia do in recent ones. Because of this similarity and because of the succession of the two in time, paleontologists have been extremely interested in their relationships. The causes for the extinction of the Rugosa seem to be beyond our reach at present—there is no evidence that competitive Scleractinia appeared until after that extinction. Conversely, though many scleractinians occupied the same ecological position as rugosan genera, there seems to be no very good reason why some Scleractinia could not have evolved before the extinction of the older order—unless the scleractinian radiation (in Middle Triassic and later) was based on a persistent, evolving rugosan line.

Some authorities have argued for independent origin of the Scleractinia from some soft-bodied anthozoa. The common ancestry of the two would then be in the Cambrian or earlier. This view is supported by the existence of skeletonless anthozoans in recent faunas that would be suitable structurally to evolve into scleractinia types, and by the occurrence of the scleractinians that are most different from the rugosans in the earliest Triassic coral assemblages.

The evaluation of coral phylogeny depends largely on the pattern of development of the septa. As already described among the Rugosa (Figure 10-9), the first six septa develop in pairs, cardinal and counter, alar and counter lateral. The remaining major septa develop in cycles of four, one pair between the counter lateral and alar septa on either side, and one pair between the cardinal and alar septa. No major septa appear between the counter lateral and counter septa. The septa of the Scleractinia, on the other hand, develop in cycles of six, and are added in the spaces between all six original septa. Some late Paleozoic rugosan corals, however, have major septa between counter and counter lateral septa, and a few Triassic scleractinian genera develop fewer septa in two adjoining sextants of the original six. These variants from the more typical rugosan and scleractinian pattern bridge part of the mor-

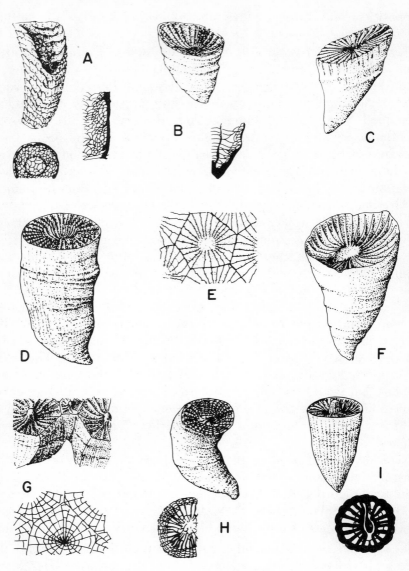

Fig. 10–12. *RUGOSAN CORALS.* A) *Cystiphyllum;* Silurian; lateral view and transverse and longitudinal sections; length 7.8 cm. Septa reduced to low, incomplete ridges
on surface of dissepiments and tabellae. Dissepimentarium wide. B) *Zaphrenthis;* Devonian; oblique view of corallite and longitudinal section; length 2.3 cm. Narrow dissepimentarium appears in calical rim; septa long, in contact in axis, bear carinae near
rim. C) *Aulacophylum;* Early and Middle Devonian; oblique view; length 8 cm. Deep
cardinal fossula; septa between cardinal and alar directed pinnately toward fossula;
others radial; marginal dissepimentarium. D) *Heliophyllum;* Early to Middle Devonian;
oblique view; length 7.6 cm. Fossula indistinct; wide dissepimentarium; carinae. E)

phological gap between orders and suggest evolution of the Scleractinia from a Rugosan source (Figure 10-13). Lower Triassic corals might provide the answer to this problem of phylogeny.

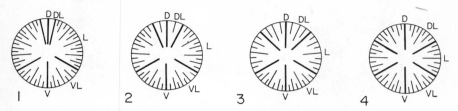

Fig. 10–13. *EVOLUTION OF THE SCLERACTINIA.* The evolutionary sequence postulated by Schindewolf (1950). 1) Rugosan septal plan—no septa in dorso-lateral sextants (DL). 2) Septal arrangement in some late rugosans—short in dorso-lateral sextants. 3) Septal arrangement in some early scleractinians—fewer septa in dorso-lateral sextants than in others. 4) Scleractinian septal plan, full hexagonal symmetry. Abbreviations: *D,* dorsal; *DL,* dorso-lateral; *V,* ventral; *VL,* ventro-lateral.

The Scleractinia. The general plan (Figure 10-14) of the scleractinians, like that of the rugosans, comprises a calcareous cup formed by the epitheca and divided internally by septa and dissepiments. The septa differ from those of the Rugosa in microstructure as well as in arrangement. The shape of the skeletal cup, the *corallum* differs considerably among different scleractinians (Figure 10-15) and is also strongly modified by environmental factors. Most families of the order have evolved colonial genera.

An important feature of scleractinia evolution has been the development of the *edge zone.* This consists of the part of the polyp that lies outside of the wall of the corallum. In some, this is merely a bulge of tissue around the end of the cup, but, in many, folds down over the side of the skeleton. In the latter, the epitheca, which is formed by the lower body wall within the cup, is suppressed and replaced by elements deposited by the edge zone.

Hexagonaria; Devonian, transverse section; width of corallite 1.1 cm. Cerioid; thin carinate septa; tabellae, dissepiments. F) *Amplexizaphrentis;* Mississippian-Pennsylvanian; oblique view; length 3.0 cm. Fossula; tabulae; no dissepiments. G) *Lithiostrotion;* Mississippian; oblique view and transverse section; width of corallite 1.8 cm. Cerioid; columella, tabulae, dissepiments. H) *Bothrophyllum;* Mississippian-Pennsylvanian; oblique view and transverse section; length 6.8 cm. Wide dissepimentarium; narrow fossula; major septa join to produce weak axial structure; septa dilate in tabularium. I) *Lophophyllidium;* Pennsylvanian-Permian; oblique view and transverse section; length 2.7 cm. Columella large; tabulae but no dissepiments. (A. Sections after Lang and Smith. B. Section after Schindewolf.)

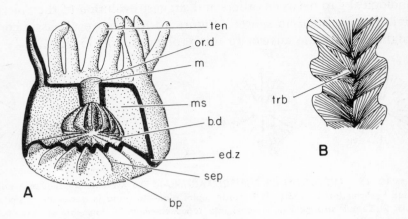

Fig. 10–14. *STRUCTURAL PLAN OF SCLERACTINIA.* A) Diagram of polyp and skeleton. Portion of body wall and mesentaries cut away. B) Transverse section of septum. Abbreviations: *b. d,* basal disk; *b. p,* basal plate; *ed. z,* edge zone; *m,* mouth; *ms,* mesentary; *or. d,* oral disk; *sep,* septum; *ten,* tentacle; *trb,* trabecula.

GLOSSARY FOR SCLERACTINIA

(Numbers following definition indicate figure that shows structure. For definitions not given here see Figures 10–3 and 10–10.)

Basal plate (bp). Skeletal plate formed initially beneath basal disk of polyp. The septa and walls extend up and out from the basal plate. (10–14A.)

Ceratoid. Corallite with angle of about 20° between sides expanding from apex. (10–15E.)

Coenosarc. Layer of soft tissue connecting polyps in a colonial coral.

Coenosteum. Skeletal tissue connecting corallites of a colonial coral. Deposited by coenosarc.

Cupolate. Corallite with flat base and convex oral surface. Rather like a button in shape. (10–15A.)

Edge zone (ed. z). Fold of body wall of polyp that extends laterally and/or downward over sides of corallite. (10–14A.)

Patellate. Corallite with angle of about 120° between sides expanding from apex. (10–15C.)

Since the edge zone extends down and latterly, these deposits broaden the base of the coral and strengthen its attachment to the substrate.

As a consequence of the edge zone and of its equivalent in the colonial types, the continuous layer between polyps, some scleractinia can build massive encrusting skeletons. This may have been a preadaptation to reef building or an adaptation for survival in the

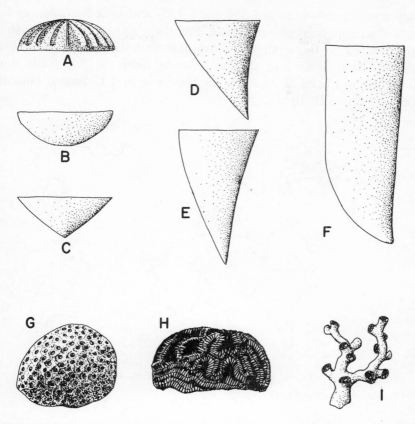

Fig. 10—15. *VARIATION IN SCLERACTINIAN FORM.* A) Cupolate. B) Discoid. C) Patellate. D) Trachoid. E) Ceratoid. F) Cylindrical G) Colonial coral, massive, distinct corallites. H) Colonial coral, massive, corallites in linear series wiah no walls between. I) Colonial coral, branching, distinct corallites. (For definitions see Figures 10—10 and 10—14.)

upper, wave zone of reefs. Regardless of its origin, it permitted expansion of the scleractinians into an environment unavailable to the Rugosa. Recent reef building scleractinians also contain within their soft tissues vast numbers of algae which apparently supply food for the polyps in return for support and protection. This relationship, of advantage to both animal and plant, seems necessary for vigorous growth of the corals and, consequently, of the reef.

The dependence of the modern reef-building corals on algae limits reef formation to shallow, well lighted waters, the zone of photosynthesis. Reef corals are further limited by temperature—

they flourish only between 25° and 29°C—and by circulation of the water to supply oxygen and food. For these reasons, reef growth is now limited to the shallows of tropical and subtropical seas. Presumably they have had similar habitats since the Mesozoic and, therefore, are used as an index to Mesozoic and Cenozoic climatic zones (Figure 10-16).

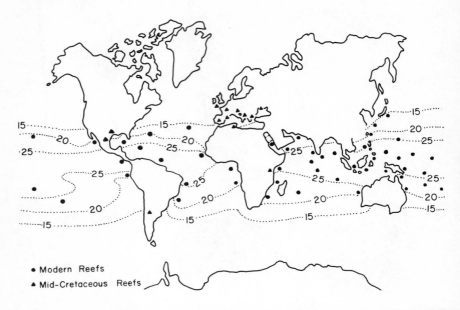

Fig. 10—16. *DISTRIBUTION OF RECENT AND MIDDLE CRETACEOUS CORAL REEFS.* The present mid-winter isotherms are shown by dotted lines. Temperatures are given in degrees centigrade. The distribution of Cretaceous reefs indicates that the 15° and probably the 20° isotherms were further north and south than at present.

The nonreef builders are less strictly limited in distribution, and some survive at temperatures as low as −1.1°C and at depths of 6000 meters. Particular species, of course, have a more limited tolerance of these factors and, in addition, are controlled in their distribution by salinity and particularly by the character of the bottom.

The Tabulata. The tabulates, a large group of Paleozoic corals, have been assigned various positions in coelenterate taxonomy. Their location here as an order among the Zoantharia follows the *Treatise on Invertebrate Paleontology.* The tabulate skeleton (Figure 10-17), consists of a simple tube partitioned by horizontal tab-

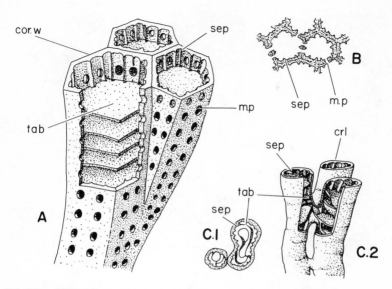

Fig. 10–17. *STRUCTURAL PLAN OF THE TABULATA.* A) Oblique view of *Favosites*, portion of wall of one corallite removed. B) *Transverse* section of *Favosites* corallites. C) *Syringopora.* C.1), transverse section. C.2), oblique view with portions of corallite wall removed. Abbreviations: *cor. w*, corallite wall; *crl*, corallite; *m. p*, mural pore; *sep*, septum; *tab*, tabula.

GLOSSARY FOR TABULATA

(See Figures 10–3 and 10–10 for definitions not given here.)

Corallite wall. Skeletal wall forming sides of corallite and comprising various elements such as edges of septa, epitheca, or accessory deposits.

Mural pore. Circular or oval hole in wall between corallites.

---

ulae. Septa are rudimentary and, in many genera, absent. They are all colonial, the individual tubes being fused or connected by short tubules. In some, the walls of the tubes are perforate, and the adjacent ones connected by *mural pores.*

The tabulates underwent a considerable radiation (over a hundred described genera) and are quite abundant in late Ordovician, Silurian, and Devonian rocks (Figure 10-18). Like the Rugosa the Tabulata had a sinking spell in the late Paleozoic, and only a few genera of doubtful affinities occur in post-Permian beds.

Because of their massive colonial habit, tabulates were important framework builders in some Paleozoic reefs. They also occurred in

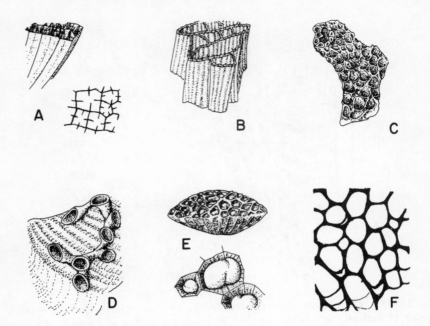

Fig. 10–18. *VARIATION IN THE TABULATA.* A) *Tetradium;* middle-late Ordovician; oblique view and transverse section; width of corallite 2 mm. Prismatic, cerioid; four septa in corallite. B) *Halysites;* Ordovician-Silurian; oblique view; length of corallites 3.7 cm. Corallites united along two sides; long slender tubes joined to form palisade-like structure; palisades interconnected to form network; chain-like in transverse section. C) *Striatopora;* Silurian-Permian; lateral view; length of fragment 3.4 cm. D) *Aulocaulis;* Devonian; lateral view; diameter of calice 2.5 mm. Fasiculate; basal portions of corallites recumbent and cemented to substrate—in this class a brachiopod shell. E) *Pleurodictum;* Early Devonian; lateral view of corallum and vertical view of several corallites; length of corallum 7.5 cm and diameter of largest corallite 7.5 mm. Corallum discoidal; corallites polygonal; tabula, thin blister-like. F) *Chaetes;* Ordovician to Permian; transverse section; diameter of corallite 0.5 mm. (F. from *Treatise on Invertebrate Paleontology,* courtesy of Geological Society of America and University of Kansas Press.)

nonreef habitats, though they apparently thrived only in low turbidity environments. Far too little is known of their paleoecology; some "species" apparently are variants which developed a particular form in a particular environment. The form of the colony and the characteristics of the individual coral both seem responsive to environmental differences.

The Heterocorallia. Two genera of Mississippian corals with an unusual septal plan (Figure 10-19) are set off in a separate order. They are a considerable puzzle to specialists on Paleozoic corals but can be only a terminus for this chapter.

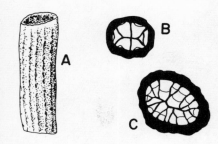

Fig. 10–19. *HETEROCORALLIA. A) Heterophyllia parva;* Mississippian; lateral view; length 2mm. *B) Hexaphyllia mirabilis;* Mississippian; transverse section; diameter 3 mm. *C) Heterophyllia reducta;* Mississippian; transverse section; diameter 5 mm. (After Schindewolf.)

REFERENCES

Bassler, R. S. 1950. "Faunal Lists and Descriptions of Paleozoic Corals," *Geol. Soc. of America, Memoir 44*, pp. 1-315. An extensive review of stratigraphic occurrence and published descriptions.

Busch, D. A. 1941. "An Ontogenetic Study of Some Rugose Corals from the Hamilton of Western New York," *Jour. of Paleontology*, vol. 15, pp. 392-411.

Carruthers, R. G. 1910. "On the Evolution of *Zaphrentis Delanouei* in Lower Carboniferous Times," *Quart. Jour., Geol. Soc. of London*, vol. 66, pp. 523-538. A classical paper on coral evolution.

Goreau, T. F. and V. T. Bowen. 1955. "Calcium Uptake by a Coral," *Science*, vol. 122, pp. 1188-1189.

Hyman, L. H. 1940. See references for Chapter 9. General coverage of biology of coelenterates.

Moore, R. C., ed. 1953. *Treatise on Invertebrate Paleontology.* New York: Geol. Soc. of America. Part F on the coelenterates was published in 1956.

————, and H. J. Harrington. 1956. "Scyphozoa," in: Above book, pp. F27-38.

Oliver, W. A., Jr. 1951. "Middle Devonian Coral Beds of Central New York," *Amer. Jour. of Science*, vol. 249, pp. 705-728. A stratigraphic study.

Schindewolf, O. H. 1950. See references for Chapter 1.

Sloss, L. L. 1939. "Devonian Rugose Corals from the Traverse Beds of Michigan," *Jour. of Paleontology*, vol. 13, pp. 52-73.

Wang, H. C. 1950. "A Revision of the Zoantharia Rugosa in Light of Their Minute Skeletal Structures," *Roy. Soc. of London, Phil. Trans., Ser. B*, vol. 234, pp. 175-246. A study of the microstructure of fossil corals.

Wells, J. W. and D. Hill. 1955. "Zoantharia—General Features," in: Moore, R. C. ed., 1953. See above, pp. F231-232.

See also Hedgpeth and Ladd, 1957, in reference list for Chapter 4 and general references for invertebrates in Chapter 3. Very complete bibliographies are given in Moore, 1953, Part F.

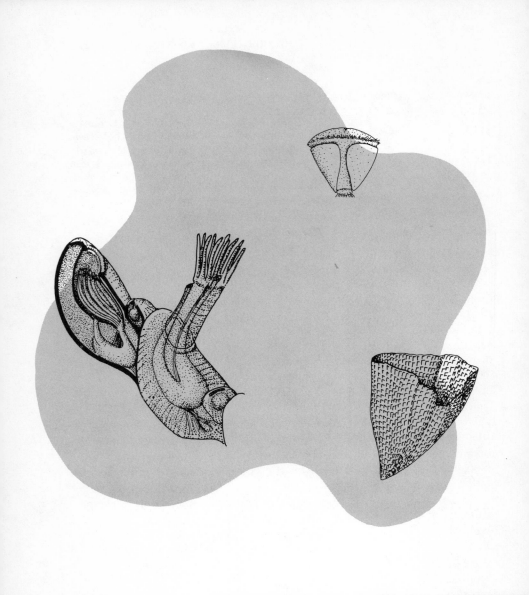

11. *A step upward:* **BRYOZOA**

*S*omewhere in the Precambrian rocks there must be a fine dark shale bearing the carbonized impressions of inhabitants of an ancient lagoon. The geologist who has the good fortune to see the glistening films of carbon will immortalize himself and help solve some of the profound problems of animal evolution. Biologists can predict, mostly from a study of the simpler living metazoans and their embryology, some of what they will find (Figures 10-1 and 10-2; p. 234ff.). There must have been a variety of protozoans, some simple types, others with the beginnings of complex organelles. Simple plants, algae, hardly different from their protozoan cousins, swung with the current and drifted with the tide. These plants furnished the primary energy for the animal community. Colonial protozoans and simple sponges, occupying the niches now held by metazoans, swarmed to browse on these microscopic pastures. Primitive medusoid coelenterates, forming the summit of the food pyramid, darted among the swimmers and floaters to feed on them. Other metazoans foraged along the bottom. The former occupied a world in which impressions of danger and of food impinged from all sides, and in which the only constant direction was that given by the animal's movement. The coelenterate was adapted with strong polarity and radial symmetry.° You saw some consequences of these adaptations in Chapter 10.

The bottom dwellers, though they may have swum above the bottom, inhabited a world with intimations of up and down as well as front and back. The feeding surface was, of course, "down," and the animals flattened out along the axis of polarity. The primary radial (or spherical) symmetry was suppressed in favor of a new bilateral symmetry with right and left and up and down. The dominant direction of perception was "forward" rather than radial, and, presumably, selection acted to concentrate organs of perception and coordination in the "forward" position. As in the coelenterates, a gut developed as a blind internal tube surrounded by the nutritive cells that originally filled the interior of the animal.

° The concept of metazoan origins expressed here is probably the most prevalent (Hyman, 1940 and 1951), but some authorities like Marcus (1958) argue for quite a different evolutionary pattern. Since the whole problem is and must remain speculative, I urge skepticism. Marcus's phylogenetic scheme seems excessively dependent on *a priori* conclusions about the significance of embryonic features. The one I have proposed here, may be too facile and superficial.

The potentialities of this structural plan have yet to be fully exploited, but it has yielded already such complex creatures as squids, praying mantises, and men. The flat worms, the phylum Platyhelminthes, have developed the immediate adaptive features of this plan without progressing in general efficiency. They are the most primitive of this great metazoan stock and retain the primitive gut which serves both in nutrition and in circulation. The nervous system, derived from the epidermal cell layer, is more complex and more highly integrated than the diffuse nerve net of the coelenterates, and a fairly complex system of visual, chemical, and tactile receptors feeds data into the coordinating centers. The mesodermal tissue, between gut (the gastrodermal cell layer) and body wall, is more abundant and important than in the coelenterates for it furnishes material for muscles, excretory organs, and nutritive glands as well as for reproductive organs.

Many of the Platyhelminthes now exist as poor relatives at the table of the more complexly organized metazoans. Only a few, such as the free living planarians, compete successfully with their more highly endowed cousins. The remainder continue as parasites, a habit for which they are preadapted by their simple body structure. The evolution of these parasitic types, which is unrecorded from fossils, has consisted primarily of a regression in complexity, of the appearance of some peculiar mechanisms connected with parasitic life, of the biochemical adjustment to the host, and of the complex reproductive cycles.

SIZE AND ACTIVITY

The increased complexity and integration in the structural plan of metazoan stock apparently created evolutionary problems and started correlated evolutionary trends. Integration means a higher level of activity; activity demands heightened efficiency and further structural modification, and greater activity results in increased resistance to the exploitation of the environment. Larger animals are, in general, better able to resist and exploit, but larger animals need superior integrative mechanisms and greater efficiency. The surface area for respiration, nutrition, and excretion increases approximately as the square of linear size increases, but the bulk increases as the cube. More cells are buried away from these functional surfaces, and mechanisms must evolve to supply food and oxygen and remove wastes from the buried cells. Such mechanisms, in turn, increase the animal's control of effects of environmental factors on the bulk of the cells. The animal, therefore, resists and exploits the environment to greater extent.

Evolutionary trends

The major trends of metazoan evolution are increased size, increased complexity of nutritive, excretory and integrative structures, and improved locomotor and perceptor adaptations. Specific adaptive requirements for smaller size have sometimes reversed the first trend; the adoption of parasitic or sessile habits, the second and third. One gathers that the most pressing needs were for an integrative structure, for a circulatory system, for excretory organs, and for improvement of the nutritive structure, the gut, since these appear in all the other metazoan phyla above the platyhelminthian level and may have evolved independently in several lineages.

In place of the diffuse nerve net of the coelenterates and flat worms, most of the other metazoa have a concentrated system. The flat worms illustrate the first steps in this change, for they possess a small number of longitudinal nerve cords that collect impulses from all parts of the body. Transverse cords connect the longitudinal trunks. The cell bodies of many of the nerve cells are concentrated in masses, the ganglia, and the anterior ganglia in more highly organized metazoa form a definite brain.

The circulation of nutrients, gases, and wastes in the coelenterates and platyhelminthes depends largely on branches from the gut which ramify through the body, and, in the mesoderm, on diffusion from cell to cell. Although this works very well in small animals which have all their cells close either to the exterior surface or the gut wall, it would hardly suffice for an elephant or even a snail. The most obvious solution is the development of fluid filled spaces * within the body—obvious at least to all organisms above the coelenterate-platyhelminthes level (Figure 11-1). The various materials to be circulated diffuse through the fluid, and currents increase the rate of circulation. Some of these spaces, those intimately related to the excretory organs, may have evolved primarily to collect the metabolic wastes. Spaces between the gut wall and

---

* These spaces have also been interpreted as adaptations to stiffen the body in locomotion (Marcus, 1958). This may be reasonable.

the body will have other functions as well. Since neither paleontologists nor zoologists have direct knowledge of the evolution of such spaces, they cannot be sure of the primary adaptation that produced them. Among most of the metazoan phyla, part or most of their functions are taken over by the blood vessels and sinuses.

Cells especially adapted for separation of metabolic wastes from body fluids occur in the flatworms. In evolution, they tend to increase in number and in efficiency, and, among the metazoa with well developed circulatory systems, they are typically grouped to form kidneys.

The coelenterates and platyhelminthes take food particles in through the mouth and expel indigestible wastes through the same opening. This obviously is inefficient, and animals with separate incoming and outgoing currents possess a selective advantage. In some coelenterates, the mouth is modified so that incoming material enters in a partly separate opening, the siphonoglyph. Among the other metazoa, the blind end of the gut breaks to the surface. In these, food enters the anterior mouth, and the undigested materials are discharged through the posterior anus. Because the direction of movement is constant, the gut is differentiated along its length for digestive and absorptive functions (Figure 11-1).

Significance of a space

Most zoologists agree that the form and mode of development of the body spaces (Figure 11-1) are the prime criteria of metazoan phylogeny. Phylogenetic schemes based on a number of other fundamental adaptations agree quite closely with this one and so tend to substantiate it. Each of the two major types of body spaces, the *pseudocoel* and the *coelom*, probably evolved independently in several different lines as an adaptation to similar selective pressures. The pseudocoel plan encompasses animals in which the body cavities are remnants of the "hollow" in the early "hollow ball" stage of development. The body cavity lies between the ectoderm and entoderm and is partly filled by the mesoderm or organs developed from it. The "pseudocoels" are less diversified and possess a simpler organization than the coelomates. Many are now parasitic; most are quite small; their organization is comparatively simple, and they comprise a relatively small number of species. They all lack a skeleton, and none of the pseudocoelomate phyla are definitely known from fossil specimens.

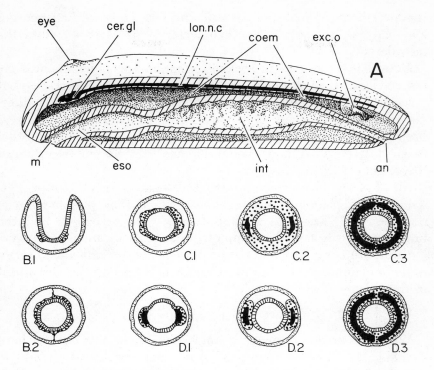

Fig. 11–1. *THE COELOMATE METAZOA. A)* General structural plan in section. *B)* Development of body cavity in pseudo-coelomates—cavity is remnant of internal space in "hollow ball" stage of development. Mesoderm, heavy stipple; endoderm, lines; ectoderm, light stipple. *C)* Development of body cavity as it occurs in molluscs, annelids, and arthropods. *C.1)* Mesoderm buds from sides of endoderm lining gut. *C.2)* and *C.3)* Coelomic cavities (solid) develop as split within mesoderm. *D)* Development of body cavity as it occurs in echinoderms and chordates. *D.1)* Pouches develop on sides of gut. *D.2)* and *D.3)* Pouches close off from gut to form coelomic spaces; lining of pouches becomes mesoderm. Abbreviations: *an*, anus; *cer. gl*, cerebral ganglion; *coem*, coelom; *eso*, esophagus; *exc. o*, excretory organ; *int*, intestine; *lon. n. c*, longitudinal nerve; *m*, mouth.

The coelomate plan includes animals in which the body cavities lie entirely within the mesoderm, i.e., the cavities are fully surrounded by tissue of mesodermal origin. In some animals, among them the echinoderms, the bryozoans, the brachiopods, the protochordates, and the more primitive chordates, the coelom forms as pouches from the cavity of the gut. The connection to the gut is closed over; the pouches expand to fill the space between the gut and body wall, and their lining becomes the mesoderm. In other animals, including the molluscs, the annelids, and the arthropods, the mesoderm buds off the gut wall and fills the space between gut and body wall. The coelom then develops as cavities within the mesoderm.

Note that these steps in coelom formation are stages in ontogeny not phylogeny. They may, indeed, repeat phylogenetic stages, but it seems more likely that they are larval adaptations. The two different methods of coelom (and mesoderm) formation may reflect a profound difference in phylogeny for they are correlated with other major differences in mode of development, but no one is certain of the origins of this divergence.

All of the animals common as fossils—except the Protozoa, Porifera, and Coelenterata—are coelomates, and they predominate in numbers and variety in modern faunas. The bryozoans and the brachiopods display the simplest organization among the coelomates; are closely related to each other, but are difficult to relate to the remaining phyla. For these reasons I'll take up these two next in this survey of animal evolution.

THE ORIGIN OF PHYLA

Were the great groups of animals, the phyla and classes, born suddenly as "hopeful monsters" from some profound change in developmental pattern initiated by a gene mutation? Or did they grow from some slight, obscure, adaptive divergence? Because paleontologists and biologists now debate the origin of these higher categories (see p. 169), I think I should briefly outline the phyletic relationships of the bryozoans and the brachiopods.

The two share a similar mode of development from the egg to the larva—characterized (Figure 11-2) by a horizontal band of cilia and a chitinous bivalve shell—a similar level of adult organization, and a ring of tentacles about the mouth, the *lophophore*. Their common ancestor probably had these features plus some lost in one or the other, less some gained independently in both. The bivalve larval shell offers a special problem because the brachiopods retain it through metamorphosis whereas the bryozoans substitute quite a different sort of external skeleton. Was the shell an independent development in either phylum? Or was it a feature of a common adult ancestor supplanted in the maturing bryozoan? Or did the ancestral line evolve it as a larval adaptation, and the brachiopod lineage later retain it to the adult stage? The peculiar metamorphosis of the bryozoans obscures the problem. In this phylum, after the larva attaches to the bottom, most of the individual tissues and organs degenerate, and the remainder generate a typical adult. This short cut in development conceals the primitive developmental pattern.

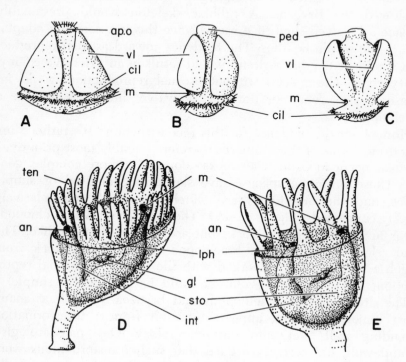

Fig. 11–2. *EMBRYOLOGY AND ORIGINS OF BRYOZOA AND BRACHIOPODA. A)* Larva of bryozoan. *B)* Larva of "primitive" brachiopod. *C)* Larva of "advanced" brachiopod. Valves develop on inner surface of mantle flaps. Flaps then turn over so valves are external. *D)* Reconstruction of hypothetical common ancestor of Bryozoa and Brachiopoda. *E)* Recent member of Enteroprocta, regarded by some specialists as bryozoan but noncoelomate. Abbreviations: *an,* anus; *ap. o,* apical organ; *cil,* cilia; *gl,* ganglion; *int,* intestine; *lph,* lopophore; *m,* mouth; *ped,* pedicle rudiment; *sto,* stomach; *ten,* tentacle; *vl,* valve of shell. (A through C and E after Borradaile and Potts, *The Invertebrata.* Copyright, Cambridge University Press, New York. Used with permission. B and C originally altered from Delage and Herouard; E originally altered from Ehlers.)

Granting this uncertainty, the ancestral bryozoan-brachiopod was a relatively simple coelomate metazoan (Figure 11-2), probably resting attached on the bottom, and collecting its food with the ciliated tentacles of the lophophore. It possibly resembled the living acoelomate Entoprocta, though more complexly organized (Figure

11-2E). The evolutionary choices for such creatures are relatively clear cut—either evolve into moderately large, shelled individuals or form colonies of small ones. Some species may have reproduced asexually and formed weak aggregates of individuals. These foreshadowed the Bryozoa. A tubular skeleton would presumably replace a bivalved shell (if present) since this is a common adaptation in the sessile benthos. The tendency toward asexual reproduction would be emphasized and would result in an extensive colony, a bryozoan. The species without asexual reproduction would increase in size, retain or develop a bivalve shell, and become a brachiopod.

How about the evidence for this reconstruction? It's rather slim, I'm afraid. Some of the simplest (therefore possibly most primitive) Bryozoa occur in Ordovician rocks—along with more complex genera. These primitive species have skeletons composed of simple tubes, and the individuals are widely separated and relatively weakly connected (Figure 11-4A). The most primitive brachiopods occur in lower Cambrian rocks but are hardly bryozoan-like. The time relation suggests the brachiopods as the basic stock from which a sessile species diverged with the benefit of asexual reproduction; however, their evolution could hardly be this simple.

The divergence of brachiopods and bryozoa, as well as many other major categories, appears to result from a transformation extending well back into the embryology. One paleontologist, Schindewolf, has recently argued that such transformations were abrupt, and, therefore, the origin of the categories was equally abrupt (see p. 169). Since fossil evidence is lacking in many such cases, proof or disproof is difficult. The brachiopods and bryozoa could have diverged in a single major step, but, as this reconstruction indicates, the changes could have been adaptive and can be explained as gradual evolution in response to low or moderate selective pressure. The inadaptive condition (or barrier) suggested in some cases does not appear here.

THE BRYOZOANS

The development of the colony (the *zoarium*) is the critical feature of the bryozoan organization (Figure 11-3). As described in the preceding section, the initial individual after attachment to the bottom degenerates, and a new individual regenerates from parts of the larval tissue. One or more buds appear and develop into distinct individuals (called *zooids*). These in turn give off additional buds. Ultimately a large colony is formed. As each zooid appears, it begins formation of its skeletal tube, the *zooecium*. The mode of budding is of course reflected in the relation of adjoining tubes, and some portion of growth, in the characteristics of the tube. As the zooid grows, it lengthens this tube. Individuals in some species form successive horizontal partitions (*diaphragms*) across the tube; each one of these may reflect a regeneration of the zooid similar to that which occurred after the initial individual metamorphosed. The wide spacing of the diaphragms and the thin walls in the lower part of the tube indicate rapid initial growth; the close spacing and thick walls in the upper portion result from slower growth. This difference in growth defines the *immature* and *mature* regions of the zooecium. The colony itself may show ontogenetic changes as younger individuals develop in different fashion than the older. Some at least of these changes during individual and colony development probably are adaptations to changing environmental conditions, for the ecology of a relatively large erect colony may be quite different from that of its initial, small, encrusting stage.

Morphology and adaptations

The primitive bryozoan zooecium consists of a simple tube of chitinoid or calcareous material (the former probably more primitive) open at one end. The zooid, while feeding, extends the tentacles and part of the body from the zooecium (Figure 11-3) but retracts rapidly when disturbed or threatened. Among more advanced bryozoa, the zooecium forms a distinct, rather box-like chamber. The opening, the *aperture*, is restricted to one end or one side of the chamber. The chamber and aperture vary in shape in different species; the aperture in some is recessed, and internal supporting structures occur in many. Most of this morphologic variation is related to extension and retraction of the lophophore. As a consequence the paleontologist, in the study of individual zooecia, deals principally with adaptations in development and in the extension-retraction function. Interpretation of life functions, of environment, and of evolution are, therefore, very much limited.

The structure of the colony, the zoarium, gives considerably more information about the natural history of the bryozoan species. Attachment is adaptive to substrate and to over-all shape and bulk

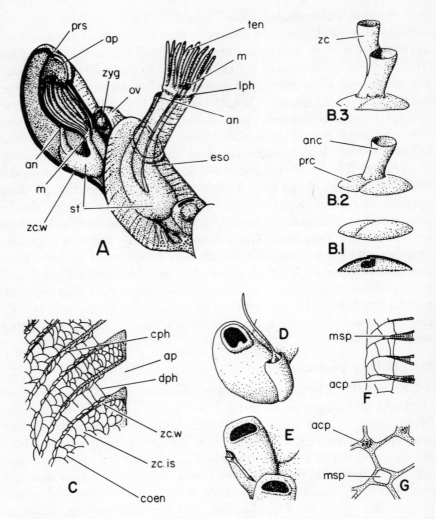

Fig. 11–3. *ESSENTIALS OF BRYOZOAN MORPHOLOGY.* A) General anatomy of recent bryozoans; zooecial wall of lower zooid cleared; wall of upper zooid sectioned. Lower polypide extended; upper retracted. Enlarged 50 times. B.1) to B.3) Stages in formation of zoarium. B.1) Skeleton formed by larva after attaching—the protoecium. Cross section and oblique view. B.2) Protoecium and ancestrula, oblique view. The latter is the zooecial tube formed by the original polypide after metamorphosis of larva. B.3) First zooecium formed. C) Longitudinal section of zoarium. Enlarged 20 times. D) Specialized zooid, a vibraculum, attached to side of normal individual. E) Specialized zooid, an avicularium, attached to another zooecium. F) Longitudinal section of Paleozoic bryozoan. Acanthopores and mesopores shown. G) Tangential section of same. (B. After Borg. D. After Hincks. E. After Busk.)

GLOSSARY FOR THE BRYOZOA

(Numbers at end of definition indicate figure that illustrates structure.)

Acanthopore (acp). Small tube adjacent and parallel to zooecial walls. Formed of cone-in-cone layers with minute central tubule—the latter may contain transverse partitions. Typically marked on surface by projecting spines. (11–3F, G; 11–6D.)

Ancestrula (anc). Initial individual of colony. Derived from metamorphosis of larva. (11–3B.)

Anus (an). Terminal opening of digestive tract. Serves primarily for discharge of indigestible materials. (11–3A.)

Aperture (ap). Opening in wall of skeleton (zooecium) through which the living animal extends lophopore and portions of body (11–3A, et al.).

Avicularium. Specialized individual bearing a beak-like structure worked by strong muscles. (11–3E.)

Bifoliate. Colony consisting of two layers of zooecia growing back-to-back. (11–4H.)

Coenosteum (coen). Vesicular or dense skeletal material between zooecia. (11–3C; 11–5C; 11–6B, D.)

Cystiphragm (cph). Calcareous plate extending from zooecial wall part-way across tube. Surface domed, convex upward and inward. (11–3C; 11–6A.)

Diaphragm (dph). Calcareous plate extending transversely across width of zooecial tube. Surface flat or gently curved.

Encrusting. Colony which forms broad sheet over substrate to which it is attached. (11–4B, C.)

Esophagus (eso). Portion of digestive tract leading from mouth to stomach. (11–3A.)

Frondose. Erect colony consisting of broad, flat branches. (11–4F.)

Interzooecial space (zc. is). Portion of zoarium between zooecia. (11–3C.)

Longitudinal section. Section of zoarium cut parallel to zooecial tubes. (11–3C, F; et al.)

Lophophore (lph). Circular or horseshoe-shaped ridge around mouth which bears a circlet of tentacles.

Macula. Cluster of small zooecia. Marked surficially by shallow depression which typically is surrounded by unusually large zooecia. (11–6B.)

Massive. Colony form consisting of thick heavy zoarium, generally hemispherical or subglobular in shape. (11–6A.)

Mesopore (msp). Zooecium of unusually small size set between larger zooecia and characterized by numerous transverse partitions (diaphragms). (10–3F, G.)

Monticule. Cluster of modified zooecia—typically of relatively small size—that project as elevation on zoarial surface. (11–4C, D.)

Mouth (m). Opening of digestive tract for intake of food.

Ovicell (ov). Specialized skeletal structure—usually a chamber that houses the bryozoan larva during development. (11–3A; 11–6E, G.)

Peristome (prs). Elevated rim surrounding aperture.

Polypide. The living portion—soft parts—of the individual bryozoan (zooid).

Protoecium (prc). Skeleton of larva formed when it attached to the substrate. Consists of the two chitinous valves of the free-living larva cemented to the substrate. (11–3B.)

Ramose. Colony form consisting of erect, round or moderately flattened branches. (11–4D; 11–5B, C; 11–6B.)

Reptant. Colony form consisting of largely separate zooecial tubes which lie attached to substrate. (11–4A.)

Stomach (st). Pouch in anterior portion of digestive tract in which part or most of digestion occurs. (11–3A.)

Tangential section. Section of zoarium cut at right angles to zooecial tubes. (11–3G; 11–4C; et al.)

Tentacle (ten). Flexible "arm" borne on ridge (lophopore) that surrounds mouth. Ciliated and functioning primarily in food getting.

Unifoliate. Colony form consisting of single layer of zooecia—all opening onto one surface. (11–4C.)

Vibracula. Specialized individual in colony consisting largely of whip-like process. (11–3D.)

Zoarium. Skeleton of entire bryozoan colony. Composed of calcite and/or chitin. (Portions of complete zoaria in 11–3, 11–4, 11–5, and 11–6.)

Zooecial wall (zc. w). Sides of skeleton (zooecium) of individual bryozoan. (11–3A, C; et al.)

Zooecium (zc). The skeleton, either chitinous or calcareous, of the individual bryozoan. Consists of tubular walls and various internal structures. (11–3A, B, C; et al.)

Zooid. The individual bryozoan—including the soft parts (polypide) and the skeleton (zooecium). (11–3A.)

Zygote (zyg). Cell formed by union of egg and sperm cells.

---

of the colony. The shape, in turn, must be adapted to current velocity (or wave action), to substrate support, to sedimentation rates, and to feeding and respiratory functions. Because the tentacles of the zooids form sort of a net to filter microorganisms from the water, the distribution of individuals as well as colony form modifies the food-getting mechanisms. Some of the different types of zoaria are shown in Figure 11-4.

Remarkable, and, therefore, important identifying features of the colonies are specialized zooids. Among modern bryozoa, some individuals develop as *avicularia* or *vibracula*. The former resemble a bird's head and consist of two "jaws" with muscles to open and close them. The latter are rather whip-like and likewise have a set of muscles that keep the "whip" in motion. These seem to be responsible for destroying or removing sedimentary particles and encrusting organisms from the colony. Some species also have (or had) individuals specialized for reproduction, typically by the formation of an *ovicell* in which one egg or a number of eggs

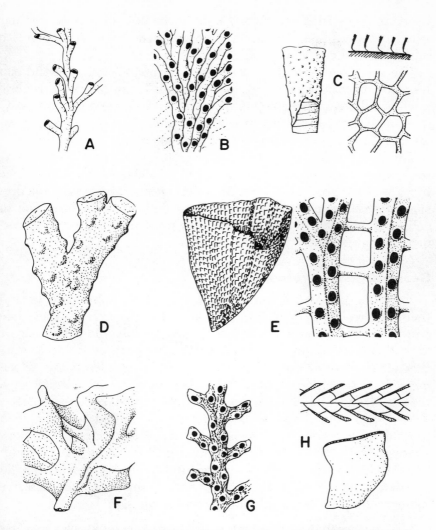

Fig. 11–4. *VARIATION IN ZOARIA.* *A)* A repant form. *Hederella;* Silurian to Pennsylvanian; lateral view; enlarged 5 times. *B)* An encrusting form. *Sagenella;* Silurian; lateral view; enlarged 8 times. *C)* An encrusting form; *Leptotrypa;* Ordovician; lateral view; longitudinal and tangential sections; lateral view natural size, sections enlarged 25 times. Zooecia polygonal in tangential section. *D)* Ramose zoarium. *Hallopora;* Ordovician to Devonian; lateral view; *E)* Reticulate, funnel-shaped form. *Fenestella;* Ordovician to Permian; lateral view of entire zoarium and enlarged view of a small part of colony; zoarium enlarged 0.5 times and detail enlarged 20 times. *F)* Frondose zoarium. A recent species. *G)* Ramose form—short, regularly spaced side branches. *Penniretepora;* Devonian to Permian; lateral view; enlarged 15 times. *H)* Bifoliate frond. *Phyllodictya;* Ordovician; longitudinal section and lateral view; section enlarged 10 times and zooarial view true size. (C. Section after Ulrich. H. After Ulrich.)

develop. Since such specialized individuals lose all or part of their usual functions, they must be supported in this share-the-wealth scheme by other zooids.

The specialized zooids, of course, have modified zooecia and can be recognized in fossil bryozoans. In those fossil groups with close modern relatives, the function of these particular zooecia are easily determined; the functions of the *mesopores, acanthopores,* and so on found only in fossil bryozoans, are unknown.

The circulatory, respiratory, and excretory functions do not have, so far as is known, any association with skeletal modifications. The bryozoa lack any definite organs for these functions and, presumably, diffusion from the water into the organism, from cell to cell, and from cell to coelom suffices to meet the moderate requirements of these small, inactive animals.

Geologists and bryozoa

The abundance of bryozoans in many post-Cambrian rocks and their relatively rapid evolution make them valuable in rock-time correlation. Since individual zooecia are microscopic, they can be identified from fragments in well cuttings—a very desirable characteristic. In spite of difficulties in preparation of identifiable specimens from the matrix and an unwieldly morphologic terminology, they contribute much to stratigraphy and could contribute more.

Most genera and species occur in a very limited series of rock types and were apparently sensitive to small environment changes. Unfortunately, these limiting environmental factors have hardly been studied. Duncan, in her review (1957), cites approximately 80 papers that touch on bryozoan paleoecology; most of these describe the more obvious features of bryozoan distribution:

1. They are most abundant in impure calcareous clastics, less abundant in shales, and rare in sandstones.

2. Species with fragile skeletons must have lived in fairly quiet waters.

3. Some robust groups contributed to reef formation.

4. Particular species tolerated a limited range of depth and temperature. For species with modern representatives, this range can be determined and used in interpretation.

5. Agitated water and low turbidity are favorable to growth of Bryozoa.

Only a few paleontologists, Stach in papers written in 1936 and 1937, for example, have examined the finer details of morphology in terms of environmental significance. He found that certain types of zoaria, the "stable" in his usage, occur only in a limited number of habitats and are controlled primarily by the nature of substrate. Other types appear in a variety of habitats and modify their growth and form to suit the particular character of the local environment. Variation in depth and in turbulence determines the development of different forms in this group of species. The potential of this sort of study appears very great—if one has patience for preparation of thin sections, for etching zoaria from calcareous matrix, and for prolonged use of a binocular microscope.

Geologic occurrence

Figures 11-5 and 11-6 show some of the most useful guide fossils in this group. The order Ctenostomata, which ranges from the early Ordovician to the Recent, comprises zoaria with membraneous or calcified zooecia. The zooecia of most are simple tubes with terminal apertures and arise as isolated individuals from a thread-like tube, the *stolon*. In most features, the Ctenostomata seem the most primitive bryozoans. Since most recent species lack calcified skeletons, their comparative rarity as fossils probably does not measure their actual abundance or diversity.

The Cyclostomata are more advanced, for they have closely grouped calcareous zooecia (though thin walled and porous) and

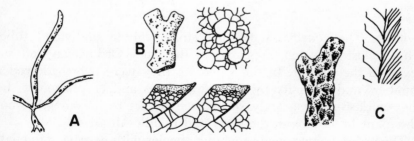

Fig. 11–5. *REPRESENTATIVE BRYOZOA: CTENOSTOMATA, AND CYCLOSTOMATA.*
A) Ctenostome Vinella; Ordovician to Cretaceous; reptant; lateral view; enlarged 12 times. B) Cyclostome Meekopora; Silurian to Permian; ramose; lateral view of zoarium and tangential and longitudinal sections; zoarium enlarged 1.0 times and sections 10 times. C) Cyclostome Pleuronea; Eocene to Pliocene; lateral view and longitudinal section; the former enlarged 12 times and the latter 12 times. (A. After Ulrich. B. Sections after Ulrich. C. After Canu and Bassler.)

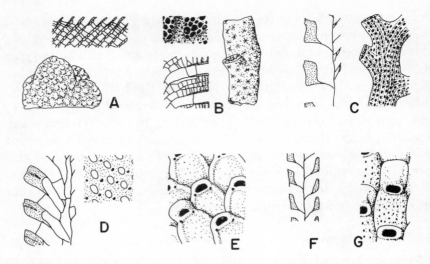

Fig. 11–6. *REPRESENTATIVE BRYOZOA: CRYPTOSTOMATA, TREPOSTOMATA, AND CHEILOSTOMATA.* A) A massive trepostome, *Monticulipora;* Ordovician; lateral view and longitudinal section; zoarium enlarged 0.5 times and section 10 times. B) A ramose trepostome, *Constellaria;* Ordovician; lateral view as well as tangential and longitudinal sections; the sections are enlarged 20 times, the zoarium 0.5 times. C) Cryptostome *Sulcoretepora;* Devonian to Permian; ramose; longitudinal section and view of fragment of zoarium; the section enlarged 20 times, the zoarium 5 times. D) Cryptostome *Rhombopora;* Devonian to Permian; mesopores; longitudinal and tangential sections; the first enlarged 20 times and the second 10 times. E) *Micropora*, a cheilostome; Cretaceous to Recent; zooecium at left with ovicell; portion of zoarium enlarged 25 times. F) Another cheilostome, *Trigonopora* shown in longitudinal section; Eocene to Recent; bifoliate. G) A final cheilstome, *Metracolposa;* Eocene; detail of zoarium; enlarged 15 times. Large ovicell above aperture. (A. Section after Ulrich and Basser. B. Sections after Ulrich. C. Section after Ulrich. D. After Ulrich. E. and F. After Canu and Bassler. G. After Bassler.)

ovicells. The zooecia, however, remain simple undivided tubes. The cyclostomes, too, appeared in the early Ordovician and survived to the Recent. In the Paleozoic they were overshadowed in numbers and diversity by the trepostomes and cryptostomes, but they outlasted these early specialized orders to become the most abundant bryozoans in the early and middle Mesozoic.

The order Trepostomata includes species with massive, lamellate, or stem-like zoaria. Their zoecia consist of long calcareous tubes partitioned by diaphragms and divided into immature and mature regions. Specialized zooids occur between the normal type in the mature region. Their form is fairly robust and some species helped, to a moderate degree, in building Paleozoic "coral" reefs (p. 107).

Trepostomes are among the oldest known bryozoans; they occur in lower Ordovician rocks, and a lower Cambrian genus has been described—though the identification is very suspect. They underwent a rapid radiation in middle Ordovician, declined in numbers and variety after the Silurian, and apparently failed to survive the Paleozoic.

The Cryptostomata have delicate frond-like or branching zoaria. The zoecia are calcareous and resemble those of the Trepostomata. The boundary between the mature and immature regions is more distinct than in the latter, and the apertures are recessed below the zooecial surface. They are another product of the early Paleozoic

TABLE 11-1

CLASSIFICATION OF THE BRYOZOA

(Based on Bassler, 1953.)

Ordovician to Recent. Colonial. Coelomate. Gut U-shaped; mouth opens in center of group of tentacles, the lophophore. Skeleton membraneous, chitinous or calcareous. Aquatic, predominately marine, sessile benthonic.

CLASS GYMNOLAEMATA

Ordovician to Recent. Lophophore circular without a "lip" overhanging the mouth. Body wall not muscular. All marine.

Order *Ctenostomata*

Ordovician to Recent. Zooecia simple tubes with terminal apertures. Zooids develop by budding from a thread-like stolon. Skeleton membraneous but calcified in some.

Order *Cyclostomata*

Ordovician to Recent. Closely grouped calcareous zooecia. Zooecia simple tubes; simple aperture.

Order *Trepostomata*

Ordovician to Permian. Massive, lamellate, or stem-like zoaria. Zooecia calcareous, long and slender; diaphragms; mature and immature regions. Some specialized zooids.

Order *Cryptostomata*

Ordovician to Permian. Frondlike or branching zoaria. Calcareous zooecia with very distinct mature and immature regions and with recessed apertures.

Order *Cheilostomata*

Jurassic to Recent. Calcareous and membraneous skeletons. Zooecia short; aperture small and may be surrounded by elevated peristome.

CLASS PHYLACTOLAEMATA

Cretaceous to Recent. Lophophore horse-shoe shaped; "lip" overhangs mouth. Skeleton chitinous or gelatinous. Fresh water. One fossil genus recognized.

radiation of the Bryozoa and had a history similar to that of the trepostomates except that they did rather better in the Devonian and Carboniferous.

No Triassic cryptostomes are known, but apparently one line, as yet undetected in the fossil record, survived and gave rise to Cheilostomata in the Jurassic. By Cretaceous, the cheilostomes had diverged into a variety of species, genera, and families, and they predominate in Cenozoic faunas. The Cheilostomata include species with either calcareous or membraneous skeletons. The zoecia are short and rounded or angular. The aperture is most commonly small, and, in some, is surrounded by an elevated rim, the *peristome*. Ovicells of different types are developed as are specialized zooids, the avicularia and vibracula.

A final group, regarded as a different class, are the fresh water bryozoans. They are known as fossils only from a single genus. The zoarium is membraneous or gelatinous. This class, the Phylactolaemata, is characterized by a horse-shoe shaped lophophore and a "lip" overhanging the mouth. The other five orders compose the class Gymolaemata which has a circular lophophore and lacks a "lip."

REFERENCES

Bassler, R. S. 1953. "Bryozoa," in: Moore, R. C. 1953. *Treatise on Invertebrate Paleontology, part G.* New York: Geol. Soc. of America. Extensive general work on Bryozoa—principally fossil forms. Includes bibliography.

Duncan, H. 1957. "Bryozoans" (annotated bibliography), in: "Treatise on Marine Ecology and Paleontology," vol. 2. *Geol. Soc. of America, Memoir 67,* pp. 783-800.

Fritz, M. A. 1947. "Cambrian Bryozoa," *Jour. of Paleontology,* vol. 21, pp. 434-435. If correctly assigned, the earliest known bryozans.

Hyman, L. H. 1951. *The Invertebrates:* Vol. 2, *Platyhelminthes and Rhynchocoela.* New York: McGraw-Hill. Extended discussion of the evolution of the metazoans.

Marcus, E. 1958. "On the Evolution of the Animal Phyla," *Quart. Rev. of Biology,* vol. 33, pp. 24-58.

Stach, L. W. 1936. "Correlation of Zoarial Form with Habitat," *Jour. of Geology,* vol. 44, pp. 60-65.

Stach, L. W. 1937. "The Application of the Bryoza in Cainozoic Stratigraphy," *Australian and New Zealand Assoc. Adv. of Science, Rept. 23rd. Meeting,* pp. 80-83.

See also the general references on invertebrates listed in Chapter 3.

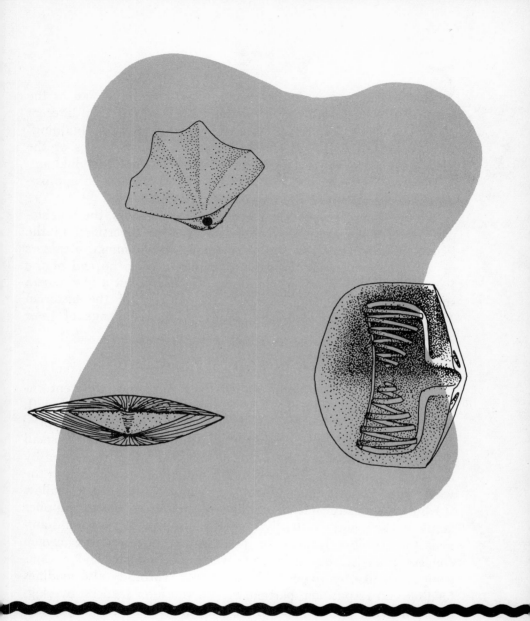

12. *Individualism reconsidered:*
the BRACHIOPODA

$\mathcal{T}$he brachiopods, with the same general structural plan as the Bryozoa and somewhat similar mode of life, evolved in a different direction. They abandoned, or never attained, asexual "budding" and colony formation. The two chitinous or horny plates of the larva become the two valves of the adult shell. The individual animal grows much larger than the individual bryozoan and approximates in size an entire Bryozoan colony.

In spite of, or perhaps because of, these differences, the brachiopods were as important, as abundant, and as diversified in the Paleozoic as the Bryozoa and were among the dominant members of sea bottom societies throughout that era. After the end of the Paleozoic, they declined in numbers and variety, but a few genera survived to the Recent. To apply the concept of the historian Toynbee, they responded successfully to the challenge of their environment.

SUCCESS IN THE SESSILE BENTHOS

Animals fixed immobile on the sea floor face quite different environmental challenges than do the active terrestrial ones with which we are more familiar. They cannot, of course, stalk their prey nor range widely to graze on algae, but must either filter the small drifting organisms from the water or seize the larger that swim by accident into tentacle reach. Waste products are expelled into the water to be carried off by currents or simply diffused. On shallow sea bottoms, the turbulence of the water removes wastes, supplies ample oxygen, and constantly renews the supply of plants and animals for the filter feeders. In quiet waters, however, the oxygen concentration is reduced, organic wastes accumulate, and noxious compounds like hydrogen sulphide appear. Turbidity also modifies feeding and respiration, particularly for the filter feeders, by clogging gills, ciliary tracts, and so on, with mud or sand. If deposition is rapid, animals on the bottom are likely to be buried; if turbulence is great, they may be broken or otherwise injured. Some require solid objects for attachment, such as coarse detritus or shells of other animals. Others live unsupported on the bottom; these may need special mechanisms to prevent sinking into the sediment. Without powers of flight, the sessile benthos are liable to the attacks of predators and parasites, and are equally exposed to the vagaries of the physio-chemical environment. Since copulation is impossible, the sperm must swim or float some distance to fertilize the egg. The larvae, if they are to find a suitable place to settle, must be motile and because of their small size and slight swimming abilities are dispersed by even weak currents.

On the other hand, requirements of circulation, of perception, of internal regulation, and of coordination are less stringent than among active animals. An oyster has little need for a highly efficient circulatory system or for a large brain. As a consequence, these systems in the bryozoans, brachiopods, pelecypods, and other sessile groups are relatively simple—either primitive or "degenerate." The brachiopod (Figure 12-1), for example, has only a pair of ganglia above and below the anterior portion of gut, with nerves to the tentacles and to the muscles of the shell; it lacks distinct sense organs; it possesses only a few simple blood vessels with a slightly differentiated muscular portion as a heart; and it has comparatively small and simple excretory organs.

THE DIFFICULTIES OF BEING A BRACHIOPOD

Brachiopods are animals of the marine sessile benthos. They construct a shell with two valves, one above the soft parts, the other below. The valves are hinged on their posterior margins and open along the anterior. Since each valve has somewhat different functions, they differ in form; since the plane of bilateral symmetry is perpendicular to the surface of the valves, each is bilaterally symmetrical—has a "right" and "left." They feed by an elaborate filter mechanism. Evolution has impressed on their form a variety of adaptations to the peculiarities of their environment. The fossil shell and skeletal structures within the shell reproduce some part of these adaptations—a greater part possibly than in any other group of sessile animals.

Feeding

Tracts of fine hair-like processes (*cilia*) on the lophophore and about the mouth form the brachiopod filter mechanisms. The lophophore consists of a pair of coiled arms (*brachia*) bearing ciliated, tentacle-like *cirri*. The beat of these cilia maintain currents into and out of the shell. Three paths of current flow are maintained, the excurrent path in the center of the gap between the

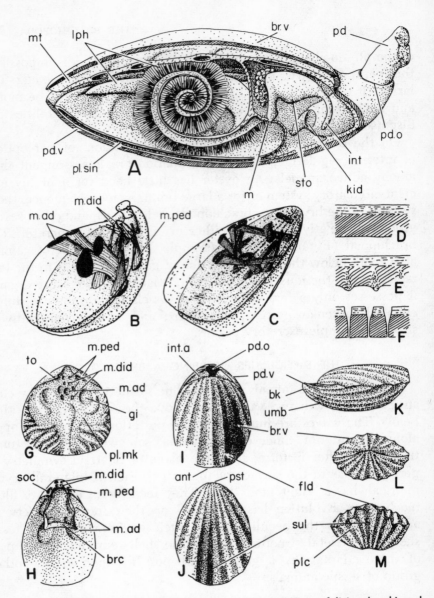

Fig. 12–1. *MORPHOLOGY OF THE BRACHIOPODA.* A) View of living brachiopod with left side of shell and mantle removed. B) Muscle system of articulate brachiopod. C) Muscle system of inarticulate brachiopod. Muscles rotate valves as well as hold them in articulation. D) Cross section of nonpunctate shell. Calcareous portion consists of outer layer, laminated parallel to surface, and inner layer of fibers inclined to shell surface. E) Cross section of pseudopunctate shell. Rods of structureless calcite in fibrous layer sometimes dissolve out in fossil shells and leave false punctate tructure. F) Cross section of punctate shell. G) Interior of a pedicle valve. H) Interior of a brachial valve. I) External view of a brachiopod, brachial valve up. J) External view of same, pedicle valve up. K) Lateral view. L) Posterior view. M) Anterior view. Note that plane of bilateral symmetry is perpendicular to plane between valves.

GLOSSARY FOR BRACHIOPODA

(Illustrations that show structure are cited at end of definition.)

Adductor muscles (m. ad). Muscles that close and/or hold valves together. May leave attachment scars on interior surface of valve. (12–1B, G, H.)

Alate. Shell form in which the valves are drawn out at the lateral ends of hinge line to form wing-like extensions. (12–5E; 12–12A.)

Anterior. Direction of shell margin where the valves separate when open. Opposite the position of the hinge line (12–1I, M.)

Beak (bk). Pointed extremity of valve adjacent to or posterior to the hinge line and in mid-line of valve. (12–1K; et al.)

Brachial valve (br. v). Valve to which brachidium is attached. In most—but not all—brachiopods the smaller valve, typically, with a small or indistinguishable beak and bearing only a small part of the pedicle opening. (12–1A, H, I, K; et al.)

Brachidium (brc). Calcareous support for the lophopore. (12–1H; 12–2.)

Brachiophore (brp). Short, typically stout processes that project from hinge line of brachial valve into the interior of the valve. Serve for attachment of lophopore. (12–2A.)

Chilidial plate. Plate at side of the opening (notothyrium) in the brachial valve for pedicle. Closes over this opening in part. (12–3G.)

Chilidium. Single plate extending across the opening (notothyrium) in the brachial valve for pedicle. May close over opening in part or entirely.

Costae (cst). Ridges on external surface of valve that extend radially from beak. Costae do not involve any folding of inner surface of shell.

Crus (cr). Basal portion of calcareous support (brachidium) of lophopore. (12–2B, C, D.)

Delthyrium (del). Opening in pedicle valve adjacent to hinge line. Serves for passage of pedicle. (12–1I; 12–3A, B.)

Deltidial plate. Plate on either side of pedicle opening (delthyrium) in pedicle valve that constricts opening or even, with its mate from opposite side, closes it off completely. (12–3E, F.)

Deltidium. Single plate filling all or part of pedicle opening in pedicle valve (delthyrium). (12–3C, D.)

Dental lamellae (den. lam). Plate extending up from floor of pedicle valve to hinge line that serves to support tooth. (12–3A.)

Diductor muscles (m. did). Muscles that open valves. Insert on floor of pedicle valve and along or adjacent to hinge line on brachial valve. Attachments may show as scars on inner surface of valves. (12–1B, G, H.)

Fold (fld). Elevation (up-arch) of a valve along the midline. Accompanied by complementary depression (sulcus) of other valve. (12–1I, K, M; 12–4E; 12–10C, D; et al.)

Foramen (frm). Circular opening adjacent to beak of pedicle valve. Serves for passage of pedicle. (12–3F; 12–6A, B; 12–12B.)

Genital impression (gi). One of a pair of shallow depressions on inner surface of pedicle valve that lie to either side of muscle scars and that presumably mark the position of genital organs. (12–1G.)

Hinge line. Edge of shell where two valves are permanently articulated and which serves as hinge when shell is opened or closed. (12–1G, H, I; 12–3A; et al.)

Hinge plate (h. pl).   Plate, simple or divided, that lies along the hinge line in the interior of the brachial valve. Typically nearly parallel to plane between valves, it bears hinge sockets and is joined to bases of crura. (12–1H; 12–3A.)

Growth lines.   Series of fine to coarse ridges or breaks on outer surface of shell. Subparallel to edges of valve and concentric about beak. (12–5C, D; 12–7A, B, C; et al.)

Interarea (int. a).   Plane or curved surface between beak and hinge line on either valve. Generally distinguished by a sharp break in angle from the remainder of the valve and by the absence of costae, plications or coarse growth lines. (12–1I; 12–3A, H through L; et al.)

Intestine (int).   Relatively long slender portion of digestive tract that connects stomach and anus. Serves for digestion and absorption of food; ends blindly in many brachiopods. (12–1A.)

Jugum (jug).   Simple or complex skeletal connection between the right and left halves of the brachidium. (12–2B, C, D.)

Kidney (kid).   Organ that filters undesirable metabolic wastes, water, and salts from fluids of coelomic cavity or of circulatory system. Serves to regulate the internal chemical environment of the animal. (12–1A.)

Loop.   Brachidium consisting of a pair of simply curved or doubly bent longitudinal "arms" and a relatively simple jugum connecting the anterior ends of these arms. (12–1H; 12–2B.)

Lophopore (lop).   Appendage extending anteriorly from mouth and consisting of a lobed disk or a pair of coiled arms (brachia). The arms or lobes attach on either side of the mouth and bear on their edges slender, ciliated threads (cirri). (12–1A.)

Mantle (mt).   Two folds of body wall that lie respectively above and below viscera and that line the inner surface of each valve. (12–1A.)

Median septum (m. sep).   Calcareous ridge built along mid-line of interior of valve. (12–2A, B; 12–9C.)

Mouth (m).   Opening into digestive tube through which food is taken. In brachiopods it lies at the base of and between the arms or lobes of the lophopore and faces anteriorly away from the hinge line and toward the free margin of the two valves.

Notothyrium (nth).   Opening in brachial valve adjacent to and outside the hinge line. Forms part of the opening for the pedicle. (12–3A, G.)

Pallial markings (pl. mk).   Shallow depressions on inner surface of valves that mark the position of canals (pallial sinuses) in the mantle. They are lateral and anterior to the muscle scars and are distinguished by their sinuous, branching pattern. (12–1G.)

Pallial sinus.   Cavities and canals within mantle lobes that connect to the coelomic cavity and that apparently serve in circulations. (12–1A.)

Pedicle muscles (m. ped).   Muscles that serve for attachment and movement of pedicle. They may leave attachment scars on the interior of the valves. (12–1A, G, H.)

Pedicle opening (pd. o).   Opening adjacent to or along hinge that serves for passage of pedicle. Opening may be in pedicle valve only or in both pedicle and brachial valves. (12–1A, J; 12–3A through G; et al.)

Pedicle (pd).   Muscular and/or fibrous stalk which is attached to the inner surface of the pedicle valve and which passes out posteriorly to attach to substrate. (12–1A.)

Pedicle valve (pd. v).   Valve to which the pedicle is attached. By convention ventral in position. (12–1A, G, I through M.)

Plica (plc).   Radial ridges and depressions that involve entire thickness of shell and thus appear as corrugations on inner as well as outer surfaces. Distinguished from fold and sulcus by small amplitude and by occurrence to sides of mid-line. (12–1*l* through *J*; 10–8B; et al.)

Posterior. Direction defined by position of hinge line and/or pedicle opening. (12–1*J*, *L*.)

Pseudopunctate. Shell microstructure characterized structureless rods of calcite in prismatic layer perpendicular to shell surface. May weather out in fossil shells, leaving tiny openings like those in punctate shells. (12–1E.)

Punctate. Shell microstructure characterized by small canals extending perpendicularly from inner to outer surface of shell. Typically appear under hand lens as closely spaced pores. (12–1F.)

Socket (soc). Depression along hinge line of brachial valve which receives the hinge tooth of the pedicle valve. (12–1H; 12–2A, B; 12–3A.)

Spiralium. One of a pair of spirally coiled calcareous ribbons that form the brachidium in some brachiopods. (12–2C, D, E.)

Spondylium (spd). Curved plate in mid-line of beak of pedicle valve. Formed by union of dental plates from either side of mid-line and serving for muscle attachment. (12–9C.)

Stomach (sto). Pouch in anterior portion of digestive tube that serves principally for digestion.

Sulcus (sul). Major longitudinal depression, down-arch, along mid-line of valve. Typically associated with up-arch, the fold. (12–1J, M; 12–9A; 12–12C; et al.)

Tooth (to). Projection along hinge line of pedicle valve that fits into socket on opposing valve. (12–1G; 12–3A.)

Umbo (umb). Relatively convex portion of valve next to (anterior to) beak. (12–1K; et al.)

Valve (v). One of the two curved, chitino-phosphatic or calcareous plates that form the brachiopod shell and that surround and lie, respectively, above and below the soft parts.

---

valves and the two incurrent paths on either side. The brachia and cirri lie before the mouth in the anterior part of the shell cavity, and, in many brachiopods, occupy the greater part of the space within the shell. They are supported by attachment to one valve, named for this attachment, the *brachial valve*. Calcified *brachidia* support the lophophore in some groups. These as well as impressions of the lophophore on the interior of the shell give information about the feeding mechanism in fossil brachiopods (Figure 12-2). The size and structure of the lophophore also probably control the shape of the valves to some extent, and modifications of shell shape, such as central folds, must influence circulation of water in and out of the shell. To repeat a statement soon to become monotonous, very little is known of the relation of variations in these structures to variations in the environment.

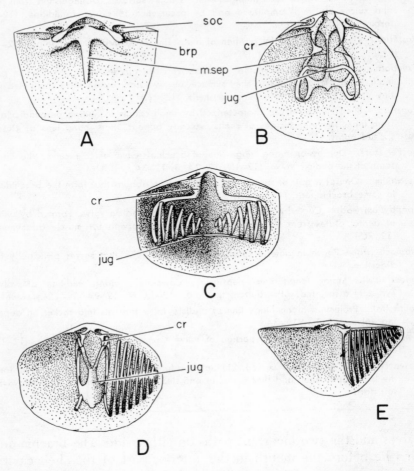

Fig. 12–2. *VARIETIES OF BRACHIDIA.* *A)* Brachiopore. *B)* Loop. *C)* Spiralium, atrypoid. *D)* Spiralium, athyroid. *E)* Spiralium, spiriferoid. Abbreviations: *brp,* brachiopore; *cr,* crus; *jug,* jugum; *m. sep,* median septum; *soc,* socket. (A. After Schuchert and Cooper. B. After Davidson. C.–E. After Beecher.)

Respiration and circulation

Respiration is accomplished primarily by the mantle lobes that line the inside of either valve, but the thin-walled cirri and their cilia may also function in exchange of gases. The adaptation may be expressed in general shell shape, possibly in *plications* of the shell if these correspond to folds in the mantle, and possibly in the *pallial markings* on the inner surface of the shell which record the position of branches on the coelomic space in the mantle (Figure 12-1). Very little is known, and so on—and on.

Support and protection

Some brachiopods attach themselves to objects by a fleshy "stem," the *pedicle;* others, by a reduced root-like or thread-like pedicle, and still others lie free on the bottom, or else cement one valve to solid objects. The pedicle is attached to the valve opposite the one bearing the brachia and gives its name to the valve (*pedicle valve*). The pedicle passes posteriorly through the hinge area, and, therefore, through an opening in one or both valves. The size of the pedicle opening and its location (Figure 12-3)reveal something of pedicle structure and function in fossil brachiopods, as do the scars left in the shell by the attachment of the pedicle and its auxiliary muscles (Figure 12-1). Robust pedicles support the shell

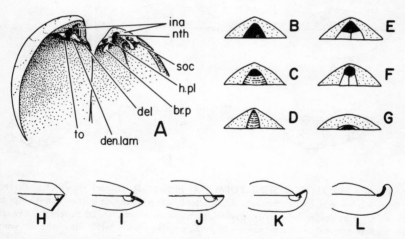

Fig. 12–3. *BRACHIOPOD HINGE LINE AND INTERAREA.* A) General hinge line features. B) through G) Posterior view of valve. B) Pedicle valve; delthyrium completely open. C) Pedicle valve; delthyrium partly closed by deltidium. D) Pedicle valve; delthyrium nearly closed by deltidium; pedicle vestigal. E) and F) Delthyrium partly covered by deltidial plates. G) Brachial valve; notothyrium partly covered by chilidial plates. H) through L) Lateral view of valves showing attitude of interarea by heavy line. H) Interarea on pedical valve, at acute angle to plane of commissure. I) Interareas on both valves, at obtuse angle to commissure. J) Interarea on pedicle valve, in plane of commissure (straight). K) Interarea on pedicle valve, at angle greater than 180° (reflex). L) Interarea on pedicle valve, changing angle with growth. Abbreviations: *brp,* brachipore; *del,* delthyrium; *den. lam,* dental lamella; *h. pl,* hinge plate; *int. a,* interarea; *nth,* notothyrium; *soc,* socket; *to,* tooth.

above the substrate; small ones anchor it as it rests on the surface of one valve or the other.

Species that lack a muscular pedicle risk settling into soft bottom sediments or burial by continued deposition. The strongly convex lower valves of some and the high *folds* (Figure 12-4) of others functioned, perhaps, to keep the valve margin, through which water was drawn, from being covered. The spines found on some brachiopod shells probably supported the animals on soft substrates. Elongate, round, and winged shapes (Figure 12-5) must also be or have been adaptive either to bottom conditions or to turbidity and turbulence. Since the substrate character, turbidity, and turbulence are determinable in some fossil occurrences, paleontologists have investigated this aspect of brachiopod paleoecology (for examples see Cooper, 1957, and the papers he cites) more than any other.

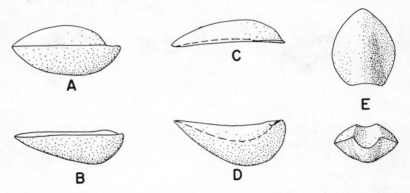

Fig. 12–4. *BRACHIOPOD SHELL FORM. A) through D) Lateral views of shell form. A) Both valves convex (biconvex). B) Brachial valve plane, pedicle convex (plano-convex). C) Brachial valve convex, pedicle plane (convexi-plane). D) Brachial valve concave, pedicle convex(concavo-convex). E) Pedicle valve and anterior view of both valves. Sulcus in brachial valve and fold in pedicle.*

A calcareous or chitinophosphatic shell protects the individual brachiopod against its predators and parasites and against some inclemencies of the physical environment. Some hold the valves in articulation with an elaborate set of muscles; others have a hinge with teeth and sockets and with a variety of supporting plates and of attachments for the muscles (Figure 12-1). Again, very little is known of the details. Are variations in the muscular apparatus that opens and closes the valves or in the articulation of valves adaptively significant? Does the thickness and composition of the shell influence predation or resistance to turbulence, or is the chemistry of the environment more important? To what extent are shape or plications related to predators and turbulence?

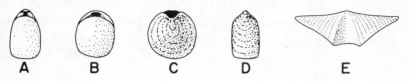

Fig. 12–5. *VARIATION IN BRACHIOPOD SHELL FORM. A)* Elongate ellipsoidal. *B)* Ellipsoid. *C)* Subcircular. *D)* Linguliform. *E)* Winged or alate. *A)* through *D)* are brachial views; *E)* a pedicle view.

THE DIFFICULTIES IN BEING A PALEONTOLOGIST

These questions about adaptive significance loom large in interpreting brachiopod phylogeny as well as in paleoecology. Many of the recognized taxonomic units in many groups of fossil animals probably are artificial, i.e., they do not correspond to phyletic units. Since paleontologists do not know and probably never will know the adaptive significance of all fossil characteristics, they can not distinguish characteristics inherited from common ancestors from those evolved to fit similar environments. In classification, they must simply do the best they can. In only a few kinds of animals like the vertebrates, do they understand adaptive trends so thoroughly that there can be very few artificial taxonomic assemblages.

Brachiopods fall tantilizingly between these two extremes. Their characteristics, obviously, have adaptive significance, but that significance is unknown for many of them. For this reason, the interpretation of brachiopod evolution has changed periodically as additional information accumulated. Paleontologists specializing in brachiopod phylogeny and taxonomy have sought conservative characteristics that appeared early in the divergence of the various stocks and remained stable through their subsequent evolution. They have not been altogether successful—unless one of the current arrangements is valid.

Parallelism and convergence

This may strike you as an academic problem, but examine the case of *Tetractinella* and *Cheirothyris* (Figure 12-6). Externally, the two are hardly more different than individuals within a single species. A nonspecialist finding them in the field would certainly believe them the same species—and probably the same age. The shell of *Cheirothyris* is punctured by minute holes, the *puncta,* and the brachidia are loop shaped. But *Tetractinella,* on the other hand, has a *nonpunctate* shell and spiral brachidia. On the basis of internal characteristics, they belong to different orders. In addition, *Tetractinella* is Triassic and *Cheirothyris* Jurassic in age—a difference of some importance to stratigraphers. This similarity of

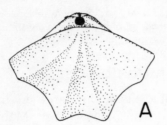 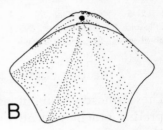

Fig. 12–6. CONVERGENT EVOLUTION IN THE BRACHIOPODA. A) Tetractinella, a middle Triassic rostrospiracean. B) Cheirothyris, a late Jurassic terebratulid. (After Cloud.)

form must result from adaptation to similar environmental factors in distinct stocks; it is, briefly, a result of convergence (p. 178). Many other examples, both of parallelism and convergence, are known in the brachiopods; surely many others exist undetected.

A provisional phylogeny

In spite of this difficulty, certain broad trends and patterns appear if one examines brachiopod evolution broadly and with reference to sets of characteristics rather than individual structures (see Table 12–1).*

The proto-brachiopod. When the first, unmistakable brachiopods appeared in the early Cambrian, they were already diversified, representing four distinct orders and both recognized classes. Most of these early Cambrian genera had chitinophosphatic shells, lacked a definite hinge between the valves, and had an elaborate set of

---

* The embryology of recent brachiopods suggests profound divergence between articulates and inarticulates and within the former group. I cannot give space here, but the reader is warned that the phylogeny is probably more complex than indicated by this classification.

TABLE 12-1

CLASSIFICATION OF THE PHYLUM BRACHIOPODA

(Based principally on Moore, Lalicker, and Fisher, 1952.)

(?) Precambrian. Cambrian to Recent. Bivalves, valves dorsal and ventral. Lophophore consists of a pair of brachia bearing ciliated cirri. Filter feeders. Attach by pedicle, lie free, or cement one valve to substrate. Sessile benthos; marine, a few brackish.

CLASS INARTICULATA

Cambrian to Recent. Valves not hinged but held in articulation by complex set of muscles. Shell chitinophosphatic or, rarely, calcareous.

Order *Atremata*

Cambrian to Recent. Opening for pedicle shared by both valves.

Order *Neotremata*

Cambrian to Recent. Opening for pedicle in pedicle valve alone or absent.

CLASS ARTICULATA

Cambrian to Recent. Valves hinged. Shell calcareous.

Order *Palaeotremata*

Early Cambrian. Hinge simple; lacks teeth and sockets.

Order *Orthida*

Early Cambrian to late Permian. Teeth and sockets on hinge. Typically with wide hinge line, biconvex shell, interareas on both valves.

Suborder *Orthacea*

Early Cambrian to early Devonian. Shell nonpunctate.

Suborder *Dalmanellacea*

Middle Ordovician to late Permian. Shell punctate.

Order *Pentamerida*

Middle Cambrian to late Devonian. Biconvex, impunctate shell; hinge line short; strong platform for hinge line structure.

Order *Strophomenida*

Early Ordovician to Recent. Pseudopunctate shell. Wide hinge line. One valve nearly plane or concave. Pedicle opening very small or absent.

Suborder *Strophomenacea*

Early Ordovician to Recent. Interarea well developed on one or both valves.

Suborder *Productacea*

Late Ordovician to late Permian. Interarea very small or absent.

Order *Rhynchonellida*

Middle Ordovician to Recent. Biconvex shells. Typically strong plications; strong beaks on one or both valves. Hinge line short and interareas very small or absent. Impunctate or punctate.

Order *Spiriferida*

Middle Ordovician to Jurassic. Shells contain spiral brachidium. Typically biconvex with interarea, large or small, on pedicle valve but none on brachial valve.

Suborder *Atrypacea*

Middle Ordovician to early Mississippian. Impunctate. Hinge line short, interarea small. Shell costate and plicate.

Suborder *Spiriferacea*

Middle Silurian to Jurassic. Impunctate. Hinge line wide; interarea moderate to large.

Suborder *Rostrospiracea*

Middle Silurian to Jurassic. Impunctate. Hinge line short; interarea small. Shell smooth.

Suborder *Punctospiracea*

Late Silurian to Jurassic. Punctate shell. Characteristics otherwise of other suborders.

Order *Terebratulida*

Late Silurian to Recent. Shell contains a looped brachidium. Biconvex; short hinge line; interarea on pedicle valve only. Pedicle opening partly closed leaving circular foramen. Shell punctate.

---

muscles to hold them in articulation (Figure 12-1). Some also had a large pedicle which extended through notches developed on both valves. Since these are most similar to larval brachiopods and since recent genera with these characters possess what seems a generally primitive anatomy, they are considered closest to the hypothetical ancestral species.

Initial radiation. This primitive stock of hingeless brachiopods forms a class, Inarticulata. When they first appear in the record, some had the pedicle opening shifted to the pedicle valve alone or had lost the pedicle altogether; some cemented themselves to the substrate by one valve; some formed calcareous shells in place of the chitinophosphatic. Two orders are recognized, the Atremata,

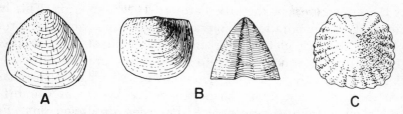

Fig. 12–7. *THE BRACHIOPOD RADIATION: INARTICULATA.* A) Atremate *Obolus;* Cambrian to Ordovician; pedicle view; length 1.6 cm. B) Neotremate *Acrotreta;* Cambrian to Ordovician; brachial view of brachial valve and posterior view of pedicle valve; length 7.5 mm. C) Neotremate *Crania;* Ordovician to Recent, brachial valve, brachial view; length 1.2 cm. (A. and B. After Walcott. C. After Piveteau, ed. *Traité de Paléontologie.* Copyright, Masson et Cie, Paris. Used with permission.)

which have a pedicle opening in both valves and the Neotremata, which have it confined to the pedicle valve (Figure 12-7).

Among the early Cambrian brachiopods that evolved calcareous shells are two groups of special interest. One, the order Palaeotremata, includes only three genera; these are distinguished by a definite hinge line for articulation at the posterior border and a flattened area next to the hinge, the interarea (Figure 12-8). Several other genera, classified in the order Orthida, have teeth and sockets along a wide hinge line and an interarea on both valves (Figure 12-8). The palaeotremates and orthids represent the suc-

Fig. 12–8. *THE BRACHIOPODA RADIATION: PALAEOTREMATA AND ORTHIDA.* A) Palaeotremate *Schuchertina;* middle Cambrian; pedicle valve, pedicle and posterior views; length 1.4 cm. B) Orthid *Nisusia* early and middle Cambrian; pedicle valve, pedicle and posterior view; length 1.4 cm. (A. After Piveteau, ed. *Traité de Paléontologie.* Copyright, Masson et Cie, Paris. Used with permission. B. After Walcott.)

cessive steps in the evolution of an articulation between the valves and are considered the initial representatives of the other brachiopod class, the Articulata.

The Second Round. The diversification of brachiopods proceeded through the middle and late Cambrian, but the only real novelty was the appearance of the articulate order, Pentamerida. This line continued the elaboration of hinge line structure with the formation of an internal platform for muscle attachment (Figure 12-9).

This progressive and moderate increase in brachiopod variety was interrupted by a burst of evolution in the Ordovician—nearly three times as many Ordovician genera are known as Cambrian. The first new group to appear was the order Strophomenida (Figure 12-10), presumably derived from unknown orthid ancestors. Their hinge line, like that of orthids, was very wide, but, typically, one valve was flattened or concave, and the shell had vertical rods of structureless calcite in the primitive laminated layer, a *pseudopunctate shell* (Figure 12-1). Two additional orders appeared in the middle Ordovician. The Rhynchonellida characteristically have biconvex shells that are strongly plicate (Figure 12-10). The posterior portion of one or both valves is commonly drawn out into a prominent beak. The hinge line is very short and the interareas rudimentary or absent. Presumably, they too had orthid ancestors, but the connecting forms have not been found, or, if found, their

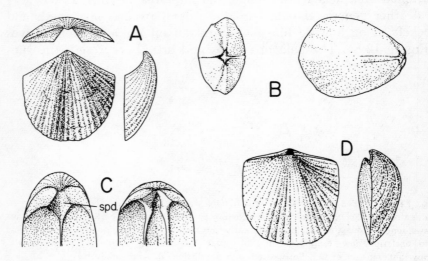

Fig. 12–9. *THE BRACHIOPOD RADIATION: ORTHIDA AND PENTAMERIDA.* A) Orthacean *Eoorthis;* middle Cambrian to early Ordovician; pedicle valve, posterior, pedicle, and lateral views; length 1.8 cm. B) Pentamerid *Pentamerus;* middle Silurian; posterior and pedicle views; length 8.0 cm. C) Pentamerid *Conchidum;* middle and late Silurian; internal views of posterior end of pedicle and brachial valves. Note specialized hinge structures. D) Dalmanellacean *Dalmanella;* early Silurian; brachial and lateral views; length 1.2 cm. (A. After Walcott. C. After Schuchert and Cooper.)

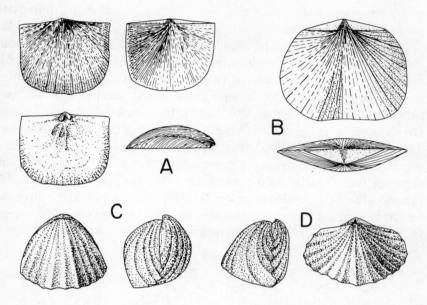

Fig. 12–10. *THE BRACHIOPOD RADIATION: STROPHOMENACEA, RHYNCHONEL-LIDA. A)* Strophomenacean *Rafinesquina;* late Ordovician; upper views pedicle and brachial, lower views interior of brachial valve and lateral; length 3.1 cm. *B)* Stropho-menacean *Orthetes;* Devonian to Pennsylvanian; brachial and posterior views; length 1.7 cm. *C)* Rhynchonellid *Rhynchotrema;* Ordovician; brachial and lateral views; length 1.9 cm. *D)* Rhynchonellid *Camarotoechia;* Silurian to Permian; lateral and brachial views; length 1.4 cm. *(B. After Piveteau, ed. Traité de Paléontologie. Copyright, Masson et Cie, Paris. Used with permission.)*

significance has not been recognized. The early members of this group retain the simple lamellate shell structure.

The Ordovician Spiriferida are somewhat similar to the Rhynchonellida in external features with a rounded biconvex shell, a short hinge line, and a small interarea limited to the pedicle valve (Figure 12-11). Internally, they are quite different, for they possess brachidia arranged in a close spiral—the first appearance of calcified supports for the lophophore. Their ancestry is unknown, though it too may lie in the Orthida.

In addition to these new groups, the older orders produced a series of advanced forms. Among the inarticulates, genera with calcareous shells appeared in both orders. This change seemingly occurred by parallel evolution, and it also paralleled an earlier event in the Articulata. The orthids now included a wide variety

of forms, some with one valve flat or concave, and a group with
punctate shells (Figure 12-9D).

Boom. By the end of the Silurian, all of the orders of brachiopods
—and all but one of the different suborders—joined the benthonic
associations; the evolutionary possibilities of the brachiopod plan
had been completely exploited. Some lines became extinct; two
suborders of the Neotremata failed to survive the end of the
Ordovician; a suborder of Atremata dropped out in the Silurian.
Three inarticulate suborders, one atremate, and two neotremate,
survived and, though never prosperous, hung on to the Recent.
Some of these inarticulate genera have extremely long stratigraphic
ranges (*Lingula,* Ordovician to Recent; *Orbiculoidea,* Ordovician
to Cretaceous; *Discinisca,* Jurassic to Recent; *Crania,* Ordovician
to Recent) and have demonstrated remarkable stability of form.

Fig. 12–11. *THE BRACHIOPOD RADIATION: ATRYPACEA. A) Zygospira;* Ordovician
to Silurian; brachial and lateral views; length 1.5 cm. *B) Atrypa;* Ordovician to Devonian; lateral and brachial views; length 3.8 cm.

The orthids with nonpunctate shells began to fall off in variety
and numbers before the close of the Ordovician, but their place
was taken by the punctate types. The pentamerids lasted out the
Devonian with a maximum of diversity in the Silurian. The
strophomenids and rhynchonellids continued to be abundant.

The spiriferids diversified in a remarkable fashion in the later
Silurian and in the Devonian (Figure 12-12). The initial group
(the Atrypacea) expanded considerably, and three additional suborders appeared. One of these lines (the Spiriferacea) typically
has a wide hinge line, a large interarea on the pedicle valve, and
costate or plicate shells. Another (the Rostrospiracea) retain the
short hinge and small interarea of the Ordovician genera but have
smooth shells and strong beaks. The final group (the Punctospiracea)
display a variety of shell form but are characterized by a punctate
shell.

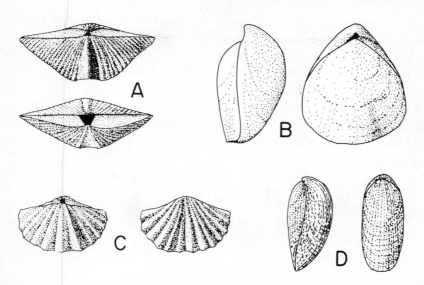

Fig. 12–12. *THE BRACHIOPOD RADIATION; SPIRIFERIDA AND TEREBRATULIDA.*
A) Spiriferacean *Mucrospirifer;* middle and upper Devonian; brachial and posterior views; length 2.0 cm. B) Rostrospiracean *Meristella;* middle Silurian; lateral and brachial views; length 2.6 cm. C) Punctospiriferacean *Trematospira;* middle Silurian to middle Devonian; brachial and pedicle views; length 1.2 cm. D) Terebratulid *Etymothyris;* lower and middle Devonian; lateral and brachial views, length 4.5 cm.

A distinctly new order, the Terebratulida, also showed up in the late Silurian, possibly as a late deviant from the orthid main line (Figure 12-12). They, like the spiriferids, have brachidia, but rather than a spire, it forms a more or less complex loop. Characteristically the terebratulids have a short hinge line and a small interarea on one valve, the pedicle. The portion of the pedicle notch next to the hinge line is closed over so that a round opening is left at the posterior edge of the interarea. Typically, the beak on the pedicle valve is strongly developed.

And bust. The brachiopods reached their zenith in the late Silurian and early and middle Devonian. The punctate orthids survived in moderate numbers to the end of the Paleozoic, but their nonpunctate relatives are unknown later than middle Devonian. The pentamerids lasted only to the end of that period. All the spiriferid suborders declined in variety. The Atrypacea became extinct in the early Mississippian. The other suborders, though they persisted until Jurassic time, are represented by only a few genera after the early Pennsylvania.

The typical strophomenids also declined in the later Paleozoic, even though they managed to survive to the Recent. An obscure group of strophomenids that evolved in Ordovician with rudimentary interareas, deeply concave brachial valves, and strongly convex pedicle valves (Figure 12-13) did flower in the late Paleozoic and are among the most common and characteristic fossils through the Mississippian, Pennsylvanian, and Permian. But this suborder, the Productacea, became extinct at the end of the Permian.

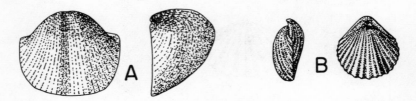

Fig. 12–13. *The BRACHIOPOD RADIATION: PRODUCTACEA AND RHYNCHONELLIDA.* A) Productid *Dictyoclostus;* Mississippian to Permian; pedicle valve, pedicle and lateral views; length 3.4 cm. B) Rhynchonellid *Kallirhynchia;* Jurassic; lateral and branchial views; length 2.8 cm.

The rhynchonellids outlasted most of their brachiopod contemporaries, underwent a considerable radiation in the Mesozoic, and survived to the Recent. Even so, they dwindled in numbers in the late Paleozoic. The latecomers in brachiopod evolution, the terebratulids, hung on in small numbers after a truncated early Devonian radiation. They, like the rhynchonellids, diversified in the Mesozoic, presumably into habitats vacated by the Paleozoic and early Mesozoic brachiopod extinctions, and they are the most diversified of recent brachiopods, numbering over forty genera.

A stratigrapher's eye view

As you should expect from the preceding description of brachiopod evolution, many genera had short stratigraphic ranges. Although most also had limited environment ranges and geographic distribution, they are of great importance as guide fossils. Many lower and middle Paleozoic sequences are zoned by brachiopod assemblages, and productid and terebratulid genera and species are useful stratigraphic markers in the late Paleozoic and in the Mesozoic. Since the various orders and suborders have a fairly short period of abundance, the brachiopod faunas have a characteristic appearance in the major time units, even though particular genera are not identified.

As sessile benthos, brachiopods show a particular sensitivity to the environment of sedimentary deposition, and a particular type of sedimentary rock is likely to bear a particular brachiopod assemblage. The significance of this to paleoecology and paleogeography is obvious. From a very general viewpoint, the occurrence of abundant brachiopods indicates water of moderate to shallow depth and of approximately normal salinity. The modern inarticulate, *Lingula,* can tolerate brackish waters, and fossil lingulids commonly occur in beds that lack a normal marine faunal assemblage and that are intimately associated with beds bearing fresh water and terrestrial plants and animals. Brachiopods are also important components of Paleozoic "dwarf" faunas. These, composed of small fossils, have long been considered the results of hypersaline, brackish, or otherwise unfavorable environments that prevented normal growth. Recent restudy, principally by Tasch, has shown that most of the "dwarfs" are either young individuals or adults of normally small species collected by some sort of sorting processes.

REFERENCES

Beurlen, Karl. 1952. "Phylogenie und System der Brachiopoda Articulata," *Neues Jb. Geol. u. Palaont.,* Mh. H. 3, p. 111-125.

Cloud, P. E. 1942. "Terebratuloid Brachiopoda of the Silurian and Devonian," *Geol. Soc. of America, Special Paper 38.* An important work on brachiopod morphology and evolution.

Cooper, G. A. 1957. "Brachiopods" (annotated bibliography), in: "Treatise on Marine Ecology and Paleoecology," vol. 2. *Geol. Soc. of America, Memoir 67,* pp. 801-804.

Elliott, C. F. 1953. "Brachial Development and Evolution in Terebratelloid Brachiopods," *Biol. Review,* vol. 28, pp. 261-179. An important recent paper on brachiopod evolution.

Greiner, H. 1957. "*Spirifer Disjunctus:* Its Evolution and Paleoecology in the Catskill Delta," *Peabody Mus. of Nat. Hist., Yale Univ., Bulletin 11.* A detailed study of a small group of late Devonian brachiopods.

Moore, R. C., C. G. Lalicker, and A. G. Fischer. 1952. See references for Chapter 3.

Thomson, J. A. 1927. "Brachiopod Morphology and Genera (Recent and Tertiary)," *New Zealand Board of Sci. and Art, Manual 7* (Wellington). A classic work on Cenozoic brachiopods.

Williams, A. 1953. "North American and European Stropheodontids: Morphology and Systematics," *Geol. Soc. of America, Memoir 56.* An example of recent work on brachiopod form and classification.

See also general references cited in Chapter 3 and P. E. Cloud (1941) in Chapter 9.

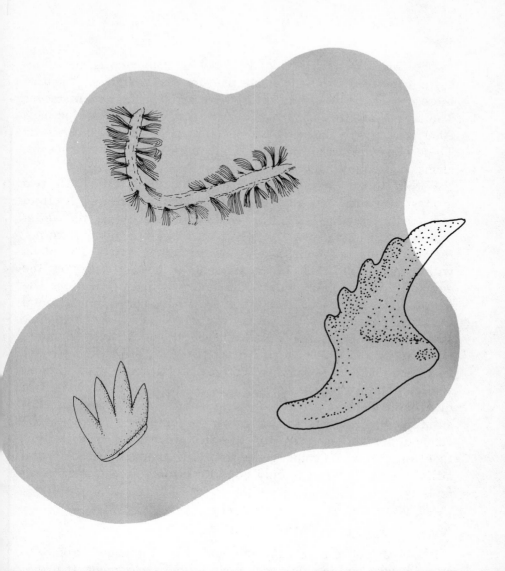

13. Segments: the ANNELIDA

$\mathcal{T}$he bryozoa and brachiopods explored many of the evolutionary possibilities of the coelomate plan for sessile animals. What of those coelomates whose ancestors were active, rather than sessile? The recent and fossil bryozoans and brachiopods number perhaps 2000 genera. Are the active coelomates more or less diversified? These questions are obviously loaded for we, insects, crustaceans, clams, snails, and many other groups are coelomates.

Within this variety of coelomates, biologists distinguish two groups of phyla which may have evolved independently from acoelomate ancestors (p. 267). One of these includes the vertebrates and echinoderms; the other comprises the annelid worms, the arthropods, the molluscs, and several "minor" phyla. The phyla within each group share a similar mode of development from the egg and a similar method of coelom and mesoderm formation. The features shared by both groups include only a few fundamental metazoan characters and a variety of things like brains, circulatory systems, and body segmentation that probably evolved independently to fill similar adaptive needs. When did they separate? In what radiation of primitive metazoans and under what circumstances? The fossil evidence, as usual, helps little to answer these questions. Rather advanced representatives of the annelid-anthropod-mollusc stock and rather primitive members of the echinoderm-chordate occur together in lower Cambrian rocks, but their form shows no convergence toward a common ancestry. Here again paleontologists can only hope for critical Precambrian fossil finds.

ANOTHER DICHOTOMY

The brachiopod-bryozoan line may have branched from the annelid-arthropod-mollusc stock early in its development. If it did, the chief feature conserved from their common ancestry was a microscopic larva characterized by an apical tuft of cilia, a girdle of cilia about its midriff, and a mouth and anus opening below the ciliary girdle. Other than this, there is little to unite the two groups of phyla—each went its own way before the beginning of Cambrian.

The annelid-arthropod-mollusc stock itself did not continue unbranched for long after it differentiated from the acoelomate stock. The annelids and the arthropods are surely very close and, as I will detail shortly, the latter phylum evolved from the annelids, possibly quite late in the Precambrian. The origin of the molluscs is not nearly so clear. The annelids have their body divided into large numbers of similar segments. Some molluscs show rudiments of similar segmentation, and one recently discovered genus displays quite distinct segmentation. These may be vestiges retained from a primitive segmented annelid ancestor or they may have evolved independently in the mollusc line. If the latter is correct, then the common ancestor of molluscs and annelids was a nonsegmented coelomate "worm" with several longitudinal nerve cords, a slightly differentiated head, and a simple circulatory system—or at least these are common features in the annelid and molluscan structural plan.

MERIT BADGE IN SWIMMING: THE ANNELIDA

The segmentation characteristic of the Annelida probably evolved as an adaptation to swimming. The reasons for this conclusion are something like this:

1. Many swimming animals progress by rhythmic contractions of the muscles on alternate sides of the body (Figure 13-1A).

2. This mechanism is most efficient if the contractions pass down the body in a series of waves (Figure 13-1B).

3. The division of the longitudinal body muscles into a succession of small groups which contract and relax in succession brings about such a series of waves (Figure 13-1C).

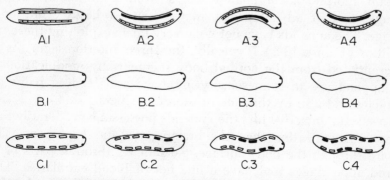

Fig. 13–1. *SEGMENTATION AND LOCOMOTION.* A) Swimming motion in nonsegmented "worm." Alternate contraction of muscles (shown in black) on either side of body. B) A more efficient pattern of swimming. A series of waves passes backward from the head. C) Successive contraction of segmented muscles (in black) produces a series of waves as in B.

This partial segmentation will, of course, be reflected in the longitudinal nervous system, and may also induce segmental development of the other organ systems. It is not clear, however, how this segmentation first arose. Some biologists suggest it was derived from a budding process in which the buds failed to develop into new individuals; others, that it arose gradually in single individuals by subdivision and modification of the primitive longitudinal muscles for this swimming method.

Rewards of virtue

But now to return from the realm of semimythologic ancestors— the segmentation of the body creates important evolutionary possibilities. Successive segments, first of all, acquire different functions and specialize for those functions. Thus, an anterior segment or segments form a distinct head. If, as in annelids, portions of the body wall are folded outward to form paired appendages on each segment, these too may be adapted to special functions. Differentiation of segments results in a body subdivided into functional areas. As the population, and, consequently, the individual animals, evolve, these areas expand or contract. The head region can, in this fashion, spread backward to include additional segments. Since the development of organisms is related to localized regions of biochemical activity, the extent of the head may increase simply through extension of the existing developmental fields. An important morphological change arises from a minor biochemical change, and, if advantageous, may initiate a large evolutionary change. The annelids have not gone very far in exploiting these possibilities (Figure 13-2). Typically, the three anterior segments are differentiated from the normal body segments by modifications of the appendages to form sensory antennae and feeding palps and tentacles and also by the lack of excretory ducts.

To sustain an active life, the annelids possess a considerably more complex organization than the brachiopods and bryozoans. They respire through the body surface, particularly through parts of the paired appendages that have a fine net of blood capillaries. Their circulatory system consists of a set of longitudinal vessels that feed into and drain capillaries. Portions of one of the longitudinal vessels are enlarged to form one or more "hearts." The excretory system consists of paired tubules in each segment (with a few ex-

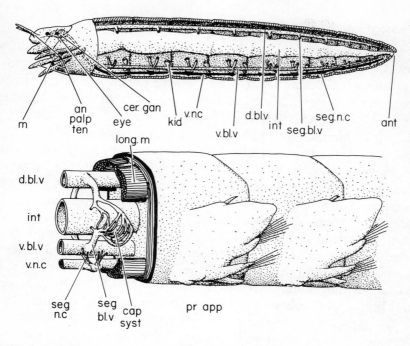

Fig. 13–2. *MORPHOLOGY OF ANNELID.* Upper drawing is a diagrammatic view of a generalized annelid. Head consists of a prostomium bearing antenna and palps and of several fused segments bearing modified tentaculate appendages. Segments behind head are shown in section with muscles, digestive glands, and reproductive organs omitted. Dorsal and ventral blood vessels give off lateral vessels in each segment. The ventral nerve cord terminates anteriorly in a cerebral ganglion and also gives off segmental nerves. The gut opens anteriorly through the mouth, leads back into an intestine and opens posteriorly through the anus. A pair of kidneys occur in each segment behind the head.

The lower drawing shows several enlarged segments, one with cuticle and portions of the muscles removed. The longitudinal are partly segmented. The segmental blood vessels give rise to a capillary network. Blood is pumped from the dorsal vessel through the capillaries into the ventral vessel.

Abbreviations: *an,* anus; *ant,* antenna; *cap. syst,* capillary system; *cer. gan,* cerebral ganglion; *d. bl. v,* dorsal blood vessel; *eye,* eye; *int,* intestine; *kid,* kidney; *long m,* longitudinal muscle; *m,* mouth; *palp,* palp; *pro. app,* paired appendage; *seg. bl. v,* segmental blood vessel; *seg. n. c,* segmental nerve cord; *v. bl. v,* ventral blood vessel; *v. n. c,* ventral nerve cord.

ceptions). A pair of longitudinal ventral nerve cords connects the sensory and motor nerves of the individual segments, and, in turn, are connected to a pair of ganglia in front of the mouth. In some, eyes are present as well as antennae.

Geologic occurrence

Since the group lacks skeletal structures, except for the chitinous jaws or the calcareous tubes of a few genera, the fossil record of the annelids is scant. Some of the "worm" burrows and trails known from Precambrian, as well as later rocks, probably are of annelid origin. The famous Middle Cambrian Burgess shale locality in British Columbia has yielded some ten genera of annelids (Figure 13-3), preserved as carbonized films in the dark, fine-grained shale. Burrows are relatively common, though no one can be certain of the zoologic affinities of the burrowers. Some burrow "species," *Scolithus, Arthrophycus,* are guide fossils. A surprising amount has been written on "worm" paleoecology (Howell, 1957). Certain distinctive burrow types are associated with particular depositional environments; calcareous tubes also occur in a restricted range of environments, and may be associated with particular kinds of shells on which they built their tubes. Some borings in fossil pelecypod and brachiopod valves may be the work of predaceous annelids.

The paucity of fossil annelids contrasts with their biologic importance in modern marine faunas. They are among the most abundant and diversified benthonic animals; they comprise free-swimming, crawling, sessile, and burrowing forms; they include some of the most common and voracious predators, many of the scavengers, and a large percentage of the filter feeders. Even if

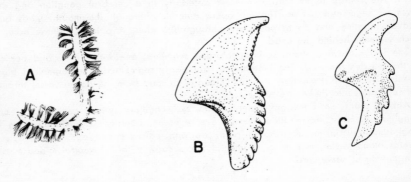

Fig. 13–3. *FOSSIL ANNELIDA.* A) *Canadia;* Middle Cambrian; enlarged about 2.0 times. Paired appendages bear long clusters of bristles. *B)* and *C)* Elements of annelids jaws. *B) Arbellites;* Silurian; upper face of left maxillae; enlarged 30 times. *C) Ildraites;* upper face of left maxillae; enlarged 50 times. (A. After Walcott. B. After Piveteau, ed. *Traité de Paléontologie.* Copyright, Masson et Cie, Paris. Used with permission. C. After Eller.)

they have just reached their climax of diversification—in itself an improbable coincidence—the most significant gap in our knowledge of paleoecology is the lack of the annelid components of ancient faunas.

Homeless waifs

Among the frustrations of the paleontologists who would arrange all animals, fossil and recent, in orderly rank are the various *"problematica."* Several of these, e.g., the archeocyathids and conularids, I have already discussed. Among these orphans are a series of jaw-like or tooth-like fossils (Figure 13-4) that occur in Ordovician to

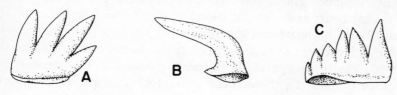

Fig. 13–4. CONODONTS. Three conodonts selected to show the general character of the group. A) *Leptochirognathus;* Ordovician; lateral view; enlarged 20 times. B) *Stereoconus;* Ordovician; lateral view; enlarged 20 times. C) *Neocoleodus;* Ordovician; lateral view; enlarged 30 times. (After Branson and Mehl.)

Triassic rocks. These fossils, the conodonts, are composed of calcium phosphate, and, in this, resemble the vertebrates. Most invertebrate paleontologists, anxious perhaps to be rid of the problem, call them vertebrates. Vertebrate paleontologists prefer to regard them as invertebrates. Since they are of some importance as guide fossils, they can't be disregarded completely.

All other things equal, unidentifiable fossil groups gravitate in the direction of the "worms." Conodonts resemble, at least vaguely, the chitinous jaws of annelids. In consequence, I place them in this chapter without judgment on their true affinities.

MISSING LINKS

One of the most interesting members of the Burgess shale fauna is a species named *Aysheaia pedunculata* (Figure 13-5). These fossils resemble a rather plump worm, show indistinct segmentation, and possess a series of short, massive, paired appendages. Details of the head and of the appendages are obscured, for, like other Burgess fossils, they are crushed and carbonized. What can be seen agrees rather closely with the features of a modern genus, *Peripatus*, and they presumably belong to the same class, the Onychophora. As I implied above, the onychophorans are rather annelid-like. Like some annelids they are covered by a thin impervious waxy layer, the cuticle, and have specialized appendages in the head region that function as antennae and jaw parts. The nervous and excretory systems also resemble those of the annelids. But *Peripatus* diverges from the annelids in several important characteristics. First, the three head segments tend to fuse and lose their distinctness. Second, respiration is carried on within the body, through the walls of minute branching tubes (the trachae) which open in a pit on the animal's surface. Third, the circulatory system consists of a tube-like dorsal heart that pumps blood into the cavities between the organs. Both the heart and the circulatory cavities (the *haemocoele*) are formed within the mesoderm, and the haemocoele replaces the coelomic cavity except in the internal cavities of the gonads and excretory tubules. In these three characteristics, the onychophores resemble the arthropods.

This group of animals, then, in a broad sense, is intermediate between the phyla Annelida and Arthropoda. Because they possess

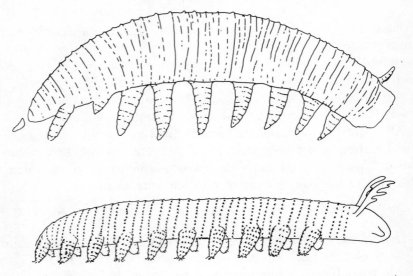

Fig. 13–5. *FOSSIL ONYCHOPORAN.* The upper drawing is of *Aysheaia pedunculata;* middle Cambrian of British Columbia; length 3.6 cm. The lower drawing is a restoration of *Aysheaia.* Even superficially the resemblances to annelids and arthropods are obvious. (After Hutchinson.)

a haemococele and trachae, they are often classified as arthropods. The morphologic similarities of annelids and arthropods, such as segmentation and the paired appendages, suggest a common ancestor with annelid structure. If this interpretation is correct, a linking form, with a mixture of annelid and arthropod features, should have appeared during the evolution of the Arthropoda. The Onychophora show this mixture and thus are a "non-missing" link.

The classification of the onychophorans is difficult. They show the same level of organization as the annelids and many structural similarities. They certainly have diverged no further from the primitive annelid stock than many forms considered "good" annelids. If one prepares a horizontal classification (p. 145) based on this radiation from the ancestral annelid, the Onychophora constitute a separate subphylum or class within the phylum Annelida. On the other hand, an onychophoran lineage (though certainly neither *Peripatus* or *Aysheaia*) probably gave rise to the arthropods. Ergo, the Onychophora form a subphylum of the phylum Arthropoda. Most authorities on these groups compromise by creating a new phylum, Pararthropoda, for the reception of the onychopores and some other arthropod-like groups. There seems to me to be little justification for dodging the issue in this way, but I bow here to the consensus.

REFERENCES

Howell, B. F. 1957. "Vermes" (annotated bibliography), in: "Treatise on Marine Ecology and Paleoecology," vol. 2. *Geol. Soc. of America, Memoir 67*, pp. 805-816.

Hutchinson, G. E. 1931. "Restudy of Some Burgess Shale Fossils," *Proceedings U. S. Nat. Museum*, vol. 78, art. 11, pp. 1-24.

Rhodes, F. H. T. 1954. "Zoological Affinities of the Conodonts," *Biol. Review*, vol. 29, pp. 419-452.

Walcott, C. D. 1911. "Middle Cambrian Annelids," *Smithsonian Misc. Coll.*, vol. 57, no. 5, pp. 109-144.

See also list of general references given at the end of Chapter 3.

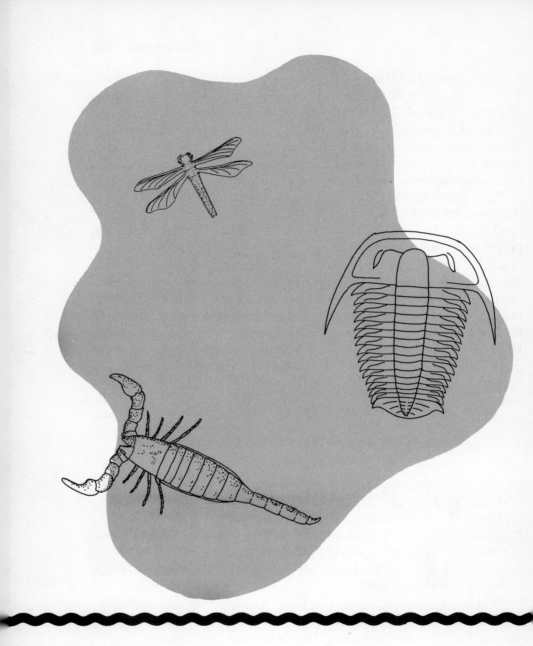

14. *Jointed limbs:* the ARTHROPODA

*A*rthropods—trilobites—characterize the basal Cambrian rocks. Arthropods—insects, crustaceans, and arachnids—by number of species and individuals, dominate nearly all modern natural societies. The fossil record preserves only fragments of this long and successful history, but even these fragments are impressive to the paleontologist.

This evolutionary success rests on a substrate of annelid characteristics, among them segmentation and paired appendages on each segment. These characteristics have been modified (Figure 14-1): (1) by progressive specialization of segments and appendages; (2) by the division of the body in distinct functional regions in which a number of segments may be fused; (3) by formation of a rigid chitinous exoskeleton beneath the cuticle; (4) by the formation of the blood cavities, the haemocoele, and (5) by a large number of changes that increase the efficiency of the nervous, respiratory, and excretory systems. Because the exoskeleton would prevent independent movement of body segments and appendages, the skeleton is divided into jointed segments. The name Arthropoda was adopted from this latter characteristic.

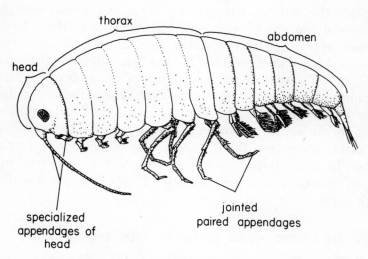

Fig. 14–1. *ARTHROPOD MORPHOLOGY.* Note segmentation, fusion of segments (six in head), differentiation of several regions (three, head, thorax, and abdomen, in this case), jointed paired appendages, and differentiation of appendages. The number of segments, the number and character of the body regions, and the form of the appendages varies widely within the Arthropoda; the general pattern does not.

313

The wide diversification of the arthropods obscures the phylogeny of the major groups. The fossil record helps very little, for here, as in the preceding phyla, most of the important lines appear suddenly. The arrangement of subphyla and classes varies from one paleontologist to another; between paleontologists and biologists, and among biologists. At present, most students of the arthropods use the structure and arrangement of the appendages as their primary criteria in classification. Some arthropod groups, like the insects, seem homogeneous and represent descendants from a single ancestral population. Others appear more heterogeneous and may represent several phyletic lines that evolved parallel or convergent characteristics. Special problem children are a variety of Paleozoic forms, among them the trilobites, that exhibit a bewildering mixture of primitive characteristics, of unique specializations, and of features otherwise limited to recognized homogeneous classes.

The classification of Table 14–1 follows Vandel's arrangement in *Traite' de Zoologie* (1949). These difficult early types are grouped in a subphylum Trilobitomorpha, united principally because of a common array of primitive characters in antennae and the other paired appendages. As thus defined, Trilobitomorpha represents the earliest arthropod radiation and should include the ancestors of the more "advanced" classes, though these have not yet been spotted. The subphylum Chelicerata includes spiders, scorpions, king crabs, euripterids, and "sea spiders" distinguished by the specialization of the single pair of appendages in front of the mouth as pincers, by the consequent absence of antennae, and by the division of the body into two parts, the head (*prosoma* or *cephalothorax*) and abdomen (*opisthosoma*). The subphylum, Antennata, comprises those classes, the crustaceans, myriapods (centipeds and millipeds), and insects, which have one or two pairs of antennae and several pairs of appendages modified as mouth parts.

EST OMNIS DIVISA IN PARTES TRES: THE TRILOBITA

The trilobites failed to equal the success of many of the arthropod classes. They diversified moderately in the early Paleozoic but then fell into a decline and disappeared into the evolutionary graveyard at the end of the Permian. Fortunately for their posthumous fame,

TABLE 14-1

THE ARTHROPODA

(Based in part on Vandel, 1949, and Størmer, 1944 and 1949.)

Cambrian to Recent. Jointed external skeleton of chitin. Segmented; paired appendages on segments. Highly organized, active animals; marine, fresh-water, and terrestrial. Aquatic forms principally benthonic; many terrestrial capable of flight.

SUBPHYLUM TRILOBITOMORPHA

Cambrian to Permian. Primitive arthropods with antennae and simple two-branched appendages. Marine, principally benthonic.

CLASS TRILOBITA

Cambrian to Permian. Body divided longitudinally into three lobes, axial and two pleural. Cephalon of six fused segments; multisegmented thorax; and pygidium of one or more fused terminal segments. Body flattened; eyes on dorsal surface. Calcite and calcium phosphate deposited in shell. Probably lived on substrate or burrowed; ate small animals grubbed from mud. Important guide fossils in early and middle Paleozoic.

Order *Protoparia*

Early Cambrian. Facial suture protoparian; eyes large and crescentic; many thoracic segments; pygidium, if developed, rudimentary.

Order *Proparia*

Middle Cambrian to Devonian. Facial suture proparian. Pygidium typically moderate or large. Thoracic segments numerous.

Order *Opisthoparia*

Early Cambrian to Permian. Facial suture opisthoparian except for a few that have a secondary protoparian suture. Pygidium typically moderate or large. Thoracic segments numerous.

Order *Eodiscida*

Early and middle Cambrian. Facial suture protoparian or proparian. Eyes generally lacking. Pygidium large; pygidium and cephalon nearly equal in size. Two or three thoracic segments. Axial lobe of pygidium segmented. Possibly burrowing.

Order *Agnostida*

Early Cambrian to Ordovician. Facial suture lacking; eyes lacking. Two thoracic segments. Axial lobe of pygidium typically unsegmented. Cephalon and pygidium of nearly equal size. Possibly burrowing.

CLASS MEROSTOMOIDEA

Cambrian to Devonian

CLASS MARELLOMORPHA

Cambrian

CLASS PSEUDOCRUSTACEA

Cambrian

CLASS ARTHROPLEURIDA

Pennsylvanian

SUBPHYLUM ANTENNATA

Cambrian to Recent. Advanced arthropods. Antennae. May or may not have simple two-branched appendages. Appendages of head, except for antennae, specialized as jaw parts. Marine, fresh water, terrestrial, aerial.

CLASS CRUSTACEA

Cambrian to Recent. Two pairs of antennae and typically some primitive two-branched appendages. Body divided into two parts, anterior covered by carapace; terminal segment of abdomen forms telson. Mostly aquatic, marine and fresh water.

Subclass Branchiopoda
Cambrian to Recent. Very small. Appendages leaflike. Carapace may be expanded to cover abdomen. Marine and fresh water. Many planktonic.

Subclass Ostracoda
Ordovician to Recent. Very small. Carapace modified to form a bivalve shell. Calcite deposited in layer of shell. Planktonic and benthonic. Important as guide fossils in well cuttings. Marine and fresh water.

Subclass Cirripeda
Ordovician to Recent. Form shell of calcified plates. Delicate curved and fringed appendages. Sessile, filter feeders. Marine.

Subclass Malacostraca
(?) Cambrian, Ordovician to Recent. Thoracic appendages form stout walking legs. May have calcium carbonate deposited in skeleton. Include recent crabs, lobsters, crayfish, and so on. Principally benthonic, marine and fresh water. A few terrestrial. Scavengers and carnivores.

CLASS MYRIAPODA

Silurian to Recent. Elongate; numerous undifferentiated segments behind head, each bearing walking legs. Single pair of antennae. Trachae. Terrestrial. Includes centipeds and millipeds.

CLASS INSECTA

Devonian to Recent. Three body regions, head, thorax and abdomen. Three thoracic segments bear walking legs. Paired appendages of abdominal segments rudimentary or absent. Most have two pairs of wings, on second and third thoracic segments. Trachae. Terrestrial and fresh water—air breathers. Many capable of flight. Scavengers, herbivores, predators.

SUBPHYLUM CHELICERATA

Cambrian to Recent. Body divided into prosoma and opisthosoma. No antennae; anterior pair of appendages bear claws; appendages about mouth only slightly modified. Benthonic; marine, (?) fresh water, terrestrial. Carnivores or scavengers.

CLASS MEROSTOMA

Cambrian to Recent. Gills on paired appendages of opisthosoma. Terminal segment bears a spine, the telson. Marine, (?) fresh water.

Subclass Euripterida

Ordovician to Permian. Opisthosoma always composed of distinct segments. Sixth pair of appendages large, oar-like. (?) Fresh water and/or marine.

Subclass Xiphosura

Cambrian to Recent. Opisthosomal segments commonly fused. Sixth pair of appendages normal walking legs. Marine and (?) fresh water.

CLASS ARACHNIDA

Silurian to Recent. No gills. Book lungs or trachae present. No appendages on opisthosoma. Four pairs of walking legs. Terrestrial. Includes scorpions and spiders.

CLASS PYCNOGONIDA

Devonian to Recent. Opisthosoma rudimentary. Legs very elongate. No gills. Marine.

---

the trilobites deposited calcium carbonate in their exoskeletons and abounded in shallow marine environments. The first assured their preservation; the second guaranteed their value to stratigraphers who must deal largely with rocks formed in those environments.

The trilobite adaptation

The trilobites exhibited most of the general evolutionary tendencies of the arthropods with particular modifications for their mode of life (Figure 14-2). The flattened body (often accentuated by compaction of sediments), the location of the mouth on the ventral surface and of the eyes on the dorsal, and the structure and arrangement of the appendages (Størmer, 1944) indicate they were benthonic animals that crept or swam along the bottom and fed on small organisms and organic debris in the bottom muds. The body is differentiated into three regions, the head, the *cephalon*, consisting of six fused segments (the most anterior segment was

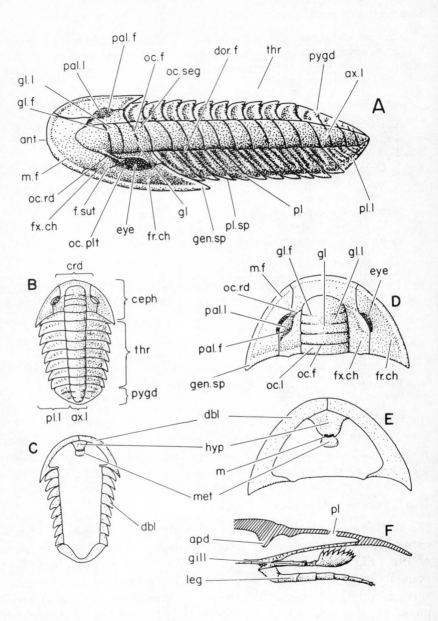

Fig. 14–2. *TRILOBITE MORPHOLOGY. A)* Diagram of trilobite, oblique view. Shown at approximately life size. *B)* Dorsal view of trilobite. *C)* Ventral view; the medial surface was covered by membraneous wall and bore legs. *D)* Dorsal view of cephalon. *E)* Ventral view of cephalon. *F)* Cross section of pleuron (cross lines) with ventral body wall restored (dashes) and leg in position (stippled shading). *(F. After Størmer.)*

GLOSSARY FOR TRILOBITA

(Illustration numbers cited at end of definition.)

Antenna (ant). One of a pair of slender, many segmented, appendages attached to the ventral surface of the head in front of the mouth.

Appendifer (apd). Downward projection from dorsal interior of thoracic segment which served for attachment of limb muscles. (14–2F.)

Axial lobe (ax. l). Portion of trilobite along mid-line. Distinguished from lateral (pleural) lobes by greater height and convexity and typically separated from them by a furrow.

Brim (brm). Portion of cranidium in front of the anterior margin of glabella and of a line from glabella to the anterior edge of eyes (the ocular ridges where developed). (14–2D; et al.)

Cephalon (ceph). Anterior portion of trilobite—the head—consisting of several fused segments and bearing the eyes and mouth. (14–2B, D; et al.)

Cheek. Portion of dorsal surface of cephalon lateral and anterior to glabella. Typically much lower and flatter than glabella and separated from it by a furrow.

Cranidium (crd). Central part of cephalon including axial lobe (glabella) and that portion of the cheek which remains attached to the glabella during molting (fixed cheek). Separated from remainder of cephalon by the facial suture. (14–2A, B; 14–3.)

Dorsal furrow (dor. f). Groove that bounds axial lobe of trilobite. (14–2A; et al.)

Doublure (dbl). Portion of dorsal exoskeleton that is bent under to form a border about the ventral surface of the animal. (14–2C, E.)

Facial suture (f. sut). Line along which exoskeleton of head split when trilobite moulted. May be limited to margin of cephalon or may pass as fine line across dorsal surface of cheek. (14–2A, D; 14–3.)

Fixed cheek (fx. ch). Portion of cheek that remained attached to glabella when animal moulted. Separated from the lateral and/or ventral portions of the cephalon along a line called the facial suture. (14–2A, D; 14–3.)

Free cheek (fr. ch). Portion of cheek lateral to line of facial suture. Freed from medial portion of cephalon along this suture when animal moulted. (14–2A, D; 14–3.)

Genal angle (gen. ang). Posterior lateral corner of cephalon. Typically terminates in spine but may be rounded. (14–2A, D; 14–7.)

Genal spine (gen. sp). Spine extending posteriorly from posterior-lateral corner (genal angle) of cephalon. (14–2A, D; 14–7.)

Gill (gill). Leaf-like appendage borne on upper branch of paired appendages.

Glabellar furrows (gl. f). Groove extending transversely across glabella. May be complete or consist of short grooves extending part way from lateral border of glabella toward medial line. (14–2A, D; 14–4.)

Glabellar lobes (gl. l). Transverse lobe on glabella bounded by complete or partial transverse furrows—remnant of original segments fused in cephalon. (14–2A, D; 14–4.)

Hypostome (hyp). Plate on undersurface of cephalon directly in front of mouth. (14–2C, E.)

Leg (leg). Long, rather slender jointed appendage that composes the lower branch of the paired appendages. (14–2F.)

Marginal furrow (m. f). Furrow extending along dorsal surface parallel to margins of cephalon (and pygidium) and just medial to them. (14–2A, B; et al.)

Metastome (met). Small plate on ventral surface of head immediately behind mouth. (14–2C, E.)

Mouth (m). Opening of digestive tract for ingress of food. In trilobites it lies in the ventral mid-line of the head a short distance behind the anterior margin. (14–2E.)

Occipital furrow (oc. f). Transverse groove that marks off the posterior segment of the glabella from the anterior portion of that structure. (14–2A, D; et al.)

Ocular platform (oc. plt). Elevated portion of trilobite cheek that extends laterally from eye. (14–2A; 14–5B; et al.)

Ocular ridge (oc. rd). Ridge connecting anterior edge of eye to sides of glabella. (14–2A, D; 14–3A, B, C; et al.)

Opistoparous. Type of facial suture which crosses cheek, passes along the medial border of the eye and intersects posterior margin of cephalon medial to genal angle. (14–2A, D; 14–3C, F.)

Palpebral furrow (pal. f). Furrow along medial border of palpebral lobe. (14–2A, D; et al.)

Palpebral lobe (pal. l). Elevated portion of cheek along medial border of eye. (14–2A, D; 14–5A; et al.)

Pleural spine (pl. sp). Lateral extremity of pleuron. Pointed or sharply rounded; narrower than the medial portion of the pleuron. (14–2A, F; 14–8A, B, C.)

Pleural lobe (pl. l). Lateral portion of thorax and pygidium to either side of axial lobe —typically lower and flatter than axial lobe and separated from it by a furrow. (14–2B; et al.)

Pleuron (pl). Portion of thoracic segment lateral to axial lobe. (14–2A, F; 14–8A, B, C.)

Proparous. Type of facial suture which crosses the dorsal surface of the cephalon, passes along medial edge of eye, and intersects lateral border of cephalon in front of, or at, the genal angle. (14–3B.)

Protoparous. Type of facial suture which passes along edge of cephalon and does not cross dorsal surface. (14–3A.)

Pygidium (pygd). Posterior portion of trilobite consisting of one or more fused segments. (14–2A, B; 14–8.)

Telson (tel). Spine mounted on terminal or one of near terminal segments and directed posteriorly along mid-line.

Thorax (thr). Portion of body between head (cephalon) and tail (pygidium). Consists of a series of separate articulated segments. (14–2A, B.)

---

probably, though not certainly, rudimentary or absent in the adult), the *thorax*, with a variable number of distinct articulated segments, and the tail, the *pygidium*, which includes one or more segments fused into a rigid plate. A pair of longitudinal furrows divide the body into three lobes—the origin of "trilobite." The *axial lobe* presumably contained the internal organs; the lateral (*pleural*) lobes may have served to protect the paired appendages. The anterior pair of appendages form antennae; the remaining four on the cephalon consist of two-branched limbs, one branch leg-like, the other gill-like. Störmer concluded that these limbs served primarily in locomotion and little if at all in food getting. In this respect, the trilobites are more primitive than other arthropods, which have the cephalic limbs modified for manipulation, cutting, and crushing. If this interpretation is correct, trilobites could have eaten only small, soft-bodied creatures.

The thoracic limbs resemble the last four on the cephalon, though longer and with more slender proximal segments. The leg-like branch presumably functioned as a walking leg, the gill-like branch a respiratory structure. The anterior limbs of the thorax are the largest, and the size diminishes toward the pygidium. The pygidium bears still smaller but similar legs, one pair for each segment.

The evolutionary trends

Within the trilobite stock, several distinct evolutionary trends are observed. These were adaptive; but paleontologists can't agree what all of them were adaptive to. Early workers generalized—and their successors have demolished their generalizations. The most I can do here is to report some of the trends and suggestions which tentatively determine their significance.

The facial suture. One of the more interesting of these trends— interesting at least to the trilobite taxonomist—was the modification of the facial suture, the line along which the external skeleton of the cephalon split during molting (Figure 14-3). Since the trilobite had to shed its rigid exoskeleton many times during growth, the manner in which it did so must have been important to its survival. In larval trilobites and in many early Cambrian genera, the head shield splits along its margin. The facial suture then is located at the border of the cephalon between dorsal and ventral surfaces. Because of its early appearance in the fossil record and because it occurs in the ontogeny of all trilobites, this type, called the *protoparous,* is thought to be the most primitive (but see footnote, p. 335).

The protoparous suture has one obvious disadvantage. Presumably, as the exoskeleton loosened in early stages of the molt, it loosened also over the eyes and interfered with vision. The molting of snakes provides an analogy. Until the molt was complete, the poor beast was partly blind. Larval trilobites, which were blind

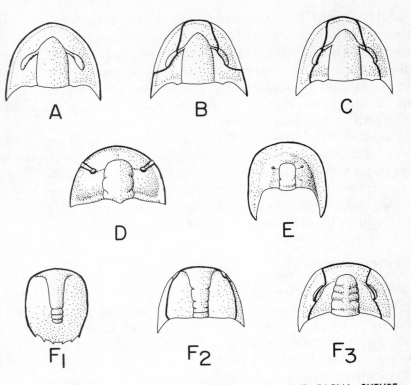

Fig. 14–3. *VARIATION IN TRILOBITE MORPHOLOGY: THE FACIAL SUTURE.* A heavy line indicates the position of the facial suture. *A)* Protoparian, suture entirely marginal. *B)* Proparian, suture passes inward to eye and back out to margin in front of genal angle. *C)* Opisthoparian, posterior end of suture intersects margin behind and medial to genal angle. *D)* Trilobite with reduced eyes. Facial suture largely margin. *E)* Trilobite with vestigal eyes, suture entirely marginal. Members of this group descended from ancestors with proparian suture. *F1)* through *F3)* Ontogeny of opisthoparian trilobite, *Sao.* Note shift of suture and of eyes. *(F. After Barrande.)*

or had their eyes along the border of the cephalon, could do perfectly well with this arrangement. In the adult trilobite, the eyes are well up on the dorsal surface of the cephalon, near the axial lobe; their molt was nearly finished before they could see properly.

The shift of the eyes to the dorsal surface was adaptive and could not be easily abandoned. The obvious solution would be to shift the facial suture also so that it continued to border the eye. In most trilobites this happened, for the suture crosses the dorsal surface of the cephalon in front of the eye, passes along its medial border and returns to the margin behind the eye. If the suture intersects in front of the posterior lateral corner (*genal angle*) of the cephalon, it is called *proparous;* if it intersects at or behind the angle, it is called *opisthoparous.* In either, the eyes would be freed early in molting as the outer part of the dorsal surface (the *free cheek*) separated from the inner (the *cranidium*).

If this interpretation is correct, large-eyed trilobites should all have proparous or opisthoparous sutures, and proparous or opisthoparous trilobites that lack eyes or have only rudimentary ones should tend to return to the protoparous suture.

The only exceptions to the prediction that large-eyed trilobites should have dorsal facial sutures are a series of early Cambrian protoparians. All later examples are proparous or opisthoparous. The exceptions, therefore, do not invalidate the interpretation, but rather suggest that evolution of the dorsal suture began near the opening of the Cambrian.

The evolution of the hypoparian trilobites fulfills the second prediction (Figure 14-3D; E). These had protoparian sutures but differ sharply from other protoparians. They do resemble some opisthoparian genera. An upper Cambrian genus, *Loganopeltoides,* furnishes a clue to their origin. In this genus, the suture crosses the anterior portion of the cephalon, passes around the eye, and then returns directly to the margin, parallel to and a short distance from the anterior part of the suture. *Loganopeltoides* had rudimentary eyes; the hypoparians had similar ineffectual eyes or were totally blind. In species that lost or reduced their eyes, the selection for a dorsal suture is removed. Since the early molts of all trilobites are protoparous, the change would be effected by a retardation of suture development prolonging the larval stage into maturity. Since here the marginal suture is a secondary development, it is named *hypoparian* to distinguish it from the primitive protoparian type.

The glabella. The axial portion of the cephalon forms a distinct lobe, the *glabella* (Figure 14-4). In the early Cambrian trilobites, the glabella is low and divided by *transverse glabellar furrows* into *glabellar lobes,* the remnants of the fused segments. This primitive type of glabella is widest at the back of the cephalon and tapers toward the front. Later trilobites tended to lose the furrows and to modify the shape of the glabella in one of several ways. The adaptive significance of these changes is not clear; some may relate to increased differentiation of the nervous system; some to specialization of the anterior part of the gut, and others to streamlining for swimming or burrowing. The very much inflated glabellas of some species may have been a floatation mechanism—sort of built-in water wings for nektonic types.

The Cheeks. The pleural lobes of cephalon are called the cheeks,

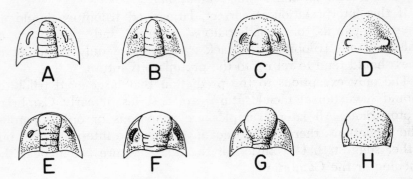

Fig. 14–4. *VARIATION IN TRILOBITE MORPHOLOGY: GLABELLA CHARACTERISTICS.* A) Primitive; glabella segmented and tapering to front. B) Anterior segments less distinct; furrows do not cros glabella. C) Glabella relatively short; two furrows missing; two coalesce and fail to cross glabella. D) Glabella broad, flat, and unsegmented; not distinct from cheek region. E) Anterior lobe of glabella expanded slightly; anterior pair of furrows incomplete. F) Anterior lobe of glabella expanded and reaching anterior edge of cephalon; occipital only complete furrow. G) Glabella inflated, extended beyond anterior margin; furrows incomplete. H) Glabella inflated, unsegmented, not distinct from cheek region.

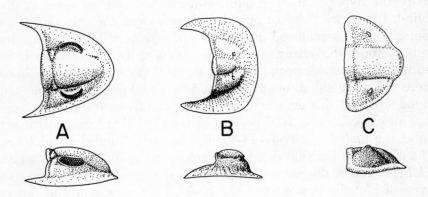

Fig. 14–5. *VARIATION IN TRILOBITE MORPHOLOGY: GENERAL SHAPE OF CEPH-ALON.* Dorsal views at top; lateral views beneath. A) *Proteus.* Glabella distinct and high; ocular platform moderately elevated; margin relatively narrow and steeply sloping. B) *Harpes.* Glabella small but moderately elevated; ocular platform very strongly elevated above margin; margin broad and flattened. C) *Homalonotus.* Glabella not distinct from ocular platform nor platform from margin, margin narrow except for "lip" in front.

that portion lateral to the facial suture is the *free cheek,* and that medial to the suture is the *fixed cheek.* The variation in width and convexity of the cheeks (Figure 14-5) may be adaptive to protection of the limbs that lie below them, to streamlining of the cephalon, or to development of a broad, stabilizing hydrofoil—or to causes unimagined.

The eyes. The trilobite's eyes resemble those of insects, for they are composed of a large number of separate lenses. In the early protoparians, they form an elongate crescent mounted on a lobe that extends laterally from the first glabellar segment. These are probably primitive characteristics, though some paleontologists have argued that some eyeless forms are more primitive. The general trends (Figure 14-6) were toward a separation of the eye lobe from the glabella and the development of a more compact eye. In some lines, the eyes are reduced or disappear altogether. In others, they are enlarged and may be raised on platforms or stalks.

There can be no question that these are adaptations to different requirements for sight. The problem would be simple if left at this vague generalization, but some researchers have not been satisfied. Large eyes have been assigned to:

1. Deep water environments with low light intensities.
2. Shallow water environments with intense lighting.

Degenerate eyes have been stated to be adaptations to:

1. Deep water environments with low light intensities.
2. A burrowing mode of life.

Possibly, each of these interpretations is correct for one or another trilobite species. Unfortunately, no one knows for certain which explanation goes with which species, although the skeletons of some appear to be adapted to burrowing habits, but detailed studies of the environments of deposition would help.

Elevated or stalked eyes increased the field of vision; they may also have permitted the animal to crawl or burrow in the bottom muds with only the eyes exposed. A few genera have extraordinarily large eyes that occupy most of the cheek and extent laterally and ventrally to form the side of the cephalon. These provided vision in all directions and may be adaptive to pelagic life in which dangers approach from below as well as above.

Genal spines. The posterio-lateral corners of the cephalon, the *genal angles,* may be modified in several ways (Figure 14-7), but

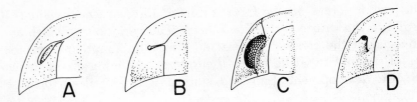

Fig. 14–6. *VARIATION IN TRILOBITE MORPHOLOGY: THE EYES.* A) "Primitive"; eye narrow, flat lobe connected by ocular ridge to glabella. B) Eye rudimentary; ocular ridge present. C) Eye enlarged. D) Eye mounted on end of stalk.

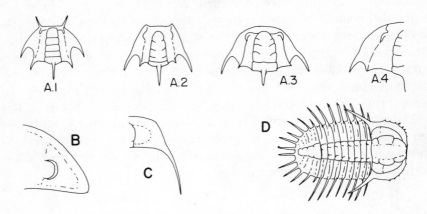

Fig. 14–7. *VARIATION IN TRILOBITE MORPHOLOGY: GENAL SPINES AND SPINOSITY.* A.1) through A.4) Ontogeny of *Leptoplastus* illustrating change in size and position of cephalic spines from larva A.1) to adult A.4). B) Genal angle rounded, no spine present. C) Genal spine slender and elongate. D) Spinose form, *Acidaspis*. Length 2.4 cm. (A. After Raw.)

the significance of these variations is not clear. The immature trilobites possess two or three pairs of spines along the genal border, one derived from the first (pre-antennal) segment, one from the fifth, and one from the sixth. During development, these spines replace one another at the genal angle by a progressive backward shift until the spines of the pre-antennal segment become the adult *genal spines*. Head spines are common among immature aquatic organisms, and function either as adaptations to floating (in the planktonic types) or for attachment to objects on the substrate (in benthonic types). They may also serve in the immature as in the adult for protection against predators. Some features of the genal spines may then be related to larval adaptations. Many genera, however, show developmental changes—enlargement of the spines or their loss—quite late in growth, which culminate in some sort of typical arrangement in the adult. Since many bottom swimmers (sharks, king crabs) have posterior lateral "horns" or similar extensions of the head, the length, size, and angle of spines might have been important in stabilizing the animal on the substrate.

Some genera carry additional spines on the cephalon and elongate spines on the thoracic segments and on the pygidium. Such spines occur in recent animals of the plankton and nekton, and by their frictional drag prevent their bearers from sinking. They may have performed similarly in some small trilobites; in others they may have discouraged predators, served as camouflage, or supported the animal on particularly soft substrate.

The thorax. Since the arthropods evolved from annelids, the ancestral arthropod presumably had a large number of similar and relatively simple segments behind the head. Some Cambrian trilobites retain this primitive condition, but even they complicate the structure by the addition of the lateral processes, the *pleura* and *pleural spines* (Figure 14-8). In the posterior portion of the thorax, these processes are quite short and the spines relatively longer than the pleura. In the anterior portion, the pleura are much wider, and the spines, though long, are shorter in comparison to the length of the pleura. Most trilobite lineages reduce, or have already reduced when first identified, the size of the pleural spines. In turn, the pleura in the posterior portion of the thorax become nearly as wide as those in the anterior. Since the pleura are related to protection and function of the limbs, this modification may echo changes or improvement in the limbs, or it could reflect changes in internal anatomy. Many trilobite lineages reduce progressively the number of thoracic segments by incorporation of some into the pygidium and/or by a decrease in the number of segments formed. Two Cambrian orders, Eodiscida and Agnostida, carried the trend so far that only two or three thoracic segments appear. Some species have axial spines arising from the axial segments— the function is uncertain, though it may have been protective. Others have enormously extended pleural spines.

The pygidium. In some early Cambrian genera, the thorax continues to the terminal segment of the body, unmodified except by diminishing size; in others, the last segment was somewhat flattened and enlarged. This primitive condition is modified by incorporation

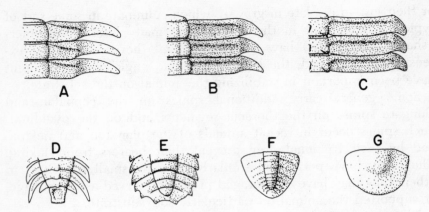

Fig. 14–8. *VARIATION IN TRILOBITE MORPHOLOGY: PLEURA AND PYGIDIA. A)* Narrow pleuron and long pleural spine. *B)* Pleuron wide and spines short. *C)* Spines very short and blunt. *D)* Pygidium consists only of terminal segment and is a small elongate plate. *E)* Pygidium of three segments. Segments strongly marked and border spinose. *F)* Pygidium of ten segments. Segments rather indistinct and those on the pleural portion do not correspond in position with the axial ones. *G)* Axial lobe shortened and merged with pleural lobes. Segments obliterated by fusion.

of additional segments into a large rigid unit (Figure 14-8). The pygidium in some is as large as the cephalon. There is a general trend toward obliteration of segmentation, and the surface becomes quite smooth. In some, the boundary between axial and pleural lobes is lost.

The pygidium may have functioned as a propeller with rapid upward and downward movements, but many paleontologists question this interpretation. Some trilobites without pygidia have a long spine extending backward for one of the posterior segments; others have pygidia with similar spines. These may have been forced downward into the mud for support in locomotion—at least the modern king crab uses a similar structure in this way.

Whatever the locomotor adaptations of the pygidium, they are difficult to identify and difficult to separate from the protective functions. Presumably, a single rigid plate gave better protection than several small separate ones. Among those trilobites that rolled up like pill bugs to protect their delicate appendages and lightly armored undersurface, the pygidium covered the underside of the head, and the larger the pygidium the better the protection.

In addition to all these possible or improbable functions, the development of the pygidium may correlate with changes in the soft anatomy, possibly in the reproductive organs. Since no close relatives survive, the character of the internal organs is largely unknown.

Appendages and ventral surface. Trilobite appendages were rarely fossilized because of their fragile attachment and structure; some apparently had only a chitinoid skeleton unsupported by calcerous deposits which was quickly destroyed after death or molting. For these reasons, the form of most genera is unknown and imperfectly known for many others. Störmer has distinguished some variations that may have had adaptive significance, but, inevitably, study of trilobite appendages lags.

For the same reasons, not much is known of modifications of the underside of the cephalon. The dorsal exoskeleton of the cephalon, pleura, and pygidium is folded onto the ventral surface (Figure 14-2) to form the *doublure*. A large plate, the *hypostome*, lies in front of the mouth; a smaller one, the *metastome*, lies behind it. The hypostome bears the antennae. The remaining paired appendages, the walking legs, arise along either side of the midline behind the mouth.

Correlated trends. To this point I have discussed evolutionary trends in terms of isolated parts, a more or less artificial division of the total organism. This isolation simplifies the problem of analysis, and, so, is justified for that reason. It does not, however, provide a complete interpretation, for these "parts" did not function in isolation. Some trends are known to be correlated with each other—the modification of eyes and facial suture already cited form one example. Unfortunately, less attention has been given to interpretation of the whole animal than to certain spectacular adaptations. Some trends, whose adaptive significance is now a mystery, may find explanation as additional studies of trilobites and their environments demonstrate the functional relationship between parts.

The material basis of evolution

In many fossil groups, the paleontologist deals primarily with the morphology of adult or near-adult animals. If he analyzes evolutionary trends, he does so from a series of adults and without knowledge of the changes in developmental pattern behind these trends. Evolutionary theorists and practical stratigraphers both suffer from this gap in knowledge. If a particular change involved many coordinated modifications in ontogeny, it must have required change in many genes and thus a considerable period of time. If the developmental change was simple, it probably involved only a few genes and could have occurred in a moment of geologic time.

The extensive growth series known in some species of trilobites (Figures 14-9 and 14-10) permit the paleontologist to trace these ontogenetic modifications. Many appear to result from relatively small changes in rate of growth in different parts of the animal.

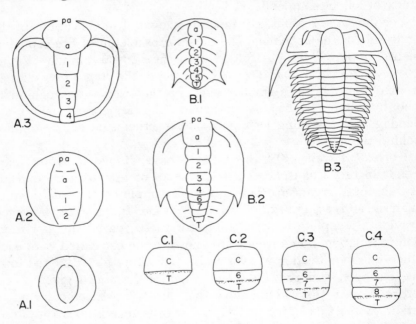

Fig. 14–9. *TRILOBITE ONTOGENY.* *A.1)* through *A.3)* Stages in the development of the cephalon in the species, *Blackwelderia quadrata.* Note progressive differentiation of segments. *B.1)* through *B.3),* Stages in the development of *Olenus.* *B.1)* shows individual just before pygidium (segments 5 and 6) separates from cephalon; the *B.2)* stage consists of cephalon and a five-segment pygidium; *B.3)* has a fully developed thorax and differs from adult only in size and minor details of proportion. *C.1)* through *C.4),* diagram of segmentation in pygidium and thorax. Segments develop at anterior border of terminal segment (stippled area). Initially they are not cut off from the terminal and form part of the pygidium *(C.2.)* and *(C.3).* Later in development they separate successively along the anterior border of the pygidium *(C.4)* so that the anterior thoracic segment of the adult is the first thoracic to appear in the larva. Abbreviations: *a,* antennal segment; *c,* cephalon; *pa,* pre-antennal segment; *T,* terminal segment; numbers indicate other segments, the thoracic and pygidial segments ar numbered in order of appearance. (A. After Endo. B. After Størmer.)

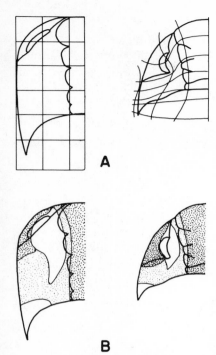

A

B

Fig.   14–10. *GROWTH   PATTERNS.* A)
Transformation of trilobite cephalon during
growth as shown by deformation of coordinate system (also see p. 28). B) Regions
of rapid (heavy stipple), moderate (light
stipple), and slow growth (white) as indicated by relative deformation of coordinates.

It is not yet possible to follow these changes in detail, but sufficient
information has accumulated for some tentative generalizations:

1. The shift of the eyes and facial suture onto the dorsal surface
from the cephalon border must have resulted from an increase in
rate of growth on the border as compared with the dorsal surface.
These structures, therefore, didn't really shift dorsally, but rather
the cephalic border moved away from them. The complexity of this
change has not been determined—it may have involved simple
acceleration of growth at the posterior lateral borders of the first
segment or complex coordinated changes in different parts of several segments.

2. The thoracic segments appeared successively at the anterior
border of the terminal, pygidial, segment. The first thoracic segment developed between the terminal segment and the back of the
cephalon, the second between the terminal and the first, the third
between the terminal and the second, and so on. If the rate of
growth at this point were reduced without a change in rate of

segmentation, the number of thoracic segments would be reduced correspondingly.

3. On the other hand, if the rate of segmentation were reduced, some segments would not be completely cut off from the terminal and would be incorporated in the adult pygidium. A very small number of changes in genes might produce either or both of these morphologic changes.

That these analyses are tentative is obvious; that they will ultimately yield interesting and valuable conclusions is, I hope, equally obvious.

Ontogeny and phylogeny

Interpretation of trilobite origins and phylogeny (Figure 14-11) depends very largely on the particular *a priori* assumptions of the particular paleontologist. If one believes single mindedly that ontogeny recapitulates phylogeny, he places full weight on features

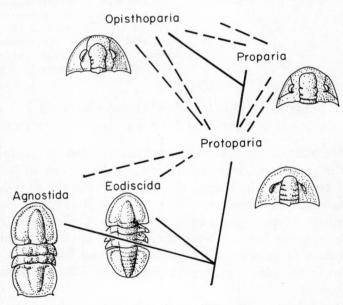

Fig. 14-11. *TRILOBITE PHYLOGENY.* Heavy lines indicate simplest (most primitive?) interpretation of trilobite phylogeny. Dashed lines indicate possible origin of agnostids and eodiscids from normal protoparian types and the probable polyphyletic origin of opisthoparians from protoparians and proparians and of proparians from protoparians.

of ontogeny. If he believes particular changes in characteristics involve large numbers of genes (or, to use pre-genetic terminology, are "fundamental" changes of form) then he arranges the phylogeny on the basis of these characteristics. If he accepts neither, it will be difficult—even impossible—to arrange the various genera in a phylogenetic scheme. All this is true in any phylum or class, but it seems particularly striking in the trilobites.

Segmentation and phylogeny. Since the arthropods evolved from annelids, the ancestral arthropod presumably had a large number of segments. Was the proto-trilobite likewise multisegmented? The consensus now holds that they were, and that genera like the protoparian *Ollenellus* with forty-five or more segments are primitive in this characteristic. In this interpretation, trilobites with fewer segments are specialized (this trend was examined back on p. 327).

Some students of the group have argued an opposite view. They point out that the early developmental stages of all trilobites have only a few segments and that the others are added later. If the rule "ontogeny recapitulates phylogeny" is taken as a dogma, the most primitive trilobites must have had no more than six segments. The trilobites of the orders Eodiscida and Agnostida, which possess two or three thoracic segments, would in this interpretation be most primitive. Members of these orders are either blind or have very small eyes, the cephalon is simple in structure, segmentation of the glabella is distinct, and the facial suture is protoparian. All these are the common characteristics of trilobite larva. Because of these presumed primitive characteristics, some paleontologists believe the trilobite ancestry lies in one of these orders.

All members of these orders, however, have a large pygidium. In most, the individual segments cannot be distinguished in the pygidium. These are surely not primitive characteristics if the annelid ancestor theory is accepted. The loss of distinct segmentation and specialization of the fused segments for a particular function occur late in evolution of the arthropod lineages, not at the beginning. If one does not accept the dogma about ontogeny, there is no reason for accepting the Eodiscid-Agnostid plan as primitive.

Facial sutures and phylogeny. The chief characteristic used in trilobite classification is the location of the facial suture. Three orders of protoparians are recognized, the order Protoparia that includes many-segmented trilobites with normal eyes and the two orders of blind trilobites with reduced segmentation and specialized pygidia. The Protoparia are considered to represent the ancestral stock for all trilobites. The remaining genera are ranked into order Opisthoparia or the order Proparia on the basis of suture type. This implies that all opisthoparian species descended from a single species that evolved the opisthoparian suture and that all proparians had a single proparian ancestor. Since some opisthoparians pass through a proparian stage in development, the proparians are conventionally considered to be ancestral to the opisthoparians.

If the change of suture involved complex changes in gene systems, then it is unlikely that the same change could have happened more than once, and the interpretation is the correct one. The complexity of the genetic change cannot be determined, of course, though some impressions can be gained by a study of the developmental pattern, but other tests are possible. First, is the mode of development similar? Second, does this classification separate species that are otherwise very similar?

To answer the first question, all trilobites in development pass through a protoparous stage. Some, then, develop a proparous suture and retain it to maturity; some develop an opisthoparous suture and retain it also, but others develop a proparous type and then go on to the opisthoparous. Either different trilobites evolved the opisthoparian suture in different ways or else the proparous stage was deleted from or added to the developmental sequence after the origin of the phyletic line. This difference in development lessens the probability that the taxonomic arrangement is correct.

As to the second question, several different opisthoparian genera resemble protoparian genera except for suture type. Other opisthoparians resemble proparous genera. Either the opisthoparian suture evolved independently in several different lineages or else the other similarities are remarkable examples of convergence. Since the suture itself is adaptive, it could well have evolved under similar selection in otherwise distinct species.

For the sake of simplicity and conformity with current usage in the United States, I retain the Protoparian-Proparian-Opisthoparian arrangement for this book, though its validity is very doubtful. As this was written, the section of the *Treatise on Invertebrate*

Paleontology on the trilobites had yet to appear—presumably some new arrangement will be attempted.*

A view from the rocks

Both protoparian and opisthoparian trilobites occur in lower Cambrian rocks as do the agnostids and eodiscids. Proparians appear in the middle Cambrian. This stratigraphic distribution, in itself, throws into question the descent of the opisthoparians from the proparians. Protoparians are not known from rocks above the lower Cambrian, and the eodiscids drop out above the middle Cambrian. Taken as a whole, the trilobites reached their maximum diversity during the Cambrian and Ordovician. The agnostids did not survive the end of the Ordovician, and, although some Silurian and Devonian trilobites are very common, the number of species declined progressively. Only eight genera, all opisthoparians, have been described from Carboniferous beds in North America; this rarity is characteristic of other parts of the world too. The class became extinct at the end of the Permian.

Trilobites are major zonal fossils for the Cambrian, and some genera and many species have short and thus useful stratigraphic ranges. Figure 14-12 shows a few of these. At any particular time, most trilobite genera were sharply restricted in geographic distribution, and, though some of these restrictions have been shown to be the result of local ecologic differences, others are of great value in defining ancient seas and lands.

Though much work has been done on the specific habits of trilobites, Brooks in a recent review (1957) cites only eight papers that deal with interpretation of particular trilobite habitats. Although some other paleoecologic studies touch on the association of trilobite and environment, this number of publications would hardly suggest an oversupply of "trilobite paleoecologists." They

---

* H. J. Harrington (1959) has proposed, in the *Treatise,* an arrangement of trilobite orders markedly different from that used here. Harrington's work was received too late for consideration in the body of this book, but it involves a re-evaluation of various suture types as well as other morphologic features. He concludes, among other things, that all protoparian sutures are specialized, not primitive. In consequence, he recognizes five orders: the Agnostida (including the eodiscids), the Redlichiida (including those forms placed here in the Protoparia as well as many opisthoparians), the Corynexochida (a small group of opisthoparians), the Ptychopariida, and the Phacopida. The two last-named orders include a mixture of opisthoparian and proparian genera as well as several groups with marginal sutures.

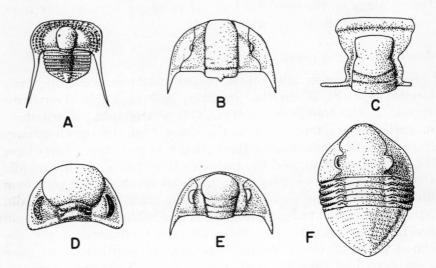

Fig. 14–12. *A HODGEPODGE OF TRILOBITES.* A) *Cryptolithus;* middle to late Ordovician, dorsal view; length 2.7 cm. B) *Olenoides;* middle Cambrian; dorsal view of cephalon; length 3.1 cm. C) *Saukia;* late Cambrian, dorsal view of cephalon; free cheeks missing; length 1.6 cm. D) *Phacops;* Silurian to Devonian; dorsal view of cephalon; length 1.5 cm. E) *Paradoxides,* middle Cambrian; dorsal view of cephalon; length 2.3 cm. F) *Isotelus;* middle to late Ordovician; dorsal view, thorax should show three more segments; length with added segments 7.4 cm.

were entirely marine animals and thrived in a variety of habitats; beyond that little is known. The importance of the trilobites to stratigraphic analyses and evolutionary theory requires that much more be done in this field.

CRUSTACEANS: THE OSTRACODS

As the trilobites slid toward extinction, the crustaceans—and others—slipped into their places. Their origin is obscure, though some of the trilobitomorphs found in the middle Cambrian Burgess shale foreshadow the crustacean form, and some may properly belong to the class. They number among themselves in the recent faunas, lobsters, crabs, crayfish, barnacles, shrimps, copepods, prawns, and water fleas; they inhabit fresh water as well as marine; and a few have adapted to terrestrial environments. They are among the commonest animals of the benthos and include, as well, a variety of planktonic, free-swimming types.

But, in spite of their abundance and diversity, only one of the six subclasses, the Ostracoda, are particularly important to a paleontologist, and two are unknown from fossils. The difficulty lies partly in the composition of the skeleton, for many recent crustacea do not deposit or deposit only small amounts of inorganic compounds in their chitinous exoskeletons. Typically, chitin would be destroyed before burial or in the early stages of diagenesis. A few fossil genera are abundant; some are found in large numbers where the conditions for preservation were unusually good, but most are represented by only a few specimens.

The members of the class Crustacea are distinguished by two pairs of preoral antennae and three pairs of appendages adapted as mouth parts. The anterior segments are fused and covered by a dorsal shield, the *carapace*. The posterior segments are distinct, and the more anterior bear paired legs adapted for walking or swimming. Some or all of the legs bear gills. The terminal segment typically is differentiated to form a spine-like or fin-like *telson*. As one expects in active animals, they have highly developed sense organs, a complex nervous system, and an efficient circulatory system.

In the ostracods the carapace extends down and back to cover the appendages and the abdominal segments (Figure 14-13). The two sides of the carapace are joined in a hinge along the middle of the back to form a bivalve shell. A calcareous layer is deposited within the carapace; this of course is the part preserved as a fossil. Ostracods are fairly abundant in many post-Cambrian beds. Their evolution, as reflected in structure and form of the valves, was rapid. They are small enough to be preserved in well cuttings, and, consequently, they supplement or replace foraminifera as guide fossils in subsurface stratigraphy.

TO LAND: MYRIAPODA

The arthropods are preadapted to life on land. The exoskeleton prevents evaporation of fluids through the body surface; the walking legs can transport an animal on land as well as on the sea bottom, and the skeletal structure is strong enough to support the animal without the help of water. The only real problem was the replacement of the external gills by some sort of internal respiratory organs. This problem was solved by a group of primitive antennate

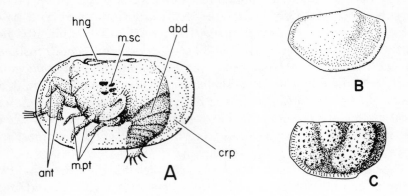

Fig. 14–13. *OSTRACODA.* A) General morphology of the ostracods. Carapace (crp) forms bivalve bivalve shell covering head and abdomen. Appendages behind head are rudimentary. B) *Lepeditia,* Ordovician to early Devonian; lateral view of left valve; length 4 mm. C) *Beyrichia;* Silurian to Permian; lateral view of left valve; length 1.5 mm. Abbreviations: *abd,* abdomen; *ant,* antenna; *crp,* carapace; *hng,* hinge; *m. pt,* mouth parts; *m. sc,* muscle scars (of adductor muscles). (A. After Sars. C. After Bassler and Kellett.)

arthropods by Silurian if not earlier; the chelicerates managed it about the same time.

The myriapods, the oldest and most primitive terrestrial antennate arthropods, include two subclasses, the millipeds (Diplopoda) and centipeds (Chilopoda). The myriapod head, though it bears eyes, antennae, and paired mouth parts, is comparatively small and is followed by a large number of similar leg-bearing segments. Respiration is carried on by diffusion of gases through the walls of internal tubules, the *trachea.* The trachea opens externally on each segment through one or two pairs of pores and may branch extensively through the viscera. Although millipeds occur from the Silurian onward and the centipeds appeared in the early Cenozoic, a geologist is more likely to find one in his boots than in a rock.

INTO THE AIR: THE INSECTA

In one line of the myriapod radiation, an extraordinary modification occurred—possibly in Mississippian time. The body wall of several segments (two at least) close behind the head developed lateral folds or flaps—for what purpose no one seems certain. Two pairs of these flaps enlarged to form wings, though, here again, the adaptive significance of the early steps in wing development are unknown. Among the other flying animals, wings developed from legs in a series of changes which, whether hypothetical or observed, had adaptive significance.

The diagnostic features of insect form apparently evolved before middle Devonian time. However wings evolved, they provided the key modification for the adaptive radiation. They did not, however, "create" the insect form. This form (Figure 14-14), as in most arthropods, is a modification of the annelid plan of similar segments bearing similar paired appendages. The segments of the head are fused; one pair of appendages forms the antennae; the remainder, the mouth parts. The three segments behind the head that form the *thorax* are enlarged and may be partly fused. Each thoracic segment bears a pair of walking legs, and the second and third develop wings in those insects that have them. The posterior

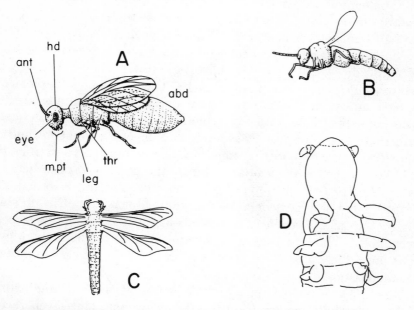

Fig. 14–14. *INSECTA. A)* External morphology of the insects. The three pairs of legs, the wings, and the division of the body into head, thorax, and abdomen are distinctive. *B) Dasyhelea;* Miocene to Recent, lateral view; length 3 mm. *C) Mischoptera;* Pennsylvanian; dorsal view, wing span 17 cm. A representative of an extinct order. *D) Rhyniella;* middle Devonian; ventral view. Abbreviations: *abd,* abdomen; *ant,* antenna; *hd,* head; *m. pt,* mouth parts; *thr,* thorax. (B. After Palmer. C. After Carpenter. D. After Scourfield.)

pair of wings was lost in the order Diptera (flies, mosquitoes, and so on). The remaining segments, typically eleven, form the *abdomen.* The paired appendages of these segments are never more than rudiments, and are typically absent in the adult. Circulatory, nervous, and excretory systems are highly developed. The tracheal respiratory system is very complex and ends in tiny tubules that supply all parts of the body.

On this plan the insects have built a tremendous diversity of form (Figure 14-19). The wings as well as the limbs and body evolved in different directions to fit divergent modes of life. The larval stages are typically adapted to different environments than the adult and undergo a distinct change of form, *metamorphosis,* immediately before they reach maturity. In two orders, social organization evolved with caste systems and elaborate integrating behavior patterns.

A paleontologist, even a hardened "splitter," is likely to quail before the taxonomic complexity of the class Insecta. Modern faunas probably include some 1,000,000 insect species; about 13,000 fossil species have been described; approximately 25 recent orders are recognized; 44 extinct orders have been established (though Carpenter, 1953, reduces this number to 10). Fortunately for paleontologic sanity, insects are terrestrial and have chitinous skeletons. They are, therefore, rare fossils and are preserved in fresh water only in fine grained lake, swamp, and lagoon sediments and in amber. The earliest insects identified are wingless types from the middle Devonian of Scotland. Since the Pennsylvanian beds in North America and Europe contain many lagoon and lake deposits, insects are relatively common and quite diversified. One modern order, that of the roaches, is present; five extinct orders have been recognized. The latter resemble several modern orders, e.g., dragon flies, may flies, and so on, but are primitive in several important characteristics.

The early Permian faunas include representatives of nine extinct orders, mostly holdovers from the Pennsylvanian, and seven recent orders, among them dragon flies and "bugs." Beetles appeared in the late Permian; primitive flies and hymenopterans (wasps, bees, ants) in the Jurassic; and lepidopterans (butterflies and moths) and isopterans (termites) in the early Cenozoic. Many recent families are represented in the Jurassic insect faunas, and many recent genera in the early Cenozoic.

CHELICERATES

Like the crustaceans, the chelicerates have structural predecessors if not actual ancestors in the middle Cambrian Burgess shale fauna. They diverge considerably from the antennate arthropods in form (Figure 14-15), particularly in the absence of antennae, in the presence of claws on the single pair of preoral appendages (*chelicera*), and in the fusion of extra segments into the head (the *cephalothorax* or *prosoma*). Some authorities have considered these divergences great enough to imply that the chelicerates evolved independently from the annelids. The mixture of chelicerate and antennate characteristics in some of the Cambrian trilobitomorphs argues against this conclusion.

The gill bearing, aquatic chelicerates, the Merostoma, first appear in upper Cambrian rocks. The earliest merostomes all belong

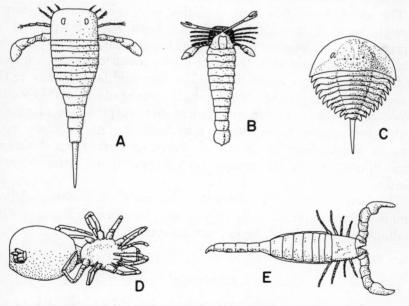

Fig. 14–15. *CHELICERATA.* A) A euripterid; *Eurypterus;* Ordovician to Permian; dorsal view; length 21 cm . Note prosoma, bearing legs, and appendageless opisthosoma. B) A euripterid, *Pterygotus;* Ordovician to Devonian; ventral view; length 20 cm. Anterior pair of appendages possess claws (chelae). C) A xiphosurian, *Neolimulus;* Silurian; length 2.2. cm. D) A spider (Arachnida) *Argenna;* Miocene to Recent; ventral view; length 1.4 mm. E) A scorpion (Arachnida), *Palaeophonus,* Silurian; dorsal view; length 4.8 cm. (A. and B. After Clark and Ruedemann. C. After Woodward. D. After Petrunkevitch. E. After Pocock.)

to the subclass Xiphosura which is chiefly remarkable for its long range (Cambrian to Recent) and for the durability of the genus *Xiphosura,* which has persisted with little change from the Jurassic to the Recent. The xiphosurans, so far as is known, have always been marine and primarily benthonic.

The other subclass of merostomes, the eurypterids, scorpion-like in form, range from Ordovician to Permian. They are very rare in most faunal associations but are common, and, indeed, form the major portion of a few. The absence of typical marine animals, corals, brachiopods, echinoderms, and so forth, from these associations, and the character and location of the rocks indicate an unusual environment of deposition, either brackish or hypersaline. These eurypterid faunal associations are of unusual interest to human vertebrates, because they include the oldest known members of our group. For this reason, I'll treat them in further detail in a subsequent chapter (p. 467ff.).

The class Arachnida now includes only air breathing forms, though some of the early scorpions have been interpreted as aquatic. This adaptation to terrestrial life appeared in the Silurian and was foreshadowed in the shift of the merostomes from marine to brackish or fresh water habits. The key modification was in the respiratory system, either *"book lungs"* formed of many thin-walled leaves or *tracheae.* The recent spiders and scorpions are of considerable importance in terrestrial communities, but they are quite rare as fossils. Several genera of scorpions have been described from Silurian rocks; the spiders do not appear until the Pennsylvanian.

The "sea spiders," class Pycnogonida, are a small group of benthonic marine animals with enormously lengthened legs and tiny bodies. Only two fossil genera are known.

REFERENCES

Bassler, R. S. and B. Kellett. 1934. "Bibliography and Index of Paleozoic Ostracoda," *Geol. Soc. of America, Special Paper 1.*

Bradley, P. C. S. 1941. "The Shell Structure of the Ostracoda and Its Application to Their Paleontological Investigation," *Ann. and Mag. of Nat. History,* ser. 11, vol. 8, pp. 1-33.

Brooks, H. K. 1957. "Chelicerata, Trilobitomorphia, Crustacea (Exclusive of Ostracoda) and Myriapoda" (annotated bibliography), in: "Treatise on Marine Ecology and Paleoecology, vol. 2. *Geol. Soc. of America, Memoir 67*, pp. 895-930.

Carpenter, F. M. 1953. "The Evolution of Insects," *Amer. Scientist*, vol. 41, pp. 256-270. A general review of fossil insects and of the evolution of the class.

Cooper, C. L. 1945. "Moult Stages of the Pennsylvanian Ostracoda, *Ectodemites Plummeri*," *Jour. of Paleontology*, vol. 19, pp. 368-375.

Evitt, W. R. and H. B. Whittington. 1953. "The Exoskeleton of *Flexicalymene* (Trilobita)," *Jour. of Paleontology*, vol. 27, pp. 49-55. A detailed morphologic study.

Harrington, H. J. 1959. "Classification," in: Moore, R. C., Ed., 1953. *Treatise on Invertebrate Paleontology, Part O*, Geol. Soc. of America, pp. 145-170. Other sections of this part of the Treatise cover over-all arthropod phylogeny and classification, as well as the morphology, ontogeny, and classification of the trilobitomorphs.

Hupe, P. 1950. "Etude Statistique de l'Evolution du Cephalon chez les Trilobites Proparia et Opistoparia," *Soc. Geol. France*, B. s. 5, t. 20, f. 1-3, p. 9-24.

―――――. 1952. "Sur les Affinities des Trilobites, *Soc. Geol. France*, B. s. 6, t. 1, f. 7, p. 469-486.

―――――. 1953. "Classification des Trilobites," *Ann. Paleont.*, t. 39, p. 59-168.

LeRoy, L. W. 1945. "A Contribution to Ostracodal Ontogeny," *Jour. of Paleontology*, vol. 19, pp. 81-86.

Palmer, A. R. 1957. "Miocene Arthropods from the Mojave Desert, California," *U.S. Geol. Survey, Prof. Paper 294-G*, pp. 237-279. Descriptions and illustrations of beautifully preserved fossil arthropods.

―――――. 1958. "Morphology and Ontogeny of a Lower Cambrian Ptychoparioid Trilobite from Nevada," *Jour. of Paleontology*, vol. 32, pp. 154-170.

Rasetti, F. 1948. "Cephalic Sutures in *Loganopeltoides* and the Origin of 'Hypoparian' Trilobites," *Jour. of Paleontology*, vol. 22, pp. 25-29.

Raw, Frank. 1953. "The External Morphology of the Trilobite and Its Significance," *Jour. of Paleontology*, vol. 27, pp. 82-129. A general discussion of the features of trilobite form.

―――――. 1957. "Origin of the Chelicerates," *Jour. of Paleontology*, vol. 31, pp. 139-192.

Raymond, P. E. 1920. "The Appendages, Anatomy, and Relationships of Trilobites," *Conn. Acad. of Arts and Sciences*, vol. 7, pp. 1-169. Covers function and paleoecology as well as form and evolution.

Ross, R. J., Jr. 1948. "Revision in the Terminology of Trilobites," *Amer. Jour. of Science*, vol. 246, pp. 573-577.

Shaw, A. B. 1957. "Quantitative Trilobite Studies II: Measurement of the Dorsal Shield of Non-agnostidean Trilobites," *Jour. of Paleontology,* vol. 31, pp. 193-207.

Størmer, Leif. 1939. "Studies on Trilobite Morphology, Part I: The Thoracic Appendages and Their Phyletic Significance," *Norsk. Geol. Tidskr.,* vol. 19, pp. 143-273. The first of a series of basic studies of trilobite form.

—————. 1942. "Studies on Trilobite Morphology, Part 2: The Larval Development, the Segmentation, and the Sutures and Their Bearing on Trilobite Classification," *Norsk. Geol. Tidskr.,* vol. 21, pp. 49-164.

—————. 1944. "On the Relationships and Phylogeny of Fossil and Recent Arachnomorpha," *Ski. Vid-Akad. Oslo, Mat.–Nat. kl. 1944,* no. 5, pp. 1-158.

—————. 1949. "Classes des Merostomoidea, Marrellomorpha, et Pseudo-crustacea," in: P. Grassé, ed. *Traité de Zoologie,* vol. 6, pp. 159-216. Paris: Masson.

—————. 1951. "Studies on Trilobite Morphology, Part 3: The Ventral Cephalic Structures with Remarks on the Zoological Position of the Trilobites," *Norsk Geol. Tidskr.,* vol. 29, pp. 108-157.

Tasch, P. 1952. "Adaptive Trend in Eyeline Development in the Olenellidae," *Jour. of Paleontology,* vol. 26, pp. 484-488.

—————. 1952. "The Taxonomy and Paleoecological Significance of Pemphigaspid Trilobites," *Jour. of Paleontology,* vol. 25, pp. 529-430.

Vandel, A. 1949. "Généralités sur les Arthropodes," in: P. Grassé, ed. *Traité de Zoologie,* vol. 6. Paris: Masson. Includes a discussion of arthropod phylogeny and classification.

Whittington, H. B., and W. R. Evitt. 1954. "Silicified Middle Ordovician Trilobites," *Geol. Soc. of America, Memoir 59.*

Also see general references given in Chapter 3; for ostracods, see D. J. Jones (1956) and M. F. Glaessner (1945) listed in Chapter 9.

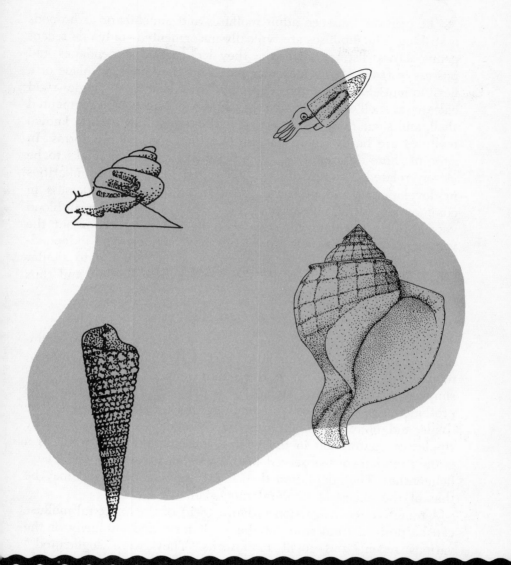

15. *Some that crawled:*
CHITONS, SNAILS,
and CLAMS

$\mathcal{T}$he contrast between adult molluscs and annelids or arthropods is striking. The molluscs are typically unsegmented—only one recent genus shows distinct segments; they lack paired appendages and possess instead a large muscular *foot;* and they have, in place of a flexible cuticle or jointed chitinous exoskeleton, a single rigid calcareous shell or pair of valves. Only the chitons have a segmented shell, and some molluscs lack a shell altogether. The earliest known molluscs are hardly more annelid-like than the modern forms. In spite of these differences, zoologists consider the two stocks to be closely related. I've already (p. 305) cited some of the similarities in development and in larval form. In addition, they possess in common a ventral nerve cord (or cords), a major dorsal blood vessel, and a circulatory system that opens into spaces about the viscera. Some of these characteristics may have evolved independently in each group. If so, they appeared in response to similar selective pressures on animals with similar organizations and thus represent parallel evolution.

THE PROTOMOLLUSC

If the annelid segmentation evolved as an adaptation to swimming, then the primitive mollusc must have adapted to a different mode of locomotion. Since the oldest known molluscs and the simplest modern types crawled (or crawl) along the sea floor, the protomolluscs, presumably, were sluggish benthonic crawlers. The snails and chitons, which preserve this adaptation, progress by ripples of contraction in the ventral musculature. The result is a gliding motion—one observed in the acoelomate worms, the Platyhelminthes. The adaptation then is extremely ancient and may be that of the ancestral bilateral metazoan.

A tentative reconstruction (Figure 15-1) of the ancestral mollusc can be derived from study of the adult form and ontogeny of the various recent and fossil molluscans. They were segmented,[*]

---

[*] Until 1957, I would have written, nonsegmented. But a dozen mollusc specimens, dredged from 3,500 meters depth in the Pacific west of Mexico (Lemche, 1957), have seriously modified all ideas about mollusc phylogeny. These specimens, genus *Neopilina*, apparently have their nearest relative in the Silurian fossil, *Pilina* and represent an order (or even a class) thought to be extinct since that time. These extraordinary "living fossils" possess a broadly conical shell (with a spiral initial stage), a broad though weak foot, and a slightly differentiated head. The head may consist of three fused segments, but the body definitely includes five segments marked by pairs of muscles attached to the shell, by pairs of gills, by segmentation of the circulatory system, and by pairs of "kidneys" in each segment.

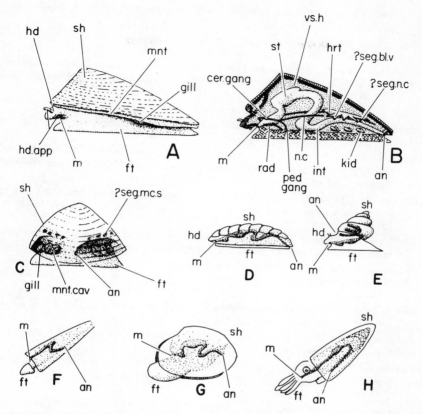

Fig. 15–1. *GENERAL MORPHOLOGY OF THE MOLLUSCA. A)* Generalized mollusc, lateral view. *B)* Generalized mollusc, longitudinal section. *C)* Generalized mollusc, posterior view. Shell and mantle cleared to show anus, mantle cavity, and gills. *D)* Amphineuran. Shell of several articulated elements; anus terminal. *E)* Gastropod. Single spiral shell; viscera twisted to bring anus alongside head. *F)* Scaphopod. Mantle folded over sides of body to form closed tube; shell tubular; anus subterminal. *G)* Pelecypoda. Bivalve shell; valves lateral to body. *H)* Cephalopoda. Viscera coiled to bring anus below head; foot formed into tentacles; chambered conical or coiled shell.

GLOSSARY FOR MOLLUSCA

(Figure numbers cited at end of definitions.)

Anus (an). Opening to egress of indigestible materials from digestive canal. Opens into posterior portion of mantle cavity in midline of body. (15–1B through *H; et al.*)

Cerebral ganglion (cer. gang). One of pair of large nerve centers in head at either side of digestive tube. Serves for reception of sensory perceptions and for co-ordination of activities. (15–1B; 15–6C.)

Foot (ft). Ventral portion of body—forming a broad sole in some molluscs, a hatchet shaped structure in some, and arms in others. Consisting chiefly of muscles used in locomotion. (15–1A to H.)

Gill (gill). Leaf-shaped structure lying in posterior portion of mantle cavity and used in respiration. Typically occur in pairs, one mounted on either side of body.

Head (hd). Anterior dorsal portion of body. Bears mouth, sensory organs, and major nerve ganglia. May be more or less distinct from foot and visceral hump. (15–1A, D, E, H; et al.)

Head appendages (hd. app). See "tentacles."

Heart (hrt). Enlarged portion of medial dorsal blood vessels that pumps through body. (15–1B, 15–3B, C, D, E; 15–6C; 16–1A.)

Intestine (int). Relatively narrow portion of digestive tube between stomach and anus. Typically consists of a number of coils occupying part of visceral hump. Serves for digestion and absorption. (15–1B; 15–3; 15–6; et al.)

Kidney (kid). Excretory organ—filters metabolic wastes, etc., from body fluids. Typically one or more pairs, one of pair on either side of body cavity. (15–1B; 15–3B to E; 15–6C.)

Nerve cord longitudinal (n. c). One of pair of nerve cords passing longitudinally from head to posterior end of body. (15–1B; 15–3C, D, E; 15–6C.)

Mantle (mnt). Dorsal and lateral portions of body wall. Typically it covers the viseral hump and forms a fold extending around the sides of visceral hump and foot. (15–1A, C.)

Mantle cavity (mnt. cav). Cavity between lateral and posterior folds of mantle and sides of visceral hump and foot. (15–1C.)

Pedal ganglion (ped. gang). One of a pair of large nerve centers which supplies nerve connections to muscles of foot. (15–1B; 15–6C.)

Radula (rad). Strip of horny material bearing teeth like those of a file. It can be protruded out through mouth from its position in the floor of the digestive canal. (15–1B.)

Segmental blood vessel (seg. bl. v). Lateral branch of dorsal blood vessel that extends to base of gill. One of several pairs in primitive molluscs that may represent earlier segmented structure. (15–1B.)

Segmental muscle scars (seg. mc. s). Paired muscle scars along posterior lateral margins of shell interior. Present in monoplacophorans and may represent remnants of segments. (15–1C; 15–2A.)

Segmental nerve cord (seg. n. c). Branch extending laterally from side of longitudinal nerve cord to base of gill. In monoplacophorans several pairs of segmental nerves appear to represent primitive segmentation. (15–1B.)

Shell (sh). Calcareous plate (or plates) deposited by cells in surficial layer of mantle and more or less covering body. (15–1; 15–2; 15–3; et al.)

Stomach (st). Pouch in anterior portion digestive tube that serves primarily for digestion. (15–1B; 15–6C; 16–1A.)

Tentacles (ten., hd. app). Used in two senses—the short, slender sensory head appendages of gastropods (15–1A; 15–3A) and the grasping arms of the cephalopods. (15–1H; 16–1A.)

Visceral hump (vs. h). Portion of body behind head and above foot in which digestive and reproductive organs are concentrated. Not set off distinctly from foot though it may form a dorsal hump. (15–1B.)

coelomate, bilaterally symmetrical, and elongate. They moved on the substrate by action of the ventral body musculature, much thickened and concentrated as the *foot*. The dorsal surface bowed upward to form the *visceral hump* and was covered by a modified "skin," the *mantle*, which may have borne calcareous spicules or a complete shell. The mantle folded laterally over the sides of the body and formed beneath the folds at the sides and posterior an extensive *mantle cavity*. The intestinal tract, excretory system, and genital tubes all emptied into this cavity. On either side of it was mounted a series of gills.

At the anterior end, the *head* was partly differentiated from the body. Very possibly it bore sensory tentacles and eyes, and the mouth opened out at its anterior-ventral end. The animal fed with a *radula*, a slender horny strip that bore a row of small teeth and could be protruded from the mouth to work like a rasp. The major elements of the nervous system were a loop about the esophagus, a pair of ventral nerve cords innervating the musculature of the foot, and the nerves to the viscera and mantle. A tubular dorsal heart pumped blood through extensive cavities about the viscera. The excretory system consisted of several pairs of simple ducts.

A recent genus, *Neopilina*, approaches this postulated ancestral plan most closely. Fossil species belonging to this same group, the order Tryblidiacea,* occur in lower Cambrian rocks, and, by their ancient stratigraphic occurrence, support the argument. The Amphineura (chitons) display somewhat similar features, though they lack segmentation and are not known earlier than the Ordovician. The lower Cambrian faunas also include some moderately specialized snails and a primitive cephalopod-like form. From the evidence of the fossil record, the ancestral molluscan line must have evolved in Precambrian times and started to diversify shortly before the beginning of the Cambrian.

THE MOLLUSCA AND LOCOMOTION

One of the primary features of molluscan evolution has been adaptation to different types of locomotion. The original "gliding" function is retained by the Amphineura, Gastropoda, and a few genera of the Pelecypoda. The "glide" is apparently satisfactory for

---

* See discussion of tryblidiacean relationships on p. 351. In this text they are regarded as a separate class.

sluggish bottom living animals—snails have done quite well with it. The late Precambrian and Cambrian communities obviously contained suitable ecologic niches for these gliders, but could employ other types even to compete with the arthropods. These potential jobs included positions for burrowers and for sessile animals. The muscular foot is preadaptive to burrowing, and it is hardly astonishing to find all members of one class, Scaphopoda, and many of another, Pelecypoda, adopting a burrowing habit. The pelecypod line in these early days also evolved a heavy bivalve shell and an elaborate filter feeding system from the gills. Both features are preadaptive for sessile animals, and many pelecypods have been and are sessile.

The step from a "glider" to a burrower is short and easy; the transformation to an active swimmer is more like a broad jump. I will always be astonished that the cephalopods made it—and with remarkable success. The modification is so great and so little documented that speculation as to its history is inevitably wild. The first change, the take-off in this evolutionary leap, may have been the development of *tentacles* from the head and/or part of the foot. They would serve to grasp and hold food (could the protocephaloped have been sessile?) but would also permit the animal to crawl along the bottom. Though arms without skeletal supports are not efficient, the tentacles could be, and probably were, used as oars in swimming, as they are sometimes in recent squids. The next change was a complex and extraordinary evolutionary improvisation. The posterior end of the cephalopod body was folded under so that the anus lay beneath the head. The anterior and posterior portions of the mantle brought together in this change fused into a cone. The shell secreted by the mantle surface likewise became conical. No adaptive significance comes to mind for these changes. They are, however, the sort of thing that occurs in sessile benthos—observe the Bryozoa for one. As the individual grew, it pulled back the mantle from the small end of the shell, and the mantle then deposited a thin partition (a septum) that sealed off the empty space. These empty chambers by their buoyancy reduced the apparent weight of the shell.

If a more efficient swimming mechanism than the tentacles were evolved, the protocephalopod would be in business. But what could serve? A skeleton for the tentacles would have been satisfactory, but there was nothing available to work on—no preadaptations for a skeleton. Some of the oldest known cephalopods may have been at this impasse, for Flower (1955) has described tentacle trails and markings that indicate the animals crawled and swam with their tentacles.

One resource remained. In many molluscs, the muscles of the mantle alternately contract and relax to pump water in and out of the mantle cavity. Distinct tubes evolve to confine and separate these currents. The proto-cephalopod almost surely had some such mechanism. This pulsating jet system could not help a clam to burrow; it assuredly does help a cephalopod to swim. Given this toehold on an adaptation, selection acted on variant mantle cavity structures to produce a highly efficient jet pump.

The evolutionary history of the molluscs seems to me sort of a Horatio Alger adventure. The annelid-arthropod stock was born with twin, silver spoons, segmentation and a flexible or jointed exoskeleton. They could hardly have failed. Molluscs retained a primitive method of locomotion and a primitive rigid skeleton suitable only for sessile or sluggish bottom animals. On this base they have equalled the arthropods in the sea and have been reasonably common and diversified in fresh water and on the land.

FORETHOUGHTS AND AFTERTHOUGHTS:
MONOPLACOPHORA, AMPHINEURA, AND SCAPHOPODA

Paleontologists originally regarded the fossil Tryblidiacea as an extremely primitive order of snails. The conical shell is generally similar to that of some recent snails, and some genera show a slight degree of coiling (Figure 15-3). In particular, the juvenal part of the *Neopilina* shell coils quite strongly. The tryblidiacean shell differs from typical gastropods in that it bears on its inner surface the scars of several pairs of muscles. The discovery of the living *Neopilina* demonstrated that these paired scars reflect distinct segmentation—not a gastropod characteristic—nor are the other characteristics particularly snail-like. The Tryblidiacea might be retained as a subclass of the Gastropoda in a vertical classification, but they also show relationships to the Amphineura and to the Cephalopoda. I here follow Lemche (1957) and place them in a horizontal classification as a separate class, Monoplacophora. This category, as defined, may include the ancestry of all molluscs.

More than any other class of mollusc, the chitons, the Amphineura, retain the ancestral mode of life. They diverge from the mythological founder of the phylum by reduction of the head, by increase in the number of gills, and by the development of a row of longitudinal calcareous plates along the mid-dorsal line (Figure 15-2). Some have a reduced foot, worm-like form, and calcareous spicules in the mantle. These may possibly be primitive character-istics but more likely are specializations that simulate the primitive. The shell-less forms are unknown as fossils; the shelled from several genera, the oldest Ordovician.

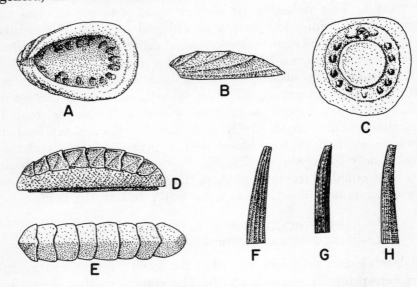

Fig. 15–2. MOLLUSCAN ODDMENTS. A) Monoplacophoran *Tryblidium*; middle Silurian; ventral view of shell, anterior to left; length 3.2 cm. Note paired muscle scars. B) Lateral view of *Tryblidium*. C) Monoplacophoran *Neopilina*; Recent; ventral view, anterior at top; length 3 cm. D) Amphineuran *Chiton*; Recent; lateral view, anterior at left; length 3.5 cm. E) Amphineuran *Helminthochiton*, Ordovician to Pennsylvania; dorsal view of valves; length 6.5 cm. F) through H) Three different species of the scaph-opod *Dentalium*, all fossil. Lateral views; length of F 3.2 cm., of G 3.8 cm., and of H 8.4 cm. (A. and E. After Piveteau, ed. *Traité de Paléontologie.* Copyright, Masson et Cie, Paris. Used with permission. C. After Lemeche.)

A small group of burrowing molluscs, the scaphopods, stands sharply distinct from the other types and may represent a distinct line from the primitive stock. The foot is conical (Figure 15-4). The mantle folds expand laterally and ventrally to fuse and form a cone. The foot extends from the wide end of the cone; the mantle cavity opens through a small hole at its apex. The mantle deposits a conical tusk-like shell. These shells first appear in Silurian rocks, but are neither varied in form nor more than locally abundant in the record.

SOLUTION IN A CURVE: THE GASTROPODS

The snails, like the chitons, remain in an environment like that of the ancestral molluscs. Unlike the chitons, they evolved a marked modification of the general molluscan structural plan. The visceral hump coils forward and the whole body above the foot twists so that the mantle cavity lies above and alongside the head (Figure 15-3). Typically, the gills and the internal organs on the inside of the curve disappear so that bilateral symmetry is lost. The form of the shell follows the torsion of the visceral mass and forms, geometrically, a spiral coiled on a cone.

The origin of the gastropod coiling and torsion is obscure. As already described, the monoplacophoran, *Neopilina*, has the initial portion of its shell curved, but the significance of that coiling and its relation to larval and adult form is yet unknown. Some early Paleozoic snails had a simple, spirally coiled shell—without any apparent torsion or asymmetry of viscera. The coiling of the visceral hump, in itself, may be adaptive to enlargement of the viscera and particularly of the digestive system. To keep the hump compact it coiled forward (Figure 15-3) and the visceral mass and shell were balanced over a relatively small foot. If the hump and shell were uncoiled, they would require a very large and heavy foot as counterbalance. The torsion of the body is less easy to explain, however, although some gastropod experts suggest it is the result of a larval adaptation.

A geometry of snails

By and large the snail shell (Figure 15-4) yields little information about the soft anatomy or adaptations of the animal. Snails with quite similar shells may have fundamental anatomical differences and very different environmental limits. The opening (*aperture*) through which the foot, head, and part of the viscera protrude and through which they may be withdrawn, is molded in part by characteristics of these organs. The shells of most groups conserve a few characteristics throughout their history, and the

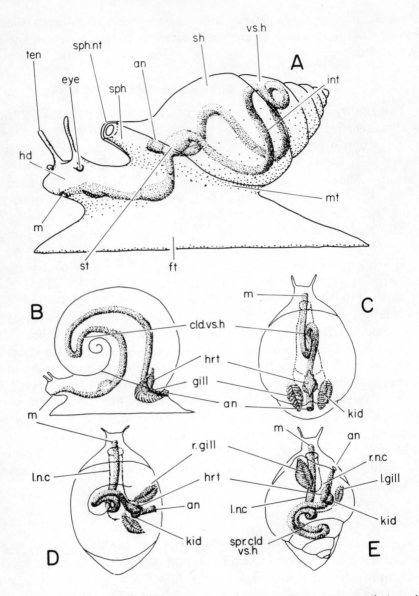

Fig. 15–3. *GENERAL CHARACTERISTICS OF THE GASTROPOD.* A) Lateral view with shell and body wall cleared to show torsion of gut. B) through E) Diagrams showing presumed evolution of coiling and torsion in snails. B) Lateral view of proto-snail; visera coiled forward over head but anus still terminal and symmetry still bilateral. C) Dorsal view of same. D) Dorsal view of intermediate stage. Viscera twisted to side so that anus and gills are lateral and plane of visceral coil is perpendicular to body axis. E) Dorsal view of specimen with torsion completed. Anus near head; right gill on left. Abbreviations as in glossary for Figure 15–4.

contradictory
see above

specialist, thus, can trace the affinities of fossil gastropod genera, known only from their shells, to recent ones distinguished primarily by their soft anatomy. Followed out in this fashion, shell evolution shows a great amount of parallelism and convergence. The result of this is a very complicated and difficult taxonomy for fossil gastropods. Identification of a genus is much simpler than determination of a subclass or order.

Most of the shell characteristics are simple properties of the geometry of the spiral curve and are, to some extent, interrelated. Critical features of morphology include the type of coiling, the spiral angle, the cross profile of shell and of the individual whorl, the tightness of coiling, the ratio of whorl number to shell height, the contact of the inner surface of the whorls, and the characteristics of the aperture. The finer subdivisions in the classification of recent snails are based on the character of the radula. Unfortunately, this is hardly ever preserved as a fossil. Knobs, ribs, spines, and so forth on the shell surface are also used, but have relatively little weight in classification.

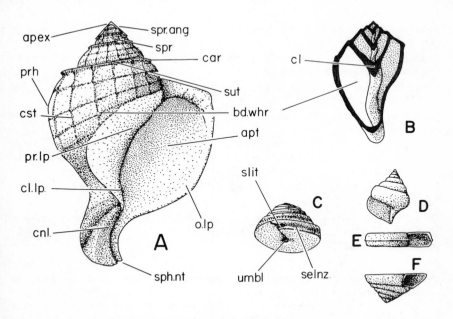

Fig. 15–4. *MORPHOLOGY OF THE GASTROPOD SHELL.* A) Apertural view—essentially ventral—with anterior down. A dextral shell. B) Cross section of snail shell. Sectioned shell in black. C) Oblique view of base. D) Apertural view of sinistral, orthostropic shell. E) Planospiral shell. F) Apertural view of dextral, hyperstrophic shell.

GLOSSARY FOR GASTROPODA

(Figures listed at end of definition show defined structure.)

Adapical. Direction opposite that of apex along axis of spiral.

Anterior. Direction along midline axis toward extremity of head. Generally defined in shell by anterior position of siphonal notch or canal and typically the adapical direction. In some Paleozoic gastropods the notch may have been posterior; in the few heterostrophic genera, the apex is anterior.

Anus (an). See 15–1. In recent snails it lies alongside—either to right or left—of head. (16–3A, E.)

Aperture (apt). Opening of shell through which body is extended or withdrawn. (14–4A; et al.)

Apex (apex). In conical shells the small end of the cone or spire. (15–4A; et al.)

Apical. In the direction of the apex or in its vicinity.

Body whorl (bd. whr). The last (and typically the largest) complete loop in the spiral. The last-formed, it terminates in the aperture. (15–4A, B.)

Canal (cnl). Grooved or partly closed tubular extension of aperture margin. Houses siphon in living snails and is anterior in position. (15–3A; 15–4A.)

Carina (car). Ridge along outer edge of shelf. Forms a more or less distinct spiral keel (15–4A.)

Coiled visceral hump (cld. vs. h). Visceral hump (see 15–1) which has developed in a coil. (15–3.)

Columella (cl). Medial pillar in spiral shell formed by coalescence of inner walls of whorls. (15–4B.)

Columellar lip (cl. lp). Part of inner border of aperture along exposed, adapical (essentially anterior) portion of columella. (15–4A; 15–5E.)

Conispiral. Shell type consisting of a spiral coiled on the surface of a cone. (15–3A; 15–4A, B, D; et al.)

Costa (cst). Ridge on surface of shell—either parallel to axis of coiling or to border of spiral. (15–4A; 15–5A, E, G.)

Dextral. Direction of coiling. With axis of coil vertical, apex up (up in orthostropic shells, down in hyperstrophic) and aperture facing observer the aperture will be to the right of the axis. (15–4A, E, F; 15–5B, D, E, G.)

Eye (eye). Photo-sensitive organ mounted on short stalk at side of head. (15–3A.)

Foot (ft). See 15–1. In gastropods a broad, flat muscular sole. (15–3.)

Growth line. Low ridge or break on outer shell surface parallel to edge of aperture. Marks previous position of aperture. (15–5G.)

Head (hd). See 15–1. (15–3A.)

Heart (hrt). See 15–1. (15–3B, C, D, E.)

Hyperstrophic. A rare shell type in which the whorls are coiled on an inverted cone so that the apex points forward rather than back. Not easily distinguished from orthostropic unless aperture shows siphon pointed in same direction as apex. (15–4F.)

Inner lip. Inner border of aperture—portion adjacent to last whorl and to columella. Comprises parietal and columellar lips—see which.

Intestine (int). See 15–1. (15–3A.)

Kidney (kid). See 15–1. Typically in gastropods one of the pair is quite small or absent. (15–3B, C, D, E.)

Left gill (l. gill). See 15–1. In all recent snails the left gill is rotated so it lies on the right anterior side of body. In dextral individuals it is typically smaller than the right or is absent. (15–3.)

Left longitudinal nerve cord (l. n. c). See 15–1. In recent gastropods torsion of the viscera loops the left cord over to the right side of the body. (15–3E.)

Mouth (m). Opening into digestive tube for ingress of food. Located at anterior ventral end of head. (15–3A.)

Orthostropic. The common shell type in which the whorls are coiled on an erect cone so that the apex points back rather than forward. If a notch for siphon is developed in aperture it will be opposite the direction of apex (adapical). (15–3; 15–4A, D; et al.)

Outer lip (o. lp). Lateral border of aperture. (15–4A; et al.)

Parietal lip (pr. lp). The portion of the inner border of aperture (inner lip) adjacent to preceding whorl. (15–4A.)

Periphery (prh). Portion of whorl most lateral to axis of coiling.

Planispiral. Shell type formed by spiral coiled in a single plane and symmetrical in that plane. Very rare in gastropods though many genera approach a planispiral. (15–4E; 15–5A.)

Posterior. The direction opposite the head along the midline axis. In nearly all shells the apical direction—see "anterior" and "heterostrophic."

Pseudoplanospiral. Shell coiled in one plane, but whorls not symmetrical in that plane. (15–5B.)

Right gill (r. gill). See 15–1. In all recent snails the right gill is rotated to a left anterior position. In dextral individuals it is the larger gill; in sinistral the smaller. (15–3.)

Right longitudinal nerve cord (r. n. c). See 15–1. Torsion of the gastropod viscera loops the right cord to the left side of the body. (15–3E.)

Selenozone (selnz). Band of closely-spaced cresentic growth lines on lateral surface of whorls. Typically it marks positions of apertural notch or slit during earlier stages of growth. (15–4C; 15–5G.)

Shell (sh). External calcareous skeleton. Consists of a single plate—typically drawn into a spirally coiled tube—which encloses the viscera and into which the head and foot may be withdrawn. (15–3A; et al.)

Sinistral. Direction of coiling. In orthostropic shells with axis of coil held vertical apex up and aperture facing observer the aperture will be to the left of the axis. See dextral. (15–4D.)

Sinus. Groove or reentrant in lateral margin of aperture (outer lip) distinguished from slit by nonparallel margins. (15–5G.)

Siphon (sph). Tubular extension(s) of mantle border. Pierced by a canal that opens into the mantle cavity from the exterior. May be indicated in shell by groove or notch. (15–3A.)

Siphonal notch (sph. nt). Notch at anterior end of aperture occupied by siphon. Where present it lies between—virtually separates—the inner and outer lips. (15–3A; 15–4A; 15–5D.)

Slit (slit). Parallel sided reentrant in lateral border of aperture. (15–4C.)

Spiral angle (spr. ang). Angle formed between two lines tangent to periphery of two or more whorls and on opposite sides of shell. Angle may change from initial whorls to later ones. (15–4A; *et al.*)

Stomach (st).   See 15–1.

Suture (sut).   Line of contact between two whorls. Typically a spiral on the outer surface—and also on the inner around the axis of coiling where that space (the umbilicus) is not closed. (15–4A; *et al.*)

Tentacles (ten).   See 15–1. (15–3.)

Torsion.   Rotation of viscera to right or left so that the anus and the mantle cavity are brought from a medial posterior to a lateral anterior position. (15–3.)

Umbilicus.   Opening along central axis of spiral formed where inner walls of whorls fail to meet. Typically a conical opening, widest in the body whorl. (15–4C.)

Visceral hump (vs. h).   See 15–1 (15–3.)

Whorl.   Single complete turn of spiral shell.

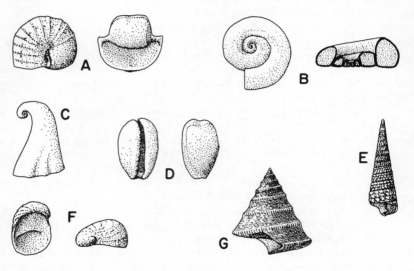

Fig. 15–5.   GALLERY OF SNAILS. A) *Bellerephon;* Ordovician to Triassic; lateral view with anterior probably at right and apertural view with anterior at top; width 2.1 cm. B) *Maclurites;* Late Cambrian to Ordovician; apical view and cross-section; maximum diameter 6.5 cm. C) *Platyceras;* Silurian to Permian;(?) apical view; length 7.3 cm. D) *Cyprea;* Cenozoic to Recent; apertural and dorsal views; length 2.6 cm. E) *Turritella;* Cretaceous to Recent; apertural view; length 4.1 cm. F) *Crepidula;* late Jurassic to Recent; apertural and lateral views; length 2.6 cm. G) *Pleurotomaria;* Jurassic; apertural view; length 2.7 cm.

As animals and fossils

The snails have from this simple plan derived a wide diversity of types (Figure 15-5). They are, indeed, the most varied of molluscs—at least at the species level. In this diversity they have largely retained the adaptation to the benthonic life. One group, the pteropods, are free swimming, adapted by a broadly flattened wing-like foot and a reduced (sometimes totally absent) shell. The pulmonate snails have the mantle cavity modified into a "lung" and inhabit a variety of aquatic (fresh water largely), semi-aquatic, and terrestrial environments. They retain, however, the basic adaptations in feeding and locomotion characteristic of the marine snails.

Snails are among the dominant predators and scavengers of the benthos and use their rasp-like radula to bore through shells and into the flesh of sluggish and sessile organisms. Others are herbivores and employ their radula to browse on aquatic plants. Presumably, a large part of the gastropod radiation corresponds to differences in food source as well as variation in substrate, turbulence, depth, and temperature. Unfortunately, little of this adaptive variation shows in the shell, and the information on gastropod paleoecology is not commensurate with their importance in marine communities.

The lack of paleoecologic data diminishes, in some measure, the value of gastropods in stratigraphic correlation. The long range of many genera and species diminishes it even more. The lot of a stratigrapher of gastropods is not a happy one. Some genera are, however, of particular value, and some, such as the fresh water and terrestrial pulmonates, occur in depositional environments otherwise devoid of fossils.

A STUDY IN SHAPE AND FUNCTION: THE PELECYPODA

Although some pelecypods retain the primitive mode of locomotion, the development of a bivalve shell and a filter feeding mechanism created additional evolutionary potentialities. The valves of the shell (Figure 15-6) are formed by a mantle lobe on either side of the body so that the plane of symmetry passes between the valves and the articulation (*hinge-line*) between them lies in the mid-dorsal line. Since the *beak* on the elevated portion (*umbo*) of the valve above the hinge typically points forward, the orientation of the shell, anterior and posterior, right and left, can usually be determined. The valves are closed by the *adductor muscles* (primitively two, one anterior and the other posterior), and are opened by tension of a *ligament* above the dorsal hinge line. The growth of the shell is recorded on the external surface by concentric growth lines.

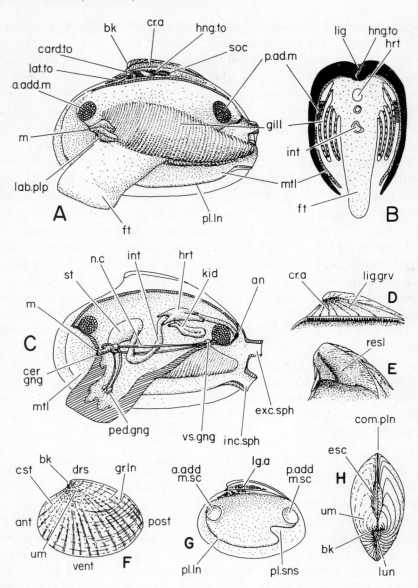

Fig. 15–6. *GENERAL MORPHOLOGY OF A PELECYPOD.* A) Lateral view with left valve and mantle fold removed. Anterior to the left. *B)* Cross-section. Shell shown in black; mantle in closely spaced stipple. *C)* Lateral view with valve, mantle fold, and body wall removed. Space around gut occupied by digestive glands and by gonad. Cavity of foot occupied by a blood sinus. *D)* Cardinal area showing ligament grooves. *E)* Cardinal area with resilifer. *F)* Lateral view of exterior of left valve. *G)* Lateral view of interior of right valve. *H)* Dorsal view of valves in articulation.

GLOSSARY FOR PELECYPODA

(Structures are shown in illustrations cited at end of definitions.)

Adductor muscles. One or two large muscles that are attached to interior surface of both valves and serve to close them. See anterior and posterior adductor.

Anterior (ant). Direction, in the plane of bilateral symmetry, of the mouth and rudiments of the head. Defined in shells by beaks which typically point anteriorly and/or by pallial sinus which occurs in posterior part of shell. (15–6F; et al.)

Anterior adductor muscle (a. add m). Adductor muscle (see which) in anterior position. Absent in some advanced groups. (15–6A, C.)

Anterior adductor muscle scar (a. add. m. sc). Area of attachment of anterior adductor. Generally a semicircular area depressed below surface of valve interior and variously scarred. (15–6G, 15–11.)

Anus (an). See 15–1. Opens in mantle cavity in posterior part of shell. (15–6C.)

Beak (bk). Projection of dorsal portion of valves above hinge line—the initial portion of the valve. Typically the beak shows strong curvature and points anteriorly. (15–6A, F, H; et al.)

Byssus (bys). Thread-like process derived from anterior portion of foot and used to attach shell to substrate. (15–8A.)

Cardinal area (cr. a). Flat or gently curved surface on valve between beak and hingle line and extending unbroken both anterior and posterior to beak. Set off from the remainder of shell by a sharp angle. (15–6A, D. H.)

Cardinal teeth (card. to). Projections along hinge line that fit into opposing sockets as part of valve articulation and that have a long axis perpendicular or oblique to hinge line. (15–6A; 15–11F.)

Cerebral ganglion (cer. gng). See 15–1.

Commissure, plane of (com. pln). Plane defined by line of juncture between valves. In pelecypods the plane of bilateral symmetry. (15–6H.)

Costa (cst). Ridge on external shell surface—one of several radiating from beak. (15–6F.)

Desmodont. Type of hinge line structure characterized by a large ligament inside the hinge line. Recognized in the shell by presence of large depression in hinge area (resilium) in which ligament was located. (15–11H.)

Dorsal (drs). Direction in plane of symmetry away from the substrate. Defined in pelecypods by the hinge line and by the beaks which form the dorsal margin. (15–6F, H; et al.)

Dysodont. Type of hinge line structure characterized by the reduction of hinge teeth and development of a large internal ligament (resilifer). Typically the hinge plate is broad and bears a deep depression (resilium) marking the position of the ligament. (15–6E; 15–11D.)

Equilateral. Shell form in which the anterior and posterior portions of valves are subequal and nearly symmetrical. (15–6F; 15–7A, B.)

Equivalve. Shell form in which right and left valves are subequal and symmetrical about plane of commissure. (15–6H; 15–7A, B, C.)

Escutcheon (esc). Flat or simply curved area between beak and hinge line and posterior to beak. Corresponds to posterior part of cardinal area and is separated from remainder of shell surface by sharp change in angle. (15–6H.)

Eulamellibranch. Type of gill structure. Each gill consists of two sheets of filaments which extend downward for a distance and then are folded back dorsally. Adjacent filaments are connected by interfilamentary junctions and the ascending and descending portions of each filament are also connected. (15–9C.)

Excurrent siphon (exc. sph). Posterior dorsal extension of mantle borders forming a tube which confines and directs outflowing current from mantle cavity.

Filibranch. Gill type. Each gill consists of two sheets of filaments which extend some distance downward and then are folded up toward roof of mantle cavity. The adjacent filaments are not interconnected though the ascending and descending branches of each filament may be. (15–9B.)

Foot. See 15–1. May be rather broad though not flattened dorso-ventrally but more commonly is compressed laterally into a broad or narrow blade. (15–6A, B, C; 15–7; 15–8.)

Gill. See 15–1. Pelecypods possess a pair, one on either side of viscera. (15–6A, B; 15–9.)

Growth line (gr. ln). Slight ridge or break in shell surface approximately parallel to the borders of valve and representing shell margin at earlier growth stage. (15–6F.)

Heart (hrt). See 15–1.

Heterodont. Type of hinge line structure characterized by a small number of hinge teeth of two types, the cardinals and the laterals. The former, directly below the beak, are perpendicular or oblique to the hinge line; the latter which lie ahead of and behind the cardinals parallel the hinge line. (15–6A; 15–11F.)

Hinge line. Line of articulation between the two lateral plates (valves) that form the pelecypod shell. (15–6A, D, E, G; et al.)

Hinge tooth (hng. to). Projection along hinge line that fits into a pit (socket) on the opposing valve and assists in articulation of valves. (15–6A, B; 15–11.)

Incurrent siphon (inc. sph). Posterior-ventral extension of mantle borders forming a tube which confines the current flowing into the mantle cavity. (15–6C.)

Inequilateral. Shell form in which anterior portion of valves is much shorter than posterior. (15–7C, 15–8A, B, C.)

Inequivalve. Shell form in which one valve is flatter (and often smaller) than the other. (15–8C, D, E.)

Intestine (int). See 15–1.

Isodont. Type of hinge line structure characterized by two large subequal teeth in one valve and corresponding sockets in the other. (15–11E.)

Kidney (kid). See 15–1.

Labial palps (lab. plp). Ciliated appendages on either side of mouth that assist in feeding. (15–6A.)

Lateral teeth. Projections along hinge line that parallel hinge line and fit into sockets on the opposing valve. See "heterodont." (15–6A.)

Left. Direction to left of plane of symmetry. Determined by placing shell with hinge line up and anterior end pointing away from observer—left on pelecypod will correspond to observer's left. (15–6F; 15–11A, G.)

Ligament (lig). Elastic tissue attaching valves along hinge line and serving to open the valves, either by tension (external ligament) or by expansion (internal ligament, resilium). (15–6B.)

Ligament area (lg. a). Scarred area between beak and hinge line that served for attachment of the ligament. May include most of the cardinal area. (15–6G.)

Ligament groove (lig. grv). Groove (typically one of several) in the area between beak and hinge line that served for attachment of the ligament. (15–6D.)

Longitudinal nerve cord (n. c). See 15–1.

Lunule (lun). Flat or curved area between the beak and the hinge line and in front of the beak. Corresponds to anterior portion of cardinal area and is distinguished from remainder of shell surface by sharp change in angle. (15–6H.)

Mantle (mtl). A pair of folds from the dorsal body wall that extend laterally and ventrally over the sides of the animal. External cell layer forms shell and is attached to its inner surface. (15–6A, B.)

Mouth (m). See 15–1.

Pachyodont. Hinge line structure characterized by one or more very large, thick teeth. (15–11G.)

Pallial line (pl. ln). Line a short distance inside shell margins marking inner border of the relatively thick edges of mantle. Typically marked by a groove or ridge and by a change in texture of shell material. (15–6A, G; et al.)

Pallial sinus (pl. sns). Inflection of posterior-ventral portion of pallial line that extends anteriorly or anterio-dorsally away from proximal shell margin. Marks position of siphons. (15–6G; 15–7B, C; 15–11F, H.)

Pedal ganglion (ped. gng). See 15–1.

Plica. Fold, involving full thickness of shell, that extends radially from beak to shell margin. Shows on inner surface of shell as well as outer. (15–8C; 15–11E.)

Posterior (post). Direction in plane of symmetry opposite position of head. Determined in shell by posterior position of pallial sinus and by anterior projection of beaks. (15–6F; et al.)

Posterior adductor muscle (p. ad. m). Adductor muscle (see which) in posterior portion of pelecypod. (15–6A, B.)

Posterior adductor muscle scar (p. add. m. sc). Area of attachment of posterior adductor. Generally a semicircular area depressed below surface of valve interior and variously scarred. (15–6G, 15–11.)

Protobranch. Gill type. Simple leaf-like gill with short simple filaments. (15–9A.)

Right. Direction to right of plane of symmetry. Determined by placing shell with hinge line up and anterior end pointing away from observer—right on pelecypod will correspond to observer's right. (15–6G; et al.)

Resilifer (resl). Depression inside margin of hinge line which holds (or held) internal ligament (resilium). (15–6E; 15–11D, E, H.)

Resilium. Portion of ligament within hinge line. Compressed by hinge plate when valves are closed.

Schizodont. Type of hinge line structure characterized by teeth diverging sharply from beneath beak. (15–11C.)

Septibranch. Gill type. Consists of a perforate diaphragm extending horizontally across mantle cavity and dividing it into upper and lower moeities. (15–9D.)

Socket (soc). Depression along hinge line that receives projecting tooth from opposite valve. (15–6A, B; 15–11.)

Stomach (st). See 15–1. (15–6C.)

Taxodont. Type of hinge line structure. Characterized by numerous small, subequal teeth along hinge line.

Umbo (um). Elevated and relatively convex portion of valve adjacent to the beak—essentially the "humped" part of the shell. (15–6F, H; et al.)

Valve. One of the two convexly curved (rarely flat or concave) calcareous plates that lie on either side of the visceral hump and foot and that are articulated along a dorsal hinge line. (15–6, et al.)

Ventral (vent). In general the direction in the plane of symmetry toward the substrate. Defined in the pelecypods by the dorsal position of the hinge line and the ventral position of the opening between the valves. (15–6F; et al.)

Visceral ganglion (vs. gng). See 15–1. (15–6C.)

The posterior mantle cavity is large and extends forward on either side of the body to accommodate the enlarged gills. A few pelecypods have a pair of simple leaf-like gills much like those of the chitons and snails, but, in most, the gills are modified into sheets of filaments, variously folded and interconnected. Cilia on the gills maintain a complex current flow into the shell along the ventral posterior border behind the foot, over the gill filaments, and back out at the posterior end. Food particles are filtered from the water and carried to the mouth on ciliated tracts. The mantle and gills are so modified that the incurrent and excurrent flow are kept separate.

The head has apparently been reduced from the primitive mollusc condition and is rudimentary, lacking eyes, tentacles, and radula. An arterial system carries blood from the heart to gills, mantle, foot, and internal organs and a venous system returns it to the heart. In the gills and mantle, the blood is confined to capillaries; elsewhere it flows through large cavities about the organs. Respiration is carried on through the surface of the mantle and, probably to some extent, in the gills.

Shell characteristics and adaptations

Those pelecypods that retain the primitive creeping mode of locomotion also have a relatively primitive, flattened foot on which the animal glides. The foot is large, and, when the valves are open, it protrudes from the anterior ventral part of the shell. The gills occupy much of the posterior part of the shells. The general shell form (Figure 15-7) is *equivalve* (the valves symmetrical) and *equilateral* (the anterior and posterior portion of each valve nearly equal). The valves are about as high as they are long and may be roughly triangular, with the apex dorsal and the base ventral. Because the anterior and posterior portions of the valves are nearly equal, the anterior and posterior adductors are of equal size. The attachments of adductors to the valve interiors (the *muscle scars*) are likewise equal.

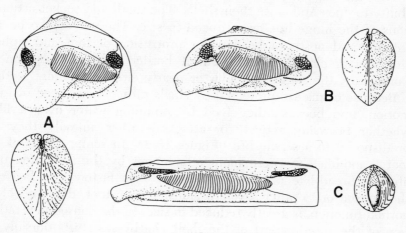

Fig. 15–7. *PELECYPOD ADAPTATION: CRAWLING AND BURROWING.* A) Lateral and anterior views of crawling pelecypod, the former with the left valve removed. Equivalvular, equilateral, triangular form. B) Same views of active burrower. Equivalvular, equilateral, quadrilateral. C) Again the lateral and anterior views, in this case of a sluggish burrower. Equivalvular, inequilateral, quadrilateral. Note gap between closed valves.

In burrowing pelecypods (Figure 15-7) the foot is laterally compressed and elongate. Rather than protruding ventrally, it extends anteriorly, and the anterior portion of the shell is long and shallow. A similar change occurs in the posterior part of the shell with the development of *incurrent* and *excurrent siphons*. These form as tubes or folds of the mantle for the incurrent and excurrent circulation of the gills and protrude as a sort of snorkle above the surface of the sand or mud. The presence of these siphons may be marked on the internal surface of the valves by an inflexion (*pallial sinus*) in the line of attachment (*pallial line*) between the mantle lobe and the shell. The shells are equivalve, but many are *inequilateral* because of unequal size of the foot and the gill-siphon space. In active burrowers the foot is large and the valves equilateral. In these the shells may be relatively deep but quadrilateral rather than triangular. The adductor muscles are, of course, nearly equal as are the adductor muscle scars. Other burrowing types live rather sedentary lives at the bottom of tubelike burrows. Their siphons are long, and the foot small. The valves are inequilateral and, in many, quite shallow. They are characteristically quadrilateral. Since they are protected by their burrows, they lose the ability to open and close their shells. The tooth and socket articulations of the hinge line are reduced in size. The valves gap on the anterior and posterior borders for protrusion of foot and siphon, and remain closed on the ventral border to exclude sediment. Commonly, the shell is circular or nearly circular in cross section.

Because clams are protected by shells rather than speed of locomotion, and because they feed by pumping water over a filter whether browsing actively or attacking other animals, they are predisposed to a sessile life (Figure 15-8). In some, a part of the foot is modified for permanent attachment by the formation of a fibrous thread-like or root-like *byssus*. This fastens the beast to the bottom or to other sessile organisms. The foot, deprived of its normal function, is greatly reduced in size. In the consequent reduction of the anterior part of the shell, the byssus shifts dorsally, or rather the anterior part of the shell fails to develop and the byssus remains near the hinge line. Because of the degeneration of the anterior part of the shell, the anterior adductor is reduced or lost. The degeneration of the anterior portion may be so nearly complete that each valve becomes symmetrical about its midline, with the morphological ventral margin becoming the new anterior margin.

Many that developed a byssal attachment rest on one valve. In adaption to this change in position, one valve may be more convex than the other and the shell *inequivalve*. Some cement portions of the "lower" valve to rocks or other shells. Some of these cemented types evolved from those with byssal attachments; others from unattached sessile types that rest on one valve. Members of this latter group evolve heavy, deep, "lower" valves to stabilize the animal and maintain it above the depositional surface. An extreme development of this tendency is shown by the coraliform rudistids. In both groups, those with a byssus and those without, there may be some torsion of the viscera as an adjustment to change in orientation. If this is reflected in shell growth, the lower valve or both valves may coil spirally much like a snail shell. The spire may support the animal above the substrate or result from attachment by the anterior dorsal margin of the valve.

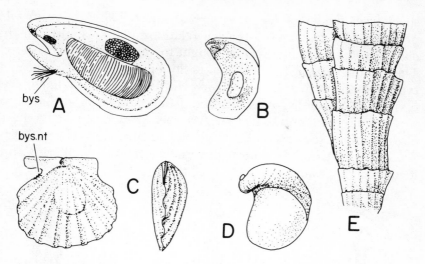

Fig. 15–8. *PELECYPOD ADAPTATION: SESSILE.* A) Partly sessile form with weak foot and byssus for attachment. Lateral view with one valve gone. B) Sessile form. Internal surface of right valve. Irregular shape of valve reflects cementation to substrate. C) Sessile form—attached by byssus. Lateral view of interior of right valve and anterior view. Lateral view demonstrates inequilateral form; anterior view shows inequivalvular form. Some members of this group swim by clapping valves together. D) Sessile. The animal rests on the strongly coiled right valve. The left valve is small and nearly flat. E) Sessile. One valve elongated into coral-like form. Some members of group form aggregates of loosely attached individuals.

Some recent genera that normally attach to the substrate by a byssus dissolve these anchoring threads at times and become free living. Since they reduced the muscular foot at an early stage of their evolution, they can no longer crawl over the bottom in typical pelecypod fashion. Instead, they swim by closing and opening the valves rapidly. This clapping motion of the valves forces water out along the ventral border and drives the animal through hinge first. They swim in the same position as they rest on the bottom, lying on one side. The single adductor muscle, the posterior, is very large and composed principally of striated muscles capable of very rapid contraction. Presumably, some fossil pelecypods with byssal attachments, a reduced foot, and a large adductor muscle had a similar swimming habit.

Shell characteristics and classification

Since these modifications of shell form are relatively simple changes in an already existing plan and are clearly adaptations to specialized modes of life, they are of questionable value in interpretation of broader evolutionary relationships. Zoologists, in their classification, give the greatest weight to variations in gill structure. The complexity of the gill makes it less likely that similar gill types could evolve independently in two or more lines. Once divided on this basis, other characteristics can be found that accord with the division, and some that disagree. As in most single criterion classifications, there is still a large risk of mistaking characteristics produced by parallelism and convergence for those inherited from a common ancestor.

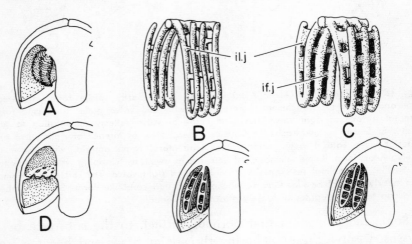

Fig. 15–9. *PELECYPOD GILL STRUCTURE.* A) Simple leaf-shaped gills, protobranch. View in right mantle cavity. B) Filibranch gills, detail and view in right mantle cavity. Each filament is folded, and the descending and ascending portions may be connected (*il. j* in drawing). C) Eulamelibrach, detail and view in right mantle cavity. Adjacent filaments connected (*if. j*) as well as branches of same filament. D) Septibranch gill, view in right mantle cavity. Gill forms a horizontal, perforate partition.

Four types of gills are recognized (Figure 15-9). The *protobranch* gill is a simple, leaf-like structure similar to that of the other classes of molluscs. The *filibranch* gill consists of a double row of closely spaced filaments, each row forming a sheet. These are attached to the gill bases and hang downward in the gill cavity, but the free end of each sheet is folded back upward, parallel to the descending sheet. In the *eulamellibranch* gill, the descending and ascending filaments are joined at intervals so that the space between the sheets is divided into a series of canals. In the *septi-*

branch type the gill forms a perforate, horizontal partition between the upper and lower moieties of the mantle cavity.

Paleontologists naturally would prefer a classification based on shell characteristics. The only one that seems to involve a fundamental change of character is that of shell microstructure (Figure 15-10). Some pelecypods have a thick layer of calcite prisms at right angles to the shell surface and a thinner layer of sheets of calcite or aragonite beneath it. Others lack the prismatic layer. This division forms the two subclasses of pelecypods Prionodesmacea and Teleodesmacea (Table 15–1). Within these subclasses, paleontol-

TABLE 15–1

THE MOLLUSCA

Early Cambrian to Recent. Typically nonsegmented. Body differentiated into foot, head, visceral hump, and mantle. Gills in cavity below mantle. Organization of circulatory, respiratory, nervous, and so on, systems near level of arthropods and vertebrates. External calcareous shell in most. Coelomic cavities reduced and replaced by haemocoel. Herbivores and carnivores. Vagrant and sessile; marine, fresh water, and terrestrial; benthonic and nektonic.

CLASS MONOPLACOPHORA

Early Cambrian to Recent. Broad foot, low visceral hump, partly differentiated head. No distinct mantle cavity. Segmented. Conical shell, coiled in some genera and in some stages of development in others. Benthonic, marine, (?) herbivorous. Fossils from early Cambrian to Silurian.

CLASS AMPHINEURA

Ordovician to Recent. Elongate foot, low visceral hump, rudimentary head. Three or more pairs of gills. Shell absent or composed of eight pieces in series along mid-dorsal line. Benthonic, marine; typically herbivorous. Few fossils.

CLASS SCAPHOPODA

Silurian to Recent. Foot reduced, compressed, conical; visceral hump high; head simple; mantle forms cone about body. No gills. Shell tusk shaped; foot protruding from large end; mantle cavity opening through apex. Marine; burrower. Feeds on small organisms encountered in bottom sediments, a mud grubber. Few fossils.

CLASS GASTROPODA

Early Cambrian to Recent. Foot large; head distinct with eyes and tentacles; visceral hump high and coiled forward. Two gills, one reduced or absent in some; some fossil genera probably had more gills. Shell typically coiled, covering visceral hump. Marine, fresh water and terrestrial. Benthonic except for a few planktonic genera. Herbivores and carnivores. Includes several classes and a number of orders but not easily determined from shell characteristics. Some genera and species are guide fossils. Snails and slugs.

CLASS PELECYPODA

Ordovician to Recent. Foot laterally compressed, hatchet shape, may be greatly reduced; head rudimentary; visceral mass large; mantle folded over sides of body. Bivalve shell, one valve on either side of body, and hinged dorsally. Two gills, enlarged and elaborated. Benthonic; marine and fresh water. Vagrant, burrowing and sessile. Filter feeders—currents through gill filaments. *hinge*

Subclass Prionodesmacea

Ordovician to Recent. Prismatic shell structure. Mantle lobes separate, Siphons poorly developed.

Order Palaeoconcha

Ordovician to Recent. Protobranch gills, no hinge teeth, subequal adductors. Predominantly burrowers.

Order Taxodonta

Ordovician to Recent. Protobranch or filibranch gills. Taxodont hinge teeth, subequal adductors. Vagrant benthonic and sessile.

Order Schizondonta

Ordovician to Recent. Filibranch; schizodont; subequal adductors. Predominantly vagrant benthonic.

Order Dysodonta

Ordovician to Recent. Filibranch and eulamellibranch; dysodont; anterior adductor reduced or absent; byssus. Chiefly sessile types. Includes six suborders, among them oysters and scallops.

Order Isodonta

Triassic to Recent. Filibranch; isodont; anterior adductor absent; some with byssus. Sessile types.

Subclass Teleodesmacea
ultimate hinges

Ordovician to Recent. Shell laminated but not prismatic. Mantle lobes connected. Siphons well developed.

Order Heterodonta

Silurian to Recent. Eulamellibranch; heterodont; adductors subequal. Predominantly vagrant benthonic. Includes most of types called "clams."

Order *Pachyodonta*

 Jurassic to Recent. Eulamellibranch; pachyodont; one valve very much enlarged, may be coral-like. Sessile benthonic.

Order *Desmodonta*

 Ordovician to Recent. Eulamellibranch except for one suborder with septibranch gills; desmodont. Burrowers and borers. Razor clams, etc.

CLASS CEPHALOPODA

(See Table 16–1, p. 393.)

---

ogists utilize variations of the articulation between the valves as taxonomic criteria. The most primitive type seems to be that of the order Palaeoconcha (Figure 15-11). Clams placed in this category lack distinct teeth and sockets on the hinge line, and the valves are held in articulation by the ligament above the hinge and by the adductor muscles. Recent genera have simple leaf-like gills, the protobranch type.

The next step in evolution is the development of many small *teeth* (and corresponding *sockets*) along the surface of articulation. This type of dental apparatus defines the order Taxodonta (Figure 15-11), but there seems no very strong reason to assume that a *taxodont dentition* evolved but once among the Palaeoconcha. The order may have a single origin and thus correspond to phylogeny, or it may be a structural grade attained in several different lines. Two suborders are recognized, one with protobranch gills, the other with more complicated filibranch gills. If the filibranch

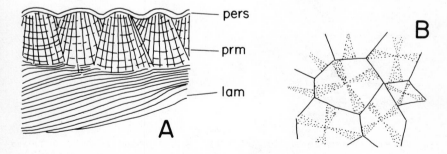

Fig. 15–10. *PELECYPOD SHELL MICROSTRUCTURE.* A) Cross section, thickness 0.5 mm., *Unio* shell. B) Transverse section through prismatic layer. Width of prisms about 40 microns. Abbreviations: *lam*, laminated layer; *pers*, periostracum; *prm*, prismatic layer. (After Piveteau, ed. *Traité de Paléontology*. Copyright Masson et Cie. Used with permission.)

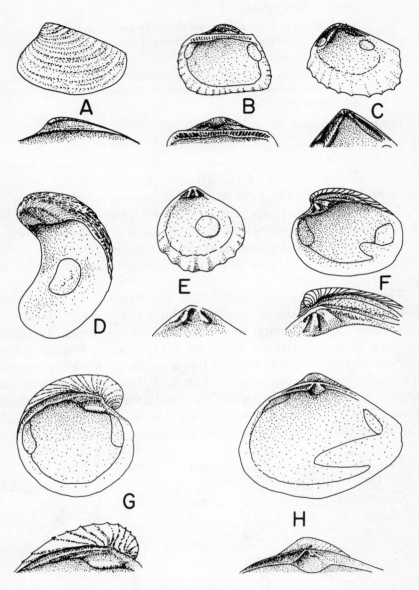

Fig. 15–11. *PELECYPOD HINGE STRUCTURE AND CLASSIFICATION.* A) Palaeo-concha, no hinge teeth. *Edmonia:* Devonian to Pennsylvanian; lateral view of left valve exterior and detail of right valve hinge line; length of upper figure 3.7 cm. B) Taxo-donta, taxodont dentition. *Arca;* Jurassic to Recent; lateral view of right valve interior and detail of hinge line; length of upper figure 3.6 cm. C) Schizodonta, schizodont dentition. *Neotrigonia;* Miocene to Recent; interior of right valve and enlarged view of hinge line; length of shell 1.9 cm. D) Dysodonta, dysodont hinge structure; single ad-

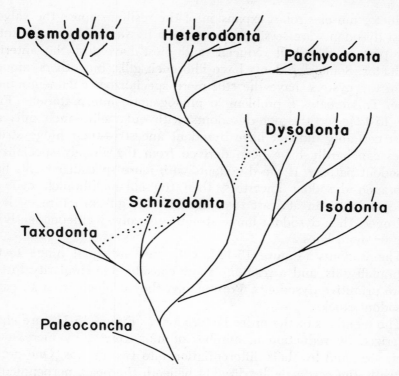

Fig. 15–12. *PHYLOGENY OF THE PELECYPODA.* The true phylogenetic relationships are not certain and may be far more complex than this. The solid lines are based principally on hinge line characters; the dotted alternatives on gill structure.

gill evolved but once, all the remaining pelecypod orders developed from this suborder of taxodonts.

The Schizodonta (Figure 15-11) have a more specialized hinge structure than the Taxodonta. The number of teeth is reduced; each is much larger, and they diverge strongly from beneath the beak. All have filibranch gills. The order Dysodonta (Figure 15-11) includes forms with reduced teeth and specialized ligaments. A portion of the ligament has shifted inside the hinge line. When the valves close, this portion, the *resilium*, is compressed. When the

ductor muscle. *Ostrea;* middle Cretaceous to Recent; right valve interior; length 8.3 cm. E) Isodonta, isodont dentition; single adductor muscle. *Plicatula;* Triassic to Recent; view of the interior of right valve and detail of dentition; length 2.3 cm. F) Heterodonta, heterodont dentition. *Venus;* Jurassic to Recent; right valve interior and dental detail; length 10.9 cm. G) Pachyodonta, pachyodont dentition. *Chama;* late Cretaceous to Recent; interior of left valve and detail of hinge area; length 4.2 cm. H) Desmodonta, desmodont dentition. *Lutraria;* Miocene to Recent; interior of right valve and detail of dental structure; length of shell 6.8 cm.

adductor muscles relax, expansion of the resilium opens the valves. Most dysodonts are sessile; many have a byssus; all have the anterior part of the shell reduced; and most have lost the anterior adductor. Some dysodonts have filibranch gills, but others, among them the oysters, have the still more specialized, eulamellibranch type. This creates a problem in phylogenetic interpretation (Figure 15-12), for the non-dysodonts with eulamellibranch gills almost certainly did not have dysodont ancestry—their hinge structures can hardly have been derived from the already specialized dysodont pattern. If the dysodonts with more specialized gills had filibranch dysodont ancestors, then the eulamellibranch evolved independently in at least two lines. If this gill structure evolved but once, then dysodont hinge structures evolved independently in two or more lines.

The isodonts (Figure 15-11), with two subequal hinge teeth, filibranch gills, and a resilium, show considerable similarity to the more primitive dysodonts. Presumably, they evolved from an early dysodont stock.

The members of the order Heterodonta (Figure 15-11) are characterized by reduction in number of hinge teeth, by increase in their size, and by their differentiation into two groups. One group of teeth, the *cardinals,* lie directly beneath the beak, perpendicular to the hinge line. The *lateral teeth* on either side are nearly parallel to the hinge line. Their gill structure is eulamellibranch.

The order Pachyodonta (Figure 15-11) have a hinge structure and gills much like that of the Heterodonta and seem to have had heterodont ancestors. Their teeth are much thickened. They are sessile, lying on one side. The valve of this side is larger and more convex, sometimes extremely so. In a group of late Mesozoic pachydonts, the rudistids, the lower valve is pyramidal or conical and the individual grew from the bottom like a coral. In these, the upper valve is reduced to a flat plate covering the open end of the cone.

The members of the order Desmodonta (Figure 15-11) are united by their possession of eulamellibranch gills (in one suborder septibranch) and of an internal ligament borne on the hinge plate or on a partly separated spoonshaped structure. They are all, primarily, burrowers and borers with similar shell adaptations. The hinge teeth are small or absent, but some have a heterodont dentition.

In geologic perspective

As I have already indicated, the pelecypods are benthonic animals. They are primarily marine, though some inhabit fresh water environments. Their adaptations of shell form for different niches in the benthos are easily recognized in most cases, though some with intermediate characteristics are not as easily diagnosed. The scanty evidence now available (see bibliographies in the *Treatise on Marine Ecology and Paleoecology,* 1957) indicates the close association of particular species and genera with particular depositional environments. Stenzel was able to associate local variation within a species population of oysters with environmental differences (see above, p. 82); very probably much more will be done along this line of investigation. The occurrence of recent genera in Mesozoic and Cenozoic rocks permits interpretation of their paleoecology in terms of the limiting factors recognized in recent ecologic studies. Schenk's paper (1945) on distribution of Cenozoic molluscan faunas along the Pacific coast of the United States exemplifies this type of study, though his statistical methods are dubious.

At present pelecypods are useful in defining the large units of geologic time, but are of little help in the correlation of finer subdivisions. This deficiency is, in part, inherent because evolution, as reflected in shell characteristics, was quite slow, and most common genera and species have long stratigraphic ranges. Very detailed analyses of large samples collected at carefully determined stratigraphic levels show, however, a gradual transformation of a population succession. The critical changes in these successions define more precisely than any ordinary guide fossils time stratigraphic units. Thus, the work of Stenzel on *Ostrea,* and of Newell (1942) on *Myalina,* not only illustrate evolutionary principles, but provide a practical guide to dating important rock sequences.

REFERENCES

Chronic, H. 1952. "Molluscan Fauna from the Permian Kaibab Formation, Walnut Canyon, Arizona," *Geol. Soc. of America, Bulletin,* vol. 63, pp. 95-166. A detailed treatment of systematics, paleogeography, and paleoecology.

Davenport, C. B. 1938. "Growth Lines in Fossil Pectens as Indicators of Past Climates," *Jour. of Paleontology,* vol. 12, pp. 514-515.

Flower, R. H. 1955. "Trails and Tentacular Impressions of Orthoconic Cephalopods (Ohio)," *Jour. of Paleontology,* vol. 29, pp. 857-867.

Lemche, H. 1957. "A New Living Deep-Sea Mollusc of the Cambro-Devonian Class, Monoplacophora," *Nature*, vol. 179, pp. 413-416. First description of the recent find of a segmented mollusc.

Newell, N. D. 1942. "Late Paleozoic Pelecypods, Mytilacea," *Kansas Geol. Surv.*, vol. 10, pp. 1-123. A detailed taxonomic and evolutionary study.

Nicol, D. 1953. "Period of Existence of Some Late Cenozoic Pelecypods," *Jour. of Paleontology*, vol. 27, pp. 706-707.

————. 1954. "Growth and Decline of Populations and the Distribution of Marine Pelecypods," *Jour. of Paleontology*, vol. 28, pp. 22-25.

Schenk, H. C. 1945. "Geological Application of Biometrical Analysis of Molluscan Assemblages," *Jour. of Paleontology*, vol. 19, pp. 504-521.

Valentine, J. W. 1958. "Late Pleistocene Megafauna of Cayucos, California, and Its Zoogeographic Significance," *Jour. of Paleontology*, vol. 32, pp. 687-696. A paleoecologic-paleozoogeographic study based principally on fossil molluscs.

Yen, T.-C. 1951. "Fossil Freshwater Molluscs and Ecological Interpretations," *Geol. Soc. of America, Bulletin*, vol. 62, pp. 1375-1380.

Yonge, C. M. 1946. "The Pallial Organs in the Aspidobranch Gastropods and Their Evolution Throughout the Mollusca," *Royal Soc., London, Philos. Trans.*, ser. B., vol. 232, pp. 443-518. A study of respiratory structures and their evolution.

See also general works cited at end of Chapter 3.

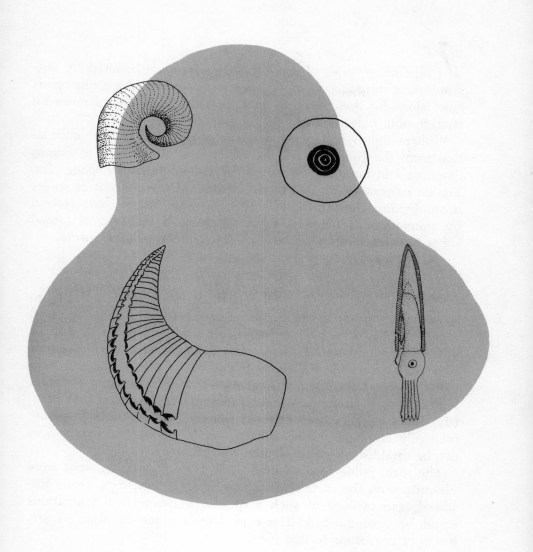

16. To correlate:
the CEPHALOPODS

*J*f obscure generals of some forgotten war are honored by out-size bronze statues, how much more deserving are the cephalopods —not alone for their intrinsic merit but also for their influence on stratigraphic paleontology.

William Smith first developed the principle of faunal correlation from the Jurassic sequence of Britain, a sequence of faunas dominated in number and variety by ammonite cephalopods. The French paleontologist D'Orbigny introduced the concept of stages in subdividing the Jurassic of western Europe, stages characterized by ammonites. A German, Oppel, developed the idea of faunal zones in these same rocks, zones indexed by ammonite species.

TO SUCCEED AS A GUIDE FOSSIL

The fossil cephalopods, particularly the ammonites, possess un-usual qualifications to justify their fame. First of all, they evolved rapidly within a lineage, and split into a large number of distinct lines. Second, many of them were nektonic and were vigorous swimmers with wide ecological tolerance. As a consequence, indi-vidual species have a wide distribution and occur in many different sedimentary environments. Third, they are relatively easy to iden-tify, many of them from external characteristics. Fourth, they are relatively common fossils. Finally, some phylogenetic sequences can be established with a degree of certainty.

The ideal guide fossils would come from populations that were ubiquitous on the earth's surface, were abundant, were easily fos-silized, and evolved at such a speed that successive generations could be distinguished. The cephalopods come as close as any group of organisms to that ideal.

The anatomy of success

Recent cephalopods, the squids, octopus, and nautilus, are all active predators, either of the marine nekton or of the benthos. What is known of fossil cephalopods suggests that most, if not all, had a similar way of life. Unfortunately for the paleontologist who would interpret cephalopod functions, one subclass of cephalopods is represented by only one recent genus and the other has few fossil representatives.

The structure (Figure 16-1) of the nautilus is closest to that of the majority of fossil cephalopods, and so can be described as an introduction to cephalopod morphology. As stated in the introductory section on molluscs (p. 350), the posterior end of the cephalopods has been rotated to lie below the anterior parts. The head bears tentacles arranged about the mouth and is distinctly set off from the remainder of the body. The eyes are large, and the major nerve ganglia of the head are of a size to deserve the name of brain. The heart, too, is large, and the circulatory system efficient. The mantle forms a cone about the viscera. Between the head and

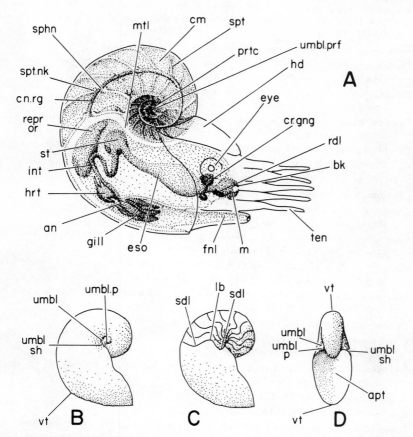

Fig. 16–1. *ANATOMY OF THE CEPHALOPODA.* A) Diagrammatic view of *Nautilus* with shell cleared to show internal structure. B) Lateral view of *Nautilus* shell. C) Lateral view of fossil *Nautilus* shell. The outer layers of shell material have been removed to show the sutures, i. e., the line of intersection of shell and septum. D) Apertural view of *Nautilus* shell.

GLOSSARY FOR THE CEPHALOPODA

(Figures cited at end of definition illustrate structure.)

Advolute. Type of coiled shell in which the outer whorl touches but does not cover any part of the adjacent inner whorls. (16–2I; 16–4D, E.)

Ammonitic suture. Type of suture characterized by complex fluting. Smaller secondary and tertiary lobes and saddles developed on larger primary set. (16–6C.)

Anus. See 15–1. In all known cephalopods the viscera are doubled back so that anus lies below head. (16–1A.)

Aperture (apt). External opening of living chamber from which the head and tentacles are extended. (16–1D; et al.)

Ascocone. Type of shell. Earlier portion is slender and curved; later short and wide with chambers above the living chamber. Initial part of shell may be detached. (16–2F; 16–4B.)

Beak (bk). Pair of horny jaws on either side of mouth. (16–1A.)

Brevicone. Shell type with short, blunt form and rapid taper from wide living chamber to initial chamber. Typically curved. (16–2E; 16–4A.)

Camera (cm). Chamber in shell representing a portion of an earlier living chamber now closed off by a septum. Presumably gas filled. (16–1A; 16–2C to G; et al.)

Cameral deposits. Calcareous deposits on septa and/or walls of camera. (16–3E. diagonal lined area)

Ceratite suture. Type of suture characterized by presence of small lobes and saddles on major lobes. (16–6D.)

Cerebral ganglion (cr. gng). See 15–1. (16–1A.)

Chamber. See camera.

Conispiral. Shell form characterized by a spiral coiled on a cone—whorls not in a single plane. (16–2P; 16–7G, H.)

Connecting ring (cn. rg). Calcareous ring forming wall of siphuncle between septa. (16–1A; 16–3B, C, D, E; et al.)

Convolute. Type of coiled shell in which part of outer whorl extends in toward center of coil and covers inner whorls. (16–1B; 16–2K; 16–5D; 16–7D.)

Crescentic cross-section. Refers to crescent shape of whorl cross-section in some coiled cephalopods. (16–2L, M.)

Cyrtocone. Type of shell. Slender, curved cone. (16–2C.)

Dibranchiate. Refers to cephalopods bearing a single pair of gills. Includes all recent cephalopods except *Nautilus*. (16–8B.)

Endocones. Conical calcareous deposits inside siphuncle. Apices of cones point toward shell apex. (16–3D.)

Esophagus (eso). See 15–1. (16–1A.)

Eye (eye). See 15–1. (16–1A; 16–8B.)

Funnel (fnl). Muscular tube just below head which extends externally from mantle cavity. Serves to confine and direct jet of water forced from that cavity. (16–1A; 16–8B.)

Gill (gill). See 15–1. (16–1A; 16–8B.)

Goniatite suture. Type of suture characterized by simple fluting consisting of single series of lobes and saddles. (See ceratite and ammonite.) (16–6E.)

Gyrocone. Type of coiled shell in which adjacent whorls do not touch each other. (16—2H; 16—4C.)

Heart (hrt). See 15—1. (16—1A.)

Hood (hd). Tough fleshy structure that lies above head of *Nautilus* and covers aperture when head is withdrawn into living chamber. In some fossil cephalopods this structure or one similar bore a pair of calcareous plates called the aptychus. (16—1A.)

Intestine (int). See 15—1. (16—1A.)

Involute. Type of coiled shell in which part of outer whorl extends in toward center of coil and covers part of adjacent inner whorl. (16—2J; 16—5A, B; et al.)

Lituiticone. Type of shell which has a coiled initial portion and a straight mature portion. (16—2G.)

Living chamber. Chamber in which soft parts of animal are housed. The last-formed chamber, it is bounded at the back by a septum and opens at the front through the aperture. (16—1A; et al.)

Lobe (lb). A flexure of the suture line away from the aperture (toward the apex). (16—1C; 16—6.)

Mantle (mtl). See 15—1. Fold of the body wall enclosing the viscera and forming a sack or cone about them. (16—1A.)

Mouth. (See 15—1. (16—1A.)

Orthocone. Shell type consisting of a slender straight cone. (16—2D; 16—3C, D.)

Phragmocone (phrag). Portion of shell consisting of camerae (gas filled chambers). Applied particularly to belemnoids. (16—1A; 16—8A, B.)

Planospiral. Type of coiled shell in which whorls lie in a single plane—that one of bilateral symmetry. (16—1D; 16—2L through O; et al.)

Proostracum (prost). Calcareous blade projecting anteriorly from dorsal border of belemnoid phragmocone. (16—8A, B.)

Protoconch (prtc). Initial chamber of shell—located at apex of cone or at center of coil. (16—1A.)

Quadrate cross-section. Shell form characterized by quadrate whorl cross-section. (16—2N.)

Radula (rdl). See 15—1. (16—1A.)

Reproductive organ (repr. or). Glandular mass responsible for production of eggs or sperm. (16—1A.)

Rostum (rst). Structure occuring in belemnites. A thick conical or subconical calcareous deposit enclosing the phragmocone. (16—8A, B.)

Saddle (sdl). Flexure of suture line toward aperture. (16—1C; 16—6.)

Septal neck (spt. nk). Flexure of septum along siphuncle forming a short tube or funnel. (16—1A; 16—3C, E; et al.)

Septum (spt). Calcareous partition transverse to walls of shell and separating camerae (chambers).

Siphonal deposits. Calcareous deposits along siphuncle. In some nautiloids of considerable thickness. (16—3E; 16—4A.)

Siphuncle (sphn). Tube extending from back of living chamber through septa to protoconch. (16—1A; 16—3B, C, D, E; et al.)

Stomach (st). See 15—1. (16—1A.)

Subcircular cross-section. Shell form characterized by subcircular whorl cross-section. (16–2P; 16–7G, H; et al.)

Suture. Line of intersection between septum and inner surface of shell wall. (16–1C; 16–6; et al.)

Tentacle. One of several slender arm-like appendages that surround the mouth and extend anteriorly in front of head. (16–1A; 16–8B.)

Tetrabranchiate. Cephalopod bearing four gills—two pairs—in mantle cravity. Known certainly only in *Nautilus.* (16–1A.)

Umbilical perforation (umbl. prf). Opening between inner sides of innermost whorl in position of axis of coiling. (16–1A.)

Umbilical plug (umbl. p). Calcareous deposit filling umbilicus. (16–1B.)

Umbilical shoulder (umbl. sh). Portion of shell bordering umbilicus and forming its outer margin. (16–1C, D; 16–5A, B; 16–7A to F. et al.)

Umbilicus (umbl). Depression (or in some an opening) in axis of coiling formed by diminishing width of whorls toward axis.

Venter (vt). Portion of whorl farthest from axis of coiling. (16–1B, D; et al.)

V-shaped cross-section. Type of shell form characterized by v-shaped whorl cross-section. (16–2O.)

---

ventral margin of the mantle is a tube (the *funnel*) extending into the mantle cavity and opening externally. Within the mantle cavity lie two pairs of gills.

The mantle, or part of it, secretes the shell. Because calcium carbonate is deposited more rapidly on the ventral and lateral sides of the mantle than on the dorsal, the shell develops in a spiral— one coiled in a single plane, that of bilateral symmetry. The axis of coiling is above the visceral mass. The mantle is attached to the shell by muscles along a sharply defined line. A partition (*septum*) is built across the shell at this position, and the line of juncture of the septum and inner layers of the shell forms a distinct *suture*. As the animal grows, the attachment periodically shifts forward, and a new septum is formed. In this way a series of chambers is formed. A slender tube, the *siphuncle*, passes back from the visceral hump through the septa. Around the opening for the siphuncle, the surface of each septum turns back sharply to form a short calcareous tube, the *septal neck*. The successive septal necks are connected by delicate *connecting rings*.

The nautilus feeds on the bottom. The tentacles are used to seize and hold the food. The animal may swim by motion of the tentacles, but rapid swimming is accomplished by rhythmic contractions of the muscular funnel and the mantle musculature (Figure 16-2). When these muscles relax, water enters the mantle cavity around the head. Contraction of the muscles seals the opening between the

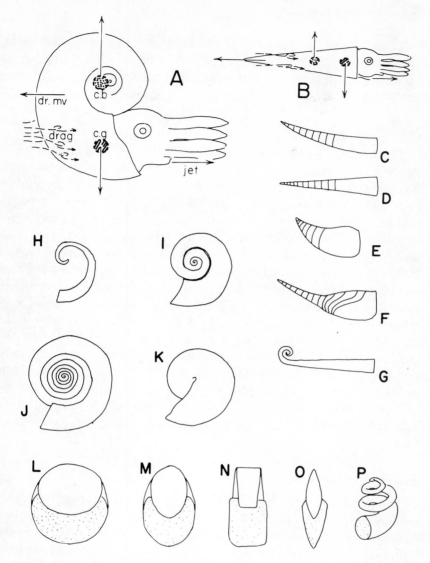

Fig. 16–2. DYNAMICS OF THE CEPHALOPOD SHELL AND VARIATION IN FORM. For definitions see Figure 16–1. A) General coiled shell type. The jet (jet) from the siphon drives the animal through the water (direction of movement, dr. mv). The buoyancy of the empty chambers (center of buoyancy, c. b) lifts the animal; gravity pulls it downward (center of gravity, c. g). "Drag" of the water around the shell opposes its movement. B) Straight shell type. The difference in location of the center of gravity (forward in the living chamber) and of buoyancy (back in the empty shell chambers) produces a rotational couple that must be opposed actively by the animal. C) Cyrtocone shell. D) Orthocone. E) Brevicone. F) Ascocone. G) Lituiticone. H) Gyrocone. I) Advolute. J) Involute. K) Convolute. L) through O) Apertural views showing cross-sectional shape of shell. L) Subcircular. M) Flattened ovoid. N) Rectangular. O) Discoidal. P) Conispiral shell.

head and mantle margin and forces a jet of water out of the mantle cavity through the funnel. A pulse of this jet drives the animal backward or if the end of the funnel is turned, obliquely through the water.

Evolutionary trends

The knowledge of fossil cephalopods is confined almost exclusively to structure and form of shell. Although many important functions of the cephalopods are not reflected in shell morphology, locomotion is (Figure 16-2). The shell, of course, serves as protection but, more important, buoys up the animal because of its empty chambers. The shape of the shell, its streamlining, determines the amount of drag. A heavy shell interferes with locomotion, particularly swimming. Too light a shell is subject to rupture under rapid changes of hydrostatic pressure, although the siphuncle probably permits gas exchange to equalize those pressures. If the center of buoyancy is far behind the animal's center of gravity, it will turn the animal so that the head, tentacles, and funnel are down and shell up. Locomotion, either crawling or swimming, would hardly be assisted by this awkward position. Knowing these problems in adaptation, one could predict many of the evolutionary trends of cephalopods. These trends show in the differentiation of the subclasses * and orders and within the particular evolutionary lineages.

Subclass Nautiloidea †

The primitive cephalopods (Figure 16-3) may have had a straight conical shell with closely spaced septa. The early Cambrian fossil *Volborthella* appears to have these features as well as a large central siphuncle. Unfortunately, preservation is very poor, and the details of the shells obscured. No middle Cambrian cephalopods have been

---

* Zoologists generally recognize two recent subclasses, the Tetrabranchiata with two pairs of gills and of kidneys and a coiled external shell and the Dibranchiata with a single pair of gills and of kidneys and a rudimentary internal shell. That division is not very practical for paleontologists who find species with a wide variety of shell types and who cannot determine the number of gills or kidneys. Therefore, they commonly recognize three subclasses on the basis of shell characteristics. Since most cephalopods are fossils, the paleontologic classification is more satisfactory and, in one sense, more valid. I use here the latter system, rather than the tetrabranchiate-dibranchiate classification.

† Classification after Flower and Kummel, 1950.

found, and, and, even if *Volborthella* is a cephalopod (which most cephalopod specialists doubt), its relation to the later types is unknown. The upper Cambrian cephalopods (Figure 16-4) are grouped along with some Ordovician species in a single suborder, Ellesmeroceroida. These have a gently curved shell with closely crowded and gently curved septa. The siphuncle is near the ventral margin, and, in early representatives, the connecting rings are thickly calcified. This weighting of the shell probably counterbalanced the buoyancy and permitted the animal to crawl or swim in a near horizontal attitude. This ballast is reduced in later ellesmeroceroids. The reduction may indicate a change in method of locomotion or in habitat.

Presumably, the remaining cephalopods were derived from ellesmeroceroid ancestors and those with flat or simply curved septa are grouped in the Nautiloidea. Eight new suborders (Figures

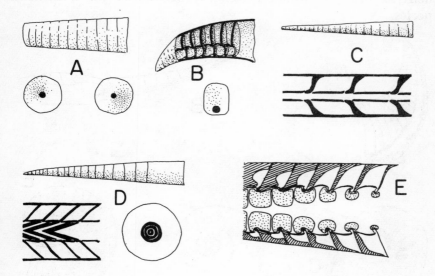

Fig. 16–3. *NAUTILOID CEPHALOPODS. A)* Ellesmeroceroid *Volborthella;* early and middle Cambrian; lateral view at top, apertural view of septal face at lower left, apical view at lower right; length 2.8 mm. *B)* Ellesmeroceroid *Plectronoceras;* late Cambrian; longitudinal section above, apertural view below; length of specimen 6 mm. *C)* Michelinoceroid *Michelinoceras;* middle Silurian to ?Triassic; lateral view above and diagrammatic cross-section below; length 6.2 cm. *D)* Endocerid *Endoceras;* Ordovician; lateral view above, cross-section at right, longitudinal section at left shows endoconces in longitudinal section. *E)* Actinocerid *Actinoceras;* Ordovician; diagrammatic longitudinal section. Siphonal deposits of calcite stippled, cameral deposits lined. (A. and B. after Schindewolf. C. after Barrande. D. and E. after Flower.)

16-3 and 16-4) appear in the Ordovician—a remarkably rapid adaptive radiation. So far as shell morphology is concerned, the differentiation was based primarily on different methods of compensating for the buoyancy of the shell. In straight and slightly curved forms, the shell was counterbalanced by calcareous deposits on the chamber walls (the Michelinoceroida) and/or on the siphuncle (the Endoceroida, Actinoceroida, and Discosoroida) or by enlargement of the siphuncle so that a large part of the visceral mass extended to the tip of the shell (the Endoceroida). In some, the Oncoceroida, the immature parts of the shell are relatively shortened, and the living chamber occupies most of the shell. All of these adaptations either carried the center of gravity back toward the center of buoyancy or brought the center of buoyancy forward, and all of them reduced buoyancy and increased the relative weight of the shell. These may have been adaptations to bottom life; certainly shells of this sort would be clumsy accessories for a nektonic species.

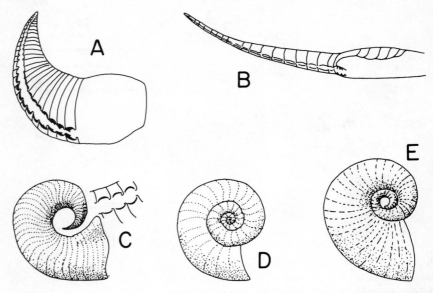

Fig. 16–4. *NAUTILOID CEPHALOPODS. A)* Oncoceroid *Valcuoroceras;* Ordovician; diagrammatic longitudinal section. Siphonal deposits shown in black. *B)* Ascoceroid *Ascoceras;* Silurian; diagrammatic longitudinal section. The slender conical portion of the shell broke off the mature portion at maturity. *C)* Discosorid *Phragmoceras;* Silurian; lateral view and section of siphuncle; greatest diameter about 15 cm. *D)* Tarphyceroid *Tarphyceras;* Ordovician; lateral view. *E)* Barrandeoceratid *Barrandeoceras;* Ordovician to Devonian; lateral view. (A. and B. after Flower; C. after Zittel.)

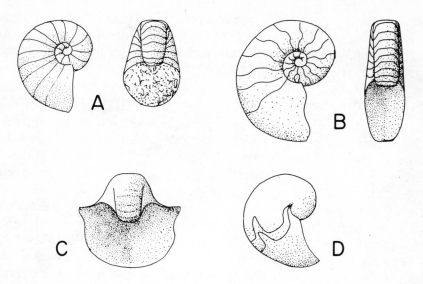

Fig. 16–5. *NAUTILOID CEPHALOPODS.* A) Rutoceratid *Endolobus;* Mississippian to Permian; lateral and apertural views of internal mold. B) Centroceratid *Domatoceras;* Pennsylvanian to Permian; lateral and apertural views. C) Solenochilid *Solenocheilus;* Mississippian to Permian; apertural view. D) Nautilid *Aturia;* Paleocene to Miocene; lateral view; maximum diameter 19 cm. (B. and C. after Miller. D after Miller and Downs.)

The other orders that appeared in the Ordovician pursued a different evolutionary path. In one, the Ascoceroida, the early, straight part of the shell broke free from the mature part of the shell and was lost. In the mature portion, the chambers extended forward over the living chamber so that the center of buoyancy lay above the center of gravity. Others, the Barrandeoceratida and Tarphyceratida, found a similar solution in a different manner. In these, the shell coiled strongly so that the axis of coiling, and thus the center of buoyancy, came to lie above the living chamber. There was no longer any need to ballast the shell, so this transformation brought a maximum of stability with a minimum of weight. Similar modifications occurred in the Discosorida and Oncoceratida, although they did not coil so tightly. In the Devonian and Mississippi, additional coiled types appeared, among them the rutoceratids, solenochilids, and centroceratids (derived probably from oncoceratid species) and the nautilids, whose ancestry is unknown. Within these orders, the genera vary in shape—some "fat" and others laterally compressed—and in tightness of coiling—

some loosely coiled and others so tightly wound that the outer whorl hides the inner ones. Presumably these changes were adaptive to different ecologic niches, and some in particular for better streamlining and greater stability.

Subclass Ammonoidea

Among the coiled Devonian cephalopods are several genera with the siphuncle placed near the ventral border of shell and with curved septa (Figure 16-6). The central part of each septum is flat or gently concave, but the margins are bent into several low folds. The suture, following the folds of the septum, curves also and traces a wavy line. These few genera are the earliest representatives of a new order, the Ammonoidea, although to a Devonian observer they would have been merely another twig in the nautiloid tree.

The ammonoids may have evolved from one of the coiled nautiloid stocks or, less probably, from straight nautiloids with a ventral

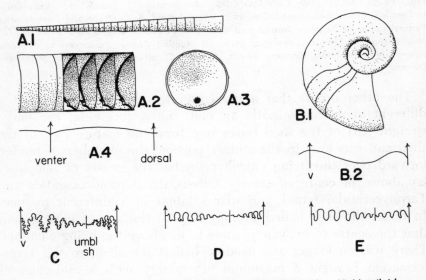

Fig. 16–6. *EVOLUTION OF THE AMMONOID CEPHALOPODS.* A) Nautiloid, possible ammonoid ancestor, *Bactrites.* A.1) Lateral view of shell. A.2) Partial longitudinal section. A.3) Septum—apertural face. A.4) Trace of suture. Arrow points in direction of aperture. B) Early and presumably primitive ammonoid, *Gyroceratites.* B.1) Lateral view. B.2) Trace of suture. C) Complex suture—ammonite *type*—with primary saddles and lobes both subdivided. D) Moderately complex suture of ceratite type. Lobes are serrate, but saddles are not. E) Simple type, goniatite, in which neither saddles or lobes are subdivided. Abbreviations: *umbl. sh,* umbilical shoulder—marked on suture by straight line without arrow. (B. after Miller and Furnish.)

siphuncle (michelinoceratids). The suture line in these early forms consists of a series of simple curves toward (the *saddles*) and away from (the *lobes*) the open end of the shell, a suture type called *goniatite*. By Mississippian time, some had evolved a more elaborate folding of septal margin, a *ceratite* suture distinguished by secondary saddles and lobes on the original lobes (Figure 16-6). A third and still more complicated suture, the *ammonite*, appeared in Permian ammonoids. Secondary folds appeared on the primary saddles as well as on the lobes, and, in some, the margin of the septa crinkles so strongly that a third set of lobes and saddles appears.

The adaptive value of these crenulations is not certainly known. They undoubtedly braced the shell wall, if it needed bracing, against hydrostatic pressure, and may have permitted the animal to dive and ascend more rapidly. So far as I know, however, no one has demonstrated experimentally or mathematically that a shell with thin walls and fluted septa is stronger than a shell of equal weight with thick walls and simple septa. Some paleontologists have suggested that the folding of the septa increased the effectiveness of the muscle attachment along the septal margin.

The ammonoids underwent at least two successive adaptive radiations, one in the late Paleozoic and Triassic, and one in the Jurassic and Cretaceous. In each, a variety of shell forms (Figure 16-7) appeared, some loosely coiled, others tightly; some globose in cross-section, others flattened and discoidal. A few coiled like snails in a conical spire. Several genera have the immature part of the shell coiled and the adult portion straight. Others formed a coil early in development, then grew straight for a while, and finally formed a loop. Those variations that produced a streamlined shape like that of some discoidal genera apparently belonged to rapid swimmers. Many of the variations, though, seem as inexplicable in function as do the ribs, spines, and nodes that occur in some ammonoids.

Subclass Dibranchiata

The dibranchiate cephalopods differ from all the preceding in the possession of an internal skeleton. Like the others, the mantle secretes a shell and builds successive septa across it. This shell (the *phragmocone*), however, is relatively small and lacks a distinct

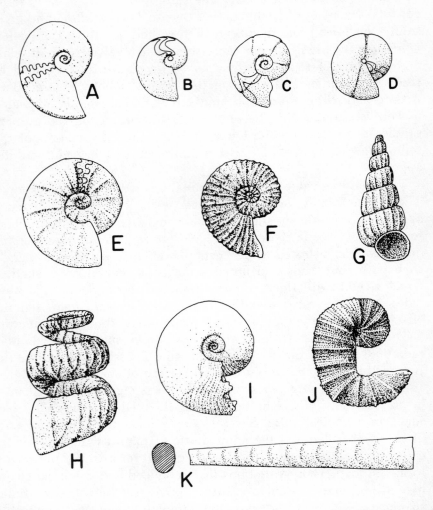

Fig. 16–7. *REPRESENTATIVE AMMONOIDS.* A) *Uddenoceras;* late Pennsylvanian; lateral view with two sutures shown; greatest diameter 1.5 cm. B) *Manticoceras;* late Devonian; lateral view with three sutures; greatest diameter 1.1 cm. C) *Muensteroceras;* Mississippian; lateral view with two sutures; greatest diameter 3.6 cm. D) *Sporadoceras biferum;* late Devonian; lateral view with two sutures shown; greatest diameter 3.3 cm. E) *Ceratites;* middle Triassic; lateral view with two sutures shown; greatest diameter 9.5 cm. F) *Nevadites;* middle Triassic; lateral view; greatest diameter 6 cm. G) *Cochloceras;* late Triassic; apertural view; height 2.7 cm. H) *Emperoceras;* late Cretaceous; height 15 cm. I) *Oxynoticeras;* early Jurassic; lateral view; greatest diameter 3.4 cm. J) *Scaphites;* Cretaceous; lateral view; greatest diameter 4.4 cm. K) *Baculites;* late Cretaceous; cross-section and a lateral view of incomplete specimen; length of specimen 17.5 cm. (A. After Miller and Furnish. F. After Smith. G. After Zittel.)

living chamber (Figure 16-8). The mantle folds back over the shell and deposits concentric laminae of calcite on its external surface to form the *rostrum*. This, typically, is much larger than the phragmocone itself. Only the dorsal portion of the shell continues growth at the normal rate. The result is a narrow blade, the *proostracum*, which projects forward in the dorsal surface of the mantle. Superficially, this dibranchiate shell differs greatly from that of any pre-Mississippian cephalopods, but if the rostrum were removed and proostracum expanded laterally to form a living chamber, it would be very like that of the michelinceroids—even to the presence of a ventral siphuncle. As shown in Figures 16-6 and 16-8, the similarity to *Bactrites* is striking. Presumably, the shell was reduced as an aid to rapid swimming, and the rostrum developed as a counterbalance or a stiffening rod for the elongate cone-shaped mantle. The rostrum was large in the extinct belemnoids but was reduced or absent in the lines that lead to the recent cuttlefish, squid, and octopus.

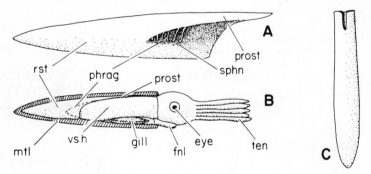

Fig. 16–8. *BELEMNOIDS.* A) Lateral view of shell, cleared to show phragmocone. B) Lateral view of reconstruction of belemnoid. The mantle has been sectioned to show the rostrum, gills, and visceral hump. C) *Belemnitella;* late Cretaceous; ventral view; length 9.5 cm. Abbreviations: *eye,* eye; *fnl,* funnel; *gill,* gill; *mtl,* mantle; *phrag,* phragmocone; *prost,* proostracum; *rst,* rostrum; *sphn,* siphuncle; *ten,* tentacles; *vs. h,* visceral hump.

CEPHALOPOD STRATIGRAPHY

I suggested in several of the preceding chapters that interpretations of phylogeny and paleoecology depended, in large measure, on interpretations of function and adaptation. Without such knowledge, the paleontologist must hesitate in separating characteristics acquired by evolution in response to similar environments from those inherited from a common ancestor. Without such knowledge, he falters in the analysis of the limiting ecological factors in the fossil environment. When a stratigrapher asks if *A* or *B* is the older species or if they lived in different environments at the same time, he can give only a very approximate answer.

Fortunately, these defects are not so serious for cephalopod stratigraphy as for cephalopod paleontology. The reason for this happy circumstance lies in the peculiarities of cephalopod geographic distribution. Many species were nektonic and vigorous swimmers. Like recent marine vertebrates, the fishes, the sharks, and the whales, they must have migrated widely across the oceans and into the confines of the epicontinental seas. Not all did so—many, such as the sluggish benthonic Paleozoic nautiloids had narrow environmental limits—but a few, at least, left "home." These wide ranging species are among the most important of zonal fossils. Admittedly, they, too, had ecologic limits and almost certainly appeared in different places at different times, but they have been found to succeed one another in local stratigraphic sections in invariable order.

PALEOECOLOGY

In spite of continued interest in cephalopod habits and environments, relatively little is known of their paleoecology. As with many fossil groups, some of the men most interested confined their studies to the museum and their speculations to an armchair. This has resulted in extensive literature on adaptation but very little on specific habitats. Some cephalopods show only very general associations with sedimentary environments and were surely nektonic; ammonoid, nautilid, and belemnoid species occur in a variety of lithologic types. On the other hand, many cephalopods, particularly the early Paleozoic types, were clearly restricted in distribution to a few habitats.

CEPHALOPOD EVOLUTION: A POSTSCRIPT

Study of cephalopod phylogeny demonstrates several phenomena which has influenced evolutionary theory and is, consequently, of great interest to the student of evolution. Arkell, Kummel, and Wright (1957) point out that, in the past century, there have been changing fashions in interpretation of cephalopod phylogeny. These fashions have followed particular trends in evolutionary thought, and have, in turn, served as examples or evidence for the favored theory. Thus, there are phylogenies based on the concept of "itera- tive evolution"; others derived from a strict application of the "biogenetic law" that individual development recapitulates phyletic changes, and still others employing Dollo's law of the irreversibility of evolution. I have no space in this book for discussion of all these ideas, but I refer you to the paper by Arkell, Kummel, and Wright just cited.

Two broad evolutionary problems do deserve some consideration at this point, however. A striking feature of cephalopod evolution is the relatively rapid rate of morphologic change and diversifica- tion. This contrasts markedly with the slow evolution of the pelecy- pods. Comparison with evolutionary rates in the other phyla sug- gests a pattern, a high correlation between rates of evolution and the degree of mobility and activity in the individual animals. Pre- sumably this correlation results from high selection pressures, but that is hardly an explanation. Why should active animals undergo greater selection than sessile? Possibly these animals enter into a feedback network in which changes in the population induce changes in the environment and these, in turn, increase or change selective pressures. One sometimes gets the impression that the population figuratively has a bear by the tail. Once sessile animals acquire a certain thickness of shell or method of support they have achieved the maximum protection for a particular environment. The population survives so long as that environment limit is not transcended. The change, however, does not modify the environ- ment—a stronger brachiopod pedicle does not change the strength of the waves; a better pelecypod gill filter system does not appre- ciably change the number of micro-organisms in the incoming water current. (I have, of course, over-simplified, for a heavier shell, for example, may require a predaceous snail with a stronger radula to bore into it.) But an ammonite—or fish—population can hardly change without affecting other animal and plant populations and the selective pressures on them.

The other major evolutionary phenomenon exhibited in the cephalopods is extreme diversification and specialization sometime prior to extinction of the group. As described on p. 182, this is sometimes ascribed to "overspecialization" or, because many of the changes do not seem to be adaptive, to "racial senility." I rejected these concepts as sympathetic magic in which a word stands in place of explanation. But here now is a specific case for explanation. The first conclusion must be that the cephalopod form and physiology were well fitted to the factors of the marine environment. They competed successfully with the vertebrates and possibly entered niches unavailable to the latter. This diversification—this adaptive radiation—fills out and, in a sense, actually creates a natural society. Natural societies evolve and, in some examples, have been modified so rapidly and destructively that one can speak of their extinction. The late Triassic and early Jurassic marine pelagic societies apparently suffered one of these "extinctions," and, in consequence, many cephalopod lineages disappeared. Another similar event occurred in the later Cretaceous.

These evolutionary catastrophies have a dangerous allure to the paleontologic observer. They attract the metaphysical theories of racial senescence and catastrophic theories of sudden climatic change, meteors, and virulent viruses. They rarely attract the hard effort of careful detailed morphologic, paleoecologic, and phyletic work. I come, therefore, to a second conclusion on this problem—that no one has yet acquired sufficient data to uncover the reasons with any certainty.

TABLE 16–1

THE CEPHALOPODA

(?) Early Cambrian. Late Cambrian to Recent. Tentacles; body bent in U-shape so that anus lies below head; viscera enclosed by muscular, cone-shaped mantle. Locomotion by forcible expulsion of water from mantle cavity through ventral funnel. Most have multichambered calcareous shell or rudiments of such a shell. Vagrant benthos and nekton; predaceous; all known marine.

Subclass Nautiloidea

(?) Early Cambrian. Late Cambrian to Recent. Large calcareous shells, either straight, curved, or coiled. Many had thick calcareous deposits inside shell chambers. Septa simple—plane or gently curved plates; sutures, in consequence, straight or broadly curved. Vagrant benthos and nekton.

Subclass Ammonoidea

Devonian to Cretaceous. Shells large, typically coiled though some are straight. Interior of chambers not filled by material deposited during life. Septa and sutures moderately to strongly folded. Most were probably nektonic.

Subclass Dibranchiata

Mississippian to Recent. Single pair of gills. Shell reduced and enclosed in mantle or absent. Vagrant benthos or nekton. Active predators. Only the belemnoids, with heavy bullet-shaped calcareous rostrum, are common fossils.

REFERENCES

Arkell, W. J., B. Kummel, and C. W. Wright. 1957. "Mesozoic Ammonoidea," in: Moore, R. C., Ed., 1953. *Treatise on Invertebrate Paleontology, Part L,* Geol. Soc. of America, pp. 80-465.

Brinkmann, R. 1929. *Statistisch-biostratigraphische Untersuchungen an mitteljurassischen Ammonitea, Ueber Artbegriff und Stammensententwicklung.* Abhandl. Ges. Wiss. Göttingen, Math Psysik., Klasse, N.F., Bd. 13, 3. A detailed study of evolution in some Jurassic cephalopod lineages.

Flower, R. H. and B. Kummel. 1950. "A Classification of the Nautiloidea," *Jour. of Paleontology,* vol. 24, pp. 604-616.

Haas, O. 1942. "Recurrence of Morphological Types and Evolutionary Cycles in Mesozoic Ammonites," *Jour. of Paleontology,* vol. 16, pp. 643-650.

Kummel, B. and R. M. Lloyd. 1955. "Experiments on Relative Streamlining of Coiled Cephalopod Shells," *Jour. of Paleontology,* vol. 29, pp. 159-170.

Spath, L. F. 1933. "The Evolution of the Cephalopoda." *Biol. Review,* vol. 8, pp. 418-462. A comprehensive review of cephalopod evolution.

Trueman, A. E. 1941. "The Ammonite Body Chamber, with Special Reference to the Buoyancy and Mode of Life of the Living Ammonite," *Quart. Jour., Geol. Soc. of London,* vol. 96, pp. 339-383.

See Arkell (1956) listed in the reference for Chapter 5 and also the general texts and treatises in Chapter 3.

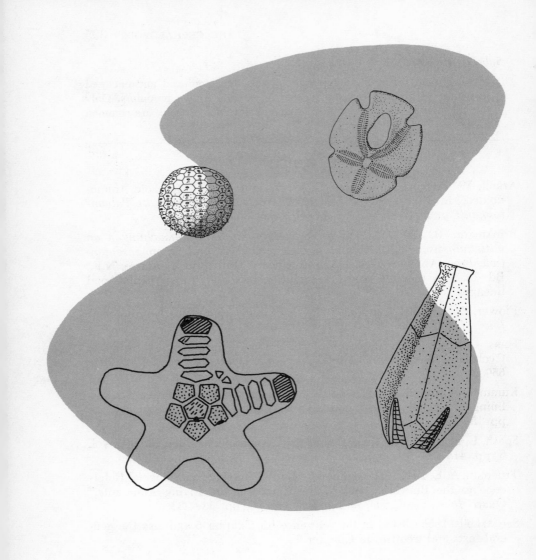

17. *Arms, stems, and spines:* *the* **ECHINODERMATA**

*S*ome time back in the Precambrian, near the time when the ancestors of the annelid-mollusc stock evolved a coelom, another population of primitive metazoa managed the same trick but in a different fashion—at least the difference in coelom development in recent animals suggests a different origin. In the annelid-mollusc stock, the coelom forms as a split within the mesodermal layer which buds off the walls of the gut. In this second group of coelomates, the coelom begins as pouches from the sides of the embryonic gut (Figure 11-1, p. 267). These separate from the gut; the cavities of the pouches form the coelomic spaces, and their walls form the mesoderm. This mode of coelom formation is obscured in some members of the group by developmental adaptations, but is nearly universal among the simpler (less evolved?) types. Further, they differ from the annelid-mollusc group in the way in which the egg divides in initial development, in the position of the mouth and anus in the larva, and in the general morphology of the larva. Their skeletal elements form internally in tissue derived from the *mesoderm* rather than externally in the superficial (*ectodermal*) layers.

Just how far back the common ancestory of this and the annelid-mollusc line lies is uncertain. The two are distinct at their first fossil appearance, and the profound differences in embryology may indicate a very long period of divergence. Like the annelid-mollusc line, this one also divided early in its history into two major stocks—so early that some authorities won't concede that the two are closely related. Again, like the annelid-mollusc line, one of the major branches, the Chordata, contained largely active animals and paralleled the annelids in the evolution of segmentation. The other branch, the Echinodermata, largely adopted a sessile or sluggish benthonic habit. They evolved a rather specialized system of canals (the *water vascular system*) from parts of the coelom, and radial symmetry but otherwise retained primitive characteristics in the circulatory and nervous system. Unlike the chordates, which penetrated or evolved in fresh and brackish waters, the echinoderms have been entirely marine in habit.

THE MYSTERIOUS PENTAGRAM

The most distinctive feature of all recent and most fossil Echinodermata is five-fold radial symmetry (Figure 17-1) in the

397

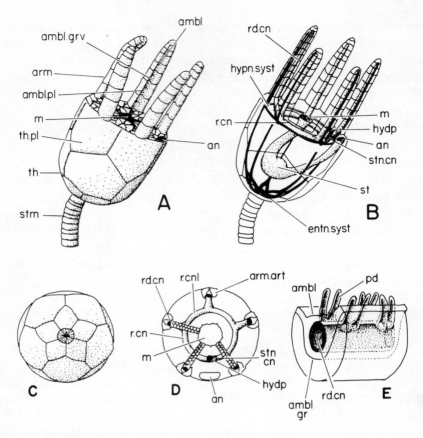

Fig. 17–1. *GENERAL PLAN OF THE ECHINODERMATA.* A) Lateral view showing theca, thecal plates, arms, and portion of stem. B) Lateral view with plates cleared to show internal anatomy. C) Aboral view of theca. D) Oral view with plates removed. E) View of arm showing details of ambulacrum, radial canal, and podia.

GLOSSARY FOR ECHINODERMATA

(Figure numbers cited at end of definition.)

Aboral. Direction opposite position of mouth. (17–1C; 17–7D, F; 17–8E; 17–13A; 17–16D; 17–19A, F, G.)

Ambulacrum (ambl). Narrow tract or groove extending radially from mouth. Typically the tissue overlying the groove is thickly ciliated and is underlain by radial canal of water vascular system. May subdivide and extend on to appendages. (17–1A, D, E; 17–2A; 17–4A; 17–5A, B, E; 17–7 A, B; 17–8E; 17–13A; 17–16A; et al.)

Ambulacral groove (ambl. grv). Groove in thecal or arm plates along course of ambulacrum. (17–1A, E; 17–2; 17–4A; 17–5A, E; 17–7A, B; 17–13E.)

Ambulacral plate (ambl. pl). Calcareous plates forming floor of ambulacral tract. (17–1A; 17–2; 17–12B; 17–13A; 17–16A.)

Ambulacral pore (ambl. p). Pore in or between ambulacral plates for passage of podium or for connection of podium to ampulla. (17–2; 17–16A; 17–17A.)

Anus (an). External opening of digestive tract for discharge of indigestible materials. (17–1A, B, D; 17–2; 17–3A, F; 17–5B; 17–7A; 17–8E; 17–11C; 17–12; 17–16B; 17–19B, E.)

Arm (arm). Appendage, typically one of several mounted on oral surface, which bears extension of ambulacrum. (17–1A, B, E.)

Columnals (col). Circular or polygonal discoid plates that form the stem. (17–1A; 17–4A; 17–5A; 17–7A.)

Covering plate (cv. pl). Small plate roofing ambulacral groove or mouth. (17–2; 17–5E; 17–7B.)

Entoneural system (entn. syst). Nerve ring and radial branches developed in aboral body wall. (17–1B.)

Hydropore (hydp). External opening of water vascular system—located in one of the interambulacral areas. May be covered by a porous plate, the madreporite. (17–1B, D; 17–4A; 17–8E; 17–11C; 17–13A; 17–16B, D.)

Hyponeural system (hypn. syst). Nerve ring and radial branches lateral to ring canal and underlying oral body wall. 17–1B.)

Interambulacral (intambl). Referring to area between rays of ambulacra—particularly the plates in these areas. (17–2; 178E; 17–12; 17–16C, D.)

Madreporite (madpt). Sieve-like plate covering external opening of water vascular system. (17–11C; 17–13A; 17–16B, D.)

Mouth (m). External opening of digestive tube serving for intake of food. (17–1A, B, D; 17–2; 17–4A; 17–5B; 17–7A; 17–8E; 17–11C; 17–13A; 17–16A, B; 17–19B, E.)

Oral. Direction—toward mouth or on same surface as mouth. (17–1D; 17–5B; 17–8E; 17–13A; 17–16C; et al.)

Podia (pd). Small tubes closed at tips and extending singly or in groups from sides of radial canal. (17–1E; 17–13A, B; 17–14B; 17–16B, F; 17–17A.)

Rays. Radial directions established by position of ambulacra. (17–1A, D; 17–8E; 17–16C, D; et al.)

Radial Canal (rd. cn). Tube extending radially from ring canal beneath ambulacrum. It is closed at its outer end and bears rows of closed branchlets, the podia. (17–1B, D, E; 17–11C; 17–13B; 17–14B; 17–16B.)

Ring canal (r. cn). Hollow tube forming a closed ring about mouth. Gives rise to radial branches—the radial canals—and is typically connected to exterior by a short tube, the stone canal. (17–1B, D; 17–11C; 17–16B.)

Stem (stm). Series of disk-like plates mounted one on top of the other and attached to aboral end of theca. Typically the terminal end is fastened to the substrate. (17–1A; 17–4A; 17–5A; 17–7A.)

Stomach (st). Pouch-like structure in anterior part of digestive tube. (17–1B; 17–11C; 17–13A; 17–16B.)

Stone canal (stn. cn). Hollow tube (typically short) leading from ring canal to external opening, the hydropore. (17–1B, D; 17–11C; 17–16B.)

Theca (th). Sac-like skeleton of calcareous plates formed in lower layer of skin and enclosing viscera. (17–1A; et al.)

Thecal plate (th. pl). Calcareous plate forming an element in the theca. Usually distinguished from ambulacral or arm plates. (17–1A; et al.)

skeleton of the body, in appendages, and in the nerve cords. This symmetry reflects the five-fold division of the water vascular system. This system develops from the anterior coelomic spaces and consists of the *ring canal* which encircles the mouth, the *stone canal* which connects the ring canal to the external opening, the *hydropore*, and the *radial canals* (typically five) which extend laterally from the ring canal. The radial canals underlie ciliated grooves, the *ambulacra*, (sometimes covered,) which extend across the body surface. The origin of the water vascular system is obscure, but it may have evolved as an accessory to a set of tentacles. The tentacles in most groups of animals are hollow, and among those that are coelomates, the cavities of the tentacles branch from the coelomic cavities. If, as would seem reasonable, respiration was carried on through the walls of the tentacles, these coelomic spaces would have taken an important part in the circulation of gases. A consequent separation of this part of the coelom and its specialization for respiration could then have occurred. All the recent echinoderms have minute branches arising from the radial canals of the water vascular system. The terminal ends of these branches are closed and form the *podia*. Subdivision of this sort is characteristic of respiratory organs, although the podia function in recent echinoderms for locomotion and food-getting as well as for respiration. If this theory of the water vascular as a respiratory organ is correct, then the respiratory adaptation proved preadaptive (p. 175) to the feeding and locomotor adaptations.

This explanation is at least logical. If however one inquires into the ontogeny of the echinoderms, several additional problems appear. The larva itself has bilateral symmetry. During metamorphosis, part of the coelom on one side of the larva subdivides and differentiates to form the water vascular system. At the same time, the position of the mouth is shifted to this side of the larva. This change involves torsion of the viscera so that the bilateral symmetry is lost. The body reorganizes about the radial branches of the water vascular system to produce a five-fold radial symmetry.

It is very difficult to make sense of this ontogenetic transformation in terms of phylogeny and adaptation. Possibly the water vascular system represents one side of a circumoral ring of tentacles like the lophopore of the bryozoa and brachiopods. That, however, does not explain why the other side degenerates. Since some of these pecularities are probably adaptations in development and others reflect characteristics from an earlier phylogenetic stage, their significance may never be determined.

Radial symmetry and tentacles are characteristics of sessile animals. Does their occurrence indicate that the proto-echinoderm species was sessile? Apparently they do, for the oldest known echinoderms are sessile types, and some of the recent free living forms attach to the bottom at some stage in their development. The phylum is conventionally divided on this characteristic, the attached forms in the subphylum Pelmatozoa; the free in the subphylum Eleutherozoa. As commonly defined, each of these subphyla represents more a stage in evolution than an evolutionary lineage, but they do provide a convenient grouping for discussion.

FORERUNNERS AND FAILURES

Subdivision of the pelmatozoans depends largely on personal predilections as to the affinities of minor Cambrian and Ordovician groups. Accordingly, one may have as few as four or as many as seven classes. Discussions of seven is simpler, paradoxically, than that of four, so I'll use the greater number for my own convenience here.

The selection of the happy few

The early Paleozoic apparently was a time of exploratory evolution for the attached crinoids. Three classes, all sharply different, are known from the Cambrian; the other four appear in Ordovician rocks, but they are rare fossils in the majority of Cambrian deposits and did not become abundant or diversified until the later Ordovician. This radiation, which apparently began in Precambrian time, produced a variety of types, each developing some aspect of the basic echinoderm adaptation. They competed with one another and with the various other animals of the sessile benthos. They were eaten and parasitized by still other animals. The majority of the pelmatozoan lines were successful only in exploitation of a very limited series of environments; a minority evolved a structure (and/or a physiology) with wider potential, and initiated their own adaptive radiation. Evolution proceeds by a selection of individuals in a species population; it also proceeds, as illustrated here, by a selection of species in an evolving natural society.

Edrioasteroids

The oldest fossil echinoderms (Figure 17-2) are several early Cambrian species that had a discoid sac-like skeleton composed of small calcareous plates and attached broadly on one surface. On the upper surface of this skeleton, the *theca,* are five arm-like tracts that radiate from the center. Typically, each arm, or, better, *ray,* consists of a double row of paired plates. These plates are depressed to form a groove where they join along the midline of the "arm." Between each plate in a row is a small pore. Another series of small plates covers the groove externally. At the center of the rays, these grooves join and open, by a single large aperture, into the inside of the theca. Between two of these rays is another smaller opening into the theca. In the same *inter-ray area* is a small plate perforated by a number of small pores.

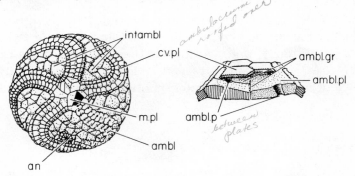

Fig. 17–2. *THE EDRIOASTEROIDEA.* One the left an oral view of *Edrioaster.* The covering plates are absent from one ambulacrum. Diameter about 3.0 cm. On the right an oblique view of a portion of an ambulacrum. See Figure 17–1 for definitions. Abbreviations: *ambl,* ambulacrum; *ambl. gr,* ambulacral groove; *ambl. p,* ambulacral pore; *ambl. pl,* ambulacral plate; *an,* anus; *cv. pl,* covering plate; *intambl,* interambulacral area; *m. pl,* mouth plate. (After Bather.)

What can one make of the animal's anatomy from these skeletal structures? The theca obviously is comparable to the calcareous skeletons that surround the viscera of recent echinoderms, and, presumably, was partly covered by a layer of living tissue. The number and arrangement of the "arms" suggests some sort of relation to the radial canals of the water vascular system. As I have already noted (Figure 17-1), one finds in recent echinoderms a similar sort of arm-like tracts, the ambulacra, in some actually borne on distinct arms. Beneath the midline of each of the ambulacra is one of the radial canals. In some, the radial canal lies directly beneath the skin and rests on the surface of the calcareous plates arranged along the ambulacral ray. The skeletal plates may be slightly or very deeply grooved for the reception of this canal. If, as in some groups, the podia are simple, small tubes, they leave no impress on the skeletal structure. Some echinoderms, however, have a large sac, an *ampulla*, connected to the base of each podium. These sacs lie either in a deep pit in the ambulacral plates, or else completely inside the skeleton at the end of a short canal. In the latter case, rows of pores within or between the ambulacral plates mark the position of the podia. Other groups of echinoderms possess radial canals that extend in a channel through the ambulacral plates or rest against their internal surfaces. In these the podia, whether they bear ampulla or not, reach the exterior through pores.

The ambulacra, typically, have a central *ambulacral groove*, roofed over in some, but open in others, and covered by ciliated skin. These grooves lead into the mouth. The water vascular system opens externally through a perforated place, the madreporite, in one of the *interambulacral areas*. The position of the anal opening is variable, but it also lies in one of the interambulacral areas.

Quite clearly, the basic echinoderm structure had already developed in the edrioasteriods, the theca of calcareous plates, the central mouth, the anus in an interray position, the radiating ambulacra, the water vascular system with podia and madreporite, and the internal torsion that brings the mouth to the center of the ambulacra. Whether the radial canals lay on or beneath the ambulacral plates is not so clear. If the former, then the podia must have had internal ampullae—accounting for the pores in these plates. But ampullae occur only in those recent echinoderms that employ the podia for locomotion. The others that are sessile, as the edriasteroids must have been, lack ampullae. If, as would seem probable from this evidence, the edriasteroids lacked ampullae, their radial canals passed along the inside of the ambulacral plates, and podia emerged through the pores.

In spite of their generalized echinoderm characteristics and early appearance. most authorities regard the edrioasteroids as a sterile side-branch from the basal echinoderm trunk. Some paleontologists believe, however, that they are early representatives of the eleutherozoan line because they, like the modern eleutherozoas, have pores between the ambulacral plates.

Eocrinoidea

The chief trends in pelmatozoan evolution were the formation of an elongate stalk, a reduction in the number of thecal plates, the development of free arms, and the arrangement of the thecal plates in symmetrical order. All of these appear in a small, precocious group of middle Cambrian echinoderms, the Eocrinoidea (Figure 17-3).

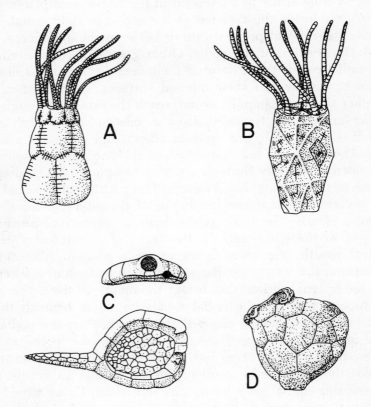

Fig. 17–3. *EARLY PELMATOZOANS.* A) Eocrinoid *Lichenoides;* Cambrian; lateral view; height of theca 3.9 cm. B) Eocrinoid *Macrocystella;* Cambrian; lateral view; height of theca 2.4 cm. C) Carpoid *Trochocystis;* Cambrian; views of oral face and of one side. D) Paracrinoid *Canadocystis;* middle Ordovician; lateral view; height of theca 4.0 cm. (A. After Jaekel. B. After Bather. C. After Gislen. D. After Hudson.)

The eocrinoids were attached by a distinct *stem* opposite the mouth and bore free arms on a globular *theca.* The stem is formed by a series of single plates, stacked one on another. The thecal plates are arranged in a series of circular rows, and have fairly *simple arm* regular radial symmetry. An arm, a *brachiole,* arises from each of the five plates in the uppermost circlet, and, in some genera, bifurcates a short distance above their base. Each brachiole consists of a double series of plates (*biserial*). The ambulacral grooves extend along the inner surface of the brachioles, and are roofed over by small plates. The forms placed in this class resemble cystoids in the structure of the arms, but lack pores in the thecal plates. The absence of thecal pores and the regular symmetry are characteristics in common with crinoids. Links with either have not been found, or, if found, have not been recognized as such. They are uncommon fossils, and, apparently, became extinct after the middle Ordovician.

Carpoidea   { *related to primitive armored fishes?*   *Save for study with vertebrates*

One other class of echinoderms, the Carpoidea, occurs in the *(very rare)* middle Cambrian deposits, (Figure 17-3). They, like the eocrinoids, have a stem, a theca of calcareous plates, and a few have brachioles. On these grounds they are obviously echinoderms—but they show hardly any of the other expected characteristics. Since the tip of the stem tapers sharply and terminates in a point or an irregular break, the adult must have lived unattached. The theca is flattened from side to side (or from front to back), and, very probably, the animal lay on one of these flattened sides. The thecal plates in some are large and completely asymmetrical. In others they are bilaterally symmetrical, the plane of symmetry perpendicular to the flattened surface. Typically, one of these surfaces is more convex than the other, and the plate arrangement differs on the "up" and "down" sides. The mouth and anus may both be on the margin opposite the stem or one or both may be shifted back along the sides. In several genera, neither mouth nor anus have been found; probably they were covered with movable plates. Several seem to lack a mouth altogether and have in its stead a row of inhalant pores like the chordate gill slits (see p. 452). The superficial appearance is very much like that of primitive armored fish with a broad, flat, head shield and a slender tail.

Without knowledge of early ontogeny and of soft parts, interpretation of carpoid adaptations and relationships is nearly impossible. Possibly they had tentacles and/or some sort of filter feeding system. If the stem were motile, they could have used it in locomotion, or, 'perhaps, they merely forced it into the substrate as an anchor. Possibly they were sessile, but at best they could have moved only slowly along the bottom. The absence of radial symmetry may be a primitive character or a highly specialized one. The bilateral symmetry could also have originated in either manner. The similarities to the early vertebrates, though intriguing, appear to be only adaptations to a generally similar mode of life. Never common, they still survived into the lower Devonian.

Paracrinoidea

The paracrinoids (Figure 17-3) are an assemblage of middle Ordovician forms with a pore system in the thecal plates, with a theca composed of small irregular plates, and with a stem. Some have free appendages consisting of brachioles with a single row of plates (uniserial) bearing uniserial branches. In others, the arms are recumbent on the surface of the theca. The pore system is a cystoid characteristic; the uniserial arms are a crinoid one. They may well be a branch of the cystoid stock that evolved crinoid-like arms. In that case, they would probably rank as a cystoid subclass or order.

A QUICK SUCCESS: THE CYSTOIDEA

A diversity of attached echinoderms with biserial arms and thecal pores appeared rather suddenly in the middle Ordovician. Obviously, their origin antedates their fossil appearance and may be back in the Cambrian. They are divided into two groups, the cystoids with irregular plate arrangements and imperfect radial symmetry, and the blastoids with perfect radial symmetry in thecal plates and ambulacra. This division is, in a sense, unequal, for the class Cystoidea encompasses a greater variety of form than the Blastoidea. The blastoid line, however, is much easier to follow than the lines within the cystoids, and underwent its major radiation after the extinction of the cystoids. The distinction is a convenient one.

The general cystoid form (Figure 17-4) is a spheroidal sac. The number and arrangement of thecal plates varies greatly from genus to genus, but, typically, they are more numerous and irregu-

lar than in crinoids or blastoids. The mouth is at the summit
of the theca. Several ambulacra, typically three or five, radiate from
the mouth. These may branch, and, in most, are extended up short
arms, the *brachioles.* If podia were present, they and the radial
canals must have lain in the ambulacral groove on the external
surface of the plates, since there are no pores for them in the plates.
The brachioles are *biserial,* i.e. they comprise a double row of
plates, and may bear biserial branchlets. The ambulacra and
brachioles characteristically show a poor grade of radial symmetry,
but some genera have very perfect five-fold symmetry; others have
bilateral symmetry, and still others are asymmetric. A high degree
of symmetry commonly correlates with a reduced number and
more regular order of thecal plates. The anus and the madreporite
lie in an inter-ambulacra area on the upper part of the theca. Many
cystoids have an additional opening, presumably for the genital
system. The stem varies greatly, long in some, absent in others.
Some with stems were not attached to the bottom.

The distinctive feature of the cystoid are the thecal pores
(Figure 17-4). Two general types are recognized. The *diploporid
system* consists of tubes oblique or perpendicular to the surface of
the plate. These are arranged in pairs, opening externally in a
common pit or short groove. The *pore rhomb system* is more complicated and comprises a series of short parallel grooves arranged
in a rhombic pattern on the external surface and a number of
tubes that connect the grooves with the interior of the theca. Each
rhomb appears on two thecal plates, half on each plate, and the
grooves are perpendicular to the suture between the plates. In
some genera, the center part of the rhomb is roofed over by a thin
calcareous layer so that only the ends of the grooves are left open;
in others, the roofing is complete.

Except for the pore system, the adaptations of the cystoids are
comparable to the crinoids. Presumably, the ambulacral grooves
were ciliated and small food particles falling on or near the
brachioles were swept down the grooves to the mouth. An increase
in the number of brachioles and of their branchlets increased the
area of this net of filters. Stemless forms may have rested directly
on the bottom and controlled their position by movements of the
brachioles. Those that did not attach their stems to the substrate
may have used the stem as a drag or as a prehensile tail to hold to
shells or seaweed. Did the cystoids compete directly with crinoids?

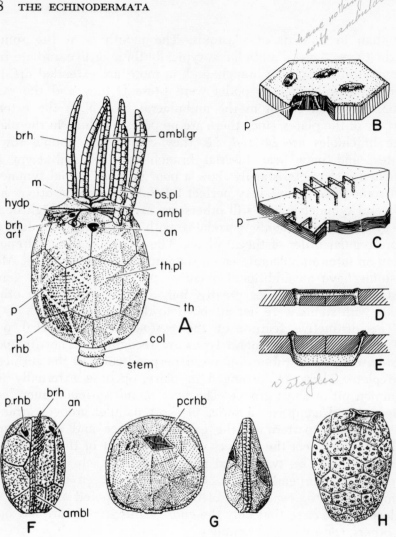

have nothing to do with ambulacrum.

~ staples

Fig. 17–4. *THE CYSTOIDS. A)* Lateral view of a generalized cystoid—based on *Caryocrinites,* a mid-Ordovician to mid-Silurian genus. Note three-fold symmetry of ambulacra. The brachioles are missing from the ray to the left. *B)* View of thecal plate sectioned to show diplopore system. *C)* View of thecal plates showing pore rhomb system. External grooves extend across adjacent plates and connect to interior by pores. *D)* and *E)* Cross-sections of two types of pore rhombs. External surface up. *F) Jackelocystes;* Silurian; lateral view; height of theca 1.5 cm. Several brachioles shown. *G) Pseudocrinites;* Silurian and Devonian; lateral views, ambulacral and interambulacral, showing compressed theca; height of theca 2.5 cm. *H) Megacystis;* Silurian; lateral view. A diploporid. (*H.* After Jaekel.)

GLOSSARY FOR CYSTOIDEA

(Figures cited at end of definitions show structure.)

Ambulacral groove (ambl. gr). See 17–1. (17–4A, F.)

Ambulacrum (ambl). See 17–1. Many genera have three distinct ambulacral rays— though some have more or less. (17–4A, F, G.)

Anus (an). See 17–1. (17–4A, F.)

Biserial arm (bs. pl). Type of arm consisting of two rows of plates from thecal articulation upward. (17–4A.)

Brachiole (brh). Arm-like appendage arising from thecal plates at ends or along sides of ambulacra. Bears extension of the ambulacral grooves. (17–4A, F.)

Brachiole articulation (brh. art). Portion of thecal plate modified for attachment of brachiole. (17–4A.)

Columnal (col). See 17–1. (17–4A.)

Diplopore. Pore system consisting of pairs of pores set in small depressions on the thecal plates. Each pore opens into the interior of the theca. (17–4B.)

Hydropore (hydp). See 17–1. (17–4A.)

Mouth (m). See 17–1. (17–4A.)

Pectinirhomb (p. rhb). Specialized type of pore rhomb system consisting of a compact rhomboidal structure of closely spaced grooves (comb-like). Typically set in a distinct depressed area on thecal plates. (17–4F, G.)

Pore (p). Small opening from exterior through thecal plates. May be closed off by deposition of calcareous material at one end or other. (17–4A, B, C, D, E.)

Pore rhomb (p. rhb). Pore system consisting of a rhomb-shaped structure on surface of theca plates. It comprises a number of grooves in plate surface at right angles to the sutures between adjacent plates and also the pores that connect ends of the grooves to thecal interior. Grooves may be roofed by thin calcareous sheet. (17–4A, C, D, E, F.)

Stem (stem). See 17–1. (17–4A.)

Theca (th). See 17–1. (17–4A, F, G, H.)

Thecal plate (th. pl). See 17–1. (17–4A, F, G, H.)

Direct paleoecologic studies have not produced any certain data on this question, but the increase of the crinoids in the later Ordovician and Silurian corresponds with a rapid decline in the cystoids.

In the absence of recent cystoids, paleontologists can only speculate about the significance of the pore system. Possibly, they served for direct exchange of gases and metabolic wastes between the coelomic fluids and the surrounding sea water. However, they could not have performed this function in those that had the pore rhombs roofed over by a calcareous sheet.

The irregularity of plate arrangement and the imperfections of the radial symmetry have induced some paleontologists to regard the cystoids as extremely primitive and near the ancestory of the whole echinoderm stock. The absence of pore systems in all Cambrian echinoderms, the high degree of symmetry in some Cambrian species, and the orderly plate arrangements in the Cambrian eocrinoids * detract considerably from this theory. Until Cambrian cystoids are found, it seems best to regard the class as one of several lines arising from an ancestor who probably possessed radial symmetry and may have had a regular plate arrangement.

The relation of the diploporid and pore rhomb cystoids and the relation of the cystoids to other echinoderms is more a question of assumptions rather than data. Some Cambrian echinoderm species have external grooves on their thecal plates. Did the pore rhomb evolve by the development of canals to connect these grooves to the surface? If so, the eocrinoids could be ancestral to the cystoids. But what does that do to the diploporid system that seems simpler and, therefore, more primitive? Are the grooved plates that occur in some crinoids and edriasteroids as well as eocrinoids the vestiges of a well developed pore rhomb system? Or, for that matter, is the difference between biserial arms (cystoids and eocrinoid) and uniserial arms (crinoids) as important as it seems? No acceptable answer can be expected until and unless additional Cambrian echinoderms are found to close the gaps.

FIRST FLOWERING: BLASTOIDEA

Some cystoid lines tend to reduce the number of thecal plates and arrange the remainder in several circlets with radial symmetry. Since the development of radial organization is related to development of the radial canals and ambulacra, these changes correspond to an increase in the size and symmetry of the ambulacra. These tendencies culminated in the class Blastoidea (Figure 17-5). Here the ambulacra are typically large and petaloid, and each has a large central plate, the *lancet*, bordered by a number of small *side plates*. The theca consists of only 13 or 14 plates in just three circlets, *basal*, *radial*, and *deltoid*. A large number of small brachioles arise in a row on either side of each ambulacrum. Each brachiole bears a small side branch from the ambulacral groove. Pores in the ambulacral plates for the tube feet and/or ampullae are lacking, and the position of the radial canals is un-

---

* The eocrinoids are thought by some to be cystoids. If so, the irregularities in Ordovician cystoids are almost certainly specialized rather than primitive characters.

known. The mouth is at the apex of the theca. The anus lies nearly adjacent in one of the interambulacral areas. The mouth, ambulacra, and grooves on the brachioles were roofed by a series of delicate covering plates. Because of their fragility, the brachioles and covering plates are only rarely found in place. Nearly all blastoids have a stem composed of separate plates, the *columnals,* stacked one on top of another.

Along either side of each ambulacrum, between the lancet plate and adjoining radial and deltoid, is a thin sheet of calcite. This sheet is folded into accordion-like pleats that parallel the ambulacral borders and extend deep into the interior of the theca (Figure 17-6). One end of the sheet is attached to a thin plate below the lancet; the other is attached to the edges of the deltoid and radial plates. These structures, called *hydrospires,* are formed by extensions of the deltoid and radial plates and, not so incidentally, the folds are approximately perpendicular to the sutures between these two plates.

The functional pattern

The habits of the blastoids must have been much like those of cystoids. Currents along the ambulacral grooves carried food particles, microscopic plants and animals from the brachioles to the mouth. Most genera were attached—those living on soft bottoms by a spreading root-like structure. Some, however, may have been free living, anchored by a prehensile stem or resting on the bottom. The purpose of the hydrospire is a mystery. The most acceptable idea would be that it was a respiratory structure, or, rather, that it supported a thin layer of living tissue that functioned in respiration. In the recent crinoids, the podia are the principal respiratory organs. Since there is no direct evidence of the water vascular system—podia, radial canals, madreporite—no one can be certain of its character or whether it was fully developed. The hydrospire may have assumed part of the function of the water vascular system.

The evolution of a pattern

Whatever the function of the hydrospire, it apparently evolved from a pore rhomb system (Figure 17-6). The position of the folds of the hydrospire perpendicular to the suture between the

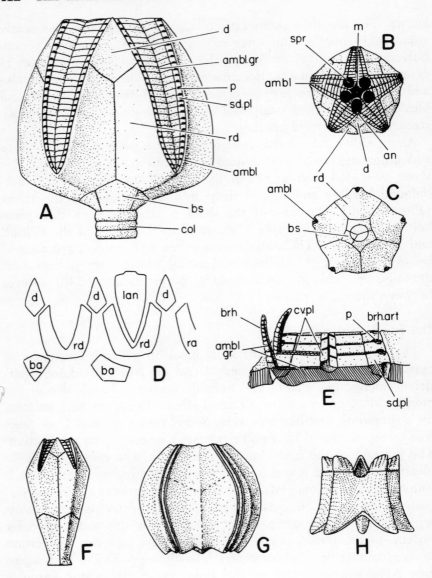

Fig. 17–5.   *MORPHOLOGY OF THE BLASTOIDEA.*   A) Generalized blastoid, based on Pentremites. Lateral view. B) The same in oral view. C) The same in aboral view. D) Relationship of thecal plates. Plates in two rays rotated into the same plane. E) Detail of ambulacrum with brachioles and covering plates. Oblique view. F) *Troostocrinus*; middle Silurian to late Mississippian; lateral view; height of the theca 1.8 cm. G) *Cryptoblastus*; Mississippian; lateral view height of theca 1.8 cm. H) *Timoroblastus*; Permian; lateral view; height of theca 1.5 cm. (H. After Wanner.)

GLOSSARY FOR BLASTOIDEA

(Illustrations that show structure are cited at end of definitions.)

Ambulacral groove (ambl. gr). See 17–1. Passes down center of ambulacral area sending off lateral branch to each brachiole. (17–5A, E.)

Ambulacrum (ambl). See 17–1. Typically one of five petal-shaped areas. (17–5A, B, C, E, F, G.)

Anus (an). See 17–1. In some the opening in theca for anus coalesced with spiracle of the anal interambulacral area. (17–5B.)

Basal plate (ba or bs). One of a circlet of plates composing the aboral end of the theca and articulated to the stem aborally and to radial plates on oral borders. (17–5A, C, D, F.)

Brachiole (brh). See 17–4. Though not often found in fossils, the brachioles formed a row on either side of the ambulacral area. (17–5E.)

Brachiole articulation (brh. art). Small area along border of ambulacrum that is modified for attachment of brachiole. (17–5E.)

Columnal (col). See 17–1. (17–5A.)

Covering plate (cv. pl). See 17–1. (17–5E.)

Deltoid plate (d). One of a circlet of plates at oral end of theca lying between ambulacra. Each deltoid terminated orally and laterally by ambulacra and aborally by radial plates. (17–5A, B, D.)

Hydrospire (hyds). Folded sheet of calcite in interior of theca beneath and parallel to ambulacral border. Axes of hydrospire folds also parallel ambulacral borders. (17–6.)

Lancet plate (lan). An elongate triangular plate that floors the ambulacral area. (17–5D.)

Mouth (m). See 17–1. Opens at free end of theca, at center of abulacral "petals." (17–5B.)

Pore (p). One of numerous small openings between side plates along ambulacral border. Connect space enclosed by hydrospire with exterior. (17–5A, E; 17–6D.)

Radial plate (rd). One of circlet of plates on sides of theca. Each deltoid embraces an ambulacral area and in consequence consists of two prongs connected below the aboral end of the ambulacrum. Bounded orally by deltoids and aborally by basals. (17–5A, B, C, D, F, G.)

Side plate (sd. pl). One of numerous small plates, arranged along ambulacral borders, that cover space between lancet plate and adjacent deltoid and radial plates. (17–5E; 17–6D.)

Spiracle (spr). Large opening at oral end of ambulacral border, adjacent to mouth. Opens into space enclosed by hydrospire. Spiracles on adjacent borders of adjacent ambulacra coalesced in some blastoids to form single opening at oral end of each interambulacral area. (17–5B; 17–6D.)

---

plates, and the contribution of each plate to its formation are precisely the character of the grooves in the pore rhombs. The initial step, as represented in the middle Ordovician *Blastoidocrinus*, was a deepening of the pore rhomb grooves so that the inner surface of the deltoid and radial plates was thrown into a series of narrow folds, each corresponding to a groove. In later blastoids, the folds are concentrated along the ambulacral borders to form the distinct hydrospire. In primitive genera, each fold opens externally by a separate slit like the pore rhomb grooves. In more specialized forms, the borders of deltoid and radial plates extend in toward the ambulacral border to form a roof just above the hydrospire. The narrow chamber between the folds and roofing plates opens to the outside through a single narrow slit along the edge of the ambulacrum. In some, still more specialized, the side plates close over this final slit and leave only a series of small pores along the edge of the ambulacrum and a large opening, the *spiracle*, at the oral end. In some blastoids, the spiracles of the two hydrospires in each interray have coalesced, reducing their number in half.

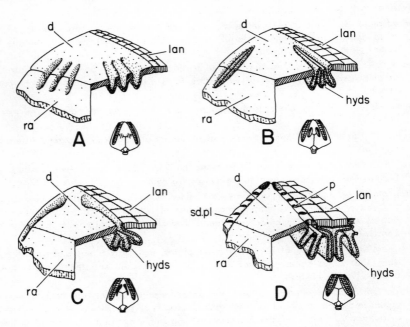

Fig. 17–6. *PRESUMED STAGES IN EVOLUTION OF HYDROSPIRE.* A) Initial, deep grooves in deltoid and radial plates like cystoid pore rhomb. B) Grooves have begun to "sink" into interior of theca. C) A definite hydrospire formed by internal, folded sheet of calcite. Each hydrospire underlies the edge of adjacent lancet plate and connects to the exterior by a long, narrow slit. D) Each hydrospire lies largely below the lancet close to the hydrospire from the other side. Side plates cover external slit except for pores and spiracle. Abbreviations: *d*, deltoid; *hyd*, hydrospire; *lan*, lancet; *ra*, radial; *sd. pl*, side plate.

In early blastoids, the anal interray lacks hydrospires, so there are only four pairs. In later genera, the anus has shifted toward the apex of the theca, and a fifth pair of hydrospires develops in that interambulacral area. In the most specialized genera with an elaborately folded hydrospire, with pore openings, and with spiracles, the primitive rhomb pore structure is hardly distinguishable.

Most of these changes occurred early in blastoid history, and conservative and advanced form continued to live side by side. Specialization of thecal structure went still more rapidly, for the blastoid features were fixed by Silurian time. *Blastoidocrinus* has four circlets of plates, five basals, five radials, a large number of small irregular plates in the next circlet, and five large deltoids between the ambulacra. Silurian blastoids, like all the later ones, have but three basals and have lost the plates between the radials and deltoids. Other than modifications in the hydrospire apparatus, blastoid evolution after the Silurian was limited to changes in thecal shape (Figure 17-5) and size of the ambulacra, most of minor importance.

The geologic record

Since the blastoids were undergoing a considerable radiation by Devonian time, some feature of blastoid anatomy must have held an important selective advantage. They reached their maximum diversity in the Carboniferous and Permian but largely on the basis of small modifications of a conservative pattern. They did not survive the end of the Permian.

Cline and Beaver (1957) conclude that blastoids were exclusively marine, thrived best in clear or only moderately turbid, quiet waters, and required a reasonably stable substrate for attachment. They commonly occur in concentrations and in association with crinoids, solitary corals, fenestellid bryozoa, and brachiopods. Future work should delimit environments and associations for individual species.

THE GOLDEN AGE: CRINOIDEA

Although the cystoid-blastoid group achieved some success, another of the pelmatozoan "investments," the Crinoidea, paid a larger return. About 140 genera of cystoids and blastoids have been described in comparison to 750 genera of crinoids. Among the pelmatozoans, only the crinoids survived beyond the Paleozoic, and the recent marine fauna includes over 600 species. They are primarily animals of the sessile benthos, attached by a slender stem, although some are not fixed permanently in one place but can crawl or swim. Even these, however, spend most of their life fastened to objects on the sea bottom or to sea weed. Like the other pelmatozoans, they were—and are—filter feeders; gentle currents along the ambulacra move small animals and plants to their mouths. The extensive branching of the arms and the numerous pinnules can create a broad filter surface.

Structural plan

Like the eocrinoids, the crinoids have a cup-shaped body * (the *calyx*) supported on an aboral *stem* (Figure 17-7). The calcareous plates that form the calyx are imperforate, but they are marked in some genera by superficial grooves resembling the pore rhombs of the cystoids. The aboral portion of the calyx bears the attachment for the stem, two or more symmetrical circlets of plates, and a ring of arms about its upper border. The top of this *aboral cup* is closed over by the small plates of the *tegmen*. The mouth lies in or near the center of tegmen. The ambulacral grooves diverge radially from the mouth, and continue up the arms. These grooves are ciliated and bear small closed tubes (podia) which arise from the radial canals of the water vascular system. The podia are also ciliated, and the beat of the cilia maintains currents of water along the grooves toward the mouth. The ring canal does not have an external opening as it does in other echinoderms but is connected with a coelom which, in turn, opens to the outside by tiny pores in the tegmenal plates. The mouth and ambulacral grooves are covered in many crinoids by small plates. The anus also opens on the tegmen in an interambulacral area.

The basal portion of an arm consists of a single row of plates (is uniserial). The more distal portions are either uniserial or biserial. In many genera, the arms branch one or more times, and each branch may bear two rows of fine branchlets, the *pinnules*.

---

* The terminology for crinoid parts varies somewhat from that in other pelmatozoans, partly because of morphologic differences but partly because of conventional usage. These changes are confusing, but are so thoroughly embedded in crinoid paleontology as to be unavoidable.

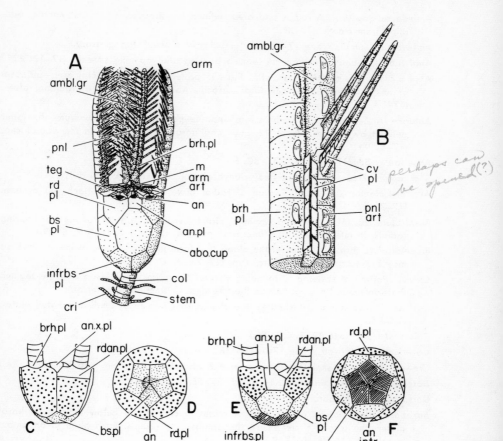

Fig. 17–7. CRINOID MORPHOLOGY. A) Lateral view of crinoid with two arms and most of stem removed. **B)** Detail of arm with most of pinnules removed. An oblique view of ambulacral face. **C)** Monocyclic crinoid—with single cycle of plates below radials (heavy stipple). A lateral view of calyx. **D)** The same in an aboral view. **E)** Dicyclic crinoid—with two cycles of plates below radials. A lateral view. **F)** An aboral view of the same calyx.

GLOSSARY FOR CRINOIDEA

(Citations at end of definition are to illustration of structure.)

Aboral.   See 17–1. (17–7D, F; et al.)

Aboral cup (abo. cup).   Cup-shaped portion of crinoid skeleton that forms the aboral and lateral walls about the viscera. Does not include free arms, tegmen, or stem. (17–7A, C, D, E, F; et al.)

Ambulacral groove (ambl. gr).   See 17–1. Grooves cross tegmen and continue up arms giving off branches to pinnules. (17–7A, B.)

Ambulacral ray (R).   A radius and area defined by direction of an ambulacrum radiating from mouth. (17–8E.)

Ambulacrum (ambl).   See 17–1 and "ambulacral groove" this glossary.

Anal tube.   Tubular elevation on tegmen bearing anal opening at end. (17–10C2.)

Anal x plate (an. x. pl *also* an. pl).   Plate in posterior interambulacral area—adjacent or next adjacent to tegmen (oral surface). Above and to left of radianal plate. (17–7A, C, E; 17–9A to C.)

Anterior (A).   Direction of ambulacrum opposite posterior interambulacrum—the latter defined by the position of the anus and/or an extra plate(s) in the aboral cup. (17–8E.)

Anus (an).   See 17–1. (17–A; 17–8C, E.)

Arm (arm).   Free extension of body above aboral cup. (17–7A; 17–10D, F.)

Arm articulation (arm art).   Portion of radial plate modified for attachment of arm. (17–7A.)

Basal plate (bs. pl).   One of a circlet of plates just below (aboral to) the arm-bearing radials. In interambulacral, "interarm" position. (17–7A, C, D, E, F; 17–9.)

Brachial plate (brh. pl).   One of the plates that form the arms. Some of lower brachials may be incorporated in aboral cup. (17–7A, B, C, E; 17–9.)

Calyx.   Portion of skeleton surrounding viscera. Comprises aboral cup and the tegmen that roofs cup. Does not include the free arms or stem. (17–7A; *et al.*)

Cirri (cri).   Appendage attached to side of stem and formed of small articulated plates. (17–7A.)

Columnal (col).   See 17–1. (17–7A.)

Covering plate (cv. pl).   See 17–1. (17–7B.)

Crown.   Portion of skeleton above stem—the aboral cup, tegmen, and arms. (17–7A.)

Dorsal.   The aboral direction. (17–7D, F; 17–8E.)

Dorsal cup.   See aboral cup.

Infrabasal plate (infrbs. pl).   Circlet of plates in crinoid cup below (aboral to) basal plates—the second circlet below the arm-bearing radials. Each plate in an ambulacral ray. (17–7E, F; 17–9.)

Interambulacral ray (IR).   Radius and area between two ambulacral rays. (17–8E.)

Interbrachial (intbrh).   Plates occurring in aboral cup between brachial plates of same ambulcral ray.

Interradial (intrad).   Plates occurring in aboral cup between brachial plates of adjacent ambulacral rays.

Left anterior (LA).   Direction of interambulacral ray and next ambulacrum to right of anterior ambulacrum as defined with mouth up and anus in posterior position. (17–8E.)

Left posterior (LP).   Direction of ambulacral ray and next interambulacrum to left of posterior interambulacrum as defined with mouth up and anus in posterior position. (17–8E.)

Monocyclic.   Cup type characterized by single circlet of plates aboral to the radials. (17–7C; 17–9A, D.)

Mouth (m).   See 17–1. (17–7A; 17–8E.)

Oral.   Direction and surface defined by position of mouth. (17–8E.)

Pinnule (pnl).   One of several branchlets arranged on either side of arm or arm branch. (17–7A, B; 17–10D.)

Pinnule articulation (pnl. art).   Portion of brachial plate modified for attachment of pinnule. (17–7B.)

Posterior (P).   Direction defined by position of interambulacral ray in which anus opens. May be recognized in aboral cup by occurrence of additional plates beyond those present in other interrays. (17–7C, E; 17–8E.)

Radial (rd. pl).   One of circlet of cup plates to which arms are articulated. Located in ambulacral rays and in line with arm axes. The lower most plate of the arm ray. (17–7A, C to F; 17–9.)

Radix.   Root-like structure at lower end of stem—attached to substrate.

Right anterior (RA).   Direction of interambulacral ray and ambulacrum next right of anterior ambulacrum—as defined with mouth up and anus in posterior position. (17–8E.)

Right posterior (RP).   Direction of ambulacral ray and next interambulacrum to right of posterior interambulacrum as defined with mouth up and anus in posterior position. (17–8E.)

Tegman (teg).   Oral surface of body. May include calcareous ambulacral and interambulacral plates or be composed entirely of soft tissue.

Tergal (terg).   Plate in posterior interambulacral ray of aboral cup just above basal plate and between radials. (17–9E.)

Uniserial arm.   Arm consisting at base of a single row of plates. (17–7A, B.)

Ventral.   The oral direction. (17–8E.)

The ambulacra branch with the arms and send off side branches to each pinnule. The stem attaches to the aboral end of the theca and consists of a column of disks (or *columnals*) with a central canal. Some of the columnals may bear side branches, the *cirri*. The end of the stem may be attached directly to the substrate or may expand to a rootlike or disklike anchor. Some recent and fossil crinoids have their stems reduced or lost altogether. These float or swim by motions of their arms and may attach temporarily by prehensile cirri.

Recent crinoids have calyx, tegmen, arms, and stem partly covered by a leathery and/or muscular skin. The plates may be rigidly joined, articulated flexibly, or held loosely by the skin and muscular connections. The latter type usually go to pieces with the death of the animal and are rarely fossilized except as loose plates. Typically, the plates of arms are articulated so that they can move by muscular contractions. The columnals and cirri are held together by ligamentous tissue.

Problems in comparative anatomy

Arms. At first glance, the crinoid arms seem comparable to the brachioles of the other pelmatozoans. They all arise in a circle

from the oral surface of the body and bear extensions of the ambulacra. Almost surely they all had a similar function. More careful examination, however, discloses several differences. One of
these, that crinoid arms are uniserial, the others biserial, was
pointed out in a preceding section (p. 409). In addition, the crinoid
arms, rather than being accessories planted on the surface of the
body, are actually extensions of the body, for the proximal plate
of each arm, the radial, develops as part of the theca.

In a strict sense, then, the theca of cystoids and eocrinoids compares with the entire crinoid calyx plus the arms and pinnules.
The brachioles or their equivalents are entirely absent and are
replaced functionally by the arms, which have an entirely different
position in the echinoderm structure plan. For this reason, the
crinoids must have arisen from a stock that lacked brachioles.

But was this lack a primitive characteristic or one that evolved
through the loss of existing brachioles? If an echinoderm had a
functioning brachiole, it seems improbable that there would be
complete selection against its presence and selection for a different
type of arm with similar functions. A brachiole, once evolved,
would have a head start on any "competitor." Therefore, the proto-
crinoid must never have had brachioles. This answer would seem
conclusive, but it obviously depends on an assumption about "competitive advantage" and has no substantiating evidence—e.g., a
middle Cambrian crinoid.

Orientation. The determination of the morphologic directions,
anterior and posterior, dorsal and ventral, in echinoderms is primarily a matter of convention. For that reason, I have avoided the
problem, as do most paleontologists, by use of "oral" and "aboral"
and by location of the anal interray. The problem becomes somewhat clearer in the crinoids because the morphologic orientation of
the embryo can be determined and applied to the adult condition
(Figure 17-8).

The larva is initially free swimming, but, after a short period,
settles to the bottom and attaches by its anterior end. The viscera
rotate 90° so that the mouth, initially ventral, opens at the free,
posterior end. The anus develops later than the mouth and finally
breaks to the surface to the left of the mouth in the same interray
as the embryonic opening of the water vascular system. The morphological anterior has become the functional ventral, and the
morphological posterior the functional dorsal. This rotation is

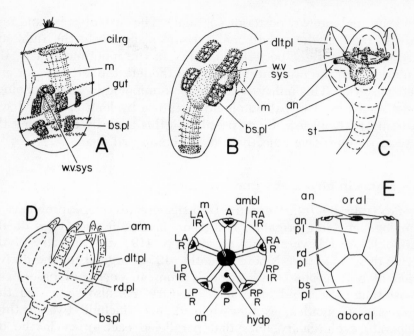

Fig. 17–8. *CRINOID DEVELOPMENT AND MORPHOLOGY.* A) Larva before attachment to bottom. Anterior is up, ventral to the left. The gut does not open to the exterior at this stage of development, but the position of the larval mouth is shown. B) Larva immediately after attachment with previous anterior end now fastened to bottom. Mouth and water vascular system have begun displacement toward free end of larva. C) Later attached stage. Deltoid folds surround mouth and a definite stem has formed. Gut now possesses both mouth and anus, the former opening in the center of the water vascular ring. D) Formation of arms. The deltoid folds and plates grow no larger and are only rudiments in the adult. E) Oral and posterior views of adult calyx with conventional morphologic directions indicated. Abbreviations: *A,* anterior; *ambl,* ambulacrum; *an,* anus; *an. pl,* anal plate; *arm,* arm; *bs. pl,* basal plate; *cil. rg,* ciliated ring; *dlt. pl,* deltoid plate; *gut,* gut; *LA. IR,* left anterior interray; *LA. R,* left anterior ray; *LP. IR,* left posterior interray; *LP. R,* left posterior ray; *m,* mouth; *P,* posterior. (A.–D. After Hyman, *The Invertebrates.* Copyright, McGraw-Hill, New York. Used with permission).

further complicated by a shift of the mouth in relation to the coelomic cavities. The water vascular system that encircles the mouth forms largely from the left anterior cavity. Thus, the mouth not only moves from anterior to posterior but brings with it the morphologic left side. Presumably, the adult could be described in terms of either the embryonic morphologic directions or the adult functional. Unfortunately, a third system has developed that corresponds to neither. The position of the stem is thus, by convention, considered dorsal (or better, aboral); the mouth ventral (or oral);

and the anal interray posterior (or anal). The two interrays and rays to the right of the mouth-anal axis are respectively the right anterior and the right posterior; the ray in the mouth-anal axis, the anterior, and the rays and interrays to the left, the left anterior and left posterior. This unhappy tangle of terminology and morphology now seems fixed in paleontologic literature by long use, but I will attempt to avoid it as far as possible in this book by continuing the use of the directive adjectives, oral, aboral, and anal.

Problems in phylogeny and evolution

Probably no other group of fossils creates more problems in phylogenetic interpretation and, thus, in classification than do the crinoids. As I have already implied (p. 419), the ancestry of the crinoids is uncertain. Moore recently (1954) argued for the derivation of both cystoids and crinoids from an eocrinoid base—or at least that they could have such ancestry. He also suggested that the class Crinoidea, as now defined, may include two or three separate evolutionary lines that paralleled each other in the development of crinoid characteristics.

The situation within the class is not much more satisfactory. Bather in the early 1900's erected two subclasses, one characterized by two circlets of plates in the aboral cup, the other by three. This division placed crinoid species with similar types of plate articulations, similar arrangements of plates in the calyx, and similar arm structure in different subclasses. More recent classifications (Figure 17-9) are based, primarily, on the mode of plate articulation and on incorporation of the interbrachial and brachial plates into the theca. These subclasses are further divided by reference to the arrangement of plates in the anal interray and to the presence of two or three circlets of thecal plates. In this interpretation, the two-circlet theca is presumed to have been derived by reduction of the lowest (*infrabasal*) circlet or by the fusion of the infrabasal plates with those of the next (*basal*) circlet.

Again, the fossil record is blank at this critical point. The oldest known crinoid, from the very early Ordovician of Europe, has a three circlet cup, but is relatively advanced in many characteristics, and could hardly have been ancestral to many—if any—of the middle Ordovician crinoids. Representatives of two of the four subclasses occur in lower Ordovician, and a third subclass in the

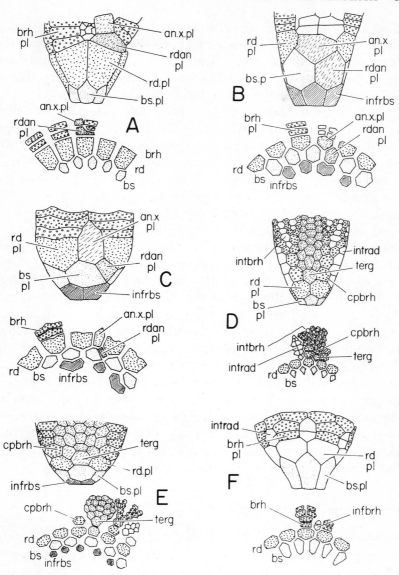

Fig. 17–9. *TYPES OF CRINOID PLATE ARRANGEMENTS.* Lateral view of calyx and diagrammatic view of plates rotated into single plane. *A)* Monocyclic cup; disparid inadunate crinoid; *Iocrinus. B)* Dicyclic cup; cladid inadunate crinoid. *C)* Dicyclic cup; flexible crinoid; *Lecanocrinus. D)* Monocyclic cup; monobathrid camerate crinoid; *Glyptocrinus. E)* Dicyclic cup; diplobathrid camerate crinoid; *Ptychocrinus. F)* Secondarily monocyclic cup; articulate crinoid; *Dadocrinus.* Abbreviations: *an. x pl,* anal x plate; *brh. pl,* brachial plate; *bs. pl,* basal plate; *cp. brh,* cup brachial; *intbrh,* interbrachial; *rd. pl,* radial plate; *rdan. pl,* radianal plate; *terg,* tergal. (A. to E. After Moore. F. After von Buch.)

middle Ordovician. All are distinct at their first appearance. Indeed, the connections between orders in the same subclass cannot be established with certainty. The fourth subclass was apparently derived from the surviving Paleozoic subclass in early Triassic time, but the phyletic links have yet to be identified.

The evolutionary trends within the orders (some of which are shown in Figure 17-10) include modification of nearly every part of the body. Many evolutionary sequences can be worked out in some detail, but, in spite of some knowledge of the adaptations in recent crinoids, paleontologists have acquired little information about the factors controlling these sequences. As Lauden (1957) observed, correlated paleoecologic and evolutionary studies of crinoid assemblages might be very useful.

Presumably, the crinoids, like other animals of the sessile benthos, adapted to specific bottom habits. Many lineages tend to increase the branching of the arms and number of pinnules and, thus, increase the size of the filtering surface. Others with reduced arms may have been adapted to turbulent environments. Presumably, the character and length of the stem and its basal attachment evolved to fit different conditions of substrate, turbidity, and turbulence. The *anal tubes* or *chimneys* of some possibly carried indigestible particles away from the filters in quiet water environments. The various modifications of cup shape and plate arrangement may be related to changes in the viscera with different diet, to variation in arm structure, or to adjustment of coelomic cavities and water vascular system to the needs of circulation, respiration, and the reproductive organs.

Identification of crinoids

Although some crinoid theca depart considerably from the simple cup shape, most retain it only slightly modified. This general similarity of form through 700 or so genera does not help in identification—nor does the tendency to reduce the infrabasal plate circlet so that it is concealed below the first columnal or fused so that it resembles a columnal. These deceptive similarities make it more difficult to determine the order or subclass than to determine the genus for some crinoids. Identification depends on careful examination of the relations of thecal plates, particularly the accessory plates incorporated in the areas between the arm bases;

on the determination of the plate arrangement, of the branching of the arms, and upon study of the tegmen and its variation.

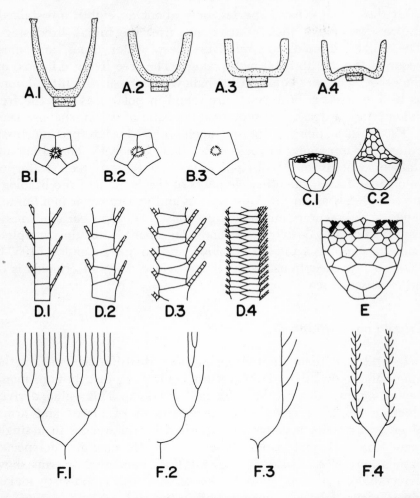

Fig. 17–10. *VARIATION IN CRINOID MORPHOLOGY. A.1) through A.4) Modification in cup shape. The deep cup A.1) the most primitive type; the degressed cup A.4) the most specialized. B.1) to B.3) Steps in the fusion of plates in the infrabasal circlet. C.1) and C.3) Development of anal chimney. D.1) through D.4) Steps in the modification of arm structure. The primitive type D.1) consists of a single row of plates with pinnules given off alternately. The most specialized has a double row of plates, each plate on each side giving rise to a pinnule. E) Incorporation of brachial and interradial plates and of pinnules in the cup. F.1) through F.4) Various types of arm arrangement. F.1) Equal branching. F.2) Unequal branching, one branch of pair larger. F.3) Unequal branching, series of secondary branches given off to one side of main branch. F.4) Unequal branching, short side branches given off to alternate sides of main branch.*

Problems in paleoecology

Of the recent crinoid species, only about an eighth are stalked; the remainder lose their attachments after the initial, fixed stage. The stalked crinoids are relatively deep water types, and most occur in the 200 to 5000 meter range. The free living crinoids, on the other hand, are common in shallow waters—in the littoral zone as well as deeper. Both types are found in polar seas, but the free living types, at least, are more characteristic of warm, shallow seas.

This information is not of much value in interpreting fossil crinoid environments in rocks older than Cenozoic. The abundant stalked crinoids of Mississippian are surely not deep water or cold water forms; the other elements of the fauna and the lithology are completely against it. Most species and genera occur in a limited range of sedimentary environments—only that seems certain. Analysis of their paleoecology depends on analysis of the complete faunal assemblages and the lithology, and, to quote Landon (1957): "With a few exceptions, work on the paleoecology of crinoids is of little consequence."

Crinoid correlation

In spite of their limited geographic distribution and of the minuscule knowledge of the factors controlling distribution, many genera and species are valuable guide fossils. This value derives chiefly from their complicated arrangement of plates and arms. Since two species may be distinguished by differences in a single plate, these characteristics show very subtle changes in species populations. Even in slowly evolving lines, the calyx or arms show detectable changes in short time intervals. The complexity makes identification laborious but pays off in the end.

Unfortunately, crinoids are of less use as guides to the major time units than to the smaller ones. Not only is it difficult to determine subclass and order by casual study, but also the major categories so overlap in time that their occurrence is not diagnostic. Although the orders show marked evolutionary changes, conservative groups and some with secondarily primitive characters survived alongside the more progressive types.

REVERSING THE FIELD: THE ELEUTHEROZOA

Many pelmatozoans tend to lose the primitive attachment and become free living, either lying on the bottom or, like some crinoids, swimming. These changes are of considerable theoretical interest because they represent one of the few documented cases of reversal of a trend toward sessility. In view of the frequency with which this reversal occurred within the pelmatozoans, it seems reasonable to believe that the classes grouped in the subphylum Eleutherozoa were derived from a sessile, pelmatozoan stock, and that this development may have occurred more than once. The first idea is substantiated by attachment of the larval starfish and by the torsion of the viscera during ontogeny; the second is given weight by differences and similarities in development within the Eleutherozoa.

The principal diagnostic feature of the Eleutherozoa, besides the lack of a stem, is the development of *ampullae* on the podia (Figure 17-16). These are bulb-like pouches opening from the podium. Contraction of the ampullae forces water into the podia; relaxation allows the podia to relax. The ends of the podia are disk shaped so that they act as tiny suction cups. By suitable rhythmic expansions and contractions of the podia, assisted by body musculature, the animals glide along the bottom. Only the brittle stars (class Ophiuroidia) lack ampullae, and their podia are limited to respiratory functions. Probably, though not certainly, they lost the ampullae with a change in method of locomotion, reversed evolution, and so regained a primitive character.

Granduncles and aunts

Among early and middle Paleozoic eleutherozoans are several genera of doubtful affinities (Figure 17-11). They resemble the sea urchins in some characteristics, but possess features that seem to bar them from a direct connection to any of the well known eleutherozoan or pelmatozoan classes. They may represent branches from the primordal echinoderm stem which paralleled the evolution of other eleutherozoans. They are not important enough as fossils to need extended discussion here; they are placed, with a question mark, as classes of the Eleutherozoa.

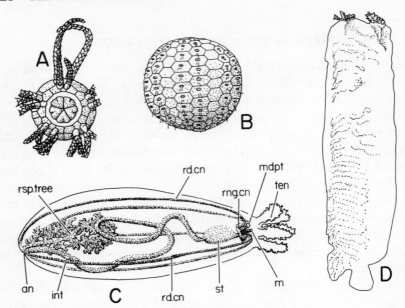

Fig. 17–11. *VARIOUS ELEUTHEROZOANS. A) Euthemon,* an ophicystoid; Silurian; oral view. *B) Bothriocidaris,* a bothriocidarid; middle Ordovicion; lateral view; diameter 1.2 cm. *C)* Diagrammatic view of holothuroid. Body wall cleared to show major visceral elements. *D)* Fossil ?holothuroid, *Louisella;* middle Cambrian; length 8 cm. Abbreviations: *an,* anus; *int,* intestine; *m,* mouth; *mdpt,* madroporite; *rd. cn,* radial canal; *rsp. tree,* respiratory tree; *st,* stomach; *ten,* tentacles. For glossary see 17–1. (A. After Fedotov. B. After Mortensen. D. After Walcott.)

Very ancient—maybe: The holothuroids

The Burgess shale fauna includes impressions of several kinds of sac-like creatures (Figure 17-11) which resemble, to some extent, the recent sea cucumbers. Unlike the recent genera, however, they lacked calcareous plates in the body wall. Walcott described four genera from these impressions and assigned them to the same class as the sea cucumbers, the Holothuroidea. Two of these are now thought to be coelenterates; the assignment of the other two is questionable. If they are truly holothuroids, they are the earliest representatives of the Eleutherozoa.

Other than these and similar vague impressions in Jurassic limestones of Europe, the holothuroids are known only from scattered plates, the oldest from the Mississippian. Recent members of the class show a mixture of primitive and specialized characteristics. The body is sac-like, and shows bilateral symmetry, and the skeleton is limited to scattered plates and spicules. The animal rests on one side, the mouth and anus at opposite ends. Some of these characteristics may be primitive; others, such as the symmetry, may be secondary—readoptions of characteristics once lost. The structure of the water vascular system is extremely specialized, for it is sunken into the interior and the ambulacral grooves are covered. Part of the podia may bear ampullae and, thus, are specialized for locomotion; others retain or have resumed their primitive respiratory and sensory adaptations.

KINDS OF STARS

The holothuroids rest on the bottom on one side; so, apparently, did many of the unattached pelmatozoans, carpoids in particular. They are, in essence, stalked forms that have fallen onto one side. The remaining eleutherozoans have returned to the primitive metazoan position with the mouth on the underside of the body. During ontogeny, the mouth shifts, in the typical echinoderm torsion, to the left, posterior side of the body,* and the anterior part largely degenerates. The anus forms on the right posterior surface, somewhat to the ventral side. The young animal settles to the bottom with the mouth on the substrate and the anus near the center of the aboral surface. A central plate and two circlets of five plates each begin to form in the middle of the aboral surface (Figure 17-12). Additional plates are added to this initial group of *apical plates* on both oral and aboral as growth continues to shape the characteristic adult form.

Whether this developmental pattern recapitulates, in any way, the evolutionary history is uncertain. What is certain is that the essential characteristics had evolved before the start of the Ordovician and various lines had taken off in diverse directions to exploit the possibilities offered by the changed body orientation and ambulatory podia.

Somasteroidea

The earliest and most primitive genera are starfish-like types (grouped as somasteroids) from lower Ordovician rocks (Figure 17-13). In them, each ambulacral plate bears a *virgalium*, which

---

* This shift does not occur in ophiuroids even though the right side of the body is reduced in normal echinoderm fashion. It would seem probable that this difference is an ontogenetic novelty rather than a profound phylogenetic divergence.

consists of a series of rods extending laterally from the edges of the arm. These were connected by skin to form broad, petal-shaped rays. The radial canals lie in deep grooves down the middle line of the ambulacral plates; the ampullae of the podia were apparently protected in cup-shaped depressions along the borders of the plates.

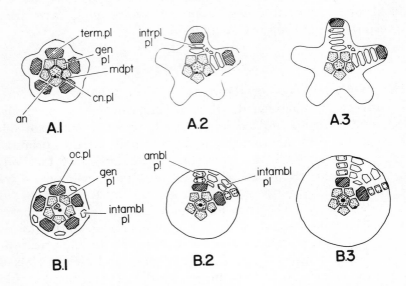

Fig. 17–12. COMPARATIVE ONTOGENY OF THE ASTEROIDS AND ECHINOIDS. Diagrammatic views of aboral surface. A.1) to A.3) Asteroid; plates added between inner and outer cycles of initial series. Ambulacral plates keep step on oral surface. B.1) to B.3 Echinoid; no plates added between inner and outer cycles. In consequence ambulacral plates appear on both oral and aboral surfaces. Abbreviations: ambl. pl, ambulacral plate; an, anus; cn. pl, central plate (dashes); gen. pl, genital plate (stipple); intambl. pl, interambulacral plate; intrpl. pl, interpolated plate; mdpt, madroporite; oc. pl, ocular plate (cross-lines); term. pl, terminal plate (cross-lines).

Asteroidea

True starfish, the asteroids, appeared by middle Ordovician. They lack virgalia, and the arms are, typically, more distinct, though still enclosing large extensions of the body cavity (Figure 17-13). In the more primitive asteroids, the ampullae were still exposed along the oral surface of ambulacra, but, in advanced types, are recessed into the cavity of the arm and communicate with the tube feet through canals between the ambulacral plates. The anus, of course, opens on the aboral surface as does the hydropore of the water vascular system, here through a perforated plate, the *madreporite*. The skeletal plates are (or were) held in a leathery skin. Typically, when the animal dies the skin decays and the plates separate. Only rapid burial in quiet water environments will preserve complete starfish skeletons; good specimens, naturally, are rare.

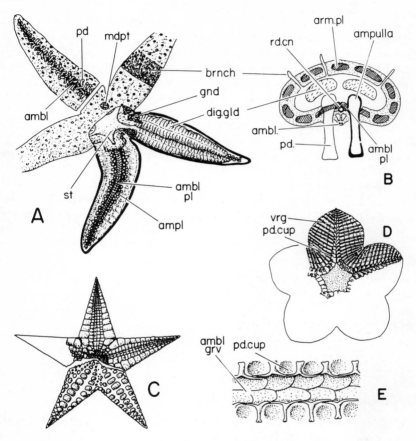

Fig. 17–13. *ASTEROIDEA AND SOMASTEROIDEA.*   A) Diagrammatic view of recent asteroid. Aboral view except that arm at upper left is rotated to show oral surface. Portion of upper right arm shows branchia. Arm at right has external surface removed to show digestive glands; digestive glands removed as well on lower arm to reveal inner surface of ambulacrum. B) Diagrammatic cross section of arm. Plates cross-lined; body wall dotted; digestive gland dashed; walls of radial canal and podia in black. C) Asteroid *Xenaster;* early Devonian; upper portion shows oral surface and the lower the aboral; length of arm from center of disk 5.0 cm. D) Somasteroid *Villebrunaster;* early Ordovician; oral view; natural size. E) Detail of somasteroid ambulacrum. Note that ampullae were set in cups and not closed off in the interior of the arm as in modern asteroids (see B). (C. After Schondorf. D. and E. After Spencer.)

GLOSSARY FOR ASTEROIDEA,

SOMASTEROIDEA, AND OPHIUROIDEA

(Figure numbers cited after definition.)

Ambulacral groove (ambl. grv). See 17–1. (17–13E.)

Ambulacral plates (ambl. pl). Plates arranged along mid-line of ambulacrum and flooring that structure. (17–13B, E.)

Ambulacral pore. See 17–1. (17–13B; 17–14B.)

Ampulla. Bulb or sac-like structure attached to internal end of podium. (17–13A, B; 17–14B.)

Ampullar cup (pd. cup). Cup-shaped depression in external surface of ambulacral plate which housed ampulla.

Anus (an). See 17–1. Located on aboral surface.

Arm (arm). Radial arm-like extension of body; bears ambulacrum.

Branchia (brnch). Slender, hollow finger-like extension of body wall. Interior connected to coelomic cavity. (17-13A, B.)

Central plate (cn. pl). Plate in center of aboral surface. (17–12A.)

Digestive glands (dig. glds). Paired digestive organs extending length of each arm.

Genital plate (gen. pl). One of circlet of five plates on aboral surface immediately around central plate. (17–12A, B.)

Madreporite (mdpt). See 17–1. Located on aboral surface. (17–12; 17–13A.)

Mouth (m). See 17–1.

Podium (pd). See 17–1. (17–13A, B; 17–14.)

Radial canal (rd. cn). See 17–1. (17–13B; 17–14B.)

Stomach (st). See 17–1. (17–13A.)

Terminal plate (term. pl). Plate at end of arm. (17–12A.)

Virgalia (vrg). An articulated series of rods that extends outward from an ambulacral plate. (17–13D.)

Ophiuroids

A third group of star-shaped echinoderms also appears in the lower Ordovician. Their arms are much more slender than those of the asteroids and are set off sharply from the body disk that surrounds the viscera (Figure 17-14). In the early genera, the radial canal is partly enclosed by ambulacral plates; in the later, it is completely covered. The early genera also appear to have had ampullae, at least of a sort; these were lost in subsequent evolution, and the podia lost their adaptations for locomotion. The madreporite opens on the oral surface, and, in most if not all genera, there is no anus. The modern ophiuroids, the brittle stars, replaced the slow, creeping locomotion possible to the asteroids

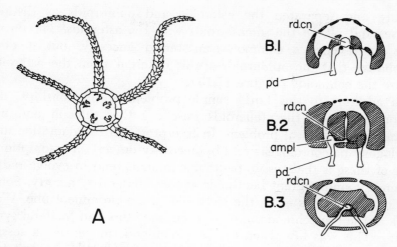

Fig. 17—14. *OPHIUROIDEA. A) Ophiaulax;* late Devonian; aboral view; diameter of central disk 6 mm. *B.1)* through *B.3)* Evolution of ophiuroid arm structure. Cross section of arm, plates patterned by diagonal lines. *B.1)* Primitive condition. Radial canal not completely enclosed; podia with ampullae. *B.2)* Intermediate condition. Radial canal enclosed between paired ambulacral plates; ampullae set in lateral cavities. *B.3)* Advanced stage. Radial canal passes through center of solid arm ossicle; podia lack ampullae. Abbreviations: *ampl,* ampulla; *pd,* podium; *rd. cn,* radial canal. (A. After Ubaghs.)

by rapid movements of their wriggling arms. Many species burrow, and most are sedentary except when disturbed.

Now the problems

Paleontologists recognize a single class, the Stelleroidea, comprising three subclasses, Somasteroidea, Asteroidea, and Ophiuroidea. The somasteroids are, without doubt, ancestral to the asteroids. The ophiuroids differ considerably, but their earliest representatives converge toward a somasteroid type. The Somasteroidea would, thus, be a horizontal grouping of primitive species; the Asteroidea and Ophiuroidea, two divergent but closely related vertical groups. On the other hand, zoologists studying recent forms are impressed by similarities of the ophiuroids and the echinoids. Both have enclosed radial canals; they have similar larva and other similarities in development. If, as is possible, they had somasteroid ancestors, the ophiuroids and echinoids may have had a common ancestory above the somasteroid level. In view of this difference in opinion, I have followed what seems the most conservative procedure and separated the asteroids and ophiuroids as distinct classes and placed the somasteroids with the asteroids. This in no way contravenes a common somasteroid ancestry, but it does emphasize that the ophiuroids are as different from the asteroids as are the echinoids (Figure 17-15).

In addition to this fairly simple problem of relationships, the characteristics of the stelleroids raise a rather difficult and important philosophical problem. In interpretation of adaptation and phylogeny paleontologists rely by necessity on certain assumptions. One of these is that sessile benthonic animals tend to evolve radial symmetry, and vagrant benthonic evolve bilateral symmetry. Some obvious exceptions exist; the stelleroids are a prominent one. Way back in the pre-echinoderm days, their ancestors had bilateral symmetry. This was lost when the proto-echinoderm became a sessile organism, and radial symmetry was superposed. Why haven't the

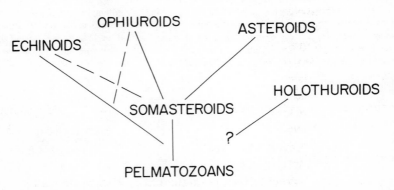

Fig. 17–15. *PHYLOGENY OF THE ELEUTHEROZOA.* Relations generalized sufficiently to be reasonably accurate. Dashed lines indicate most probable alternatives.

stelleroids redeveloped bilateral symmetry? Is the whole concept wrong? Is the interpretation of metazoan origins reported back on p. 236 a fairy tale? Are the interpretations of habit from symmetry in fossil groups erroneous? Or have I overlooked an explanation for stelleroid symmetry?

A ONE-TRACK MIND: THE ECHINOIDEA

If the starfish and brittle stars failed to meet expectations by not developing bilateral symmetry, another eleutherozoan group, the echinoids, did so, and did so within the discernible fossil record.

Superficially, the globular or discoid echinoid seems quite different from either asteroid or ophiuroid, but careful comparison of adult form (Figure 17-16) and ontogeny reveals some remarkable relationships. They, like the asteroids, have podia with ampullae specialized for locomotion. This, of course, is an ancient echinoderm adaptation and means little in itself. Their radial canals are covered by overgrowths of the ambulacral plates. The podia then protrude through pores in the plates. This is reminiscent of the ophiuroid structure, though, in that group, the podia have lost their locomotor

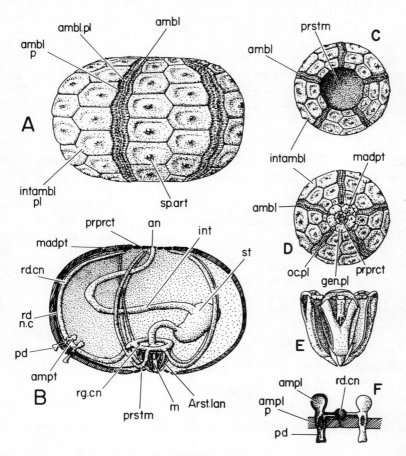

Fig. 17–16. *MORPHOLOGY OF THE ECHINOIDEA.* A) Lateral view of echinoid test. B) Oral view. C) Aboral view. D) Diagram of soft morphology, lateral view, one side of test removed. In a living echinoid the space around the viscera shown here is partly filled by digestive glands and gonads. E) Echinoid "jaw" structure—Aristotle's lantern. F) Diagrammatic cross section of ambulacrum showing radial canal and two podia.

GLOSSARY FOR ECHINOIDEA

(Figures cited at end of definitions show structures.)

Ambulacral plate (ambl. pl).   See 17–1. (17–16A, F; 17–17A; 17–18.)

Ambulacral pore (ambl. p).   See 17–1. (17–6A, F; 17–17A; et al.)

Ampulla (ampl).   See 17–13. (17–16B, F; 17–17A.)

Anterior.   In echinoids the direction of the ambulacral ray opposite the anal interray-
—where the anus has shifted from the apex of the skeleton. (17–19A, B, G; et al.)

Anus (an).   See 17–1. May be located in periproct in center of aboral surface or be
shifted down onto oral surface. (17–16B; 17–19B, E, G.)

Aristotle's lantern (Arst. lan).   Complex system of calcareous elements that surround
mouth and function as jaws. (17–16B, E.)

Bourrelets (bour).   Elevated areas adjacent to peristome—located in interrays. (17–17C.)

Genital plate (gen. pl).   Plate belonging to iner circlet in center of aboral surface. Arranged in interray positions. In some echinoids they surround periproct. (17–16D.)

Interambulacral area (intambl).   See 17–1. (17–16C, D.)

Interambulacral plate (intambl. pl).   Plate in interambulacral area. (17–16A, C, D;
17–18.)

Interray.   Radius between two rays—corresponds to radius of interambulacral area.

Madreporite (madpt).   See 17–1. Located in right anterior genital plate. (17–16B, D.)

Mouth (m).   See 17–1. (17–16B; 17–19B, D.)

Ocular plate (oc. pl).   One of a circlet of plates around genital circlet in center of aboral
surface. Each marks the aboral terminus of an ambulacrum. (17–16D.)

Oculogenital ring (ocg. rg).   Two circlets (ocular and genital) of plates in center of
aboral surface. Represent initial plates of skeleton. (17–16D; 17–18B; 17–19A.)

Periproct (prprct).   Area surrounding anus—covered by skin in which small plates are
embedded. Plates lost in most fossils. (17–16B, D; 17–18B.)

Peristome (prstm).   Area surrounding mouth. Covered with leathery skin supplemented
in some by small calcareous plates. The latter are typically lost in fossils. (17–16B,
C; 17–17C.)

Petal.   Petal-shaped portion of ambulacrum on aboral surface. In some depressed
below level of skeletal surface. (17–17B; 17–19F, G.)

Phyllode (phyd).   Depressed petaloid portion of ambulacrum adjacent to mouth. Bears
specialized podia. (17–17C.)

Podium (pd).   See 17–1. (17–16B, F; 17–17A.)

Radial canal (rd. cn).   See 17–1. (17–16B.)

Radial nerve cord (rd. n. c).   Nerve cord just outside radial canal and parallel to it.
(17–16B.)

Ray.   Radius defined by location of ambulacrum.

Ring canal (rg. cn).   See 17–1. (17–16B.)

Spine articulation (sp. art).   Tubercle to which spine is attached. (17–16A to D;
17–18B.)

function. The mouth lies on the undersurface of the body; the anus, in early echinoids at least, lies near the center of the aboral surface. The ambulacra radiate from the mouth and terminate on the aboral surface very near the center.

The critical feature of the comparison is the group of plates in the center of the aboral surface. They include a *central plate* (lost in many echinoids) and two cycles of five plates each (Figure 17-12). The plates of the inner cycle lie along the midline of the interambulacral areas; four of them have a central genital pore and so are called *genital plates;* one is perforated by canals of the water vascular system, and thus is a madreporite. The plates of the outer, *ocular* cycle alternate with the genital plates and, consequently, lie in the midline of the ambulacra, in fact, terminate the ambulacra on the aboral surface. This is, essentially, the arrangement of plates in the apical plate system of very young starfish and brittle stars already described (p. 430).

Since these plates are the first to form in the echinoderm, the immature of the two classes are very similar. These similarities in ontogeny probably conserve a developmental stage of their common ancestor. After this stage in development, however, the starfish and sea urchin begin to diverge. In the starfish and brittle stars, a series of plates is added between those of the ocular cycle, the plates that are terminal to the ambulacra, and the inner genital group. As the plates form, the end of each ambulacrum is carried out laterally. The development of ambulacral plates keeps pace with this series, but the interambulacral plates are added very slowly. In consequence, arms develop from a central disk, each arm bearing on its oral surface an ambulacral groove. In the echinoid, no plates are added inside the apical system; so ocular plates and the ends of the ambulacra remain near the center of the aboral surface. Plates are added in the ambulacra and interambulacral areas at equal rates so that a spheroidal skeleton is formed, growing out and down from the apical plate system.

A few, very simple changes in gene systems might have produced these differences in development. If so, these three classes of Eleutherozoa could have had a common ancestor not long before their first appearance in the geologic record. Whether this ancestor was a proto-starfish and the echinoids evolved by retaining embryonic features into maturity, or whether it was a proto-echinoid to which starfish and brittle star characteristics were added in two separate lines cannot now be determined. The oldest known representatives of either type are the somasteroid starfish which, in itself, suggests a starfish ancestry for all. Since the early representatives of all three have flexible skeletons of plates held together principally by skin, paleontologists cannot be certain that the first representatives of any of the three classes do not antedate by a good span their first fossil appearance.

Though the basic echinoid plan was firmly established by their first fossil occurrence in the middle Ordovician, quite a lot of important changes occurred after that time. Some of these have simple explanations as adaptive modifications; others are difficult to explain.

Water vascular system

The Ordovician echinoids show a transition between the external radial canal of the primitive echinoderm and the internal canal of the later echinoids (Figure 17-17). In these primitive echinoids, the canal still lies in the ambulacral groove, but the groove is roofed by the growth of the ambulacral plate toward the midline. The ambulacral plates thus enclose the canal completely. In later echinoids, the internal flanges of the ambulacral plates are first reduced to a ridge so that the canal lies in a groove on the internal surface of the ambulacrum, and, finally, are lost altogether.

In the primitive types, the bases of the podia and the canals connecting them to the radial canal lie between successive ambulacral plates and are partly covered by them. The ampullae were, already, completely inside the skeleton. In more advanced echinoids, the edges of the ambulacral plates grew around the basal part of the podia so that they projected through pores within the plates. Some Ordovician echinoids had a single pore for each podium, but all later ones had a double pore. The principal result of these changes —presumably the cause for them—is protection of the water vascular system by the skeleton.

Paleozoic echinoids and their more conservative descendants had ambulatory podia that were extremely similar throughout the ambulacral areas. The more advanced Mesozoic and Cenozoic genera tended to modify this simple setup by specialization of the podia on the aboral surface for respiration and of those about the mouth for assistance in feeding. In the correlated modifications of the ambulacra the aboral portions form elongate *petals* with slit-

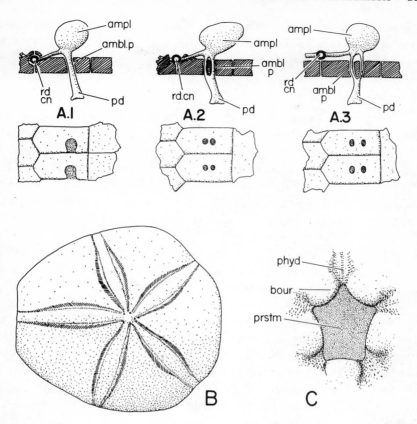

Fig. 17–17. *VARIATION IN ECHINOID MORPHOLOGY. A.1)* to *A.3)* Evolution in structure of podia and radia canal. Upper views, sections through ambulacrum; lower views of external surface. *A.1)* Condition in early echinoids. Radial canal enclosed in ambulacral plates; podium opens through single pore; pore opens between ambulacral plates. *A.2)* Intermediate stage. Radial canal in groove, and branch to podium passes through short canal in plate; podium opens through pair of pores; pores open within ambulacral plate. *A.3)* Advanced stage. Radial canal lies entirely inside ambulacral plates, and connection to podium is not enclosed in canal. *B)* Irregular echinoid, aboral view. Ambulacra petaloid. *C)* The same, oral view of the peristome and adjacent surface of test. Grooves, the phyllodes (phyd.), at ends of ambulacra and intervening elevations, bourrelets (bour.), form flower-like structure, the floscelle. Abbreviations: *ambl. p,* ambulacral pore; *ampl,* ampulla; *bour,* bourrelet; *pd,* podium; *phyd,* phyllode; *prstm,* peristome; *rd. cn,* radial canal.

like, closely crowded pores, and the oral may have short petaloid grooves (*phyllodes*), with enlarged pores about the mouth. Many of these advanced forms tend to lose the locomotor adaptations of the podia altogether and to replace them functionally by movable spines. In these, podia, other than those used in respiration and food getting, are reduced in size and serve minor respiratory and sensory functions.

The skeleton

That part of the echinoid skeleton beyond the apical plate system is distinguished as the *corona*. In Paleozoic and some later echinoids it is typically nearly spherical with mouth and anus at opposite poles and shows regular fivefold symmetry (Figure 17-16). The mouth lies in a circular area of leathery skin, the *peristome*, on the lower surface. The anus lies in a similar area, the *periproct*, on the upper surface. If the central plate is reduced, the anus may lie in the center of the apical system; if not, it is displaced toward the right posterior ray, but still within the apical system. Each ambulacral and interambulacral area comprises two parallel rows of plates, rather loosely articulated.

One group of echinoids, the Regularia, retain the primitive shape and symmetry throughout their career (Figure 17-18). In general, they evolve a firmer articulation between plates so that the corona becomes a rigid structure. Some lines increase the number of rows of plates in the interambulacra areas and/or in the ambulacra. If the latter, the number of podia are increased correspondingly. Small plates typically appear within the peristome and periproct. Many genera appear with large spines more or less articulated to the coronal plates. Internal calcareous supports for the viscera and jaws are developed. The jaws themselves are formed into an elaborate apparatus called *Aristotle's lantern*—"lantern" for obvious reasons. The strengthening of the test and development of spines is obviously protective. The spines also play a part in locomotion and in burrowing, for the animals can move them by muscles attached to their base. Changes in jaws and jaw supports are, presumably, related to adaptation to different types of food. The increase in coronal plates and in the number of podia is less obviously adaptive, and little is known of its significance.

Bilaterality

These modifications, however, are far less striking than those in body symmetry (Figure 17-19). Among some regular echinoids,

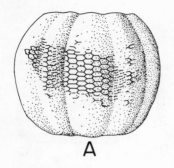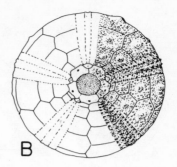

Fig. 17–18. *REGULAR ECHINOIDS.* A) *Melonechinus;* Mississippian; lateral view; length 11.2 cm. B) *Acrosalenia;* early Jurassic to early Cretaceous; aboral view; length 3.1 cm. Only two rays shown in detail.

the anus (and the periproct) has shifted to one border of the apical system. In the lower Jurassic, echinoids appeared with the periproct outside of this ring, shifted into one of the interareas. Similarities of these Jurassic forms to certain regular echinoids suggests that this change evolved in two separate orders of regular echinoids. The shift of the periproct produces, of course, a bilateral symmetry. The theca is characteristically somewhat flattened. In a few Jurassic forms—and many later genera—the periproct appears far down the upper surface of the theca, on the margin of the flattened lower surface or the lower (oral) surface itself. In some, the mouth, in turn, shifts forward so that it lies near the anterior margin. In many, these changes are associated with great flattening of the test and/or with anterior-posterior elongation; some lose their jaw structures.

These modifications are also associated with modification of the podia on different parts of the ambulacra for respiration and food getting and with the development of tracts of fine spines, the *fascioles,* which maintain a current over the body surface, even when the animal is in a burrow.

Why did the echinoids, apparently successful as radially symmetrical forms, develop bilateral symmetry? The answer may be change of habit. Most irregular echinoids burrow or else crawl along the bottom with only the upper part of the test exposed. Animals with these habits are characteristically flattened and many are elongate. An anus on the upper surface of the body would

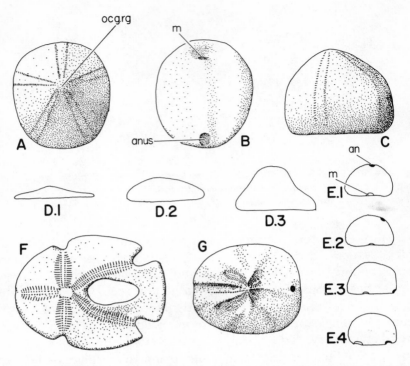

Fig. 17–19. *IRREGULAR ECHINOIDS.* A) to C) *Ananchytes;* aboral, oral, and lateral views. The anus opens on the oral surface rather than through the oculogenital ring. As a consequence the test assumes bilateral symmetry, the plane of symmetry along the mouth—anus axis. D.1) to D.3) Lateral views showing variation in body shape from flattened burrower to high domed surface dweller. E.1) through E.4) Variation in position of anus and mouth. E.1) Anus in oculogenital ring but not central; mouth in center of oral surface. E.2) Anus on aboral surface but not in oculogenital ring. E.3) Anus on border of oral and aboral surface; mouth shifted out of center. E.4) Anus on oral surface. F) *Encope;* Miocene to Recent; aboral view; length 7.5 cm. G) *Hemiaster;* Cretaceous; aboral view; length 4.0 cm.

hardly be satisfactory for the discharge of wastes. If it were shifted down (and by its shift producing the direction "back"), it could function much more efficiently. Once shifted, the proper functioning would occur only if the animal crawled or burrowed in just one direction. Elongation and modification of the arrangement of the ambulacra would follow as an adjustment to this single direction of movement. Since some irregular echinoids are closely related to regular species, a study of fossil environments in relation to the change in form might provide a test of this hypothesis.

The geologic record

Though abundant in some rocks and with short stratigraphic ranges, most species and genera of echinoids were so limited by ecologic factors that they are of little use as guide fossils. This implies that they would be excellent subjects for paleoecologic work, but Cooke (1957) cited only fourteen papers that deal with ecology of post-Paleozoic echinoids; Cooper (1957) eight papers on the ecology of the much rarer Paleozoic echinoids.

TABLE 17-1

THE ECHINODERMATA

Early Cambrian to Recent. Coelomate. Level of organization about that of Brachiopoda, and distinguished by possession of water vascular system developed from coelomic cavities. No heart or circulatory system. Nervous system not highly centralized. Skeleton of calcareous plates developed in mesoderm. Typically five-fold radial symmetry; some asymmetric or bilaterally symmetrical. All marine; predominately vagrant and sessile benthos; some weak swimmers.

SUBPHYLUM PELMATOZOA

Early Cambrian to Recent. Typically attached forms; some specialized lines lose stem.

CLASS EDRIOASTEROIDEA

Early Cambrian to Early Mississippian. Discoidal; attached broadly on flattened base. Oral surface bears five curved ambulacra. Pores between ambulacral plates may indicate presence of podia with ampullae. Sessile benthos, presumably filter feeders.

CLASS EOCRINOIDEA

Middle Cambrian to Middle Ordovician. Cup-shaped theca with stem. Small number of thecal plates, arranged in circlets with radial symmetry. Five biserial brachioles (bifurcated in some) from upper circlet of plates. Brachioles bear roofed ambulacral grooves. Sessile benthos; filter feeders.

CLASS CARPOIDEA

Middle Cambrian to Early Devonian. Cup-shaped theca; typically flattened; with or without stem. In many stem was not attached to substrate. A few have brachioles. Plate arrangement varied, asymmetric or bilaterally symmetrical. Sessile and possibly vagrant benthos; probably filter feeders.

CLASS CYSTOIDEA

Middle Ordovician to Late Devonian. Cup-shaped theca with stem. Arrangement of plates varied, from small number with imperfect radial symmetry to large number with asymmetric pattern. One or more biserial brachioles; typically three to five ambulacra on theca and extending up brachioles. Thecal plates bear system of double pore or pore rhomb openings. Sessile benthos; filter feeders.

CLASS BLASTOIDEA

Middle Ordovician to Late Permian. Cup-shaped theca with stem. Three circles of plates; radial symmetry with five ambulacra. Series of brachioles borne along edges of ambulacra. Hydrospire system. Sessile benthos; filter feeders.

CLASS CRINOIDEA

Early Ordovician to Recent. Cup-shaped theca with or without stem. Three or more circlets of thecal plates, typically with five-fold radial symmetry. Arms bear extensions of ambulacra. Arms, uniserial at base, may branch extensively and bear rows of branchlets, the pinnules, on either side of ambulacral groove. Some free living, weak swimmers; others sessile benthos; filter feeders.

SUBPHYLUM ELEUTHEROZOA

(?) Middle Cambrian. Ordovician to Recent. All forms unattached. Five-fold symmetry well developed. Vagrant benthos.

CLASS HOLOTHUROIDEA

(?) Middle Cambrian. Mississippian to Recent. Elongate sac-like body. Skeleton of loose spicules and plates in leathery skin. Ambulacra covered, internal. Bilateral symmetry. Animal rests on one side with mouth and anus at opposite ends. Ambulatory podia. Mud grubbers; vagrant benthos and burrowers. Rare as fossils.

CLASS STELLEROIDEA

Ordovician to Recent. Star-shaped body; arms broad; body cavity extends into arms. Ambulacra and mouth on substrate; anus and madreporite on upper surface. Skeleton of loosely articulated plates. Ambulatory podia. Ambulacral grooves and radial canals open or only partly covered by skeletal plates. Scavengers and predators. Vagrant benthos.

Subclass Somasteroidea

Early Ordovician. Primitive starfish. Ambulacral plates bear lateral rods, the virgilia.

Subclass Asteroidea

Middle Ordovician to Recent. Lack virgilia. Ampullae of tube feet more or less enclosed inside cavity of arm. Not common as fossils.

CLASS OPHIUROIDEA

Early Ordovician to Recent. Star-shaped; arms slender; body cavity does not extend into arms. Radial canal enclosed by arm plates. Podia project through pores. No ampullae; podia primarily respiratory. Scavengers and predators. Vagrant benthos. Not common as fossils.

CLASS ECHINOIDEA

Ordovician to Recent. Rigid globular tests; no arms. Ambulacra enclosed; podia primarily ambulatory with ampullae; podia project through pores in ambulacral area. Mouth on lower surface. Most bear calcareous spines articulated to plates. Scavengers and predators.

Subclass Regularia

Ordovician to Recent. Regular pentameral symmetry. Anus in center of aboral surface. Vagrant benthos.

Subclass Irregularia

Radial symmetry partly suppressed in favor of bilateral. Anus not in center of aboral surface. Vagrant benthos and burrowers.

REFERENCES

Bassler, R. S. and M. W. Moodey. 1943. "Bibliographic and Faunal Index of Paleozoic Pelmatozoan Echinoderms," *Geol. Soc. of America, Spec. Paper 45.*

Bather, F. A. 1900. "The Echinoderma," in: E. R. Lankester, *Treatise on Zoology,* Part 3, London: Black, pp. 1-344. A classical study; in spite of its age, still a standard reference.

Clark, A. H. 1915-1950. "A Monograph of the Existing Crinoids, *U.S. Nat. Museum, Bulletin,* vol. 82. A series of parts of this study have appeared over a 35 year period.

Cline, L. M. and H. Beaver. 1957. "Blastoids" (annotated bibliography), in: "Treatise on Marine Ecology and Paleoecology," vol. 2, *Geol. Soc. of America, Memoir 67,* pp. 955-960.

Cooper, G. A. 1957. "Echinoids of the Paleozoic" (annotated bibliography), in: "Treatise on Marine Ecology and Paleoecology," vol. 2, *Geol. Soc. of America, Memoir 67,* pp. 979-980.

Cooke, C. W. 1957. "Echinoids of the Post-Paleozoic" (annotated bibliography), in: "Treatise on Marine Ecology and Paleoecology," vol. 2, *Geol. Soc. of America, Memoir 67,* pp. 981-982.

Croneis, C. and H. L. Geis. 1940. "Microscopic Pelmatozoa: Part I, Ontogeny of the Blastoidea," *Jour. of Paleontology,* vol. 14, pp. 345-355. One of the few studies on ontogeny of fossil echinoderms.

Durham, J. W. and R. V. Melville. 1957. "A Classification of Echinoids," *Jour. of Paleontology,* vol. 31, pp. 242-272.

Eaton, T. H., Jr. and K. E. Caster. 1956. "Microstructure of the Plates in the Carpoid Echinoderm *Paranacystis*," *Jour. of Paleontology*, vol. 30, pp. 611-614.

Hyman, L. H. 1955. *The Invertebrates:* vol. 6, *Echinodermata*. New York: McGraw-Hill. Echinoderm morphology, ontogeny, physiology, ecology, and evolution; with extensive bibliography.

Jaekel, O. 1918. "Phylogenie und System der Pelmatazoen," *Palaeont. Zeitschriften*, vol. 3, pp. 1-128.

Laudon, L. R. 1957. "Crinoids" (annotated bibliography), in: "Treatise on Marine Ecology and Paleoecology," vol. 2, *Geol. Soc. of America, Memoir 67*, pp. 961-972.

Moore, R. C. 1940. "Early Growth Stages of Carboniferous Microcrinoids and Blastoids," *Jour. of Paleontology*, vol. 14, pp. 572-583. See also Croneis and Geis.

————. 1954. "Pelmatozoa," *Mus. Comp. Zoology, Harvard, Bulletin*, vol. 112, pp. 125-149.

Mortensen, T. 1928-1951. "A Monograph of the Echinoidea," Copenhagen: Reitzel. Five "volumes," each composed of several parts covering recent and fossil echinoids.

Raup, D. M. 1956. "*Dendraster:* A Problem in Echinoid Taxonomy," *Jour. of Paleontology*, vol. 30, pp. 685-694. An example of recent work on echinoids.

————. 1958. "The Relation between Water Temperature and Morphology in *Dendraster*," *Jour. of Geology*, vol. 66, pp. 668-677.

Spencer, W. K. 1951. "Early Paleozoic Starfish," *Royal Soc. of London, Philos. Trans., Ser. B*, vol. 235, pp. 87-129. Description of early starfish and a discussion of their evolution.

See also general references for Chapter 3.

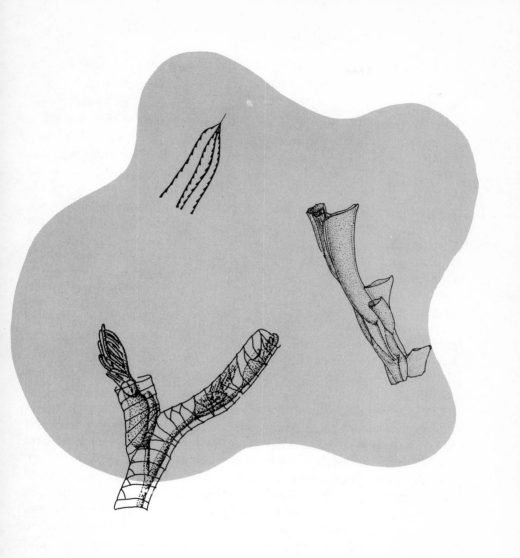

18. *Brothers under the skin:*
PROTOCHORDATA

*A*pparently, sessile animals adapt, primarily, to the physical and chemical factors of their environment. Once they attain a satisfactory adjustment to the demands of the sessile habit, they evolve slowly, fitting themselves to new niches and to long-term changes in the natural society. Active animals adapt, in large measure, to the biological factors of their environment. By their adaptation, they change the factors as well as their response (see p. 393). Because they can escape from unfavorable environments, they are likely to evolve further mechanisms of escape as well as adjustments to the environment. They rarely attain a satisfactory adjustment to the demands of their active habit and continue to evolve rapidly—always trying to catch their own tail until they fail of exhaustion.

The evolutionary consequences are profound. The changes of structure that create new and wider potentialities occur in active species not in sessile. The concept need not be belabored further; the evidence is clear, and nowhere is it clearer than among the vertebrates and their relatives. Unfortunately, in this group (chordates and protochordates) as in so many others, palentologists lack direct evidence of the animals and the times when they established this dichotomy of habit. They have, as fossils, the vertebrates, first known from Ordovician rocks and thereafter reasonably common, and the graptolites, an extinct group whose relationships are questioned and whose specialized structure gives little information on their ancestry. The other members of the group, the ones that could contribute most to a reconstruction of evolutionary pattern, are known only from relatively specialized recent species. The next few pages, therefore, will be primarily zoological, will deal largely with details of ontogeny, and will be highly speculative.

CHARACTERISTICS OF THE PROTOCHORDATES AND CHORDATES

Burrowers and tube dwellers

The acorn worms and the pterobranchs are, in some ways at least, the simplest and, presumably, the most primitive of the whole chordate-protochordate complex. The acorn worms have an elongate, bilaterally symmetrical body (Figure 18-1). The mouth is anterior, of course, and the anus posterior but not terminal. The body wall immediately behind the mouth is quite thick and distinct from the remainder; this structure is called the *collar*. A conical *proboscis*, stiffened by a short internal rod, lies in front of and above the mouth. A dorsal nerve cord extends backward from the base of the proboscis. The anterior end of the cord is swollen and hollow. The ventral cord begins farther back near the posterior margin of the collar. On either side of the body for a distance behind the collar, are a series of openings, the *gill slits*. These pierce the body wall and open into the anterior part of the gut. The coelom is capacious and develops, like the echinoderm coelom, as side pouches from the embryonic gut. The ciliated planktonic larva also resembles that of the echinoderm. They burrow by use of the collar and proboscis and feed on organic particles in the bottom muds. They include only a few species, are entirely marine, and are entirely unknown as fossils.

The pterobranchs differ from the acorn worms principally in the presence of branched arms on the collar and in the small size of the proboscis (Figure 18-1). Unlike the acorn worms who are active burrowers, the pterobranchs live in chitinoid tubes. They, too, are marine, but feed on particles and organisms filtered from the water by the ciliated arms. Probably as an adaptation to this sessile mode of life, the gut turns upward and forward so that the anus lies above the head. Pterobranchs bud and, consequently, may form colonies. They seem to connect the protochordate stock with the extinct colonial Graptolithinia. I'll cover this problem at greater length in a succeeding section.

Sea squirts

The acorn worm with its elongate shape and bilateral symmetry at least suggests a vertebrate form. The adult sea squirts could hardly be less like a vertebrate (Figure 18-1). They are sessile sac-like animals. The upper end of the sac is drawn into two tubes—one opening into the mouth, the other into a large chamber, the *atrium*. The gut for a distance below the mouth is much expanded and perforated by gill slits that empty into the atrium. The anus likewise empties into the atrium. The beat of cilia around the gill slits maintains a current of water in through the mouth, through the gill slits into the atrium, and back out through the atrium's external opening. The animal filters small food particles from the

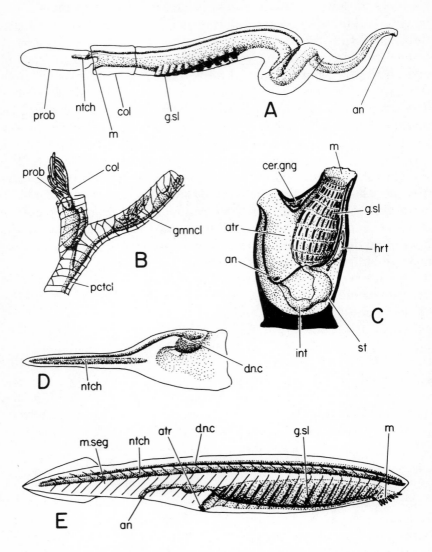

Fig. 18–1. *PROTOCHORDATES AND CHORDATES.* A) Lateral view of acorn worm; body wall cleared to show part of viscera. B) A portion of a pterobranch colony showing a mature individual to the left and an immature individual and the "parent bud" to the right. Skeleton cleared to show soft parts. C) A diagrammatic lateral view of a sectioned sea squirt. D) The larva of a sea squirt—body wall cleared to show viscera. E) Amphioxus. A lateral view with body wall and muscle segments cleared. Abbreviations: *an,* anus; *atr,* atrium; *cer. gng,* cerebral ganglion; *col,* collar; *d. n. c,* dorsal nerve cord; *g. sl,* gill slit; *gmncl,* gymnocaulus (growing stem); *hrt,* heart; *int,* intestine; *m,* mouth; *m. seg,* muscle segment; *ntch,* notochord; *pctcl,* pectocaulus (chitinized stem); *prob,* proboscis. (B. After Thomas and Davis.)

water as it passes through the gill slits. There is no trace of a coelom. Remarkably, the external covering of the animal is a cellulose-like material. No fossil sea squirts are known.

As in most sessile marine organisms, the sea squirts have a planktonic larva. These somewhat resemble a tadpole with a large "head" and a slender muscular tail. At metamorphosis, the larva attaches by the anterior end of the head; the tail degenerates; because of the relative growth, the mouth shifts toward the posterior free end; the atrium forms, and an external, atrial opening develops. The most interesting feature of the larva, however, is the structure of the tail. In its dorsal part is a nerve cord. This extends into the "head" where it is enlarged and hollow. Below the nerve cord is a stiff rod, the *notochord*, which ends before entry to the head.

Almost an ancestor

There is one other recent group of animals, the cephalochordates, that show affinities to the vertebrates. Unlike the preceding two, they look a good deal like vertebrates, for they are small, slender, fish-like animals (Figure 18-1). Like the others, they have an extensive series of gill slits. These slits open out like those of the sea squirts into a chamber, the atrium, which has an excurrent pore in front of the anus. Again, like the sea squirts, they filter food particles from water passing through the gill slits. The anus itself is subterminal so that a distinct tail lies behind it. The animal has a hollow dorsal nerve cord running the length of the body. Below it and extending into the tip of the head is the notochord. This latter structure consists of a tough cover and a nearly gelatinous interior, and functions as a stiff but a flexible beam on which the body muscles can pull. The muscles themselves are divided into a series of transverse segments, the *myomeres*.

Although capable of swimming actively, the animal spends most of its time partly buried in the bottom sediment. The beat of cilia in the anterior part of the gut maintains an inflowing current through the mouth; food particles are filtered out as the water passes through the gill slits into the atrium.

The reinforced notochord

This brief description of the cephalochordates need not be altered much to fit the vertebrates (Figure 18-2). The vertebrate noto-

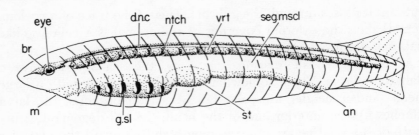

Fig. 18–2. *GENERAL PLAN OF THE VERTEBRATA.* Lateral view of a hypothetical vertebrate. Abbreviations: *an,* anus; *br,* brain; *d. n. c,* dorsal nerve cord; *eye,* eye; *g. sl,* gill slit; *m,* mouth; *ntch,* notochord; *seg. mscl,* segmented muscle; *st,* stomach; *vrt,* vertebra.

chord does not reach the tip of the head but ends some segments behind. Otherwise they (we) have a hollow dorsal nerve cord and at least rudiments of gill slits. In all living vertebrates and most, if not all, fossil ones, the notochord is supplemented or replaced by articulated bony or cartilagenous blocks, the *vertebrae,* that form around it. Since the muscles in each segment attach to two adjoining vertebrae, they produce more efficient and controlled motion than the muscles working on an unsegmented notochord. Finally, vertebrates lack an atrium of the cephalochordate type.

STRUCTURAL PLANS AND ANCESTORS

All of these various friends and relatives of ours possess, in common, gill slits, a notochord or some pretense of one, a hollow dorsal nerve cord, and a distinct tail behind the anus. These form the major elements in the structural plan of the protochordate-chordate group. Presumably, their common ancestors must have had these characteristics; each, by itself, might be considered a parallel development, but, because each structure has a constant topographic relationship within the body and a similar mode of development, more than likely they were inherited.

If so, what were the other characteristics of the common ancestor, and what was his mode of life? Everyone concerned with vertebrate origins wishes he knew. The acorn worm has specialized for burrowing with the proboscis-collar structure; the pterobranchs for a sessile tube dwelling habit with "arms;" the sea squirts for a sessile filter-feeding existence; the cephalochordate and vertebrates for locomotion with segmentation. Perhaps the common ancestoral species was like an acorn worm which lacked a proboscis and collar and which lived crawling or swimming along the bottom. But gills seem to have developed as a filter-feeding mechanism—a feature of sessile animals. If so, perhaps the ancestral protochordate was like the sea squirts but without their peculiarities. The other protochordates and chordates would have evolved by retardation of development so that the larval form was retained in maturity. Anyway, speculation is good, clean fun.

Classification of the protochordate-chordate complex varies with the classifier. One extreme is to place each group in a separate phylum; the other is to lump them all under Chordata. Or the primitive protochordates may be shoved together, and the advanced protochordates and vertebrates thrown into the phylum Chordata. For example, Moore, Lalicker, and Fischer (1952) place acorn worms (and pterobranchs) and sea squirts together in phylum Protochordata and leave the Cephalochordata go as a subphylum of the Chordata. Many zoologists feel that the sea squirts are closer to cephalochordates than to acorn worms and place them, also, as a subphylum of the Chordata. Table 18–1 expresses this last viewpoint, which seems to me to be the most nearly correct.

A PROBLEM IN MULTIPLE PERSONALITIES: GRAPTOLITHINA

The witches of *Macbeth* with their "Double, double, toil and trouble" prophesied the paleontological career of the graptolites. Probably no other common group of fossils has produced so much argument abut its taxonomic affinities. The work of Kozlowski on the fine details of their morphology may have settled the problem. We can hope so anyway.

The morphologic problem

As commonly seen, the graptolite skeleton is relatively simple (Figure 18-3). It consists of a series of cuplike chitinoid *thecae* arranged in series along a branch, the *stipe*. The stipes may be solitary or form a branching net. The stipes may also be connected by cross bars, the *dissepiments*. The colony, the *rhabdosome*, was supported at one point by a thread, the *nema*. The stipes branch from the end of the nema. The first cup, the one at the end of the nema, is termed the *sicula*. Presumably each theca bore an individual animal, and the sicula represents the initial individual of the colony.

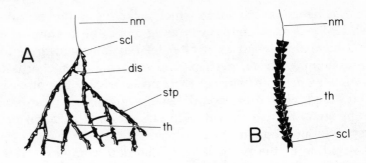

Fig. 18–3.   *GENERAL FORM OF THE GRAPTOLITES.*   A) Dendroid graptolite. B) Graptoloid graptolite.

GLOSSARY FOR THE GRAPTOLITHINA

Autotheca (ath).   Largest tube of three produced at each budding in the development of a dendroid colony. (18–4A, B.)

Bitheca (bth).   Small tube formed at each budding in the development of a dendroid colony. (18–4A, B.)

Dissepiment (dis).   Cross-bar uniting adjacent branches (stipes) of dendroid colony. (18–3A.)

Fusellar layer (fs. l).   Inner layer of the two that compose the graptolite tube. Consists of chitinous "half" rings. (18–4B, C.)

Half ring (h. rng).   One of series of chitinous half rings that are joined to form the inner wall of the graptolite tube. (18–4B, C.)

Lamellar layer (lm. l).   Outer layer of graptolite tube. Consists of concentric chitinous laminae. (18–4C.)

Nema (nm).   Delicate chitinous tube to which the base of graptolite colony is attached. (18–3A, B; 18–5.)

Rhabdosome.   The entire graptolite colony. (18–3A, B; 18–5.)

Sicula (scl).   Tube formed by initial individual in colony. (18–3A, B.)

Stipe (stp).   Branch of graptolite colony comprising a series of tubes (thecae). (18–3A; 18–5B to H.)

Stolon (stl).   Dense chitinoid tubule extending through successive stolothecae and sending off branches to base of each autotheca and bitheca. (18–4A, B.)

Stolotheca (sth).   Tube (theca) which contains stolon and which gives rise to three new thecae (autotheca, bitheca, and stolotheca) by budding. (18–4A, B.)

Theca (th).   Individual tube in graptolite colony. (18–3; 18–4; 18–5.)

So much can be observed in the ordinary graptolite preservation in black shales. The great compaction characteristic of this type of sediment during diagenesis leaves the graptolite only as a carbonized streak hardly distinguishable from a pencil mark. According to the position of the stipe in burial, the individual thecae are more or less distinct.

Occasionally graptolites are found in limestone or chert matrix. Because of the massive character of the rock, the fossils are only slightly distorted. Because of the difference in composition between matrix and fossil, the paleontologist can use acids that dissolve calcite or chert but do not attack the chitinous fossil. Freed from the rock, the graptolite can be studied directly in a free mount or can be imbedded in plastic or paraffin and sectioned.

The earliest graptolites, from late Cambrian deposits, have a many branched leaf-like (dendroid) structure. Free mounts and sectioned specimens show three distinct types of thecae on the stipes (Figure 18-4). In the growth of the stipe, a single individual, the *budding zooid,* gave rise to three zooids corresponding to the three types of thecae.* One of these was a new budding zooid. It

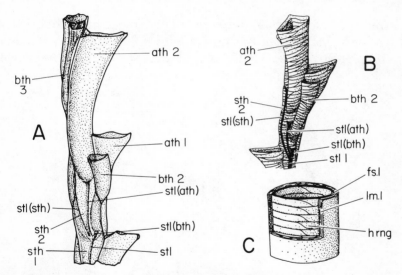

Fig. 18–4. *DETAILED MORPHOLOGY OF THE DENDROID GRAPTOLITES.* A) Lateral view of portion of stipe. Three buds arise from stolotheca 1 (sth. 1). One of these forms stolotheca 2 (sth. 2), one forms bitheca 2 (bth. 2), and one forms autotheca 2 (ath. 2). A chitinoid tube, the stolon (stl.) extends along the stolotheca and gives off side branches to the bitheca [stl. (bth.)] and to the autotheca [stl. (ath.)]. B) Lateral view of portion of stipe showing fuseller half rings that form part of skeleton. Labeling of thecae corresponds to that in A. C) Detail of skeleton showing inner and outer layers. Based on Kozlowski, 1947. Abbreviations: *ath,* autotheca; *bth,* bitheca; *fs. l,* fuseller layer; *h. rng,* half ring (of fuseller layer); *lm. l,* lamellar layer; *sth,* stolotheca; *stl,* stolon—abbreviations in parenthesis indicate which branch. (After Kozlowski.)

---

* Decker, 1957, described two other thecal types, gonotheca, which he attributes to female individuals, and nematotheca, which he believes housed nematocysts of coelenterate type.

built a slender tube, the *stolotheca*. Since this, in turn, gives rise to another set of zooids, stolothecae form the axis of the stipe. The other two individuals construct thecae that open laterally from the stipe. These two zooids differed in some unknown way, for one formed a larger theca, the *autotheca*, than did the other, the *bitheca*. Probably each one was adapted for a different function in either food getting, protection, respiration, or reproduction. The thecae are connected internally by a delicate tubule, the *stolon*, which extends through the stolotheca and divides into three branches, one to each theca of the next generation. The wall of the theca consists of two layers. The inner is composed of half rings that dovetail to form zigzag longitudinal sutures. The outer layer consists of thin concentric sheets deposited on top of one another.

In the early Ordovician, graptolites appeared that lacked stolons and had only one kind of theca on a stipe (Figure 18-5). Although their simpler structure would suggest that they were more prim-

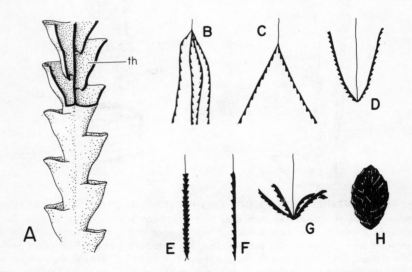

Fig. 18–5. *FORM AND VARIATION OF GRAPTOLOIDS.* A) View of detail of stipe—upper portion sectioned. B) *Tetragraptus;* early Ordovician. Four branched type; stipes pendant. C) *Didymograptus,* early to middle Ordovician. Two branched type; stipes pendant from nema. D) *Dicellograptus;* middle to late Ordovician. Two branched type—stipes turned upward. E) *Diplograptus.* Two stipes—turned upward along and attached to nema. F) *Monograptus;* Silurian. Like *Diplograptus* but reduced to single row of thecae. G) *Tetragraptus* (see B); stipes turned upward. H) *Phyllograptus.* Four stipes turned upward and attached to nema.

itive, they are connected to the earlier types by a series of inter-mediate forms, and a simpler form evolved from the more complex. Characteristically, the rhabdosome in these specialized types had fewer stipes, and the stipes, rather than growing downward from the end of the nema, turned laterally or even upward so that they grew back up along the nema. Internally, each theca opens into a common canal.

The perfect crime

The relationship of the graptolites to other animals, either fossil or recent, has been and, perhaps still is, the major mystery of pale-ontology. They have been considered inorganic structures and remnants of plants. Even after their animal origin was agreed on, they were assigned to the sponges, the hydroid coelenterates, the alcyonnarian coelenterates, the bryozoans, the cephalopods, and the pterobranchs.

Certainly they are colonial and are not sponges or cephalopods. Ulrich and Ruedemann (1931) argued for their affinities to the Bryozoa, but most specialists now believe that the similarities are the consequence of convergent evolution in two distinct colonial groups. They seem closest to the hydroids among the coelenterates in that they have a chitinous tubular skeleton and several different types of theca—presumably corresponding to individual, special-ized polyps.

Unlike the hydroids, however, the graptolite colony and the individual thecae display a degree of bilateral symmetry (Koz-lowski, 1947). Further, the stolon that connects the thecae is quite different from the hydroid structure. As Kozlowski observed, the character of the stolon corresponds to that of the pterobranch stolon, and the half ring elements, with their zigzag sutures which form the skeletal tube, are nearly identical with those of the ptero-branchs (Figure 18-1).

On this evidence, Kozlowski placed the graptolites with the pterobranchs. This concept received wide acceptance, and Bulman has used it for Part V of the *Treatise on Invertebrate Paleontology*. Some paleontologists, Bohlin in 1950 and more recently, Decker and Gold (1956 and 1957), question this relationship and emphasize the differences between graptolites and pterobranchs.

The crime may not be perfect—the ancestry of the graptolites

forever lost—but it is very nearly so. I place them with the protochordates—with a question mark.

The elephant graveyard

A common African legend holds that dying elephants travel great
distances to a common, secret graveyard. The distribution of graptolites has very nearly produced a similar legend among paleontologists. Graptolite fossils are common in fine-grained black shales
and extraordinarily rare in other rock types. The characteristics of
these shales suggest that the water above the bottom had little or
no oxygen and was loaded with hydrogen sulphide. Very few animals can tolerate this environment—called anerobic—for even short
periods of time. Fossils of all kinds, except graptolites, are rare in
these shales. Early paleontologists were struck by this peculiar
distribution, and their interest increased after the environmental
significance of the black shales was recognized.

Did the graptolites live in an anerobic environment? Certainly
their occurrence would suggest this. Even though their skeletons
were light, it seems improbable that currents otherwise capable
of transporting only fine clay could have carried them into the
area of deposition. But this conclusion rests on an assumption, i.e.,
that graptolites were benthonic animals. The early dendroid types
may have been, for their structure and associations indicate they
lived as upright branching colonies like the "erect" bryozoans. The
evidence is not so clear, however, for later, more specialized species. In these, the nema is so delicate that it could hardly have
supported the weight of the rhabdosome above the bottom if it
functioned as a stem, but the rhabdosome could have dangled
downward from the nema, which, in turn, was attached to floating
seaweed. Some apparently had a bladder-like float to which the
nema attached. As long ago as 1865, Hall suggested that the graptolites were planktonic, and the direct evidence for a planktonic life
is supported by the wide geographic distribution of many graptolite species. Nektonic or planktonic animal species commonly inhabit wide areas; benthonic forms rarely do so.

On this evidence, many, if not all, graptolites were planktonic.
They floated and lived in the well aerated surface waters, and only
after death did they sink into the poisonous black mud environment. "Fine," you say, "but if they floated over wide areas why are
they so rare except in black shales?" Consider now the composi-

tion of their tests. The chitinoid material is an organic compound particularly susceptible to attack by micro-organisms and generally unstable in an oxidizing environment. Arthropods and other animals with chitinous skeletons are rare fossils except for those that deposit calcium carbonate or phosphate in the chitinous matrix. On the other hand, the chitinoid and chitinous compounds are more stable in reducing environments than is calcium carbonate. On bottoms high in oxygen, chitinoid skeletons would be destroyed. On anerobic bottoms, the kinds and activities of micro-organisms are limited, and the organic compounds preserved. Planktonic organisms with calcite tests would dissolve in this reducing environment.

Note that special factors produced a rock-fossil association that leads to an erroneous paleoecologic interpretation. These factors were identified, and the error recognized through a careful study of the morphology and its functional significance.

The importance of being planktonic

Within a limited time range, Ordovician and Silurian, and within a limited series of rock types, black shales, the graptolites are the most useful guide fossils, for they evolved rapidly and single species appeared in widely separated seas. Since they are the only common fossil of the black shale environment, they permit correlation of rocks otherwise dated only from questionable interpretations of physical stratigraphy. Since several major geosynclines developed black shale phases during this time, their stratigraphic importance far outweighs their biologic.

TABLE 18–1

PROTOCHORDATA AND CHORDATA

PHYLUM PROTOCHORDATA

Cambrian to Recent. Coelomate; level of organization approximates that of Annelida. Possess some trace of notochord and gill slits. Nonsegmented. Distinguished by muscular collar that may bear tentacles. Marine; burrowing, benthonic or planktonic.

CLASS ENTEROPNEUSTA

Recent. Solitary; worm-like; collar simple; muscular proboscis. Burrowing. Mud strainer.

CLASS PTEROBRANCHIA

Ordovician to Recent. Colonial; chitinoid skeleton; collar bears tentacles. Lack specialized initial cup, the sicula. Sessile benthonic. Filter feeders.

(?) CLASS GRAPTOLITHINA

Cambrian to Mississippian. Branching colonial; chitinoid skeleton; soft parts largely unknown. Sicula. Planktonic and/or sessile benthonic. (?) Filter feeders.

PHYLUM CHORDATA

Ordovician to Recent. Coelomate; level of organization approximates that of Arthropoda. Notochord and gill slits present, at least in embryo.

SUBPHYLUM TUNICATA

Recent. Larval has notochord in tail region. Notochord lost but gill basket much enlarged in adult; body enclosed in sac-like, cellulose tunic. Marine, predominately sessile benthos. Filter feeders.

SUBPHYLUM CEPHALOCHORDATA

Recent. Notochord large, extends to tip of head. Gill basket large; body segmented and fishlike. Vagrant benthos; Marine and brackish. Filter feeders.

SUBPHYLUM VERTEBRATA

Ordovician to Recent. Notochord primitively large but not extending to tip of head. Skeletal elements develop in mesenchyme. Notochord supplemented or replaced by series of cartilaginous or bony vertebrae. Marine, fresh-water, and terrestrial. A wide variety of adaptations.

CLASS AGNATHA

Ordovician to Recent. Notochord large. Gill chambers. Elongate, fishlike but without paired appendages or jaws. In most, head is covered by bony armor. Most lineages extinct after Devonian. Fresh water and marine. Sluggish to active, benthonic and nektonic. Filter feeders and mud grubbers.

CLASS PLACODERMI

Silurian to Mississippian. Notochord large. Gill chambers generally reduced. Elongate, fish-like; with bony or cartilaginous jaws and some type of paired appendages. Fresh-water and marine, nektonic. Predators and herbivores.

CLASS CHONDRICHTHYES

Devonian to Recent. Skeleton entirely of cartilage. Notochord reduced; cartilaginous vertebral elements. Jaws propped against skull by hyoid gill arch. Two pairs of paired appendages. Predominately marine, nektonic, and predaceous.

CLASS OSTEICHTHYES

Devonian to Recent. Bony skeleton. Notochord reduced. Jaws variously attached to skull. Two pairs of paired appendages. Marine and freshwater; nektonic; predators, and herbivores.

Subclass Actinopterygii

Middle Devonian to Recent. Fins suported by slender rays. End of vertebral column turned into upper lobe of tail. Nostrils have no internal openings.

Subclass Choanichthyes

Early Devonian to Recent. Paired fins supported by stout bony rods. Nostrils have internal openings. Lungs variously developed. End of vertebral column is straight with lobe of tail above and below. Predominately fresh water, predaceous.

CLASS AMPHIBIA

Late Devonian to Recent. Internal nostrils and typically well developed lungs. Paired limbs; most have ossified vertebrae; except in primitive forms no fish-like tail. Eggs laid and develop in fresh water only. Fresh water and terrestrial; predominately predaceous, some herbivorous.

CLASS REPTILIA

Pennsylvanian to Recent. Well developed limbs and limb girdles; vertebrae, bony and well articulated. Gill slits absent in adult. Eggs laid on land with protective shell and membranes. Marine, fresh water, terrestrial, and aerial. Predators and herbivores.

CLASS AVES

Jurassic to Recent. Fore limbs modified into wings. Feathers. Homiothermal. Terrestrial and aerial; secondarily aquatic. Predators and herbivores.

CLASS MAMMALIA

Latest Triassic to Recent. Hair; mammary glands. Most bear young partly developed; some have marsupium; others have internal embryonic development with placenta. Terrestrial, aerial, aquatic. Predators and herbivores.

REFERENCES

Bohlin, B. 1950. "The Affinities of the Graptolites," *Bulletin Geol. Instit., Univ. of Uppsala*, vol. 34, pp. 107-113. An argument for the coelenterate affinities of the graptolites.

Bulman, O. M. B. 1938. "Programme Evolution in the Graptolites," *Biol. Review*, vol. 8, pp. 311-334. An interpretation of evolutionary trends among the graptolites.

Decker, C. E. 1956. "Place of the Graptolites in the Animal Kingdom," *Amer. Assoc. of Petr. Geologists, Bulletin*, vol. 40, pp. 1699-1704. This and the following reference argue for assignment of the graptolites to Coelenterata.

————— and I. B. Gold. 1957. "Blithecae, Gonothecae, and Nematotheca on Graptoloidea," *Jour. of Paleontology*, vol. 31, pp. 1154-1158.

Kozlowski, R. 1947. "Les Affinites des Graptolithes," *Biol. Reviews*, vol. 22, pp. 93-108. A description of graptolite morphology and an argument for the protochordate affinities of the graptolites.

—————. 1948. Les Graptolithes et Quelques Nouveaux d'Animaux du Tremadoc de la Pologne. *Palaeontologia Polonica*, vol. 3, pp. 1-235. Detailed morphologic studies of graptolites and related protochordate fossils.

Moore, R. C., S. G. Lalicker, and A. G. Fischer. 1952. See references for Chapter 3.

Ruedemann, R. 1947. "Graptolites of North America," *Geol. Soc. of America, Memoir 19*.

Ulrich, E. O. and R. Ruedemann. 1931. "Are the Graptolites Bryozoans?" *Geol. Soc. of America, Bulletin*, vol. 42, pp. 589-603.

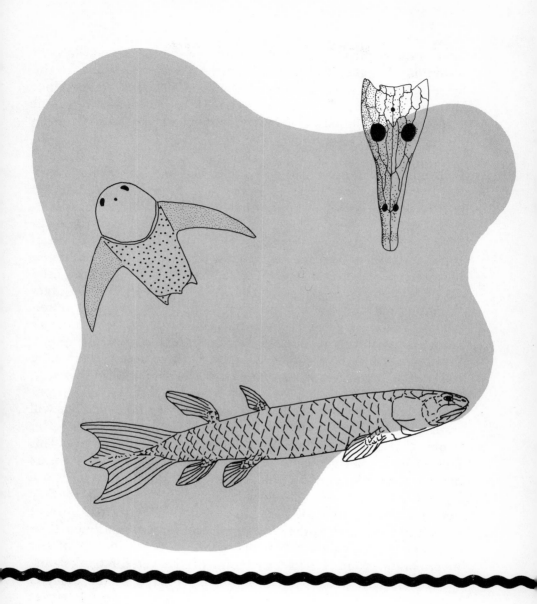

19. *The coming of the vertebrates:*
FISH and AMPHIBIA

*A*s the arthropods stand at the apex of one of the great lines in evolution of multicelled animals, so the vertebrates stand at the apex of the other. In individuation and intelligence, those things that we self-centered vertebrates consider the most important measures of evolutionary advance, they have risen far above even the most advanced arthropods.

In spite of their long divergence from a common ancestor and their profound morphologic differences, the vertebrates and arthropods resemble one another to a surprising degree. The vertebrates also show primary segmentation modified by specialization of segments and their fusion in functional regions. They, like arthropods, have a jointed skeleton extending to the limbs, though the vertebrate skeleton is internal rather than external. Most vertebrates, like arthropods, have or had paired limbs. All have a definite head with brain and sense organs. These similarities cannot be other than the results of similar selective pressures acting on quite different initial forms, because the proto-arthropod was a worm with paired appendages and a stiff, external cuticle, and the proto-vertebrate a larval sea squirt with gill slits, an internal stiffening rod, and a muscular tail for swimming. The similarities evolved in spite of these differences.

Vertebrates are rare fossils—any one who has hunted them will testify to that—but, despite this rarity, their phylogeny is better known than any of the far more abundant invertebrate groups. This knowledge is partly due to our intense interest in our forebears and all our uncles, cousins, and aunts. You have only to inspect a natural history museum to see the results of this interest. Since they are so rare and, thus, of slight importance in correlation, except of continental deposits, they have been collected primarily for their evolutionary, their phyletic, significance. This is hardly true of any invertebrate group. Finally, the form of the vertebrate skeleton, like that of the arthropods, is intimately related to the animal's adaptations. The vertebrate paleontologist can therefore interpret adaptive trends and separate adaptive similarities and differences from phylogenetic with at least some certainty.

THE ORIGINS OF THE VERTEBRATES

The picture of the ancestral vertebrate is, in part, a reconstruction from modern protochordates, but it is not too different from the

oldest known vertebrates (Figure 19-1). Some vertebrate bone
fragments have been found in Ordovician rocks, but the first good
specimens come from the lower Silurian. These "fishes" consist
basically of a large set of gills protected by bony armor and of a

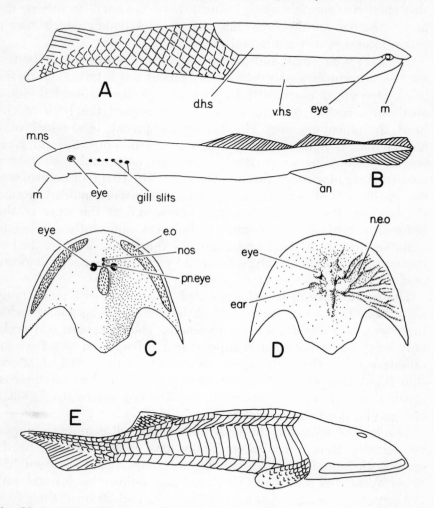

Fig. 19–1. *THE AGNATHA. A) Poraspis;* Late Silurian; lateral view; length about
15 cm. as restored. *B) Petromyzon;* Recent; lateral view. The lamprey. *C) Cephalaspis;*
late Silurian to early Devonian; dorsal view of head shield; length about 10 cm. *D)
Cephalaspis* with bony armor removed to show internal mold of brain case. *E) Hemicy-
claspis;* late Silurian to early Devonian; lateral view; length about 20 cm. Abbreviations:
an, anus; *d. h. s,* dorsal head shield; *ear,* ear; *e. o,* electric (?) organ; *eye,* eye; *m,*
mouth; *m. ns,* median nostril; *n. e. o,* nerve to electric (?) organ; *nos,* nostril; *pn. eye,*
pineal eye; *v. h. s,* ventral head shield. *(C. and D. After Wangsjo. E. After Stensio.)*

tail hung onto the back end of the gills. The mouth was a simple slit, without jaws, at the anterior ventral margin—hence the name Agnatha, "no jaws," for the class. The gills were supported by bony bars more or less fused to the head armor. In some the gill slits opened separately along either side of the head; in others, the gills opened on either side into an internal pouch which had a single lateral or ventral-lateral opening.

The eyes were small and placed laterally. The nostrils, or better, *nares,* were simply a pair of olfactory pits at the anterior end of the head. One group is characterized by a single median nostril. Some also had a medial opening in the armor toward the back of the head, the pineal opening. This housed the pineal "eye" which may have detected light and dark but not much more. Several Norwegian paleontologists, particularly Stensio, have made painstaking studies of serial sections through the skull. The brain, of course, was not fossilized, but portions of the head armor were molded around the brain and nerves. The support below and at the sides of the brain was, typically, cartilagineous but was sufficiently ossified in some so that it too was preserved. As the result, a good deal is known of the brain structure from the form of the cavity it occupied.

The trunk and tail were unarmored or covered with small bony plates. No traces of the internal skeleton have been found—what there was, presumably, was cartilagenous. The notochord was probably large and functioned in support of the body and as a base for muscle action. Although one or two genera had a pair of lateral skin flaps back of the head, these apparently lacked an internal skeleton and are not true paired limbs. The tail was relatively small and turned downward near the tip.

The lack of jaws and the large size of the gill chambers suggest the Agnatha were filter feeders. Many have broad, flattened heads, some with lateral "horns," probably an adaptation to bottom life. Some agnathans may have burrowed just below the surface with the top of the head and the trunk exposed, and strained their food from the mud drawn in through the mouth. Most of them were probably poor swimmers because of their oversized head, short body and tail, and the lack of paired fins to act as ailerons or elevators. I suspect they passed most of their life lying in bovine contemplation on the bottom, or grubbing placidly in the mud.

Although the agnathans show definite morphologic similarities to the cephalochordates and probably had a similar way of life, they are clearly much advanced over the cephalochordate condition. Unfortunately, the specializations of the living cephalochordates and agnathans confuse this comparison. The former are probably a good deal more sedentary, and their sense organs, brain, and circulatory system may have regressed in complexity. The recent agnathans, the lamprey and the hagfish, have developed an unpleasant semipredatory-semiparasitic habit in which they attach themselves to a fish by a specialized sucking mouth and burrow into its flesh with a rasp-like tongue.

The vertebrates did not leap to the center of the evolutionary stage quite as suddenly as did the trilobites and other invertebrates, for these fragments in Ordovician rocks give warning of their imminent appearance. On the other hand, they are pretty well diversified on this first appearance, and it seems unlikely that the several evolutionary lines developed bony armor at the same time so that they could be preserved for posterity. For that reason vertebrate paleontologists have given quite a lot of effort to reconstruction of early vertebrate evolution and to attempts to determine why fossils from that period are unknown.

The problem centers on the normal environment of early vertebrates. After careful consideration of the lithology and paleontology of Ordovician and Silurian fish localities, Romer and Grove (1935) concluded that the early vertebrates lived only in fresh water habits. Denison (1956), after an equally careful study, concluded that they were not fresh water but marine—or at least brackish. The faunal associates of these early fish are not typically marine—if by typical, neritic is meant. On the other hand, paleontologists know very little of Paleozoic brackish faunas, and it is uncertain whether they can always distinguish them from fresh water faunas. Either interpretation would account for the absence of vertebrates from the well known Ordovician deposits which are predominately of neritic origin. Almost surely someone, some day, will find well preserved fish in Ordovician rocks to end this argument and to establish, more clearly, the relation of the vertebrates to the more primitive chordates.

Whether estuarine or fresh water, many early fish species lived in waters with strong currents. Even though they were sluggish beasts who grubbed for food or filtered it from the passing water there was a selective premium in swimming. Only by swimming could they move in those currents and adjust to the shifting environments of streams or tidal passes. Because of these environmental factors, they could not evolve, as do most filter feeders, into sessile animals. The bony armor about the head gave protection against predators—possibly the euripterids which are commonly found in the same localities—but this armor by its weight and rigidity interfered with swimming. Caught between fires the agnathans tended to reduce or even lose entirely their armor and to protect themselves by swifter flight—at least the majority of the later members of the class have smaller and thinner head shields. The reduction of euripterids in numbers and variety at the same time may be either cause or effect.

A TIME FOR EXPERIMENTS

For most animals, filter feeding has become an evolutionary blind alley. The bryozoans, brachiopods, pelecypods, and crinoids succeeded within the limits of this adaptation, but, to use a figurative phrase, they lost the will for higher things. The vertebrates escaped their fate through no virtue of their own but by circumstance of their physical environment. Their ultimate success, however, depended on an extraordinary evolutionary event—the development of jaws. The annelid-arthropod line accomplished it by transformation of some paired appendages, but the vertebrates had no such resource.

The morphological development of the vertebrate jaw was demonstrated by zoologists over seventy-five years ago in a series of remarkable studies of vertebrate anatomy and embryology. The jaw, in its initial stages of development, consists of four elements—one above and one below on either side (Figure 19-2). In the embryo, these are cartilaginous and are replaced functionally by other bony elements in the adult. They are, however, retained in sharks. These jaw elements are in line with the cartilaginous bars that lie in the fleshy gill arches between the gill slits and resemble them considerably. Still more important, the nerves and major blood vessels of the jaw region resemble those of the normal gill arches in structure and arrangement. Continued development modifies the gill bar behind the jaw in size and form so that it supports the jaw against the brain case. The gill slit between the jaw and this specialized arch is reduced to a tiny hole. The ontogeny of the

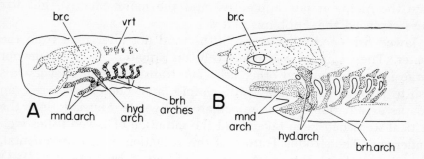

Fig. 19–2. *DEVELOPMENT OF THE JAWS IN SHARK ONTOGENY.* A) Embryo. B) Adult. The gill arches and jaws are shown in close stipple; the brain case in open stipple. Abbreviations: *br. c,* brain case; *brh. arch,* branchial arch; *hyd. arch,* hyoid arch; *mnd. arch,* mandibular arch (jaws); *vrt,* vertebra. (A. After Goodrich. B. After Watson, *Paleontology and Modern Biology.* Copyright, Yale University Press, New Haven. Used with permission.)

vertebrate jaws therefore indicates that the jaws evolved from a set of gill bars.*

If this interpretation is correct, paleontologists should observe the intermediate steps between gill bar and jaw in fossils. Unfortunately most of the connecting forms are still listed among the "missing links," though some early jawed fish appear to have a normal large gill slit just behind the jaw. Can we reconstruct the evolutionary sequence and predict the characteristics of these missing links? I think we can and with some certainty (leaning heavily on a discussion by D. M. S. Watson in *Paleontology and Modern Biology*). ~~Chap.1 - origin of jaws -~~

Some agnathans had their gill bars free of the head shield rather than fused into it. Very probably, the arches between the gill slits were muscular, and these muscles pumped the whole gill basket like a bellows to force the water—or mud—out. Some had small movable plates around the mouth that could be used to nibble on plants or small invertebrates. The musculature of the gill arches assisted in moving these plates. In this fashion, the anterior arches became part of the functional biting mouth. Selection could then act to incorporate variants with larger and stronger anterior gill bars

---

* This is not an illustration of "ontogeny recapitulates phylogeny" for the jaws are never functional gill bars as they must have been in the ancestral population. Rather the ontogeny of the recent forms resembles the ontogeny of the ancestors. Many, if not most, of the examples given for the rule are of this sort.

into the incipient jaw apparatus, and the more effective gill bar jaws replaced the "nibbling plates."

Jawed fish need not burrow in the mud nor filter food from the water. They can browse effectively on aquatic plants or devour large invertebrates and other fish. The transformation of a jawless fish to jawed was probably rather rapid, and, once it occurred, an adaptive radiation began immediately. By late Silurian time the critical steps had been taken, and the radiation of jawed fishes well underway. The striking feature of this radiation is its experimental, almost tentative, nature. A variety of jaw types (Figure 19-3) appeared—some of them dissimilar adaptations to quite similar function.

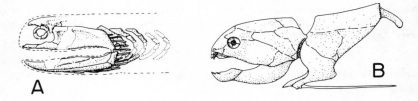

Fig. 19–3. *JAW STRUCTURES IN PRIMITIVE FISH.* *A) Acanthodes, a early Permian placoderm. The gill arch (hyoid) immediately behind the jaw bears a full set of gill rakers. These indicate the hyoid slit was a normal functional slit rather than the reduced pore-like opening (the spiracle) known in sharks and bony fishes. B) Dinichthyes, a late Devonian placoderm. The skull is articulated to the shoulder girdle with a ball-and-socket joint and may have moved up and down on a stationary lower jaw. (A. After Watson. B. After Heintz.)*

The primitive jawed fishes first appear with agnathans in those controversial brackish or fresh water associations. By Devonian, however, they adapted to normal marine salinity and occur with characteristic marine organisms. Some apparently retained the ancient mud-grubbing habit, for they have a flattened body and heavy cranial armor like the agnathans (Figure 19-4). Many, however, have a deeper bodied form and a torpedo shape complemented by large powerful jaws. These were carnivores of the open waters like the recent pelagic sharks and bony fishes. Some lost their cranial armor altogether; others had it transformed to small, relatively thin plates, and still others elaborated and enlarged it and supplemented the head shield by heavy bony scales on trunk and tail.

To catch smaller fish or to escape from larger ones, these first jawed fishes had to swim more swiftly and maneuver more agilely.

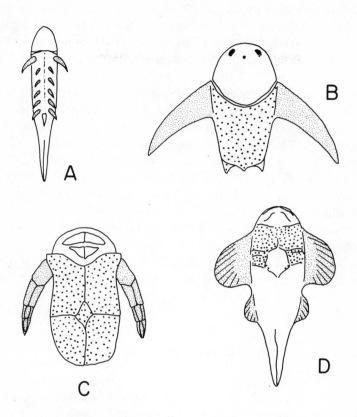

Fig. 19–4. *VARIATION OF FORM IN THE PLACODERMA.* Paired appendages shown by light stipple; limb girdles by heavy stipple. A) *Climatius,* an early Devonian genus with seven pairs of spines on either side of the ventral mid-line. B) *Arctolepis;* early Devonian; dorsal view of head and shoulder armor. A pair of hollow spines extend laterally from the shoulder girdle and are fused to the girdle. C) *Pterichthyodes;* middle Devonian; ventral view of head and shoulder armor. A pair of externally armored limbs are articulated to the sides of the heavy thoracic armor. D) *Gemuendina;* early Devonian; ventral view. The body is rather broad and flat and bears both anterior and posterior paired appendages. (B. After Heintz. C. After Traguair. D. After Broili.)

The agnathans were like an airplane without aeilerons or elevators. They attained directional control by torsion of the entire trunk and tail—an extremely wasteful mechanism. Obviously paired lateral flaps would be much more effective. The initial steps in the evolution of the paired fins are unknown, but several different types appeared in the primitive jawed fishes (Figure 19-4). Some had a lateral fold on either side extending part of the length of the body;

others had paired lateral spines—some with as many as eight or ten pairs; others had a pair of appendages at the back end of the head. These latter, supported by bone developed just below the skin, were jointed and articulated in a manner somewhat like that of arthropod legs.

The diverse products of this radiation are collected in the class Placoderma. They are characterized positively by the presence of jaws, negatively by the possession of a normal gill slit and bar behind the jaw. The class may be an artificial grouping of several lineages with separate agnathan ancestors, but, since none have been linked directly with any agnathan, it still represents the most satisfactory statement of current knowledge. On the other side, the class includes the ancestors of the advanced fishes, but these ancestors are still hypotheses. Some placoderms obviously could not be these ancestors; others could be if they were not too late in time or too specialized in this characteristic or that. The evolutionary tenure of the placoderms was short, for only a few survived beyond the Devonian and even these went down to extinction before the beginning of the Mesozoic.

VERTEBRATES WITHOUT BONES

Out of this welter of experiments in the late Silurian and early Devonian evolved two lines that found the correct combination—though this correctness was not immediately apparent. These two, the sharks and the bony fishes, were distinct at their first appearance in the fossil record. Whether they had a common ancestor in an advanced placoderm or represent separate, parallel developments from the primitive jawed fish has yet to be determined. The sharks resemble a group of placoderms, the acanthodians, but the well known acanthodians are too late in time to be ancestral to the sharks, and the early ones too poorly known for palentologists to assess their relationships.

The ancestral shark population advanced beyond the placoderm condition in three essentials (Figure 19-5). They evolved two sets of paired fins, an anterior *pectoral* pair, and a posterior *pelvic* pair. They had the gill bar behind the jaws modified so that it propped the upper jaw against the brain case and, as a result, had the anterior gill slit reduced to a small hole, the *spiracle*. Finally, they lost the bony armor so characteristic of primitive fishes. Sharks, or more broadly, the class Chondrichthyes, are further characterized by a cartilaginous internal skeleton and by separate external openings for each gill slit. These are commonly taken to be primitive characteristics conserved from their placoderm ancestry, although it is unlikely that the primitive placoderms used cartilage as extensively as do sharks, and some placoderms had a large operculum covering all the gill slits.

The adaptive radiation of the chondrichthyans is but poorly known. Cartilage decays rapidly; only when it is partially calcified or when it leaves its impression in fine grained shales is it fossilized; otherwise fossil shark species are teeth and nothing more. The first, primeval species was probably marine; probably a carnivore; probably pelagic. Those anyway are the interpretations from the occurrence of the early sharks in marine associations, from their teeth, and from their slender, fusiform bodies. One group penetrated to and evolved in fresh waters. These, the pleurocanthids, occur along with amphibians and reptiles in late Paleozoic river channel, flood plain, and lake deposits. In these beds, large coprolites associated with shark teeth and bits of ossified cartilage include fish scales and fragments of amphibian bone. From this we can infer that the pleurocanthids were predaceous, and from their size that they were the dominant predators of those waters.

Most sharks however remained marine, though a few recent species tolerate brackish or even fresh waters. They largely retained the carnivorous pelagic habit, but some, like the modern skates and rays, foraged on bottom invertebrates. In adaption to this habit, the latter have a broad, flattened body, and some evolved heavy flat teeth to crush thick-shelled animals. Even if we recognize that paleontologists know most sharks only from their teeth, they have been far less diversified than the bony fish. They have had an important but subsidiary role in the drama of vertebrate evolution— the elderly character actor always on the stage but with only a few lines to speak. The chondrichthyes are a terminal group in themselves; they did not, as is sometimes implied in elementary zoology courses, evolve into bony fish; they evolved only into sharks.

The race to the swift

If the chondrichthyes have supporting roles in the evolutionary play, the bony fish, the Osteichthyes, and their weird side branches are the leads. It is commonplace to state that evolution of a group

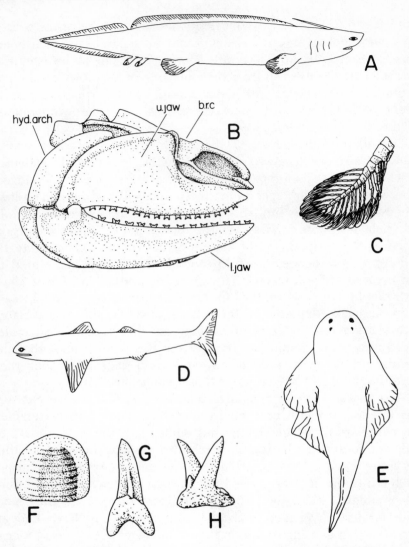

Fig. 19–5. *THE CHONDRICHTHYES.* A) General body plan—a late Paleozoic fresh-water shark, *Pleuracanthus.* B) Brain case and jaws of *Pleuracanthus;* lateral view. C) Skeleton of anterior (pectoral) paired fin of *Pleuracanthus.* D) *Cladoselache;* late Devonian; lateral view. A slender, fusiform shark—probably an active predator. E) *Rhina;* late Jurassic to Recent; dorsal view. A flattened, bottom feeder. F) Tooth of *Ptychodus;* Cretaceous; crown view. A broad flat tooth—probably used to crush molluscs and arthropods. G) *Isurus;* early Cretaceous to Recent; lateral view of tooth. H) A pleuracanth tooth; Carboniferous to Permian; lateral view. Abbreviations: *br. c,* brain case; *hyd. arch,* hyoid arch; *l. jaw,* lower jaw; *u. jaw,* upper jaw. (B. and F. After Romer, *Vertebrate Paleontology;* reprinted by permission of the University of Chicago Press. Copyright, 1945, University of Chicago Press. All rights reserved.)

is limited by previous adaptations—I gave many examples in preceding chapters. I also gave a few examples of adaptive changes that created new and diverse evolutionary possibilities, changes that broke the mold of the organic world. No group, not even the arthropods, illustrates this phenomena so clearly as the Osteichthyes. As good swimmers with paired fins they should have gone on, getting to be better and better "fish." And so they have, for over ninety per cent of recent fish are bony fish, and, even more significant, they have eliminated most of their competitors and have come to dominate the vagrant benthos and the nekton. But they had some poor relations who could not survive in the water and clambered onto land to share the terrestrial environments with the arthropods.

The earliest osteichthyians have been found in lower Devonian rocks with their placoderm and chondrichthyian cousins. Although their source in the placoderms is unknown, from their occurrence and from the physiological adaptations of recent bony fish, paleontologists suspect that they evolved in upland rivers and lakes.[*] Unlike the sharks, they retained part of the primitive dermal bony armor and augmented it with internal bone (Figure 19-6). The skull comprises a large number of separate dermal elements more or less tightly sutured for rigidity. The eyes were large and set well forward. The gill slits were protected by a movable operculum that helped control the flow of water through the gill chambers. The body is covered by a mosaic of heavy bony scales. Internal bone varies from genus to genus—typically, parts of the brain case, vertebrae, and supports for the paired appendages are ossified.

Like sharks they had settled for two sets of paired fins. These are named on the basis of their later evolution in the tetrapods, the pelvic, and the pectoral. The fins have an internal skeleton of heavy bony rods or slender *rays* and articulate with bony elements in the body wall, the *pectoral* and *pelvic girdles*.

To rule the seas

Among the best known of these Devonian fishes are two genera of similar form (Figure 19-6). A Devonian ichthyologist, impressed

---

[*] Denison (1956) notes that middle Devonian lungfish apparently occur in both marine and fresh water environment, but the other middle Devonian osteichthyians were limited to fresh waters. He feels that the evidence does not support the hypothesis of evolution in rivers and/or lakes.

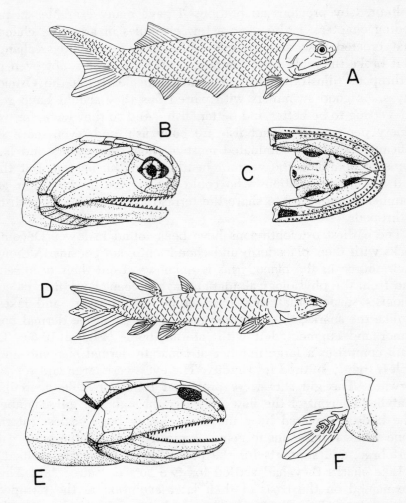

Fig. 19–6. *EARLY OSTEICHTHYES. A) Cheirolepis; middle Devonian; lateral view; length about 20 cm. B) Lateral view of skull of Cheirolepis. C) Ventral view of Cheirolepis skull—lower jaw removed. D) Eusthenopteron; late Devonian; lateral view. E) Osteolepis; middle Devonian; lateral view of skull. F) Eusthenopteron; view of pectoral fin and shoulder girdle. (A. After Traguair. B. and C. After Watson. D. and E. After various sources. E. After Save-Soderbergh.)*

by these similarities and their common differences from placoderms, might have placed them in the same family. Modern vertebrate paleontologists classify them in different subclasses. The differences between them are small, but these differences have been perpetuated through 300,000,000 years and through a rapid succession of evolutionary changes and radiations. Only the perspective of time permits this extreme separation.

What of the differences? One has blind pits for nostrils, rays supporting the fins, and the tip of the vertebrae turned up in the base of the fin tail. The other has nostrils that open into the mouth cavity, bony rods in the paired fins, and tail vertebrae that run straight back into the tail fin. They also differ minutely in the arrangement of bones in the skull. These structural differences imply an adaptive divergence but a very slight one, for they both inhabited fresh water environments, both had slender torpedo-shaped bodies, and both possessed the sharp teeth of carnivores. If not directly competitive, they certainly excluded each other from niches both could otherwise have easily occupied.

The ray-fins (subclass Actinopterygia), although they started slowly in the Paleozoic, steadily shoved their vertebrate and invertebrate competitors into extinction. They have diverged continuously into new niches and have developed new forms for old niches. They include rapid swimmers of the open seas with elongate torpedo shapes, and flattened bottom dwellers like the flounder. Many are still predaceous, but many have become herbivores or feed on the tiny animals and plants of the plankton. They include giants and dwarfs, eels and sea horses.

But throughout this almost continuous, explosive radiation runs a common evolutionary progression. Among the more important changes in this progression have been the reduction of the bony scales to thin horny plates; the shift of the pectoral fins up the side of the body and the pelvic fins forward below the pectorals; an increasing ossification of ribs and vertebrae; and a reduction of the thickness and rigidity of the dermal skull bones. Typically, they have large eyes, and the brain is modified by the correlative change of the optical centers.

These features have evolved in many lines, cross-cutting adaptive diversification and so, alas, cross-cutting the hapless taxonomist. He can recognize three major radiations, late Paleozoic and early Mesozoic, Mesozoic, and late Mesozoic and Cenozoic, but each radiation is a phylogenetic thicket rather than a family tree. By this token the species in each radiation are of a similar structural grade, but they attained this similarity by parallel evolution. As more fossils are collected and more carefully studied, some of the central stems in the thicket can be discerned and separated from sterile shoots, but this effort has scarcely begun.

Black sheep

The other subclass of bony fish represented in Devonian faunas includes a moderate number of Paleozoic, a few Mesozoic and Cenozoic, and four or five recent genera. They would hardly be worth mentioning—except because they gave rise to the terrestrial vertebrates. But why did a group otherwise obscure produce such important offspring? The answer lies in two of the characteristics that distinguish them from the ray fins. The internal nares permitted them to breathe when their mouths were closed—breathe, that is, by intake of water or air. The rods in their paired fins were sufficiently sturdy to bear their weight out of water. This combined with two characteristics, heavy scales and paired sacs attached to the esophagus, held in common with the primitive ray fins, permitted them to survive on land. The scales protected them from the drying action of the air; the sacs formed chambers into which air could be drawn for respiration. Finally, the early choanichthyes were probably fresh water forms, for they are found in channel fills and lake deposits. They may have been driven to land because of the drying of the streams or lakes or in a search for food. The early stages may simply have involved moving from one channel or pond to a nearby one.

Presumably, only one choanichthyian population evolved into tetrapods. The remainder plodded along into obscurity or extinction. Even in the middle Devonian, two separate lines can be distinguished (see also p. 148ff.). One group, marked by elongation of the body to an eel-like form and reduction of the paired fins, leads to the modern lungfishes, the Dipnoi (Figure 6-12). The dipnoans have adapted to life in the intermittent streams and ponds characteristic of a monsoonal river delta. Two of the recent genera, *Protopterus* and *Lepidosiren*, burrow into the mud, during the dry season and aestivate. This habit appears to be of ancient origin because Permian lungfish occur in vertical "pipes" that seem to represent sediment-filled burrows. The other recent genus does not aestivate but survives in pools of muddy water by breathing air. The dipnoans feed principally on small, hard-shelled invertebrates and evolved crushing and cutting plates to handle this adamant fare. The skull, in turn, changed greatly to support these plates and the powerful jaw muscles.

The other group of choanichthyes (Figure 6-12) is distinguished primarily by broad based, paired fins with a sturdy skeleton—hence the name Crossopterygia, lobe-fin. The crossopterygians also differ from the Dipnoi in arrangement and number of skull bones. The structure of the paired fins foreshadows that of the tetrapod limb, and the skull structure is close to that of the earliest amphibians. The Crossopterygia are important members of late Paleozoic fresh water faunas, at least in number of fossils. In Devonian, they were probably the dominant predators. If the proto-amphibian was chased out of the water, it was probably by a crossopterygian cousin.

By Permian time, a number of marine genera had evolved to form a distinct order, the Coelocantha. The fresh water crossopterygians are unknown after the Permian, but the coelocanths managed with some success in the Mesozoic. Long thought to be extinct, a living coelocanth, very like the Cretaceous ones, was collected off the African coast in the late 1930's. More recently additional specimens have been found, and detailed studies of their morphology have begun.

AN EXCESS OF OXYGEN

A Danish expedition to eastern Greenland in 1931 found outcrops of a fossiliferous red sandstone, and, in them, made a dramatic discovery. Most of the vertebrate fossils were typical late Devonian forms including several genera of placoderms, lungfish, and crossopterygians. Among these, however, were partial skulls and isolated limb bones of two species of amphibians. Though fragmentary Devonian amphibian material had been collected some years before from rocks in Canada, this was the first opportunity to learn the details of their anatomy. Previously, comparison of Carboniferous amphibians with Devonian fish had indicated that amphibian ancestory almost surely lay in the crossopterygian group. If this interpretation were correct, the Devonian amphibians would be intermediate in form.

The study of these Devonian amphibia, though not yet finished, has completely borne out this expectation (Figure 6-14). The limbs are of the typical tetrapod form, though short and undoubtedly clumsy (Figure 19-7). The pelvic and pectoral girdles are also more amphibian than fish-like, but these structures are easily derived from those of the crossops. The vertebrae are essentially like those of the crossopterygians except that the dorsal (*neural*) arches that covered the spinal cord are more closely articulated. The body of each vertebra consists of two crescentic pieces, a small one (the *pleurocentrum*) that lay on the upper surface of the notochord and a larger one (the *intercentrum*) that wrapped around its lower part and extended up its sides to articulate with the neural arch. The notochord was large and still bore a large share of the load on the back.

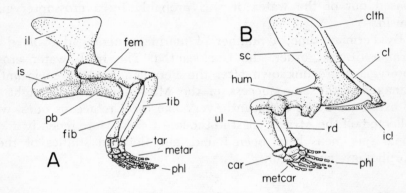

Fig. 19–7. *THE TETRAPOD LIMB.* General structure of limbs in early amphibians and reptiles. A) Posterior (pelvic) limb and girdle. B) Anterior (pectoral) limb and girdle. Abbreviations: *car*, carpal; *cl*, clavicle; *clth*, cleithrum; *fem*, femur; *fib*, fibula; *hum*, humerus; *icl*, interclavicle; *il*, ilium; *is*, ischium; *metar*, metatarsal; *metcar*, metacarpal; *pb*, pubis; *phl*, phalanges; *rd*, radius; *sc*, scapula; *tar*, tarsal; *tib*, tibia; *ul*, ulna.

The pattern of bones in lateral and anterior parts of the skull (Figure 19-8), the arrangement of dermal bones in the palate, and the structure of the lower jaw also resemble those of the crossopterygians. On the other hand, the head looks more amphibian than fish-like. The snout is relatively long; the part of the skull behind the eyes is relatively short. The opercular bones are gone, except for two small elements. The teeth are simple sharp cones borne on the bones of the palate as well as on the margins of the jaw. The enamel around the base of the tooth is infolded to form a labyrinthine pattern in a cross section. These characters of the teeth are primitive, since the crossopterygians have similar dentition, but they are also typically amphibian and were retained in many later species.

The general form of body reminds one of a fish. The neck is non-existent, for the back of the skull lies almost against the pectoral girdle. The tail is long and, most remarkably, the vertebrae bear short ventral and dorsal spines. These spines are clearly the rays supporting a fish-like tail—one very like that of the Crossopterygia.

The mixture of fish-like characteristics with those of the tetrapods demonstrates that these Devonian amphibians were very near the origin of the tetrapod stock. This mixture also demonstrates that the evolution of tetrapod characteristics went on at different rates in different parts of the body. What makes a land animal? Obviously, legs to crawl on and lungs to breathe with. These early amphibians have the legs; that can be seen. The lungs cannot be seen, but, since the operculum is gone, the gills must be too. If the gills are lost, the lungs must have replaced them. Besides, the legs are too good for animals that only ventured from the water momentarily. Legs and lungs evolved under intense selective pressure, but, once these critical adaptations were made, the other changes, the refinements as it were, could go on more slowly, and indeed some were not completed until late in the evolution of the reptiles.

The great invasion

The early terrestrial vertebrates had a whole new world to conquer, to exploit. The floodplains, at least in their wetter parts, were covered by a variety of plants. The insects and other arthropods had begun their radiation in the terrestrial environment. With this opportunity, the Amphibia began to diverge in form almost before they became amphibians. Although the Devonian genera are extremely primitive, they already represent two distinct families. Since specializations of skull structure debar any of the three well known genera from a direct ancestry of Carboniferous amphibians, there must have been still other Devonian types.

Fossilization in the terrestrial environments

The origin of the class is, as I have shown, fairly well known; the evolutionary paths within the class are known only imperfectly. The reasons for this latter situation lie both in the nature of fossilization in the terrestrial environment and in the peculiarities of the geologic record of the Carboniferous.

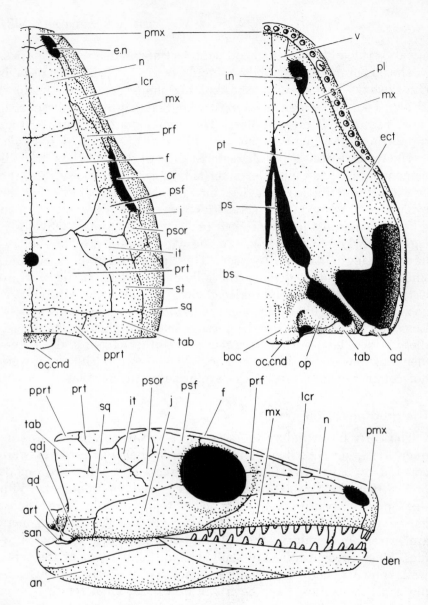

Fig. 19–8. *GENERAL FORM OF THE TETRAPOD SKULL.* Drawing at upper left is a dorsal view of the right side of the skull; at upper right is a ventral view of the left side. Lower drawing is a lateral view. Abbreviations: *an*, angular; *art*, articular; *boc*, basioccipital; *bs*, basisphenoid; *den*, dentary; *ect*, ectopterygoid; *e. n*, external nostril; *f*, frontal; *it*, intertemporal; *j*, jugal; *lcr*, lacrimal; *mx*, maxillary; *n*, nasal; *oc. cnd*, occipital condyle; *op*, opisthotic; *or*, orbit; *pl*, palatine; *pmx*, premaxillary; *pprt*, postparietal; *prf*, prefrontal; *prt*, parietal; *ps*, parasphenoid; *psf*, postfrontal; *psor*, postorbital; *pt*, pterygoid; *qd*, quadrate; *qdj*, quadratojugal; *san*, surangular; *sq*, squamosal; *st*, supratemporal; *tab*, tabular; *v*, vomer.

First of all, fossils are rare in all sedimentary rocks of terrestrial origin. The reasons are several: terrestrial animals, even aquatic ones, are rarely as abundant in any one place as are marine animals; if threatened they can all pack up and leave, but marine faunas have many sedentary species; terrestrial environments of deposition, because of their very local and shifting occurrence, rarely provide rapid permanent burial; and the alternate wetting and drying and high oxygen concentrations destroy much of what is buried. In major river channels vertebrate skeletons are disarticulated and the bones broken, worn, and scattered. On the flood plains a dying animal is attacked by scavengers, and the indigestible remains left to the bacteria and the corrosive atmosphere. A paleontologist finds fossils in main channel sands or in floodplain clays more by luck than by careful search. Occasionally, swamp deposits contain accumulations of vertebrate bones, although the chemistry of most swamp environments is unfavorable for fossilization. Where can vertebrate skeletons accumulate and be buried in numbers? Around ephemeral lakes and ponds where animals bog down and are buried in mud holes or where their carcasses sink undisturbed to the bottom of a pond. Or in the back waters of small channels where isolated bones or whole skeletons accumulate.

An extensive exposure of marine rocks will almost always yield fossils to a patient collector. An extensive exposure of terrestrial rocks will rarely do so unless it cuts into one of the extremely localized ponds or minor channels. If vegetation and soil cover most of the bed rock, the chances of finding vertebrate fossils become almost infinitesimal. For example, lake and pond deposits are unusually abundant in the Dunkard (Permo-Carboniferous) beds of West Virginia, Ohio, and Pennsylvania. Yet in some seven field seasons only about ten significant vertebrate fossil localities have been found in an area of over 7000 square miles. The search of course was limited to road cuts because of the extensive mantle cover.

Mississippian rocks in most parts of the world are of marine origin. Many of those that are continental, such as the Pocono and Mauch Chunk formations in the Appalachian basin, are poorly exposed. The amphibian species known from the Mississippian represent, then, only a small fraction of those that existed during the period. Paleontologists can recognize the fact of an extensive amphibian radiation but not the details nor the origins of the separate lines. The Pennsylvania record is somewhat more satisfactory but limited principally to one type of environment—the coal swamp.

Long after most of the major events in amphibian evolution, paleontologists find numerous amphibian fossils in the extensive Permian and Triassic deltaic deposits of the western United States, Russia, and South Africa. Any description of amphibian evolution must be based in large part on a reconstruction of pre-Permian events from Permian fossils.

Amphibian evolution

The most wide-spread and consistent trend in the Amphibia was for modification of the vertebrae to reduce the stresses on the notochord and on back muscles and to place the static and dynamic loads on the bony arches and centra. This was accomplished differ-

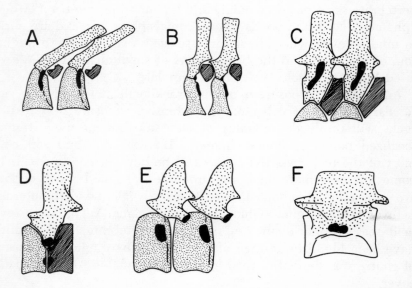

Fig. 19–9. *AMPHIBIAN VERTEBRAE.* Neural arch shown by heavy stipple; pleurocentrum by diagonal lines; intercentrum by fine stipple; and rib articulations by solid black. A) Vertebrae of crossopterygian fish. B) Vertebrae of primitive amphibian (ichthyostegalian). C) Vertebrae of moderately advanced amphibian. Rhachitomous type of vertebra. D) Vertebra of moderately advanced amphibian. Embolomerous type. E) Vertebrae of advanced amphibian. Stereospondylus type. F) Vertebra of lepospondylus amphibian. Body of vertebra formed by deposition of bone around notochord, not by ossification of intercentral and pleurocentral cartilages. (A. After Gregory. B. Altered from Jarvik. C. and D. After Williston.)

ently in different primitive stocks (Figure 19-9), and for this reason vertebral characteristics form the principal basis of amphibian classification. These modifications of the vertebrae were certainly functional, but the exact mechanial advantages of any particular vertebral type have not yet been established. Most lines also show reduction of the bones of the palate—this may be related to some sort of diet change, to a general lightening of the head, or, very possibly, to some other cause.

The skull of early amphibians, like that of their fish ancestors, is deep and compressed from side to side. Nearly all later amphibians have the skull flattened dorso-ventrally so that it is wide but shallow (Figure 19-10). The functional significance of the change

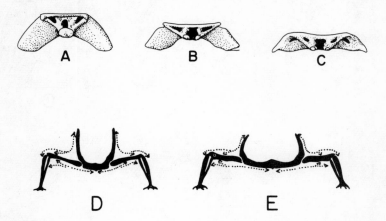

Fig. 19–10. *EVOLUTION OF SKULL AND BODY FORM. A)* through *C)* posterior view of amphibian skulls. *A)* Primitive, deep skull; Carboniferous embolomere. *B)* Moderately flattened; Permian rhachitome. *C)* Strongly flattened; Triassic stereospondyl. *D)* and *E)* Diagrammatic cross section of front limbs and pectoral girdle. Bones in solid black; muscles dotted. *D)* Primitive form with deep narrow body. *E)* Advanced form with wide, flat body. (A.–C. After Watson.)

is not clear but would seem related to the generally flattening of the body. The change in body shape from narrow to flat correlates with the position of the limbs and their use. The proximal limb segments, the humerus in the fore limb, the femur in the hind, stuck out laterally and nearly parallel to the ground. The next segment, comprising the ulna and radius bones in front and the tibia and fibula behind, were at right angles to the ground and actually carried the animal above it. The gait must have been awkward and sprawling much like that of a turtle. The real load rested on the long muscles of the arm and leg working over the levers at the shoulder and hip and at the elbow and knee. These muscles would work best if long and nearly parallel to the proximal limb segments. They would be longest and most nearly parallel if the body were flat rather than narrow. With these short, wide-spraddled legs, a flat body and head would also give more clearance above the ground.

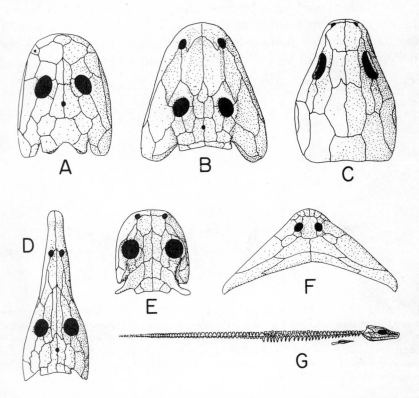

Fig. 19–11. *VARIATION IN AMPHIBIAN FORM.* A) *Ichthyostega;* late Devonian; dorsal view of skull; length 20 cm. A relatively deep, fish-like skull. B) *Eryops;* late Pennsylvanian to early Permian; dorsal view of skull; length about 50 cm. Flattened skull with eyes high on head and far back. C) *Euryodus;* early Permian; dorsal view of skull; length about 2.5 cm. Short snouted form. D) *Platyops;* middle(?) Permian; dorsal view of skull. Long snouted form. E) *Stegops;* Pennsylvanian; dorsal view of skull. Note short "horn" at posterior corners of skull. F) *Diplocaulus;* late Pennsylvanian to early Permian; dorsal view of skull; width about 27 cm. A "long-horned" amphibian. G) *Sauropleura;* Pennsylvanian; lateral view; length 18 cm. Snake-like amphibian with rudimentary limbs. (A. After Jarvik. B. After various sources. C. After Olson. D. and E. After Bystrow. F. After Williston. G. After Steen.)

Adaptive radiation

Left to themselves until the evolution of the reptiles, the amphibians adopted a variety of aquatic, semiaquatic, semiterrestrial, and terrestrial habits. The terrestrial types are poorly known but include short bodied types, some of which had bony armor on the back. Those found so far are relatively small, predacious forms that must have eaten insects and smaller terrestrial vertebrates. The semiaquatic and semiterrestrial probably corresponded ecologically to alligators and predaceous turtles, lived along the banks of streams and lakes, and preyed on fish, aquatic amphibians, insects, and unwary terrestrial vertebrates that came to drink or lay their eggs. Some were of large size and certainly capable of holding their own with the early carnivorous reptiles.

Some of the most important subsidary trends are shown in Figure 19-11 as adaptations to particular environments or modes of life. Many of these appeared independently in otherwise distinct lines and are the result of parallelism and convergence.

REFERENCES

Camp, C. L., *et. al.* 1940-1953. "Bibliography of Fossil Vertebrates," *Geol. Soc. of America,* Special Papers 27 and 42, Memoirs 37 and 57. A continuing series now covering the period 1928-1948.

Denison, R. H. 1941. "The Soft Anatomy of *Bothriolepis,*" *Jour. of Paleontology,* vol. 15, pp. 553-561. A study of one of the agnathids.

———. 1956. "A Review of the Habitat of the Earliest Vertebrates," *Fieldiana: Geology,* vol. 11, pp. 361-457. An argument for brackish or marine environments for the early vertebrate habitat.

Eaton, T. H. 1951. "Origin of Tetrapod Limbs," *American Mid. Naturalist,* vol. 46, pp. 245-251.

Goodrich, E. S. 1930 (Reprinted 1958). *Studies on the Structure and Development of Vertebrates.* New York: Dover. A group of classic essays on form, ontogeny, and evolution of the vertebrate structure.

Gregory, W. K. 1951. *Evolution Emerging.* New York: Macmillan. In spite of the title, a richly illustrated book on vertebrate morphology and evolution.

Hay, O. P. 1901. "Bibliography and Catalogue of the Fossil Vertebrata of North America," *U. S. Geol. Survey, Bulletin 179.*

Jarvik, E. 1955. "Ichthyostegalia," in: J. Piveteau, *Traité de Paléontologie.* Paris: Masson et Cie. A consideration of the earliest and most primitive amphibians.

Moy-Thomas, J. A. 1939. *Palaeozoic Fishes.* New York: Chemical Publishing Co. The best general book on early fish.

Romer, A. S. 1941. *Man and the Vertebrates.* Chicago: University of Chicago Press. A semi-technical account of vertebrate evolution.

──────. 1946. "The Early Evolution of Fishes," *Quart. Rev. of Biology,* vol. 21, pp. 33-69.

──────. 1947. "Review of the Labyrinthodonta," *Bulletin Mus. of Comp. Zoology,* Harvard, vol. 99. The standard work on the largest group of fossil amphibians.

──────. 1957. *The Vertebrate Body,* 2nd ed. Philadelphia: Saunders. A brief but relatively complete text on vertebrate morphology—both fossil and recent.

──────. 1958. "Tetrapod Limbs and Early Tetrapod Life," *Evolution,* vol. 12, pp. 365-369. Most recent paper of several discussing the factors controlling the evolution of the first tetrapods.

────── and B. H. Grove. 1935. "Environment of the Early Vertebrates," *American Mid. Naturalist,* vol. 16, pp. 805-856. An argument for a fresh water habitat for the first vertebrates.

Stensiö, E. A. 1927. *The Downtonian and Devonian Vertebrates of Spitzbergen: I, Family Cephalaspidae,"* Skr. om Sval. og Nordishavet, no. 12, 2 vols. An extraordinarily careful and detailed study of agnathid morphology.

Watson, D. M. S. 1951. *Paleontology and Modern Biology.* New Haven: Yale University Press. A series of essays on evolution of *a*) first vertebrates, *b*) jawed fishes, *c*) amphibians, *d*) primitive reptiles, and *e*) the mammal-like reptiles.

──────. 1954. "A Consideration of Ostracoderms," *Roy. Soc. of London, Philos. Trans.,* ser. B, vol. 238, pp. 1-25. A review of agnathan fishes.

Westoll, T. S. 1943. "The Origin of the Tetrapods," *Biol. Review,* vol. 18, pp. 78-98.

White, E. I. 1946. "*Jamoytius kerwoodi,* a New Chordate from the Silurian of Tanarkshire," *Geol. Magazine,* vol. 83, pp. 89-97. Description of primitive agnathid without exoskeleton and extremely primitive in fin folds and myomeres.

See also general references cited in Chapter 3.

20. *Victory on land:*
the **REPTILES**

$\mathcal{T}$he large number of amphibian lineages that returned to entirely aquatic habits demonstrate the uncertainty of their terrestrial adaptations. Regardless of the efficiency of lungs or legs, they must return to the water to lay their eggs. Though some have evolved mechanisms to reduce or circumvent this need, these mechanisms are stop-gaps, successful only because the animals live in exceptionally humid environments. To free themselves from the uncertainties of the ephemeral, stagnant pond an amphibian lineage had to evolve an egg that could be laid on land.

The problem is relatively simple—just build a shell of low permeability. Oxygen enters freely, but the water, essential to development, cannot diffuse back out. But what is to be done with excretory wastes spilled out into the fluid surrounding the embryo? How can it be ensured that sufficient oxygen reaches the embryo in its watery envelope? To make matters even more complex, the young on hatching must be capable of surviving under terrestrial conditions; that means a longer period of development before they leave the egg. The answer, of course, is the amniote egg with its respiratory membranes, its external bladder for storage of excretory products, its large yolk sack for food—plus a series of physiological and morphological adaptations in the embryo so that it can use these structures and survive.

EX POST FACTO ANCESTORS

If paleontologists knew when and how this egg evolved, the separation of reptiles and amphibians would be easy. Fossil eggs are of no help, for they are so rare that their absence is meaningless. It is customary to set the boundary line between fossil reptiles and amphibians on morphologic differences—principally details of the vertebrae and of the arrangement of bones in the skull roof. Just one feature seems to be completely diagnostic—if it can be found in the fossil. Fish and many amphibians have—and had—grooves on the snout and sides of the skull that are the impressions of the *lateral line system*. This system consists of canals and associated nerves and blood vessels lying immediately below the skin. In modern fish and amphibia, these lateral lines have a sensory function—probably they perceive pressure changes and the movement of the water. If traces of the lateral lines occur on a fossil

490

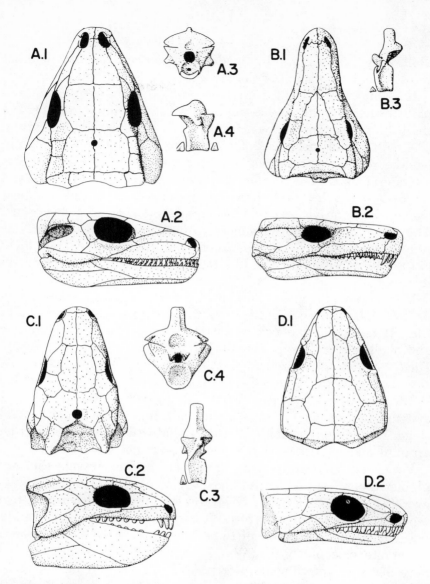

Fig. 20—1. *PRIMITIVE REPTILES AND REPTILE ANCESTORS.* *A) Seymouria;* early Permian; *A.1)* dorsal view of skull, *A.2)* lateral view of same, and *A.3)* and *A.4)* anterior and lateral views of vertebra. A genus close to reptile-amphibian boundary and assigned by various paleontologists to one or other of these classes. *B) Limnoscelis;* early Permian; *B.1)* dorsal view of skull, *B.2)* lateral view of skull and *B.3)* lateral view of vertebra; length of skull 24 cm. A primitive reptile. *C) Diadectes;* early Permian; *C.1)* dorsal view of skull, *C.2)* lateral view of same, and *C.3)* and *C.4)* lateral and anterior views of vertebra; length of skull 22 cm. A primitive reptile very similar to *Seymouria.* *D) Cardiocephalus;* early Permian; *D.1)* dorsal view of skull and *D.2)* lateral view; length 1.8 cm. A microsaur amphibian thought by some paleontologists to be near the ancestry of some reptiles. (A. After White. B. After Williston. C. After Olson. D. After Gregory.)

skull, they are presumptive evidence of aquatic life or, in other words, the development of the larva in a stream or pond.

If we now go to the fossil record and study the reptile-like amphibians and amphibian-like reptiles, we should be able to draw a sharp line between the two. Immediately another problem arises. The most useful specimens of reptile-like amphibians and amphibian-like reptiles are contemporaneous and some 25 million years too late in time. Since the amphibian ancestors of the reptiles and the earliest reptiles surely lived on dry land, they shouldn't appear among the Pennsylvania coal swamp assemblages, and they don't. The few known Pennsylvanian reptiles include some relatively primitive forms, such as the Conemaugh *Desmatodon,* but these are hardly more amphibian-like than their better known Permian relatives.

Many paleontologists consider the early Permian genus, *Seymouria,* to be a survivor of the stock connecting amphibians and reptiles. It resembles the reptile *Diadectes* very closely in vertebrae and skull and differs principally in the characteristics in which *Diadectes* has specialized for herbivorous diet (Figure 20-1). For this reason, it was accepted for many years as a primitive reptile. White, however, showed (1939) that grooves of the lateral line system could be seen in some skulls. This implies an aquatic larval stage. In addition, a middle Permian relative of *Seymouria* has an array of characteristics that imply it was completely aquatic.

Very well, *Seymouria* is an amphibian and represents the amphibian stock from which reptiles evolved. A puzzle remains however. *Seymouria* is more like *Diadectes* than it is like other primitive reptiles (the captorhinomorphs). It has characteristics that seem to debar it from the ancestry of these others. For this reason, several vertebrate paleontologists (Westoll and Olson, in particular) believe that the captorhinomorph reptiles had a separate origin—probably in a group of amphibians called microsaurs (Figure 20-1). If this interpretation is correct, the class Reptilia had a double origin, the diadectids from a seymouria-like species, the captorhinids from a microsaurian species. Others (Romer and Watson) disagree and believe both diadectids and captorhinids had a seymouria-like ancestor.

The late Pennsylvanian and early Permian vertebrate faunas include several, more advanced, reptile groups which must have had diadectimorph and/or captorhinomorph ancestors. The commonest and best known of these are members of the order Pelycosauria. These must have evolved very early in the radiation of the reptilian stock, for relatively specialized pelycosaurs appear in upper Pennsylvanian rocks. Details of skull structure indicate they were derived from the captorhinomorphs. The pelycosaurian species share a variety of characteristics, an extensive common structural plan. The most characteristic, though probably not most critical, feature of that plan is in the skull, a single *lateral temporal opening*. The primitive reptile stocks have a solid skull roof; the dermal bones formed just below the skin extend down and laterally from the midline to cover the cheek region; many of the muscles that close the jaw are attached to the inner surface of this roof; the brain is separated from these muscles by an inner wall of cartilage and bone (Figure 20-2). Turtles retain this structure, but all other recent reptiles have a different arrangement. One or two openings occur in the skull over the great muscles of the cheek region. When these muscles contract, they bulge laterally through these temporal openings. The pelycosaurs are distinguished by a single opening low on either side of the skull. The middle Permian therapsids evolved from a pelycosaurian stock and, in turn, gave rise to the mammals; thus, pelycosaurs and therapsids are termed mammal-like reptiles. The details of this sequence are fairly well understood; I'll discuss them further in the following chapter.

The other reptiles, other than the primitive groups and pelycosaurs, are represented in the lower Permian by only a few, tantalizing specimens. For example, the genus *Araeoscelis* has been variously interpreted as a lizard ancestor, as a close relative of the pelycosaurs, or as a specialized member of a stock that gave rise to ichthyosaurs, plesiosaurs, and the diapsids (lizards, dinosaurs, birds, and so on). Like the pelycosaurs, it has a single temporal opening, but the opening is high up on the skull rather than on the lower cheek region (Figure 20-2). At the present time, these specimens help very little in interpreting the ancestry of more advanced reptiles.

DOMINATION OF THE LAND:

Act I; Scene I

The mists of Pennsylvanian swamps that largely conceal the origins of the reptiles began to dissolve near the end of that period.

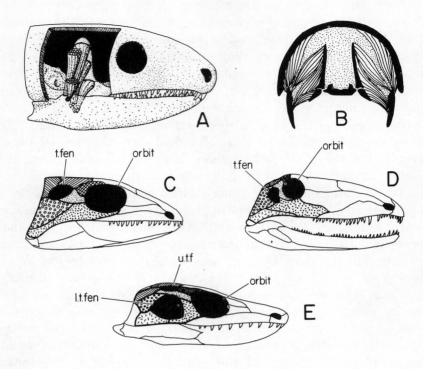

Fig. 20–2. *JAW MUSCULATURE AND TEMPORAL OPENINGS. A)* Diagrammatic lateral view of primitive reptile skull. A window has been cut in the skull roof and cheek to show the muscles. In the animal the attachment of the muscles to the interior of the skull roof would be much wider. Note that part of them originate from the bones of the palate and at the sides of the brain case. *B)* Diagrammatic cross section of same. Bone shown in solid black. *C)* through *E)* are lateral views of reptile skulls that show various types of temporal openings. Different patterns indicate different bones of cheek and skull roof. *C) Araeoscelis.* A single temporal opening surrounded by the parietal (lines diagonal to right), postorbital (light stipple), squamosal (circles), and supratemporal (lines diagonal to left) bones. The parapsid condition. *D) Ophiacodon.* A single opening surrounded by the postorbital, jugal (heavy stipple), and squamosal bones. The synapsid condition. *E) Youngina.* Two openings present; the diapsid condition. Abbreviations: *l. t. fen,* lower temporal fenestra; *orbit,* orbit; *t. fen,* temporal fenestra; *u. t. fen,* upper temporal fenestra. (*C.* and *D.* Altered from Romer. *E.* Altered from Broom and Olson.)

By mid-early Permian the scene was brightly illuminated. At that time, river deltas had accumulated from the east and south to fill the shallow seas that had covered Oklahoma and north central Texas for most of the Pennsylvanian. A wide variety of reptiles and amphibians (see Table 5–5, p. 120) lived on the terrestrial

TABLE 20–1

THE REPTILIA

(Classification from Romer, 1956.)

Subclass Anapsida
Pennsylvanian to Recent. Generally primitive reptiles without temporal openings.

Order *Cotylosauria*
Pennsylvanian to Triassic.

Order *Chelonia*
(?) Permian, Triassic to Recent. The turtles.

Subclass Lepidosauria
Permian to Recent. Primitive diapsid reptiles.

Order *Eosuchia*
Permian.

Order *Rhynchocephalia*
Triassic to Recent.

Order *Squamata*
Jurassic to Recent.

Subclass Archosaura
Triassic to Recent. Advanced diapsid reptiles.

Order *Thecodontia*
Triassic. Primitive archosaurs.

Order *Crocodilia*
Jurassic to Recent. Crocodiles and alligators.

Order *Saurishia*
Triassic to Cretaceous. Dinosaurs.

Order *Ornithischia*
Jurassic to Cretaceous. Dinosaurs.

Subclass (Uncertain).
Order *Mesosauria*
Permian. Aquatic reptiles

Subclass Ichthyopterygia.
Triassic to Cretaceous.

Order *Ichthyosauria*
Triassic to Cretaceous. Marine reptiles.

Subclass Euryapsida.

> Permian to Cretaceous.

Order *Protorosauria*

> Permian to Triassic. Conglomeration of small reptiles with single upper temporal opening.

Order *Sauropterygia*

> Triassic to Cretaceous. Aquatic and marine reptiles.

Subclass Synapsida

> Pennsylvanian to Triassic.

Order *Pelycosauria*

> Pennsylvanian to Permian. Primitive "mammal-like" reptiles.

Order *Therapsida*

> Permian to Triassic. Advanced "mammal-like" reptiles.

---

portions of these deltas, and many were buried and fossilized. The area subsequently was tilted gently, and, in the Cenozoic, a thin cover of young rocks was stripped away. Because of the low dip, these beds are exposed over a wide area. Because of the present semi-arid climate there are extensive outcrops. As a result, the badlands of the Wichita River Valley are a paradise for vertebrate fossil collectors.

The deltas were apparently well vegetated, except possibly for the dryer interfluves. The climate was warm with marked wet and dry seasons; this can be seen from the nature of the fauna and the lithology. The deltas were crossed by distributory channels of the rivers. On the flood plain were shallow lakes and, at least in the early part of the sequence, local swamps. The lakes probably were reduced to muddy ponds during the dry season; the distributaries, to trickles and pools. In the lakes and channels lived xenocanth sharks, lungfish, crossopterygians, and a variety of amphibians.* The xenocanths were sharklike in behavior as well as appearance. Their coprolites contain bones of fish and amphibians. The lungfish were well on their way to their recent form; they had elongate bodies, slender paired fins, and broad crushing plates in place of teeth. The crossopterygians and most of the amphibians were predaceous forms, though some, such as the "longhorned" *Diplo-*

---

* These interpretations of habitat and habit are based largely on the structure of limbs and teeth and on occurrence in various lithotopes.

caulus (Figure 19-11) and the tiny, limbless *Lysorophus,* probably grubbed along the bottom for small invertebrates. Large predaceous amphibians and reptiles crawled along the banks and returned to the water like recent crocodiles to eat fish and aquatic amphibians. Several species of small captorhinomorph reptiles and a few amphibians foraged on the flood plains; some probably ate plants; others, insects or smaller vertebrates. *Diadectes* and some of the *pelycosaurs,* including one (*Edaphosaurus*) with long dorsal spines, were the larger herbivores. *Edaphosaurus* may have lived primarily in the swamps. A number of medium and large-sized pelycosaurs were the dominant terrestrial carnivores. The largest of these, *Dimetrodon,* also had long dorsal spines on their vertebrae and a "sail" of skin between the spines.

Olson (1952 and earlier papers) made an extremely detailed study of the late early Permian fauna in north central Texas (see also pp. 120 and 181). He developed the paleoecologic interpretation summarized above and was able to show gradual changes in the fossil assemblages as the climate became drier. Near the end of the early Permian, the Texas delta apparently became too dry for survival of a vertebrate fauna. A somewhat different assemblage of more advanced pelycosaurs and captorhinomorphs appeared briefly at the base of the middle Permian sequence. Though deposition continued until near the end of the Permian, no vertebrate fossils have been found in these upper beds.

Act I; Scene 2

At about the same time that the vertebrate fossil record fails in North America, it begins in Russia and South Africa. Recent collecting at the top of the fossiliferous sequence in Texas (San Angelo formation) and at the base of the Russian indicates the two may overlap in time. The oldest South African fauna is probably slightly younger. In both Russia and South Africa, deposition was nearly continuous from middle Permian through early Triassic.

So far as is known, the environment of the Russian and African deltas was much like that of the Texas one—warm with seasonal rainfall. The faunas, however, show a sharp change (Figure 20-3). The amphibians were reduced in variety. Those that remained were aquatic types, some with flattened heads and reduced limbs and others with elongate snouts adapted to catching fish. Captorhinomorphs had nearly disappeared and did so before long.

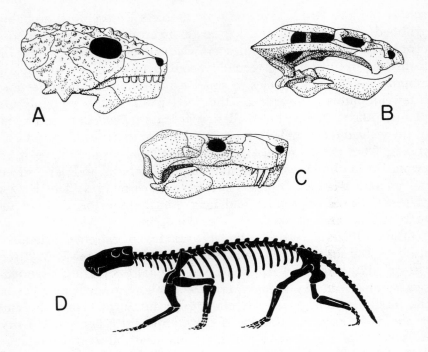

Fig. 20—3. *REPRESENTATIVES OF THE PERMO-TRIASSIC RADIATION. A) Parei-asaurus;* late Permian; lateral view of skull. A cotylosaur. *B) Dicynodon;* middle to late Permian; lateral view of skull. A herbivorous therapsid. *C) Lycosuchus;* middle Permian; lateral view of skull. A carnivorous therapsid. *D) Lycaenops;* late Permian; lateral view. A carnivorous therapsid—quite mammal-like in form. (A., B. and C. After Broom. D. After Colbert.)

The diadectimorphs were represented by large, heavy-bodied herbivores, the procolophonids and pareisaurids. The primitive herbivorous and carnivorous pelycosaurs had disappeared. They were replaced by herbivorous and carnivorous therapsids—both of which probably evolved from a carnivorous pelycosaur stock. The therapsids were clearly the dominant members of the fauna and would seem to be the first thoroughly successful terrestrial vertebrates. They evolved with some rapidity and radiated to different adaptations even more rapidly. Watson and Romer in a recent summary (1956) list over 180 genera of carnivorous therapsids representing 40 families, and over 90 genera of herbivores in 7 families. They were of moderate to large size; the skull and jaw form and the teeth were considerably modified for specialized diets; and the limbs were brought under the body rather than spraddled laterally as in early Permian types.

Because of the great thickness and extent of these beds, because of the abundance of fossils, and partly because of their remoteness from centers of paleontologic research, study of the Russian and South African faunas has hardly gone beyond the initial, descriptive stage. The existing phylogenetic interpretations are tentative and based on very tentative stratigraphy. Paleoecologic studies have hardly begun.

Act II

A dispassionate observer in the early Triassic could hardly have avoided concluding that the therapsid reptiles had taken the final step in tetrapod evolution and would live happily ever after. Of course, the diapsid reptiles were on the scene. But they were only subsidiary characters whereas the therapsids were well on their way to being the heroes. Then the stratigraphic sequence was interrupted, in South Africa by the break between uppermost Beaufort (lower Triassic) and the Stormberg (upper Triassic). In that interval the diapsid villains (the archosaurs) got the upper hand, and the therapsids faded into obscurity. The reasons for this evolutionary upset are unknown.

Ancestors and conservatives. The early history of the diapsids is obscure. *Petrolacosaurus,* a primitive reptile from the late Pennsylvanian of Kansas, may be a diapsid ancestor. Certainly *Youngina* and a series of related genera, the eosuchians, from the late Permian of South Africa, are diapsids (Figure 20-2). They have the characteristic pair of temporal openings, upper and lower, on each side of the skull and retain a sufficient number of primitive reptilian adaptations to stand as satisfactory ancestors for the three advanced lines— the lizards, the rhynchocephalians, and the archosaurs. In general, these late Permian proletarians are small, lizard-like in form and probably lizard-like in habits.

The rhynchocephalians have been the most conservative diapsid lineage (Figure 20-4). Their teeth are fused to the edge of the jaws rather than set in sockets, and they have a small beak on the upper jaw. But they retain the pineal eye (see p. 466), and the palate has a movable articulation on the brain case like the ancestral crossopterygian fish. The history of the order has been modest; the oldest fossil representatives date from the early Triassic; they underwent a small radiation in that period; and a single genus, *Sphenodon*, survives today in the protective isolation of New Zealand.

The lizards and snakes (order, Squamata, suborders Lacertilia and Ophidia) have been the true heirs of primitive diapsids. Most retain the pineal eye and the primitive palate (Figure 20-4) and retain or are logical extrapolations of the late Permian form in size and adaptations. They are characterized by three major specializations—the development of ball and socket joints between the vertebrae, the loss of the bar below the lower temporal opening, and fusion of the teeth to the inner or outer margins of the jaw. The modification of the vertebrae provides a very strong but flexible backbone. The loss or reduction of the bony elements in the cheek frees from rigid connection with the rest of the skull, the bone (the *quadrate*) that articulates with the lower jaw. The jaw is, in essence, double-jointed. The added flexibility assists in holding and swallowing large pieces of food.

The modification of vertebrae and jaw articulation has been carried furthest in the snakes. The ball and socket vertebrae pro-

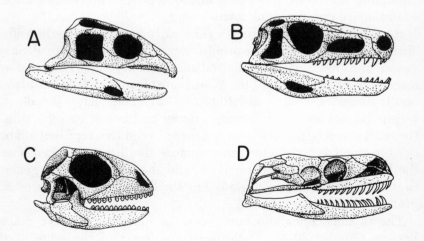

Fig. 20—4. *DIAPSID REPTILES.* A) Rhynchocephalian *Mesosuchus;* early Triassic; lateral view of skull. B) Thecodont *Euparkia;* early Triassic; lateral view of skull. C) Squamate *Iguana;* Pleistocene to Recent; lateral view of skull. A herbivorous lizard. D) Squamate *Python;* Pliocene to Recent; lateral view of skull. A snake. (A. and B. After Brown. D. After Smith.)

vided an efficient mechanical framework for the body muscles, so efficient that a wriggling locomotion substitutes for limbs. The snakes also lost the bony bar between the upper and lower temporal opening so that the quadrate is very loosely attached to the skull. In addition, the palate has only a loose connection with the quadrate; the palate and upper jaw move freely on the brain case; the lower jaw has a joint on either side midway of its length; and the two halves of the lower jaw are only loosely connected by a ligament.

The oldest fossil lizards are of Jurassic age, and the oldest snakes late Cretaceous. Triassic lizard ancestors are not known nor are the precise origins of the snakes among the various lizard lineages. Both are essentially modern groups and have survived and radiated widely in competition with the mammals.

Kings of the hill. The archosaurs have been the most spectacular successes—and failures—of the three diapsid lineages. Primitive archosaurs, thecodonts, appear first in lower Triassic rocks. In upper Triassic rocks we can distinguish four suborders and a dozen families of archosaurs; in upper Jurassic rocks, seven suborders and twenty families. The primitive thecodonts retained the slender, lizard-like body of the eosuchians (Figure 20-5) but otherwise departed from that plan (Figure 20-4). The pineal eye, conserved in the rhyncocephalian and lizard lines, was lost; the upper temporal openings were reduced in size; an opening was developed in the skull immediately in front of the orbits. Yet more significant of the archosaur future, they had relatively long hind legs. The legs, like those of the advanced mammal-like reptiles, were directly under the body rather than sprawling to the sides. The ventral part of the pelvis was extended fore-and-aft so that the muscles of the hip could swing the limbs fore-and-aft. Their tail was long, large, and, presumably, heavily muscled, the muscles attached in part to the upper leg. By analogy with later archosaurs and modern bipedal lizards, they must have run on the hind legs, the body and tail balanced about the fulcrum of the hip joint. This characteristic and adaptation, though suppressed in many later archosaur lines, shows even in the crocodiles and alligators. In them the hind limbs, though small relative to body size, are much larger than the fore-limbs.

Very early in their history some thecodont lineages abandoned the biped habit and adopted a sluggish aquatic life (Figures 20-5

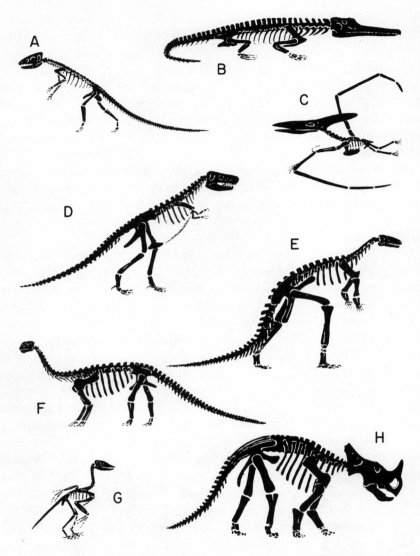

Fig. 20–5. *VARIOUS ARCHOSAURS.* *A) Hesperosuchus;* late Triassic. A thecodont. *B) Mystriosuchus;* late Triassic; length about 3.3 m. An aquatic thecodont—a phytosaur. *C) Pteranodon;* late Cretaceous; wing span about 7.0 m. A pterosaur. *D) Aublysodon;* late Cretaceous; length about 9.0 m. A carnivorous saurischian. *E) Camptosaurus;* late Jurassic to early Cretaceous. An ornithischian. *F) Camarasaurus;* late Jurassic to early Cretaceous; length about 5.5 m. A "small" herbivorous saurischian. *G)* The primitive bird *Archaeornis;* Jurassic. *H) Monoclonius;* late Cretaceous; length about 5.2 m. An ornithiscian. (A. After Colbert. B. After McGregor. C. After Eaton. D. After Lamb. E. After Gilmore. G. After Heilmann, *Origin of the Birds.* Copyright, Appleton-Century-Crofts, New York. Used with permission. H. After Brown.)

and 20-6). There they competed with the giant predaceous amphibians and ultimately displaced them. The phytosaur lineage made the adaptive shift in the early Triassic, underwent a modest radiation in the middle and late Triassic, and disappeared by the end of the period. Crocodilian in general form with a large, long-snouted skull and a heavy, short-limbed body, they differed considerably in detail from the crocodiles.

The other lineage of aquatic archosaurs included the crocodiles and alligators (Figure 20-6). Although anticipated by the phytosaurs they outdid them in diversity and persistence and survived all their more spectacular archosaurian relatives. Some Jurassic crocodilians apparently expanded into marine environments.

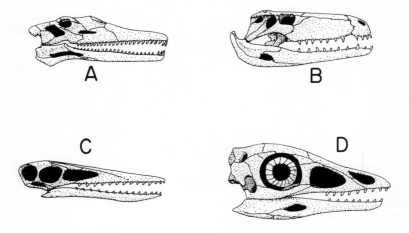

Fig. 20—6. *ARCHOSAUR SKULLS.* A) Thecodont phytosaur *Machaeroprosopus;* late Triassic; length of skull about 1.0 m. B) Crocodilian *Sebecus;* Paleocene to Miocene. C) Pterosaur *Rhamphorhynchus;* late Jurassic; length of skull about 12 cm. D) The primitive bird, *Archaeornis;* Jurassic; length of skull about 5.0 cm. (A. After Camp. B. After Colbert and Mook. C. After Jaekel. D. After Heilmann, *Origin of the Birds.* Copyright, Appleton-Century-Crofts, New York. Used with permission.)

Two groups of archosaurs also took up flying. The pterodactyls, who developed a flight membrane from a sheet of skin stretched between elongate fingers (Figure 20-5), were moderately successful but failed to survive the big kill at the end of the Cretaceous. The group appears at the beginning of the Jurassic with well developed wings—transitional stages should occur in the late Triassic.

The other flying archosaurs did sufficiently well to found a new company of their own, the class Aves. The birds are distinguished from the primitive archosaurs primarily by the presence of wing and feathers, the extreme shortening of the tail, and the loss of teeth. The primitive bird *Archaeopteryx* known from Solenohofen lithographic limestone (late Jurassic) had wings and feathers, the latter preserved as impressions in the fine-grained limestone, but also had a long tail and teeth (Figures 20-5 and 20-6). These fossils were found in 1861 and played an important role in the controversy over Darwin's theory of evolution. In structure, *Archaeopteryx* is almost exactly intermediate between later birds and the primitive archosaurs—a "missing link" discovered really before anyone thought of it being missing. I will have more to write about the origin and evolution of birds in the concluding chapter.

The remaining archosaur lineages, loosely the dinosaurs, formed the dominant elements of the later Mesozoic faunas and evolved into some of the largest and most bizarre of vertebrates, fossil or recent. To men, another group of bizarre vertebrates, they have been the most fascinating of fossils. They occupy the centers of museum halls and form the *pièce de résistance* of popular books on fossils. In spite of this—or perhaps because of it—their paleoecology and evolution are but poorly known. Their very size diminishes their scientific worth, for few museums or universities can afford to collect large numbers of dinosaurs. In recent years some paleontologists have undertaken the necessary careful studies of the dinosaurs but still less is known than of less common and perhaps less interesting animals.

Paleontologists now recognize two distinct lines of dinosaurs. The saurischians first appeared in the late Triassic. The earliest members of the group are hardly more than slightly aberrant thecodonts (Figures 20-5 and 20-8), and would surely be classified with them if later, more specialized saurischians were unknown. This phyletic line is particularly characterized by the form of the pelvis; a broad plate, the *ilium,* above the hip joint; a slender bone, the *pubis,* extending forward and down, and a similar element, the *ischium,* extending backward and down (Figure 20-7). The primitive saurischians were bipeds and probably swift runners. The smaller species have hollow bones somewhat like those of birds. Their teeth were sharp, serrate, compressed, and thereby fit for a diet of flesh.

By the end of the Triassic, this primitive stock had begun a radiation (Figures 20-5 and 20-8). Some species retained the primitive

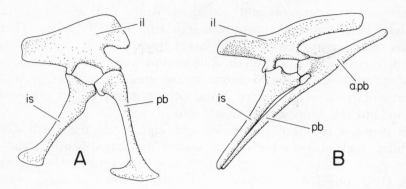

Fig. 20–7. *DINOSAUR PELVES.* A) Saurischian pelvis. B) Ornithischian pelvis. Abbreviations: *a. pb,* anterior process of pubis; *il,* ilium; *is,* ischium; *pb,* pubis.

characters and adaptations. Others evolved long slender hind limbs, long, delicate forelimbs fitted for grasping, and a long neck. Among these types the teeth are often small or even absent. Except for the long tail they resemble an ostrich. Probably they ate small verte-

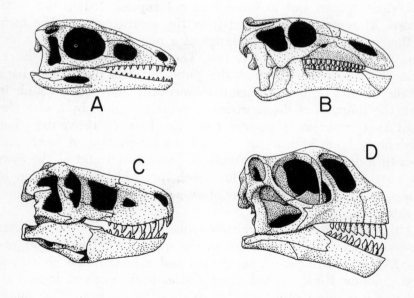

Fig. 20–8. *DINOSAUR SKULLS.* A) *Compsognathus;* late Jurassic. A small predaceous saurischian. B) *Iguanodon;* late Jurassic to early Cretaceous. An ornithiscian. C) *Tyrannosaurus;* late Cretaceous. A large carnivorous saurischian. D) *Apatosaurus;* late Jurassic. A large herbivorous saurischian. (B. After Hooley. C. After Osborn. D. After Gilmore.)

brates and invertebrates and succulent plants. Still another series evolved large size and massive though still bipedal bodies. Their heads were large; their jaws still larger in proportion and set with sharp, recurved, cutting teeth. These types must have been the master carnivores of the Mesozoic as the great cats are at present. Representatives of all three lines persisted or, better, thrived, throughout the Jurassic and Cretaceous.

In contrast to these carnivores and omnivores, the basal saurischian stock also produced herbivorous dinosaurs. Most of these were giants, some up to eighty feet long. Because of their great bulk they returned to a quadruped habit. Tails and necks were long; the body short though massive; and the head diminutive. Because of their small head, weak jaws, and reduced, peg-like teeth they must have fed on soft vegetation. They are best known from Jurassic deposits but are variously represented from late Triassic to late Cretaceous.

The other major dinosaur line, the ornithischians, first appeared in the Jurassic and, unlike the saurischians, have no close connection with the known thecodonts. Presumably they evolved from a thecodont species but in some area not represented in the fossil record. They are distinguished from the saurischians by the form of their pelvis and by the presence of a new element, the *predentary*, in the front of the lower jaw. The ornithischian pelvis differs from the saurischian in that the pubis extends down and back parallel to the ischium rather than forward. The position and, in part, the function of the saurischian pubis are taken by a new element that arises as a process from the base of the pubis. The predentary bone appears as part of the adaptation of teeth and jaws to a diet of plants; the teeth in the anterior end of the jaws are lost; a beak replaces the lost teeth, probably in adaptation to cropping leaves; and the predentary serves as the lower element of this beak.

Although many of the ornithischians are bipedal, there appears a persistent tendency to return to the quadrupedal habit (Figure 20-5). They all remained herbivores and exhibited the characteristic dinosaur trend toward greater size. Some evolved large batteries of grinding teeth—probably to chew harsh plants. The quadrupedal types evolved either heavy body armor or large horns and a protective neck shield. The ornithischians, though common and varied in Jurassic deposits, are more characteristic of the Cretaceous and thrived to the very end of the period.

RETURN TO THE WOMB

The success of the reptiles is expressed most clearly in their invasion of a wide variety of habitats; the dinosaurs, of course,. on the ground; the phytosaurs and crocodilians in lakes and streams; the pterodactyls and birds in the air. But even more striking are the variety of reptiles that thrived in the sea. Five distinct groups of marine reptiles have been identified—the ichthyosaurs, the sauropterygians, the mosasaurs, the geosaurs, and the turtles. The first two appeared in the Triassic and underwent a moderate radiation through the Jurassic and into the Cretaceous. The third evolved from a lizard ancestry in the Cretaceous; the fourth from a crocodilian stock in the Jurassic.

The order Ichthyosauria comprises a group of rather large, very fish-like reptiles (Figure 20-9) characterized by a single large temporal opening high up on either side of the skull. At their first appearance they had already assumed most of the adaptations necessary for aquatic survival, a fish-like tail fin, a dorsal fin, paddle-like limbs, and an elongate, fusiform body. They were apparently active predators, or so their elongate jaws with sharp teeth, their large eyes, and their streamlined shape imply. Some apparently bore their young alive, for adult specimens have been collected with young icthyosaurs lying in and emerging from the pelvic region.

Ancestors for the ichthyosaurs have yet to be collected. Their characteristics, other than the adaptations for marine life, are those of primitive reptiles. The temporal opening bears a different relationship to the bones of the skull than in other reptiles, so this tells nothing of their origin. They apparently reached their acme of diversification in the Jurassic and slowly declined in the Cretaceous.

The sauropterygians form a somewhat more diversified group (Figure 20-9). The Triassic nothosaurs had begun adaptation to the aquatic environment and had long slender bodies, short limbs, and a bony, secondary palate to separate the air passages from the mouth. The placodonts, also Triassic, were more heavy-bodied,

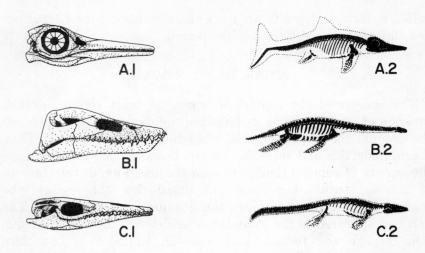

Fig. 20–9. *MARINE REPTILES.* A.1) Ichthyosaur *Ophthalmosaurus;* middle to late Jurassic; length of skull 1.0 m. A.2) Skeleton and body outline of advanced ichthyosaur. B.1) Sauropterygian (plesiosaur) *Hydrotherosaurus;* late Cretaceous. B.2) Skeleton and body outline of a plesiosaur. C.1) Squamate (mosasaur) *Tylosaurus;* late Cretaceous. C.2) Skeleton and body outline of a mosasaur. (A.1 After Gilmore. B.1 After Welles. C.1 After Williston.)

evolved a bony armor, and bear wide, crushing teeth on jaws and palate. The plesiosaurs apparently evolved from an early nothosaur species and appear in Jurassic marine deposits. They have a broad, heavy body with a relatively short tail. The limbs are large, massive paddles—evidently they served to row the animal. Two groups of pleisosaurs are recognized, those with small heads and long necks and those with large heads and short necks.

The marine crocodiles are less important and are limited to the Jurassic. Their most noteworthy specializations are paddle-like limbs and a fish-like tail fin. The mosasaurs occur only in late Cretaceous deposits and had diverged only slightly from their lizard ancestors by evolution of paddles and of long, laterally compressed tails. Both groups were probably predaceous, living on fish—and probably on cephalopods.

The marine turtles are an obvious extension of the typical turtle habit. The most marked changes are the loss of armor and the broadening of feet into paddles. Some are of large size—*Archelon* is 12 feet long. The turtles, alone of the marine reptiles, survived the end of the Cretaceous and persist to the present.

REFERENCES

Colbert, E. H. 1951. "Environment and Adaptations of Certain Dinosaurs," *Biol. Review,* vol. 26, pp. 265-284.

Olson, E. C. 1947. "The Family Diadectidae and Its Bearing on the Classification of Reptiles," *Fieldiana: Geology,* vol. 11, pp. 2-53. A discussion of reptilian phylogeny. Olson concludes that reptiles had a double (diphyletic) origin in two separate groups of amphibians.

————. 1952. See references for Chapter 5.

Romer, A. S. 1950. "The Nature and Relationships of the Paleozoic Microsaurs," *Amer. Jour. of Science,* vol. 248, pp. 628-54. A consideration of an amphibian group and a negative conclusion on the hypothesis that they gave rise to one of the two reptile lineages.

————. 1956. *The Osteology of the Reptiles.* Chicago: University of Chicago Press. An extended discussion of form, phylogeny, and classification of recent and fossil reptiles.

Swinton, W. E. 1934. *The Dinosaurs.* London: Thomas Murby. A semipopular presentation on dinosaurs and on their habits, habitats, and evolution.

Watson, D. M. S. 1954. "On *Bolosaurus* and the Origin and Classification of Reptiles," *Mus. of Comp. Zoology, Harvard, Bulletin 111,* pp. 297-449. A consideration of broader problems of reptile phylogeny.

———— and Romer, A. S. 1956. "A Classification of Therapsid Reptiles," *Mus. of Comp. Zoology, Harvard, Bulletin 114,* pp. 37-89.

Westoll, T. S. 1942. "Ancestry of Captorhinomorph Reptiles," *Nature,* vol. 149, pp. 667-68. Another argument for a double origin of the reptiles. See also Olson, 1947; Romer, 1950; and Watson, 1954.

White, T. E. 1939. "Osteology of *Seymouria Baylorensis,*" *Mus. of Comp. Zoology, Harvard, Bulletin 85,* pp. 325-402.

See also general references in Chapters 3 and 19.

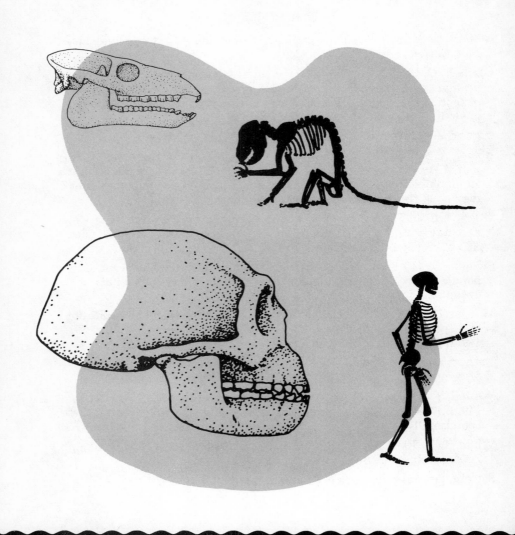

21. *The ascendency of the*
BIRDS *and* MAMMALS

$\mathcal{T}$o the end of the Cretaceous, the archosaurs dominated the terrestrial vertebrate associations; the ichthyosaurs, plesiosaurs, and aquatic lizards (the mosasaurs) shared the seas with the ray-finned fishes, the sharks, and the cephalopods.

The mammals throughout the late Cretaceous formed an insignificant element in the terrestrial vertebrate faunas. The ornithischian dinosaurs were represented by a series of horned quadrupedal genera, another group of large biped forms, and a third of armored types; the saurischians by a group of large carnivores, and by a number of light-bodied, ostrich-like forms. The latter have been variously considered herbivores or egg eaters or, most probably, omnivores that ate mammals and lizards as well as eggs and succulent vegetation. The ranks of the insectivores and small herbivores numbered a variety of lizards as well as mammals. Turtles and crocodilians occupied the lakes and rivers along with a number of small amphibians (frogs and urodeles). The birds, though very rare as fossils, were probably abundant and diversified. The fauna as a whole would seem to be well balanced, and most, if not all, major adaptative types were present.* The flora had a relatively modern aspect including many flowering plants.

The climate of the late Cretaceous was warmer than at present; this is evidenced by the occurrence of cold-sensitive vertebrates in what are now cold temperate areas, and is further substantiated by temperature determinations based on the oxygen isotope method.

THE FALL OF THE MIGHTY

In some areas in the western United States, continental Cenozoic beds overlie continental Cretaceous without any physical break. Because of the lack of physical criteria, the two series are separated primarily on faunal differences. The Cretaceous beds have the typical late Cretaceous assemblage just described. Above these are twenty or so feet of barren beds. At the top of the barren zone is a variety of specialized mammals, including fairly large herbivores and moderate sized carnivores. Accompanying these are turtles and crocodilians, many of them Cretaceous genera. Some primitive

---

* No thorough study of paleoecology of Jurassic or Cretaceous terrestrial communities has yet been made. Speculations about dinosaur extinctions would be on considerably firmer ground if something of the sort were done.

511

mammals, in particular the multituberculates, also cross the systematic boundary without major change. But no archosaurs other than the crocodiles managed it; all dinosaurs, small and large, are gone.

What happened? Change of temperature? Change in the plants? Blasts of heat from a meteor; mammals eating dinosaur eggs; hyperpituitarism; change in oxygen concentration; overspecialization and senility of the dinosaur stalk; and so on . . . and on . . . and on? Some of these explanations seem absurd, but this illustrates the desperate straits into which paleontologists have been pushed by the mysterious extinction of the dinosaurs. Only primitive mammals are found with dinosaurs, never advanced forms. If the advanced mammals crowded the dinosaurs out, they should be found together. Besides, I find it hard to imagine a mammalian herbivore, weighing three or four hundred pounds shouldering a two-ton ceratopsian away from a juicy leaf or a fox-sized carnivore at the throat of a forty-foot long saurischian carnivore.

Some explanations seem to disregard ecologic common sense—surely Cretaceous mammals ate dinosaur eggs, but so did Jurassic ones and so did the therapsids back in the middle Triassic. A mammal may even have eaten the last dinosaur egg, but something must have already upset the balance between eggs laid and eggs eaten. If temperature grew hotter, they should have survived in the polar regions; if cooler, then in the equatorial. Possibly a change in the physical environment triggered an ecologic imbalance; but that's just words until we know something of the late Cretaceous ecologic system.

BIRDS

The fall of the dinosaurs left two vertebrate groups, the birds and the mammals, to exploit the unguarded provinces of the terrestrial environment. As already indicated they had evolved in the mid-Mesozoic and filled secondary roles in the Cretaceous terrestrial communities. They began the Cenozoic—marked its boundary—with an explosive adaptive radiation.

The fossil history of birds is fragmentary. The find of the Jurassic fossil bird, *Archaeopteryx* (Figures 20-5 and 20-6), must be considered an extraordinary stroke of luck. Only two Cretaceous birds are well known, a tern-like form and an aquatic bird with vestigial wings. Both are primitive in retaining teeth but otherwise are "good" birds with a reduced tail, essentially modern wing structure, and an enlarged breast-bone (*sternum*) for attachment of the flight muscles. Between these advanced forms and *Archaeopteryx* there are no intermediates; if *Archaeopteryx* had not been found, one might well imagine the bird lineage arising as some sudden "hopeful monster" within a Cretaceous archosaurian stock.

A few puzzling and intriguing fossils suggest the evolution of toothless birds by late Cretaceous time. Over half the modern orders are known from fossils no younger than Eocene and very probably many of the other orders are as old. The recent giant cursorial birds, the ostriches, the rheas, the emus and the cassowaries, though unrecognized as fossils in rocks earlier than Pliocene, are more primitive in skull structure, more reptile-like in palate, than the known early Tertiary birds and probably derive from a radiation near the close of the Cretaceous.

The birds achieved their basic adaptations to flight before the end of the Mesozoic and accomplished the major steps in their radiation before the end of the Eocene. Fixed in adaptations to flight and unable to compete with mammals on the ground,* birds have been without significant evolutionary issue in the later Cenozoic. Their evolution in structure (Figures 20-5 and 21-1) and behavior has been remarkable but apparently self-limiting, for each successful *tour de force* has closed the boundaries of specialization tighter about them.

MAMMALIAN ORIGINS

I reported in the preceding chapter that the mammal-like reptiles faded into ecological obscurity with the radiation of the diapsids in the later Triassic. We must flash back in our story to find how they were saved.

As noted, the therapsids composed the major part of the early Triassic terrestrial fossil assemblages. Some of these approach the mammals in characters of skull and skeleton, and only the most mammal-like of the mammal-like reptiles survived the archosaurian break-through in middle Triassic. Only one group of therapsids, ictidiosaurs, is known from the late Triassic (Figure 21-2). These would be classified as mammals except that the lower jaw still

---

* The cursorial birds are an exception; but, by their small diversity, restricted distribution, and limited ecologic importance, they prove the rule.

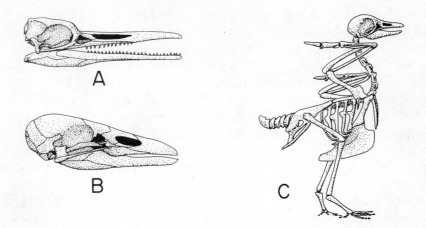

Fig. 21–1. *AVES*. A) *Hesperornis;* late Cretaceous; lateral view of skull; length 25 cm. Skull of loon-like, toothed bird. B) *Anas;* Oligocene to Recent; lateral view of skull. The duck. C) Skeleton of an advanced bird. (A., B., and C. After Heilmann, *Origin of the Birds.* Copyright, Appleton-Century-Crofts, New York. Used with permission.)

includes bones other than the dentary—though these are rudimentary. The well-known members of the group could not, because of aberrant specializations, have evolved into the recognized mammal stocks. Proto-mammals, however, must have been in existence, although many paleontologists believe that they had a separate origin (or several separate origins) from the middle Triassic therapsids. Late Triassic vertebrate localities are not abundant, and many of the best known are apparently wet deltas with aquatic amphibians and phytosaurs and other heavy-bodied and probably semi-aquatic archosaurs. As a consequence, even the early dinosaurs are rare, except in unusual occurrences. The absence of the proto-mammals—surely active upland forms—is to be expected.

The earliest recognizable mammals occur in the very late Triassic in association with ictidiosaurs. Late Jurassic rocks have yielded four distinct mammalian groups (Figure 21-4), but of these only the multituberculates lasted beyond the early Cretaceous. More modern mammals appear in the lower Cretaceous Trinity formation of Texas along with survivors from the Jurassic. In all these cases the specimens consist of isolated teeth and fragmentary jaws. At best they say mammals were here, were small, and were primarily carnivorous or insectivorous (excepting the herbivorous, rodent-like multituberculates). Little is known of the development of the

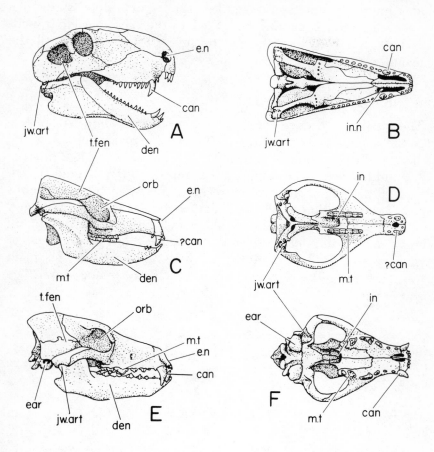

Fig. 21–2. *THE ORIGIN OF MAMMALS.* 1. *The Skull.* A) and B) Advanced pelyco-saur, *Dimetrodon*, an early Permian genus near the ancestry of the therapsids. Note differentiation of canine tooth and the anterior position of the internal nostrils. C) and D) Advanced therapsid, *Oligokyphus*, a late Triassic genus. Note the differentiation of the canine and cheek teeth, the presence of a secondary palate, and the relative size of dentary bone in the lower jaw. E) and F) A mammal, *Canis*. The jaw articulation has shifted forward to the squamosal and dentary; the bones that originally formed this articulation (the quadrate and the articular) have become part of the middle ear. Abbreviations: *can*, canine; *den*, dentary; *ear*, ear; *e. n*, external nostril; *i. n*, internal opening of nostril; *jw. art*, jaw articulation; *m. t*, cheek tooth; *orb*, orbit; *t. fen*, temporal fenestra. (A. After Romer. B. After Kühne.)

cranial portions of skull or of the post-cranial skeleton. A few skulls, as well as teeth, are known from the late Cretaceous of Mongolia and the very late Cretaceous of western North America. These include multituberculates, primitive oppossums, and shrew-like species, the latter commonly classified in the recent order Insectivora but sufficiently primitive to be near the ancestry of all the placental mammals.

The origin of a class

The fossil record does not impress the observer—but it does provide the documentation for the evolution of a major animal group, a class. And the origin of the class Mammalia was a gradual process, not a sudden leap. The mammal-like reptiles show a gradual approach to the mammalian structure—particularly in the carnivorous types. The definition of the boundary between fossil reptiles and mammals depends on osteological characteristics observed in all modern mammals and correlated in them with the presence of mammary glands, hair, a four-chambered heart with the main artery passing to the left, and a constant body temperature. The

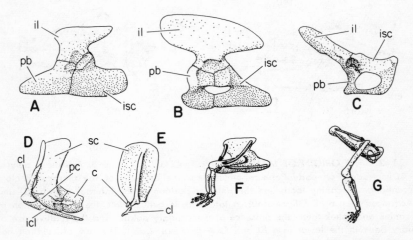

Fig. 21–3. *THE ORIGIN OF MAMMALS.* 2. *The Limbs.* A) Lateral view of pelvis of pelycosaur. Note relative size of ventral elements. B) Lateral view of left pelvis of therapsid. Note reduction of ventral elements and expansion of dorsal. C) Lateral view of pelvis of mammal. In this, the pubis and ischium have been rotated posteriad. D) Lateral view of pectoral girdle of pelycosaur. As in the pelvis (A) the ventral elements are relatively large. E) Lateral view of pectoral girdle of mammal—ventral elements very much reduced. F) Limb position in primitive reptile. The musculature (arrows) lies principally above and below the limb. G) Limb position in a mammal. The musculature lies in front and behind the limb. Abbreviations: *c,* coracoid; *cl,* clavicle; *icl,* interclavicle; *il,* ilium; *isc,* ischium; *pb,* pubis; *pc,* precoracoid; *sc,* scapula.

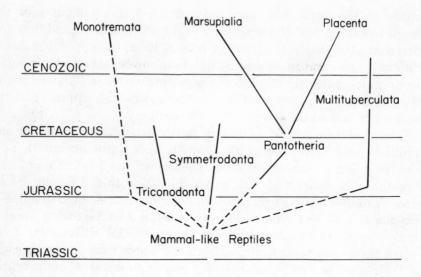

Fig. 21—4. *PHYLOGENY OF THE MAMMALIA.* Solid lines indicate known history; dashed indicate probable relationships.

osteological features include (Figures 21-2 and 21-3) the development of a bony secondary palate; the reduction of the bones in the lower jaw to a single element, the dentary on either side; the shift of the lower jaw articulation forward; the incorporation of the two bones of the old jaw articulation into the middle ear; adaptation of teeth in the front part of the jaws for biting and in the rear for chewing; rotation of the pelvic girdle so that the dorsal element shifted forward and the two ventral elements backward; and reduction of the size and commonly the number of the ventral elements of the pectoral girdle. These changes from the primitive reptile conditions are all adaptive: the change in limb girdles to the fore and aft movement of the limbs *under* rather than at the sides of the body; the modification of the middle ear to better hearing (particularly if, as Watson (1951) believes, the tympanic membrane was borne on the articular bone); the change in jaw articulation to changes in jaw musculature and the biting mechanism; and the formation of the secondary plate to permit uninterrupted passage of air above the palate to the back of the throat.

All of these features, except the shift of ear ossicles, began to appear in the mammal-like reptiles during the early Triassic and appeared independently in several different lines. Olson's (1944) study of the brain case and the indicated characteristics of the brain has confirmed this approach to the mammalian condition and demonstrated that it occurred in several lines, though at somewhat different rates and in somewhat different combinations. After vertebrate paleontologists studied the structure of these Triassic forms, they began to wonder whether the therapsids also approached the mammals in the character of the soft anatomy.

The evolution of the secondary palate is suggestive. In the amphibians and most reptiles the nostrils open into the mouth near the front end of the snout. When the animal has food in its mouth, breathing is difficult if not impossible. But this difficulty really doesn't matter since its metabolism is so low that a small amount of oxygen is sufficient—you need only observe a snake eating another snake. Aquatic reptiles, however, have special difficulties. Even when they raise their nostrils above the water they cannot breathe if their mouths are open. For this reason, several aquatic reptile lineages evolved a bony secondary palate. This palate closes over the roof of the mouth and forms a separate air passage from the internal openings of the nostrils back to the throat.

Among recent terrestrial vertebrates, only the mammals have a secondary palate. In them the structure serves as an adaptation to continuous high metabolism. They deplete the oxygen in the cells, blood stream, and lungs so rapidly that they must breathe at short intervals. Mammals also chew their food into small pieces that can be quickly swallowed—for this they have an elaborate set of cutting and crushing teeth. Many reptiles bolt their food whole so that the throat is blocked for long periods. Breaking food into small pieces assists the digestive system, but it also reduces interruptions in respiration.

It seems reasonable to assume that the carnivorous therapsids, with secondary palate and well developed chewing mechanisms (teeth and muscles), had a constant body temperature—were *homiotherms*. This is further confirmed by the development of bony scrolls in the nasal air passages, since, in recent mammals, these bear mucous membranes that warm and filter the incoming air. If they had constant body temperature, they probably also had a four-chambered heart to separate oxygenated blood from the oxygen depleted venous blood. Very probably, they had an insulating layer (hair) to reduce the effect of external temperature variations.

To pile hypothesis on hypothesis, we can say that their eggs would have required a constant incubation temperature—a feature perhaps attained by carrying the eggs in an abdominal pouch or by retaining them within the body during development. The latter adaptation would require development of a placenta to supply the embryo with oxygen and food and to remove metabolic wastes. The newly hatched young would require an abundant and constant supply of food that could be provided by mammary glands.

Very probably, some of these features appeared fairly early—temperature regulatory mechanisms perhaps as early as middle Permian. The frequency of independent developments of secondary adaptations to this primary change (the palate for example) implies that the unknown advanced pelycosaur, which was ancestral to the therapsids, may have had some control of internal temperatures. The other features surely appeared at different times in different lines and in different combinations. But regardless of where and when these events occurred, we cannot question the origin of mammals from one or more evolving populations of therapsid reptiles. So far as the fossil record ever "proves" anything about evolution, that evolution was gradual—extending over 45,000,000 years—and consistent with the concept of selection of slight variants within a species population. No "hopeful monsters" need apply.

Development of the mammals

The proto-mammals obeyed the adage and placed their eggs in several baskets; at least two distinct lineages, the symmetrodonts and triconodonts, appear at the very beginning of the mammal record. The two additional Jurassic orders, the multituberculates and pantotheres, may represent further independent lineages, and the recent monotremes may form a fifth stock, all derived separately from a proto-mammal source—or even from different therapsid genera.

Of these experimenters in mammalness only the pantotheres achieved a large success. They did so by evolving into marsupial and placental mammals. The marsupials (Figure 21-5) are characterized by an abdominal pouch (*marsupium*) in which the young are housed during the later stages of development and, in the skeleton, by marsupial bones to support the pouch; by the inward inflection of the back corner of the lower jaw, and by a particular pattern of cusps on the molar teeth. The placentals, on the other hand, carry

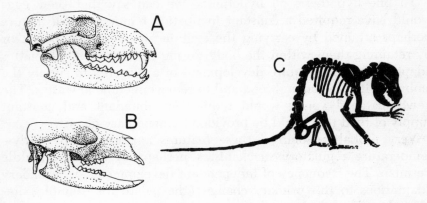

Fig. 21–5. *MARSUPIALIA. A) Thylacinus;* Pleistocene to Recent; Australia; lateral view of skull. A marsupial carnivore. *B) Macropus;* Pleistocene to Recent, Australia; lateral view of skull. A marsupial herbivore. *C) Didelphis;* Pliocene to Recent, New World; skeleton. An unspecialized omnivore of primitive structure. (*A., B,.* and C. After Gregory, *Evolution Emerging.* Copyright, The Museum of Natural History, New York. Used with permission.)

their embryos to a full term of development; lack marsupium, marsupial bones, and the inflection of the jaw angle; and possess a different molar pattern. The two lines separated early in the Cretaceous, as shown by the Trinity placental-style teeth and by marsupial and placental skulls and jaws in upper Cretaceous beds.

THE CAUSE OF OUR PARTY

Before them lay an entire world and no competitors but the birds, already bound in adaptations to flight. The mammals, marvelously equipped for terrestrial life, could not fail. Adaptive radiation may have begun in some unknown isolated area in very late Cretaceous time—the oldest Paleocene faunas include five orders, three of them new. By the close of the epoch, seventeen orders had appeared. Seven of these, mostly large, precociously specialized herbivores later became extinct, and, within the others, the earliest suborders and superfamilies, were later supplanted. By and large, the products of this first radiation failed to withstand the competition of later adaptive experiments but managed quite well through the Paleocene and into the Eocene. The Eocene was a transitional stage, with evolution of the modern orders and suborders well underway. In general, the archaic orders are heavy bodied and short limbed. Their brains were small. The teeth of herbivores were short and had a simple pattern of cones or ridges not well adapted to tough, abrasive plants. The modern orders typically are light bodied (at least primitively), long limbed, and large brained. The herbivores tend to evolve highly crowned teeth with complex crown patterns for grinding.

The complexity of the mammalian radiations and the extensive collections of fossil mammals preclude all but the most general description here (Figures 21-6, 21-7 and 21-8; Table 21–1). The origins of the different mammalian orders, whether "archaic" or "modern," are not well known. The order Carnivora is represented in the early Paleocene by the archaic carnivores, suborder Creodontia. The more primitive creodonts and the primitive members of the archaic herbivorous order, the Condylarthra, are so close as to indicate an immediate common ancestor. The odd-toed hooved animals, Order Perissodactyla, which includes the horses, may have evolved from the base of the condylarth stock; the even-toed ungulates, Order Artiodactyla, almost certainly did. Probably some extinct orders of South American herbivores also evolved from the Condylarthra. The elephants (and some obscure relatives of theirs), the sea cows, and some extinct South American orders may form another group with a primitive condylarthran ancestry. Two archaic orders of herbivore known only from the early Cenozoic may have been derived from the condylarthran stock, but they may be separate lines from the latest Cretaceous or earliest Paleocene radiation.

TABLE 21–1

The Mammalia

(A summary classification based on Simpson, 1945.)

Subclass Prototheria
  Order *Monotremata*
    Pleistocene to Recent. Egg laying mammals.

Subclass Allotheria
  Order *Multituberculata*
    Jurassic to Eocene. Primitive mammals with rodent-like adaptations.

Mammalia of uncertain subclass
  Order *Triconodonta*
    (?)Triassic. Jurassic to Cretaceous.

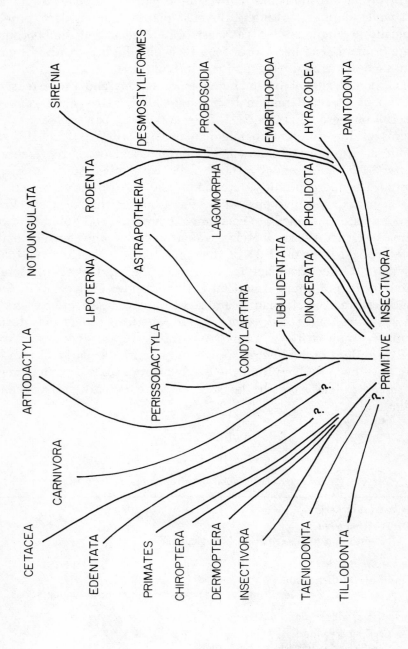

Fig. 21–6. *PROBABLE PHYLOGENY OF THE PLACENTAL ORDERS.* (Based primarily on Simpson, 1945.)

Subclass Theria

Infraclass Pantotheria.

Order *Pantotheria*
Jurassic. (?) Cretaceous.

Order *Symmetrodonta*
(?) Triassic. Jurassic to Cretaceous.

Infraclass Metatheria.

Order *Marsupialia*
Late Cretaceous to Recent. The pouched mammals.

Infraclass Eutheria.

Order *Insectivora*
Late Cretaceous to Recent. Shrews, moles, etc.

Order *Dermoptera*
Paleocene to Recent. "Flying lemurs."

Order *Chiroptera*
Eocene to Recent. Bats.

Order *Primates*
Paleocene to Recent. Lemurs, monkeys, etc.

Order *Tillodontia*
Paleocene to Eocene.

Order *Taeniodonta*
Paleocene to Eocene.

Order *Edentata*
Paleocene to Recent. Sloths, armadillo, anteater, etc.

Order *Pholidota*
(?) Oligocene to Recent. Scaly anteaters.

Order *Lagomorpha*
Paleocene to Recent. Rabbits.

Order *Rodenta*
Paleocene to Recent. Squirrels, rats, etc.

Order *Cetacea*
Eocene to Recent. Whales.

Order *Carnivora*
Paleocene to Recent. Cats, bears, dogs, etc.

Order *Condylarthra*
Paleocene to Eocene. Primitive herbivores.

Order *Litopterna*
Paleocene to Pleistocene. South American herbivore group.

Order *Notoungulata*
Paleocene to Pleistocene. South American herbivore group.

Order *Astrapotheria*
Eocene to Miocene. South American herbivore group.

Order *Tubulidentata*
Pliocene to Recent. Aardvark.

Order *Pantodonta*
Paleocene to Oligocene. Archaic herbivores.

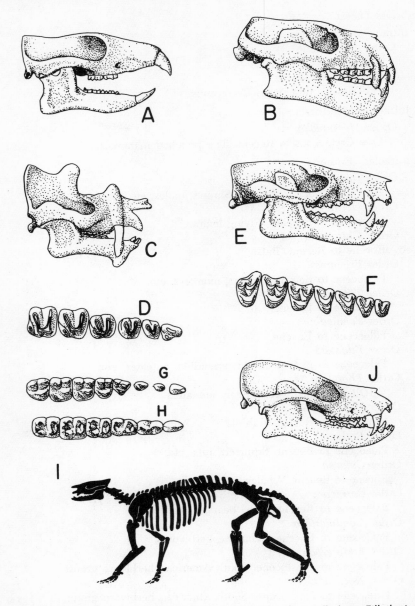

Fig. 21–7. *THE ARCHAIC MAMMALIAN RADIATION. A)* A tillodont, *Tillotherium;* middle Eocene; lateral view of skull; length 32 cm. A herbivore with rodent-like incisors. *B)* A taeniodont, *Psittacotherium;* middle Paleocene; length of skull 22 cm. A herbivore. *C)* A dinocerate, *Uintatherium;* middle Eocene; length of skull approximately 75 cm. A large herbivore. *D)* Right upper cheek teeth of *Uintatherium. E)* and *F)* A pantodont, *Pantolambda;* a moderate sized herbivore. *E)* Skull, length of skull approximately 1.5 cm. *F)* Upper right check teeth. *G)* through *I)* A condylarth, Phenacodus; late Paleocene to

Order *Dinocerata*
    Paleocene to Eocene. Archaic herbivores.
Order *Pyrotheria*
    Eocene to Oligocene. South American herbivore group.
Order *Proboscidea*
    Eocene to Recent. Elephants.
Order *Embrithopoda*
    Oligocene.
Order *Hyracoidea*
    Oligocene to Recent. Hyrax.
Order *Sirenia*
    Eocene to Recent. Dugongs, sea cows.
Order *Perissodactyla*
    Eocene to Recent. "Odd-toed" ungulates. Horses, rhinos, etc.
Order *Artiodactyla*
    Eocene to Recent. "Even-toed" ungulates. Pigs, camels, cattle, etc.

The primates clearly developed directly from the latest Cretaceous—earliest Paleocene placental stock. This appears to be true also of the bats, insectivores, and probably also of the edentates (anteaters, armadillos, and sloths both tree and ground), and of the whales. The rabbits and rodents appear suddenly at the end of the Paleocene without any apparent affinities to each other or to any other order of mammals.

PALEOECOLOGY, PALEOGEOGRAPHY, AND EVOLUTION

Cenozoic terrestrial deposits cover wide areas of western North America, central Asia, and southern South America. Less extensive but very significant deposits occur on the other continental areas. A very large number of fossils has been collected. Because the complex mammalian molar tooth is distinctive even for genera and species, fragmentary jaws and isolated teeth, useless in other vertebrate class, are of great value in mammalian paleontology. As a consequence, some evolutionary lines, e.g., the horses, have been traced out in detail; enough specimens exist for similar studies in many other groups. This abundance of material taken with the great knowledge of functions, adaptations, and ecology of recent

early Eocene. G) Upper right cheek teeth. H) Lower left cheek teeth. I) Skeleton of *Phenacodus*—length about 1.6 m. An extremely primitive herbivore near the ancestry of the carnovores, artiodactyls, perissodactyls, and several other herbivore orders. J) A primitive carnivore, *Delthatherium;* middle Paleocene. (A. After Marsh. B. After Matthew and Wortman. C. After various sources. D.-H. After Mathew. I. After Gregory, *Evolution Emerging.* Copyright, The American Museum of Natural History, New York. Used with permission. J. After Matthew.)

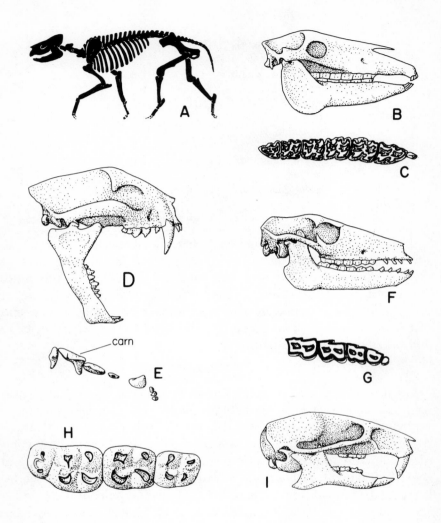

Fig. 21–8. *THE MODERN MAMMALIAN RADIATION.* A) Skeleton of the perissodactyl, *Hyracodon,* an early and middle Oligocene herbivore. B) and C) *Equus,* another
perissodactyl; late Pliocene to Recent; B) is a lateral view of the skull, C) a crown view
of the upper right cheek teeth; length of skull 55 cm. The enamel in the teeth is shown
in black, and the dentine in white. D) and E) A Oligocene carnivore, *Dinictis.* D) Lateral
view of skull—length 13 cm. E) Upper right dentition. F) An artiodactyl, *Poebrotherium;*
middle Oligocene; length of skull about 12.5 cm. A small primitive camel. G) *Camelops;*
Pleistocene; upper right cheek teeth. An advanced camel. H) Upper left cheek teeth of
a rodent, *Cricetops,* a late Oligocene genus. I) Skull of *Cricetops,* length approximately
2.4 cm. (A. After Scott. C. After Simpson. D. and E. After Matthew. F. After Wortman.
G. After Merriam. H. and I. After Schaub.)

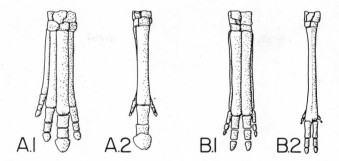

Fig. 21–9. *EVOLUTION OF THE FEET IN THE HOOFED MAMMALS. A.1)* Forefoot of a primitive perissodactyl (and ancestral horse) *Hyracotherium. A.2)* Forefoot of an advanced horse, *Merychippus. B.1)* Forefoot of a primitive artiodactyl, *Leptomeryx. B.2)* Forefoot of an advanced artiodactyl, *Merycodus. (A.1* after Cope; *A.2* after Osborn; *B.1* after Romer, *Vertebrate Paleontology,* reprinted by permission of the University of Chicago Press; copyright, 1945, University of Chicago Press. All rights reserved. C after Matthew.)

mammals has made the mammals the most useful group of animals for evolutionary studies.

Of particular importance, both for current knowledge of evolutionary processes and for future study, are the relations between these phylogenetic lines and changes in the physical environment, the natural societies, and continental relationships.

For example, North America and Eurasia were connected intermittently during the Cenozoic. Each gained immigrants during the connections. Some of these immigrants replaced native species; others filled unoccupied adaptive zones. This repeated upsetting of the mammal ecological systems intensified selection by bringing together competitors that evolved in different communities. As a consequence, when northern hemisphere mammals reached South America in the Pliocene and Pleistocene, they rapidly disposed of the less highly adapted South American forms which had had less competition and thus were subjected to lower selective pressures.

Within the North American-Eurasian faunal system, we can recognize two or three major shifts related to climatic changes—warm and moist in the early Cenozoic, warm and arid during the middle Cenozoic, and cool and arid in the last epochs. The hunter, returning from a safari on the modern African plain, would find the Pliocene and Pleistocene mammals of North America quite commonplace; he would see affinities with the Oligocene and Miocene species, though they would be small and less specialized; but he would discover the Paleocene and Eocene faunas to be very strange.

By and large, the Paleocene and Eocene mammals appear to be forest animals. Arboreal types like the primates are moderately abundant. The fossil reptiles, particularly the crocodilians, and the plants from the same beds indicate a moist subtropical climate in western North America, as far north as Canada. The expansion of the modern orders and suborders appears to connect with the spread of grassland in Oligocene and later times. The short-legged, splay-footed jungle browsers (leaf eaters) gave place to long-legged, hooved grazers (grass eaters). The clumsy, small-brained carnivores fell before the agile, clever dogs and cats.

Less is known of mammalian evolution in the southern continents. Africa must have been isolated during parts of the Cenozoic, for several unique groups, most strikingly the elephants, apparently evolved there. On the other hand, the persistence of warm-humid and warm-arid environments in Africa provided a refuge for groups that disappeared from the northern continents.

Australia and South America were still more isolated from the main stream of mammalian evolution. A marsupial population reached Australia at an early date—a date by inference, for the earliest fossil localities are late Pliocene—and evolved in isolation into a wide variety of adaptive types. South America received in the Paleocene a partial sample of North American placental mammals. In the subsequent isolation, these species, primitive condylarths and insectivores, evolved a wide variety of herbivores and some omnivores (Figure 21-10). Some of these resemble northern types; others are quite different. No placental carnivores appear in South America before the Pliocene, but their place was taken by carnivorous marsupials.

THE SOCIABLE APE

The jungles of Africa, South America, and South Asia harboured, among other refugees, a variety of primates. The order is a very ancient one—part of the Paleocene deployment in a forest environment. Fossil primates are relatively rare, but the lineage is fairly obvious—from insectivore to tree shrew to lemur to monkey to ape (Figure 21-11). In response to selection in the arboreal environment, the line evolved prehensile hands and feet (and some, prehensile tails), large eyes with stereoscopic vision, and a notably

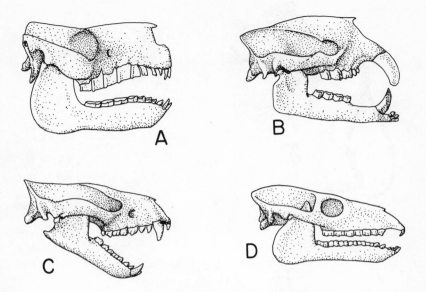

Fig. 21–10. *THE SOUTH AMERICAN MAMMALIAN RADIATION* A) A large herbivore (notoungulate) *Nesdon;* early to middle Miocene; length 38 cm. B) A large herbivore (astrapothere) *Astrapotherium;* late Oligocene to late Miocene; length 67 cm. C) A marsupial carnivore, *Borhyaena;* late Oligocene to early Miocene; length 22 cm. D) A horse like herbivore (a litoptern) *Thoatherium;* early Miocene; length 17 cm. (A., B., and D. After Scott. C. After Sinclair.)

large brain. Within the tropical forests they thrived, but an event more important to us occurred along the grassland-forest boundary. This new environment placed in action a new set of selective factors. Primates could have become, like dogs, runners on the plains; but the other mammals, both herbivores and carnivores, had a long head start. Primates survived, therefore, by clinging to the forest border, to its plainward extension along rivers or to the "forest" of rocks on isolated inselbergs or cliffs. They adapted to running but retained some of their ability to climb. The monkey species that shifted to this marginal environment were initially quadrupeds and remained so. Their descendants are the baboons.

The apes, on the other hand, attained a partial bipedal habit, and their "ground ape" descendants emphasized this adaptively. The history of this adaptation is fragmentary (Figure 21-12). The oldest fossil ape known is *Propliopithecus* from the early Oligocene of North Africa. Probable ancestors of modern arboreal apes have been collected from the Miocene—these may include ground ape

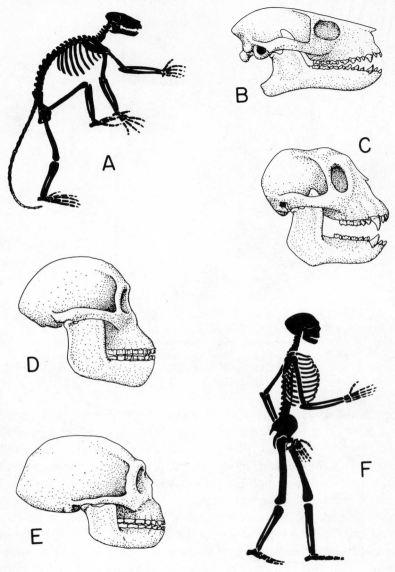

Fig. 21–11. *THE PRIMATES.   A)* *Notharctus;* early to middle Eocene. A primitive primate near the ancestry of the more advanced groups. *B)* Skull of *Notharctus*—length slightly over 7 cm. *C) Mesopithecus;* early Pliocene; length of skull about 7.5 cm. A monkey. *D) Australopithecus;* Pleistocene; length approximately 17 cm. A very man-like ape or ape-like man. *E) Pithecanthropus;* Pleistocene; A primitive man. *F)* Skeleton of *Homo neanderthalenis.* A primitive species of our genus. *(A.* and *B.* After Gregory, *Evolution Emerging.* Copyright, The American Museum of Natural History, New York. Used with permission. C. After Gaudery; *D.* after Broom and Robinson; *E.* after Weidenreich.)

ancestors as well. *Oreopithecus*, a very late Miocene or early Pliocene ape, may be on the ground ape line, at least Hürzeler (1958)
believes so. *Australopithecus*, a man-like ape from the Pleistocene
of South Africa, may be a late survivor of later Pliocene ground
apes and thus of human progenitors. True men, though of a different species and possibly a different genus, appeared well back in
the Pleistocene; *Homo sapiens* probably antedates the last glacial
age.

The human evolutionary lineage attained three striking structural changes: the modification of the prehensile simian foot to a
more rigid walking foot with small stiff toes, an arch, and a heel;
the rotation and expansion of the pelvis to support the body in an
upright position; and the enlargement of the brain case. All three
trends may have been established in the late Miocene *Oreopithecus*
—study of several skeletons found recently by Hürzeler should
settle this. *Australopithecus* approaches *Homo* in foot and pelvic
structure, though the brain is only about half the size of that in
Homo sapiens. The middle Pleistocene fossil-man, *Pithecanthropus*,
has essentially a "modern" skeleton though the brain is slightly
smaller.

Australopithecus presents special problems. In form it represents
a true intermediate between ground ape and man and might well
be classified with the latter in spite of the ape-like skull. The initial
discoverers suggest that some of the remains were late Pliocene—
sufficiently early to be ancestors of *Pithecanthropus*. Stratigraphers
now believe that the earliest possible date is early Pleistocene and
that middle Pleistocene is more probable. Certainly some australopithecines coexisted with *Pithecanthropus*, or, rather, with other
members of that phyletic complex, and may have been contemporaneous with *Homo*. By this evidence, the australopithecines
populations known from fossil samples were too late to be human
ancestors. Were they late survivors of the Pliocene ape-men ancestral to *Homo* lineage? Or were they a group of ground apes that
evolved humanoid characteristics in parallel and in response to similar environmental factors? The authorities cannot yet agree which
phyletic inference is correct.

The ground-dwelling apes probably lived, as do the modern
ground dwelling primates, baboons and men, in social groups. In
such groups, intelligent cooperation could offset physical disadvantage. Even the cleverest brain helps little when a baboon is

caught alone in the open by a lion. Social organization reduces the chance of such occurrence, but social organization also demands further mental adaptations. One suspects that man was a social animal before he could become a man.

Even so, what are baboons or ground apes alongside lions or water buffalo? Little except intelligent and therefore adaptable. But conditions arise where adaptability is, itself, a superior adaptation. Those conditions arose at the close of the Pliocene. Several varieties—(?)subgenera or species—of *Pithecanthropus* occur in middle Pleistocene deposits throughout Eurasia and Africa and thus evidence an abortive radiation of hominids. One of these lineages apparently lead directly to an archaic species of *Homo*. In normal human fashion, this species helped dispose of its contemporaries. No substantial evidence of specific radiation of *Homo* has yet been offered—*H. neanderthal* may be a slightly aberrant subspecies of the archaic *Homo*. The species *Homo sapiens* derived from the earlier *Homo* and completed the geographic and ecologic dispersal begun by the early Pleistocene hominids.

REFERENCES

Boule, M. and H. V. Vallois. 1957. *Fossil Men*. New York: Dryden Press.

Brink, A. S. 1956. "Speculations on Some Advanced Mammalian Characteristics in the Higher Mammal-like Reptiles," *Palaeont. Africana*, vol. 4, pp. 77-96.

Butler, P. M. 1939. "Studies of the Mammalian Dentition; Differentiation of the Post-canine Dentition," *Proc. Zool. Soc. of London*, Ser. B, vol. 109, pp. 1-36. An original and stimulating approach on the evolution of mammalian teeth.

———. 1946. "The Evolution of Carnassial Dentitions in the Mammalia," *Proc. Zool. Soc. of London*, vol. 116, pp. 198-220.

Clark, W. E. LeGros. 1955. *The Fossil Evidence for Human Evolution*. Chicago: University of Chicago Press. A recent summary of the human fossils.

De Beer, G. 1954. Archaeopteryx lithographica: *A Study Based upon the British Museum Specimen*. London: British Mus. (Nat. Hist.). A recent restudy and reinterpretation of the oldest fossil bird.

Heilmann, G. 1926. *The Origin of Birds*. New York: Appleton. Still the best general work on this topic.

Hürzeler, J. 1958. "*Oreopithecus Bamboli* Gervais: A Preliminary Report." *Verh. Naturf. Ges. Basel,* vol. 69, pp. 1-48. On the morphology and stratigraphic occurrence of a possible ancestor for the hominids. Additional finds have been made since this paper was published.

Kühne, W. G. 1956. *The Liassic Therapsid* Oligokyphus. London: British Mus. (Nat. Hist.). Thorough study of a very advanced mammal-like reptile with a discussion of mammalian origins.

Kurtén, B. 1957. "Mammal Migrations, Cenozoic Stratigraphy, and the Age of Peking Man and the Australo pithecines," *Jour. of Paleontology,* vol. 31, pp. 215-227.

Olson, E. C. 1944. "Origin of the Mammals Based upon Cranial Morphology of the Therapsid Suborders," *Geol. Soc. of America, Spec. Paper 55.* A detailed consideration of the evolution of the mammal-like reptiles and the origin of the mammals.

Robinson, J. T. 1954. "Prehominid Dentition and Hominid Evolution," *Evolution,* vol. 8, pp. 324-334.

Scott, W. B. 1937. *A History of Land Mammals in the Western Hemisphere.* New York: Macmillan. A semi-popular but very valuable survey of Cenozoic mammalian faunas.

Shotwell, J. A. 1955. "An Approach to the Paleoecology of Mammals," *Ecology,* vol. 36, pp. 327-337. An interesting paper illustrating a new approach to paleoecologic interpretation.

Simpson, G. G. 1945. See references for Chapter 6.

Watson, D. M. S. 1951. See references for Chapter 19.

Weber, M. 1927-28. *Die Säugetiere,* 2 vols. Jena: Verlag von Gustav Fischer. An original if sometimes erratic survey of the mammals and their phylogeny.

See also general references for Chapters 3 and 19.

Index

INDEX

Morphologic terms mentioned only in glossaries or in glossaries and illustrations are not indexed. Individuals mentioned only in parenthetical references are not indexed. Citations to illustrations are italicized.

C